What's it WORTH?™

Planning to take in an auction?

Selling or trading in some of your newer iron?

Have to put a value on your fleet
of machinery for a bank loan?

Then you must have this book!

Greg "Machinery Pete" Peterson packs this
guide with over 14,000 sales transactions.
Mind you, the prices listed here are not guesses,
estimates, or rules of thumb. They are based
on real sales transacted in just the past two
years. This companion book to the ultimate
guide on antique tractors, *Rust Book*, provides
you with a farmyard of machinery from across
the country.

What's it Worth?™

Successful Farming® Magazine	*What's It Worth?* by Greg Peterson
Publisher: Scott Mortimer	Editor: Dave Mowitz
Editor in Chief: Loren Kruse	Art Director: Kathy Grove
New Product Manager: Diana Willits	Copy Editor: Paula Barbour
Consumer Marketing: Brenda Torsky	Project Manager: Pamela Garbett

Contributing Designers: Nancy Itani and Mark McManus

Senior Vice President: Doug Olson   Group Publisher: Tom Davis

What's it Worth? (ISBN 978-0-696-23699-0) is published by Meredith Corporation,
1716 Locust Street, Des Moines, IA 50309-3023. ©Copyright Meredith Corporation
2007. All rights reserved. Write to *What's it Worth?* at 1716 Locust Street, LS253,
Des Moines, IA 50309-3023, or e-mail us at dave.mowitz@meredith.com.
Printed in the United States of America.

Actual prices on actual machinery

What's it worth?

Trying to help folks answer that simple question has been my passion since November 1989, back when I began to track auction sale prices on all types of farm and construction equipment across North America.

That was a lot of auctions ago.

What an incredibly fun ride it has been, building this business from the ground up. I think of the 700-plus auctioneers I've worked with to compile this data. So many great people and stories.

So how did this book come to be? In great part due to the success of our previous effort, the *Rust Book* (**www.rustbook.com**), which contained price data I had compiled on equipment over 30 years old.

This book is the opposite in that it contains auction sale price data I've collected on all types of equipment less than 30 years old.

Bring on the shiny new stuff.

You'll find auction sale prices on all types of equipment in this book. We cover everything. Wondering what a Wilson 42-foot grain trailer is worth? We got you covered.

How about a Bush Hog 2615 batwing mower? Yep, those too.

Garden tractors, disks, drills, sprayers, trucks, trailers, hay balers, rock pickers. It's all here for you.

When I say "all," I mean more than just sale prices. We give you all the details that affect a sale. I don't want to simply tell you a 1979 Chevy C70 truck sold for $21,500 on an April 2006 auction in northwest Minnesota. We tell you more: the truck was a twin screw with a 427 engine, Eaton 5x2-speed transmission, had a 20-foot Buffalo box, hoist, roll tarp, three-piece end gate, was plumbed for drill fill, and had 61,064 miles on it.

Compare that with the other 25 Chevy C70s sold at auction that we've got listed, and now you know what C70s are worth.

My sincere hope is that this book's information can help you make more informed buy/sell/trade decisions that keep more of your hard-earned money in your pocket. And I hope you enjoy it on a personal level, by the sheer fun of seeing what all this equipment has sold for at auction.

Machinery Pete

The expert on all things used and iron

Around 17 years ago, the son of a Minnesota equipment dealer set out on a mission – to report actual auction prices for machinery. No one offered such a service, and dealers were anxious to know the worth of equipment they were dealing on.

Greg Peterson's purpose seemed simple. The work was not. Consider the challenge.

He set out to amass tens of thousands of prices from hundreds of auctioneers and equipment dealers across North America.

And, for good measure, he validated those prices with invaluable insights listing the quality of machinery, its geographic location, and sale specifications. These details are critical when putting a price on iron.

Greg's determination to be the one-stop source for actual machinery values paid off. Today no one knows more about equipment values than Machinery Pete.

No one.

Sure, there are other price guides out there. Pick one up sometime. Take a look at the listings.

Many such publications merely estimate values.

Others base their figures strictly on dealer trade-in values, not actual sale price.

Worse yet, I've bought guides with sale prices that were years old! How did I know that? I compared the price listing from a current book to a copy I had purchased five years earlier. Imagine how much those prices had changed in five years. Shoot, the price of used machinery has skyrocketed in just the last six months!

When you are buying machinery, you need to know what machinery sold for recently.

When selling or trading iron, it is crucial to know the actual sale prices of similar equipment.

When applying for a loan application or scheduling depreciation, you must have accurate comparables.

Anytime you deal with machinery, you must have this book.

Thousands of farmers, dealers, and agricultural bankers depend on Greg's guidance to put a value on farm iron. This book allows you to join their ranks.

Dave Mowitz

Contents

Contents

Abbreviations

AC – air conditioning
AHHC – auto header height control
auto – automatic transmission
aux. – auxiliary
bkt. – bucket
bu. – bushel
CH – corn head
CAH – cab, air, heat
cyl. – engine cylinders
DAS – Dial-a-Speed
EROPS – enclosed rollover protection structure
gp – general purpose
gpm – gallons per minute
GPS – global positioning system
GVWR – gross vehicle weight rating
hi-lo – high/low speed transmission
hd – heavy-duty
hp. – horsepower
hyd. – hydraulics
hydro – hydrostatic
IHC – International Harvester Company
K – 1,000
KW – kilowatts
L – litre
LP – liquefied petroleum (propane)
MF – Massey Ferguson
MFWD – mechanical front-wheel drive
OD – overdrive
OH – overhaul

Abbreviations

OROPS – open rollover protection structure

pkg – package

power adj. – power adjustable rear wheels

ps – powershift

PS – power steering

pw/pl – power windows, power locks

pt – pull type

pt. – point

PTO – power take-off

R – row

ROPS – rollover protection structure

RN – narrow row

RW – wide row

RWA – rear-wheel assist

RWD – rear-wheel drive

sep – separator

SP – self-propelled

SN – serial number

spd. – speed

ss – stainless steel

std. – standard front axle

TA – torque amplifier

TLB – tractor/loader/backhoe

trans. – transmission

V – volt

WF – wide front

1 pt. – one-point hitch

2 pt. – two-point hitch

3 pt. – three-point hitch

2WD – two-wheel drive

4WD – four-wheel drive

Area

The abbreviation under this column represents the region of a state in which the machinery sold.

Example:

SCMI – south-central Michigan

Cond. – Condition

The following indicates the overall condition of the machinery as it sold at auction.

P – poor

F – fair

G – good

E – excellent

Honesty *is* the best policy

Everyone wants top dollar for his or her machinery. But misrepresenting the condition of your iron can come back to bite you, warns Randy Olson. "We call 'em as we see 'em. If something is seriously wrong and we know it, we announce it at the sale. The seller might be mad, but I've also got to protect my buyers," he says.

When not farming, Olson, brother Scott (below, left), and father Bob are operating auctions or a semi-annual consignment sale they hold near their home in Tekamah, Nebraska.

Some 30 years of selling used iron has convinced them that word gets around about people who misrepresent machinery. "You may have sold it today for top dollar. But a reputation follows folks around," Olson says.

Part of the situation may be that, in an effort to get fair market value, sellers believe they should conceal problems with machinery. "Yet I had a guy selling a Deere 4430 with a bad transmission at one of our sales. He told people that fact," Olson recalls. "I was selling a similar 4430 in good shape at the same sale. Guess what? My tractor only brought $200 more than the one with the bad tranny."

In this and many other cases Olson has witnessed, potential buyers knew what they were getting and felt comfortable with the purchase. "They sure sense when something is fishy," he adds. "Good luck getting a good price on that machine."

Getting iron ready to sell

Best intentions can cost you when selling machinery. Investing in a new paint job or engine overhaul to improve the salability of machinery rarely pays, say auctioneers and dealers.

"As a rule, you won't recoup the expense of an overhaul or major transmission job, for example," says Gene Ryerson of Ryerson Auction and Realty in Eagle Grove, Iowa. "If you do major work, run the machinery a couple years to justify the investment, and then sell it."

Of course, there are exceptions. "Let's say you had a nice, low-hour machine with a bad clutch," says Ron Gehling of Gehling Auction Company, Preston, Minnesota. "In this case, with that repair I would say you'll be OK. But overhauling an engine to get it sold is risky."

The same can generally be said about repainting machinery. Rarely will a complete paint job pay off, particularly if it's a bad effort. "Actually, it can reduce a machine's value," warns Randy Olson of Lee Valley in Nebraska.

Paint jobs often cause potential buyers to suspect that the seller is trying to cover something up, says Mark Stock of Stock Realty and Auction in Columbus, Nebraska. "Keep it light when it comes to paint," Stock says. "Touching up dings or dents or even repainting wheels is fine. Any more than that is risky."

It's important to keep machinery as original as possible. "Doing so reassures prospective buyers. They know what they are getting," Olson explains. "This is especially true of antique machinery, which many collectors prefer in its original condition."

There is much you can do, however, to improve the appeal of your machinery:

Clean machines completely. This includes a wash job that removes all dirt and grime. Waxing and buffing to improve paint luster is a must. Detail the cab

Providing repair and service records reassures potential buyers of a machine's quality.

since "a clean cab leaves a great first impression. This includes washing windows and maybe using deodorizer in the cabs of tractors used in a livestock operation," Gehling says.

Make sure the battery works. "Like cleaning, this is an absolute must," says Doug Walton of Walton Realty & Auction, Sycamore, Ohio. "It must be able to start, turning over with strength."

Check all fluids and fill to full levels. Change engine or hydraulic fluid if existing oil is dirty.

Inflate all tires. Repair or replace tires that don't hold air. "Maybe replace the front tires on a front-wheel-assist tractor if they are smooth," suggests Ryerson. But avoid buying expensive tires, like the rear rubber on tractors, as "it rarely pays off," he says.

Make sure all lights are OK.

Have repair records, work orders, and invoices available

for inspection. "This gives buyers peace of mind," adds Stock.

Be honest about the condition of your machinery. "I really can't stress this enough," says Gehling. "I've seen tractors and combines with major problems still sell well simply because the owner explained how the machine had been used and what was wrong with it."

Cleaner is better, provided the machine is presented in its original condition.

A bad paint job can scare off serious buyers and cause an item to sell poorly. Buyers become suspicious of paint that covers potentially serious rust problems or hides major repairs. It's best not to paint such machinery so buyers are reassured it really is "as is."

Successful bidding

By Dwayne Leslie

To be the successful highest bidder is easy at any auction. But to be a successful bargain bidder requires a plan.

Talking to bidders from across North America, the most consistent advice is to research the value of an item before the auction. Do this by calling your local dealer, reading ads in the paper, or searching Internet sites like Ag Dealer.com (**www.agdealer. com**) and the F.A.C.T's Report (**www.factsreport.com**). These sites provide a value range for the piece of equipment you are planning to purchase.

You've probably been to an auction and seen a buyer pay more for a two- to three-year-old item than what it cost new. The best way to prevent this is to set a value before the auction and adjust that value after inspecting the item's condition at the sale.

With a target price in mind, watch the auctioneer in action to see his technique. Auctioneers all have different styles of selling. Watch to see how each one starts the bidding. For example, does the auctioneer start the bidding low and try to gain momentum? Or does he start out high initially and then drop the price until the first bid?

In the latter case, you might have to step in with a starting bid to guard against the call getting too low and causing interest in the crowd.

Do you start the bidding and continue fast and aggressively to show determination to deter competition? Or do you wait until near the end of bidding and then jump in to dishearten any remaining bidders? Then again, do you bid slowly to give your opponents time to think about how much they are paying, or do you enter the ring quickly and decisively at the end with a couple of fast bids?

There is no one method that is better than another, although auctioneers certainly appreciate bidders who step forward and quickly get things moving. Having the auctioneer on your side is always a good thing.

Another consideration is where you stand. Many people stand in front of the equipment in good view of the auctioneer. An option is to stay in the crowd while bidding through a ring person. That way you stay anonymous until the end.

Successful bidding uses a combination of these strategies to suit the situation. But everyone certainly agrees on one strategy: If the price is too high, don't bid at all!

Internet iron abounds

By Dave Mowitz

Maybe it was only a matter of time before the impact of the Internet would be felt in the world of used farm machinery. I assumed some machinery would exchange hands via cyberspace. Yet I had doubts it would make major inroads into the iron market.

The major stumbling block I perceived was one of accountability. Would farmers come to trust a transaction involving machinery they would often never see in person? Kicking tires, after all, seems a major prerequisite to any iron purchase.

And then there was the issue of dealing with people through a computer screen. Farmers are honest to a fault. Yet we've all heard those stories of unscrupulous operators.

Considering such stumbling blocks, one rightfully wondered if the eBay phenomenon would ever establish itself as a major market for used machinery.

Well, wonder no more. Interest in Internet iron sales is nothing less than astonishing. The first hints of this trend were witnessed in the antique tractor world. Large numbers of collectors were reporting great finds on the Net.

Auction guru Greg Peterson began hearing from growing numbers of auctioneer houses that were turning to cyberspace sales. "The concept has been simmering on the back burner for years," Peterson says. "But its use has just recently taken off to the point that some auctioneers employ it as a major part of their business."

Or in the case of West Auctions (**www.westauction.com**) out of Woodland, California,

Internet trading is the only way of doing business. "We view it as the preferred method," says West's Jack Young. "We don't even put our phone number on our sale bills anymore. We just put on the Web site address."

Young offers a humorous example of the power of the Internet. "A year ago an auction firm in California sold – during a hailstorm, I might add – a piece of repossessed equipment sitting in Oklahoma City that was owned by a bank in Germany to a guy sitting on an oil rig in the Gulf of Mexico. None of us touched that piece of equipment."

The West Auctions example may represent the extreme in the market. But a growing number of auctioneers, as well as dealers, report turning to the Net. "We e-mail pictures of equipment to potential customers across the country all the time," says Kevin Bauman with Haug Implement in Willmar, Minnesota. "This year alone we've sold a plow to Oregon, scrapers to California, a planter to Florida, a four-wheel-drive tractor and skid loader to Montana, and numerous other items in our five-state area."

Even early Internet adopters are surprised by this media's recent growth. "We initiated our Web site in the early 1990s," recalls Geri Paul of Steffes Auctioneers (**www.agiron.com**), Fargo, North Dakota. "In the beginning, our individual auction page views were under 500 per auction."

With time, interest climbed to 2,000-plus views per auction, Paul reports. And then, interest took off. "We are now up to 8,600-plus page views," Paul says. "Advertising on the Internet gives our audience a chance to shop 24/7."

That last point is key in explaining the growth in Internet iron sales. Farmers have discovered the convenience of viewing a nation's worth of machinery from the comfort of their desks.

Looking for a tracked tractor with low hours? Not long ago your search was limited to local classifieds, auction listings, and dealers' lots. Today an Internet search will turn up tractors from every corner of the continent.

Plus, the variety of exchange methods is equally diverse. You can choose to buy from and sell to fellow farmers, machinery jockeys, auction houses, and dealers employing transactions ranging from private treaty sales to bidding at an auction broadcast live online.

Still, there are security issues that surround Internet sales. Experienced Internet users have found that putting common sense to work – like only buying from established firms or never paying for Internet iron sight unseen – is the key to avoid getting burned.

Avoiding Internet scams

By Jim Meade

Like an increasing number of farmers, I've bought supplies and equipment online. That experience has taught me the hard way to be cautious.

The tractor I'm pictured with at right was one purchase that didn't work out as well as I'd hoped. It looked good in the pictures and had a glowing write-up. Yet its three-point hitch was broken and incomplete, the power steering was nonstandard, and so was the paint job.

Iowa City, Iowa, farmer and Internet guru Jim Meade has bought tractors, such as this Oliver 770, as well as other equipment online for several years.

Buyer-beware credo applies

True, the modern marketplace has many buyer protections built in. But trading online is very much a buyer-beware business. When you are buying a new item, you have some expectation of the condition. But if it's used, and you're buying from someone who is not a dealer or familiar with the item, the seller's description may not agree with the way you'd assess it.

"We have bought a handful of items over the Internet. The fourth one hurt us kind of bad," relates Bron in the Machinery Talk discussion group at www.agriculture.com. "It was an articulated tractor from Canada. The pictures looked great. It was a one-time-owner tractor from an older guy that sounded very honest over the phone. We paid a little more for it. When it came, it looked good. But deeper there were problems: engine, hydraulic cables, other items."

Larry, in another Machinery Talk posting, describes how he makes sure the machine is as represented before he pays for it. "I don't send any down payment. I go to pick up the item in person and take cash."

That's a good practice, but some online sellers demand a sizeable down payment within days and payment in full soon thereafter.

When you buy from a local dealer, it's easy to check the seller's reputation. But you don't always know online sellers, who may use nicknames or conceal their identity. Online auction sites like eBay have a feedback mechanism designed to give buyer and seller confidence that both are trustworthy.

"Feedback score should be very high," advises Cutshay from a Machinery Talk posting. "Also, don't buy if it's only the first few items they've sold on the Net. Read other buyers' comments about them," he says.

Use feedback scores with caution. There is a lot of pressure on some sites to swap favorable feedback scores.

One benefit of buying online is finding a machine at an attractive price. But high bidders expecting to win the auction may find themselves suddenly outbid. "Be ready for the price to shoot up the last 20 seconds of the sale," Cutshay adds. "It's my preferred way to buy. It's called sniping, and it usually shakes out the rookies."

What to do with a sour deal

What can you do if you feel you've been cheated in an online purchase? Options depend on state laws and any rules associated with the online site. The first recourse is to appeal to the site manager and the other party. If that fails you may want to consult your attorney. If the deal goes sour, raise your concerns right away. Keep the discussion objective and try for a compromise that is fair to both parties before resorting to lawsuits.

There are out-and-out scams online. One popular scam is to offer to buy your equipment but pay with a larger check than the purchase price, with you sending a refund back. Naturally, the big check that you got is no good.

Many purchasers keep prices low enough that if they have a problem they can stand the loss.

Allison Wiediger used that approach. "We bought an IH Model 140 on eBay. We checked the seller's feedback, which was good. He delivered, and the tractor was as good as advertised. We were very pleased."

Bear in mind that purchase price doesn't cover the cost of getting the item home. Freight rates may run from $1.50 to $3.00 per loaded mile.

There are plenty of positive experiences with online purchases. For example, I bought two tractors that were worth the money. They were sold by a major company with a good reputation.

ATVs

"Is that thing for sale today?" I heard the question asked a couple times at an auction I attended recently. Guys were asking the young fella riding around on the late-model ATV if it was up for sale on the auction. It wasn't, but just goes to show the high level of interest out there in used ATVs in good condition. They seem to hold their value pretty well.

ATVs

Make	Model	Year	Hrs.	Cond.	Price	Sale	Location	Comments
Arctic Cat	250			G	$2,700	12/06	SCMI	2×4 quad auto
Arctic Cat	250			G	$2,700	12/06	SCMI	2×4 quad auto
Arctic Cat	400			G	$3,250	11/06	SCCA	4WD
Arctic Cat	400			G	$3,850	12/06	SCMI	Quads
Arctic Cat	400			G	$4,050	12/06	SCMI	Quads
Arctic Cat	454		984	G	$1,400	11/06	WCMN	Quads, 2×4, 1 owner
Arctic Cat	500		446	E	$4,100	8/06	WCKS	4-wheeler, 4×4, 20-gal. poly tank w/ 12V pump
Arctic Cat	500	2005	446	E	$5,550	1/06	SCNE	4-wheeler, 4×4, 20-gal. poly tank w/ 12V pump
Arctic Cat	NA			G	$2,800	4/06	NEND	4-wheeler
Bombardier	NA	1977		G	$1,100	8/06	NCMI	Trail groomer w/ cab, 4-cyl.
Honda	110			P	$110	8/06	WCMN	3-wheeler, not running
Honda	110			G	$400	6/06	ECND	3-wheeler
Honda	125			G	$500	4/06	NWMN	3-wheeler
Honda	185			F	$300	11/06	SCNE	3-wheeler
Honda	200			F	$250	1/06	NEMO	3-wheeler
Honda	200			P	$290	8/06	SWWI	Fourtrax, needs repair, sold as is
Honda	200	1981		G	$375	3/06	ECNE	Big Red 3-wheeler
Honda	200	1984		F	$400	12/06	WCMN	3-wheeler
Honda	250			G	$1,025	2/06	SCMI	250 SE, 3-wheeler, electric start
Honda	250	1984		G	$500	3/06	ECNE	Big Red 3-wheeler, shaft drive
Honda	250	1999		G	$1,600	12/06	SCMI	2×4
Honda	250	2001		G	$2,200	12/06	SCMI	2×4, auto, winch
Honda	300			G	$1,000	8/06	NCNE	4-wheeler, 2WD
Honda	300			G	$1,200	9/06	NEIN	Fourtrax, gas
Honda	300			G	$1,300	9/06	NCIA	Fourtrax, 4-wheeler
Honda	300			G	$1,700	3/06	SWNE	Sprayer kit w/ tank
Honda	300	1988		F	$1,100	3/06	NWMN	Fourtrax
Honda	300	1998		G	$2,400	12/06	SEIA	Fourtrax, 4×4, 4-wheeler
Honda	300	1999		G	$2,600	3/06	SEND	Fourtrax 4-wheeler
Honda	300	2001		G	$2,150	9/06	NCMI	300EX, 4-wheeler
Honda	350	2002		G	$3,000	9/06	SEIA	Rancher 4×4, 4-wheeler
Honda	400	1999		F	$2,400	11/06	NEND	Foreman, manual shift
Honda	Foreman			E	$3,250	9/06	NEIN	4×4
Honda	Foreman	1999		E	$3,800	3/06	SWIN	450 Foreman ESP, 4×4, front & rear racks
Honda	Fourtrax	1995		G	$2,350	11/06	WCMN	4×4, plow
Honda	Fourtrax	2002		G	$4,400	4/06	WCSD	Rancher ES, 4-wheeler
Honda	Recon	2002		G	$2,500	3/06	ECNE	Recon 4-wheeler, 2WD
Honda	Recon	2004		E	$1,800	12/06	SWIL	Recon
Honda	Rancher			E	$4,400	4/06	ECNE	4WD, 1 year old, like new
Honda	Rancher	2000	2,542	G	$3,000	12/06	ECNE	Rancher ES, 4-wheeler
Honda	Rancher	2004	2,941	G	$2,500	5/06	SEND	Rancher ES, 4×4, air cooled
Honda	Rancher	2004		E	$3,000	12/06	SWIL	4×4, 350
Honda	Rancher	2006		G	$3,800	12/06	SCMI	4×4, quads
Honda	Rancher	2006		G	$3,800	12/06	SCMI	4×4, quads
Honda	Rancher	2006		G	$4,000	12/06	SCMI	4×4, quads
Honda	Rancher	2006		G	$4,000	12/06	SCMI	4×4, quads
Honda	TRX 200			F	$800	3/06	NWKS	4×2
John Deere	500	2005	400	E	$3,500	12/06	NWIL	Trail Buck, 4×4, automatic
John Deere	500	2005	16	E	$4,500	8/06	SCNE	Buck ,semiautomatic, warranty

ATVs

Make	Model	Year	Hrs.	Cond.	Price	Sale	Location	Comments
John Deere	500	2006		G	$4,500	11/06	WCMN	Buck, auto, demo
John Deere	AMT 600			P	$325	11/06	WCIL	Utility vehicle
John Deere	AMT 622			F	$675	12/06	ECMO	5-wheeler
John Deere	Buck	2006		G	$5,100	11/06	WCMN	Demo
John Deere	Gator			G	$925	8/06	WCNC	
John Deere	Gator			G	$2,400	11/06	SWCA	4×2, 3' bed, gas
John Deere	Gator			G	$2,400	12/06	ECMO	4×2
John Deere	Gator			G	$2,600	3/06	NWIL	Gas, 6×4
John Deere	Gator			G	$2,700	11/06	SCCA	2×4 gas
John Deere	Gator			G	$2,900	12/06	ECMO	6×4, knobby tires
John Deere	Gator			G	$3,000	6/06	NCIL	6×4
John Deere	Gator			G	$3,200	12/06	SCMN	4×2
John Deere	Gator			G	$3,300	12/06	WCMN	
John Deere	Gator			G	$3,400	12/06	NWMO	6×4
John Deere	Gator			G	$3,500	6/06	NEIN	6×4
John Deere	Gator			G	$3,600	12/06	SCMN	4×2
John Deere	Gator			F	$3,600	1/06	NCCO	2WD
John Deere	Gator			G	$3,750	11/06	SECA	4×2
John Deere	Gator			G	$4,300	3/06	NCUT	4×2
John Deere	Gator			G	$4,400	1/06	SEPA	6×4, good paint
John Deere	Gator			G	$4,400	11/06	NCKY	2×4
John Deere	Gator			G	$4,500	11/06	SECA	4×2
John Deere	Gator			G	$4,500	11/06	NCKY	2×4
John Deere	Gator		814	G	$4,650	12/06	ECMO	6×4, knobby tires, diesel, hd tires, bedliner, front bumper
John Deere	Gator			G	$5,400	9/06	NCIA	6×4
John Deere	Gator			G	$5,500	12/06	SCMN	HPX Gator
John Deere	Gator		250	G	$6,750	11/06	SCCA	4WD, gas
John Deere	Gator		2	E	$7,250	8/06	SEPA	Gator HPX, new, 4×4, manual dump
John Deere	Gator	2002	1,400	G	$3,500	8/06	NWIL	4×2, gas
John Deere	Gator	2002	250	G	$5,000	3/06	NWIL	Diesel, 6×4, electric dump
John Deere	Gator	2003	125	G	$6,250	6/06	NEIN	6×4, diesel
John Deere	Gator	2004	500	G	$3,650	8/06	NWIL	4×2, gas
John Deere	Gator	2004	160	G	$3,900	8/06	NWIL	4×2, gas
John Deere	Gator	2004	45	E	$5,450	3/06	NWOH	4×2, like new
John Deere	Gator	2004	102	G	$9,500	9/06	SEIA	4×4, all-terrain tires, deluxe cab, electric bed hoist
John Deere	NA		148	G	$6,750	12/06	ECMO	HPX 4×4 Trail Gator, roll guard, brush guard
Kawasaki	110			P	$50	11/06	SCNE	3-wheeler
Kawasaki	110			F	$200	11/06	SCNE	3-wheeler
Kawasaki	110			F	$350	11/06	SCNE	3-wheeler
Kawasaki	250			G	$1,750	3/06	NCND	Mojave 250, liquid cooled, 4-wheeler, 2WD
Kawasaki	2510		5,566	P	$2,500	9/06	NCOH	4×4 Mule, windshield and canopy, rough, lots of hours to feed calves 6-8 hours a day, ran OK, they had little trouble with it
Kawasaki	2510		1,465	G	$3,250	2/06	SENE	Mule, 4×4, new engine 400 hours ago
Kawasaki	2510	1998	1,548	G	$3,500	5/06	SEND	Mule ATV, 4×4, liquid cooled, 25 hp., manual dump body
Kawasaki	300			F	$550	11/06	SCNE	Bayou, 4-wheeler, 2×4
Kawasaki	300			F	$700	3/06	NWKS	Bayou, 2WD

ATVs

Make	Model	Year	Hrs.	Cond.	Price	Sale	Location	Comments
Kawasaki	300			G	$800	3/06	NENE	Bayou, one owner
Kawasaki	300	1995		F	$700	2/06	WCMN	4×4, 4-wheeler
Kawasaki	300	1996		G	$3,000	3/06	WCKS	4-wheeler, Bayou
Kawasaki	300	2001	1,922	G	$2,200	11/06	SCNE	Prairie, 4-wheeler, 4×4
Kawasaki	300	2004		G	$3,250	8/06	SEMN	Bayou
Kawasaki	3010	2003	175	G	$5,800	12/06	NWIL	Mule, 4×4
Kawasaki	360	2003	2,000	G	$2,900	11/06	SCNE	4-wheeler, 4×4
Kawasaki	400			F	$950	8/06	NCNE	Prairie 4-wheeler, dozer blade, 4×4
Kawasaki	400		3,097	G	$1,550	2/06	SEKS	4-wheeler
Kawasaki	400			G	$1,850	9/06	NCIA	Prairie, 4-wheeler
Kawasaki	400	1982		G	$1,200	4/06	WCKS	4-wheeler, sprayer
Kawasaki	650	2001	650	G	$3,750	8/06	SEMN	4×4, V-twin
Kawasaki	Bayou			F	$450	8/06	NCNE	4-wheeler
Kawasaki	Bayou 300			G	$1,300	1/06	SCMI	4-wheeler, 2WD
Kawasaki	Mule			F	$900	4/06	NWSD	4-wheeler
Kawasaki	Mule			G	$5,400	12/06	ECMO	
Kawasaki	NA			G	$1,800	3/06	NCND	4-wheeler, 2WD
Kawasaki	Prairie			G	$2,800	3/06	NCUT	300 Prairie
Kawasaki	Prairie	1999	511	G	$3,800	2/06	WCKS	4×4
Polaris	250			G	$1,000	3/06	ECND	Trailblazer, 4-wheeler
Polaris	250	1999		G	$1,850	12/06	NENE	4-wheeler, 4×4
Polaris	300			G	$1,500	3/06	NWKS	Xplorer, 4×4
Polaris	300			G	$1,900	11/06	SCCA	4WD
Polaris	300			G	$1,900	11/06	SCCA	4WD
Polaris	300	1996		G	$925	3/06	ECMN	Xplorer, 4×4, recent engine rebuild
								+10% buyers premium
Polaris	300	1996		G	$1,600	10/06	NCWI	Express, 4-wheeler, 2WD
Polaris	300	1997		G	$1,100	3/06	NEKS	Express, 2×4
Polaris	325	2000		G	$2,100	4/06	ECND	4×2, Trail Boss
Polaris	325	2000		G	$2,400	11/06	WCMN	Magnum 325, 4×4
Polaris	325	2002		G	$3,100	11/06	WCMN	Expedition, 4×4
Polaris	350	1993		G	$1,300	3/06	WCMN	4-wheeler, 4×4, liquid cooled
Polaris	400			G	$3,000	8/06	SWWI	Big Boss, 6×6, dump box
Polaris	400	1998	2,948	G	$1,950	3/06	NEKS	Explorer, 4×4
Polaris	400	2003		G	$3,100	8/06	SEMN	4×4
Polaris	400	2004		G	$4,000	11/06	WCMN	Sport 400, 4×4
Polaris	400	2004		G	$4,750	8/06	SEMN	Sportsman
Polaris	425	1998		G	$2,250	11/06	ECNE	Magnum, gas, 4×4, hd tires, liquid-cooled engine,
								front snow blade, rear racks, front bumper
								lights, 2,924 miles
Polaris	500			G	$2,550	3/06	SWNE	4×4, liquid cooled, shaft ride system,
								front & rear racks, new tires
Polaris	500			G	$3,400	3/06	NCUT	
Polaris	500	2000		F	$3,100	11/06	NEIA	4×4, Magnum
Polaris	500	2000		G	$3,300	12/06	WCMN	6×6
Polaris	600	2003		G	$3,500	11/06	WCMN	Sportsman, 4×4
Polaris	700	1999		G	$1,700	11/06	WCMN	XC SP700, high-performance twin,
								adult ridden, garaged
Polaris	90	2001		G	$1,000	10/06	NCWI	4-wheeler

ATVs

Make	Model	Year	Hrs.	Cond.	Price	Sale	Location	Comments
Polaris	Explorer			G	$1,200	12/06	ECMN	
Polaris	Explorer		3,060	G	$1,600	11/06	ECNE	4×4, auto
Polaris	Explorer			E	$2,500	3/06	SENE	4-wheeler, 400
Polaris	Explorer	2000		G	$1,500	8/06	NCNE	4-wheeler, 4×4
Polaris	Hawkeye			G	$4,100	8/06	NECO	
Polaris	Hawkeye			G	$4,200	8/06	NECO	
Polaris	Magnum 425	1995		G	$1,900	11/06	WCMN	4×4
Polaris	NA			G	$3,900	3/06	NCUT	4×2
Polaris	Ranger	2001		G	$5,100	12/06	WCMN	2×4
Polaris	Ranger	2003		G	$5,600	9/06	NCMI	4×4
Polaris	Sportsman			G	$3,200	12/06	WCMN	700 Sportsman 4-wheeler
Polaris	Sportsman			G	$3,450	8/06	SEIA	Sportsman 500, 4×4, 4-wheeler
Polaris	Sportsman	1997		G	$3,000	3/06	NEMI	Sportsman 500, 4×4
Polaris	Sportsman	2002		G	$3,500	12/06	WCMN	4×4, new winch
Suzuki	125			F	$300	3/06	NENE	4-wheeler
Suzuki	250	2004		G	$1,500	11/06	WCMN	LT250Z
Suzuki	80	2001		G	$1,150	12/06	SCMI	Electric start, automatic
Suzuki	80	2005		G	$1,800	12/06	SCMI	
Yamaha	125	2001		G	$1,000	11/06	SECA	4-stroke motorcycle
Yamaha	200			F	$375	11/06	SCNE	3-wheeler
Yamaha	350			G	$800	3/06	WCMN	ATV, 2×4
Yamaha	350			G	$800	3/06	WCMN	ATV, 2×4
Yamaha	350			G	$1,700	3/06	NWKS	Big Bear, 4×4
Yamaha	400	1995		F	$1,700	1/06	NECO	Kodiak, 4×4
Yamaha	80	2001		G	$500	11/06	SECA	2-stroke motorcycle
Yamaha	Big Bear	1991		G	$1,600	11/06	WCMN	Big Bear 350, 4×4
Yamaha	Moto 4			F	$800	10/06	SWNE	4-wheeler, 2WD, reverse
Yamaha	Moto 4	1986		F	$400	11/06	WCMN	200 cc, 2×4
Yamaha	NA	1998		G	$1,500	4/06	NWKS	4-wheeler
Yamaha	Timberwolf			P	$325	10/06	SWNE	4-wheeler, 4×4, needs work

Notes

Augers & Elevators

"Yeah, but what does a new one cost now?" That was the explanation an auction buyer recently gave for paying $7,750 for a grain auger that sold new for $7,250 a few years back. Hard to reason with his logic. Big demand out there now for good-quality used augers.

Augers & Elevators

Make	Model	Year	Cond.	Price	Sale	Location	Comments
Adrian Mfg.	NA		G	$5,700	1/06	SCMN	Drive-over hopper dump pit auger, low profile
Allied	30×8		F	$400	11/06	WCMN	
Allied	33×7		F	$185	6/06	WCMN	PTO, auger
Allied	42×6		F	$40	5/06	SEND	PTO
Allied	NA		F	$100	8/06	NCIA	27' truck auger
Alloway	1220		G	$2,000	4/06	ECND	61'×8" auger, 10-hp. single-phase motor
Alloway	1320		G	$1,900	2/06	NWMN	Grain auger, 70', hyd. drive, swing-out hopper
Alloway	1405		G	$1,750	9/06	NWMN	60'×10" auger, PTO, mechanical swing hopper
Alloway	31×8		F	$80	8/06	NCIA	Auger set up for electric motor
Alloway	31×8		G	$1,500	3/06	NCIA	16-hp. Briggs
Alloway	36×8		F	$425	11/06	NWMN	PTO
Alloway	61×10		E	$2,000	3/06	SEMN	GS20 grain auger, PTO drive, hyd. lift, looks new
Alloway	62×10		E	$1,800	11/06	WCIA	
Alloway	62×8		F	$650	3/06	NCIA	PTO, auger
Alloway	71×10		F	$1,200	4/06	NWMN	Hyd. swing hopper
Batco	1335	2002	E	$4,600	12/06	SWIA	Electric single phase, 5 hp., bottom controls
Batco	1375		G	$8,000	3/06	NEND	Belt conveyor, PTO, hyd. lift
Batco	NA		G	$3,600	2/06	SCMI	Custom 26'×8" belt auger
Brandt	28×7		G	$900	11/06	NEND	5 hp., single phase
Brandt	35×6		G	$500	6/06	ECND	11 hp., Briggs ES
Brandt	35×7		G	$750	3/06	ECND	5 hp., single phase
Brandt	35×7		G	$2,100	6/06	ECND	Kohler 16 hp., Wheatheart bin sweep
Brandt	36×6		G	$350	3/06	NEND	16-hp. Briggs
Brandt	36×6		G	$500	3/06	NEND	16-hp. Briggs
Brandt	42×8		G	$1,000	3/06	NEND	Supercharged auger, Honda 18 hp., electric start
Brandt	57×8		F	$350	3/06	NCIA	PTO, auger
Brandt	60×10		G	$850	12/06	SEND	Auger, swing-out hopper, hyd. drive
Brandt	60×10		G	$900	10/06	NCND	Auger, swing out
Brandt	60×10		G	$2,700	3/06	ECND	Mechanical drive, PTO
Brandt	60×10	1995	G	$4,000	4/06	WCMB	Canadian sale, swing-away unload hopper
Brandt	60×8		G	$750	6/06	ECND	PTO, auger
Brandt	61×10		F	$650	7/06	NEND	Hyd. swing hopper auger
Brandt	70×10		G	$1,900	4/06	NEND	PTO, swing hopper, light kit, downspout
Brandt	70×10		G	$4,000	3/06	NCND	Mechanical swing hopper
Cardinal	18'		F	$75	5/06	SWWI	Elevator, transport and electric motor
Cardinal	30×8		F	$450	1/06	NWIL	5 hp., electric drive, auger
Cardinal	57×8		E	$1,600	9/06	NEIN	
Convey-All	NA		G	$700	11/06	NEND	Jump auger, Honda 5.5-hp. motor
Farm King	31×10		F	$1,800	2/06	NWIL	PTO, auger
Farm King	31×10	1999	G	$1,350	2/06	NWIN	Loading auger
Farm King	36×7		G	$800	3/06	ECND	7.5 hp., single phase
Farm King	40×6		F	$50	8/06	SCMN	PTO
Farm King	40×6		F	$100	4/06	WCSD	
Farm King	51×8		G	$700	4/06	SEMN	Canadian sale
Farm King	56×8		P	$110	1/06	NWIL	
Farm King	56×8		G	$880	1/06	NWIL	
Farm King	60×10		G	$950	11/06	SWIA	Swing hopper
Farm King	60×10		G	$2,600	3/06	NEND	PTO, swing-away auger

WHAT'S IT WORTH?

Augers & Elevators

Make	Model	Year	Cond.	Price	Sale	Location	Comments
Farm King	61×10		G	$4,400	4/06	SEMN	Canadian sale, swing-away unload hopper, PTO, mechanical drive
Farm King	70×10		F	$1,250	8/06	NWIL	Auger, swing-away hopper
Farm King	70×10		G	$1,800	6/06	NWMN	PTO, mechanical drive swing hopper
Farm King	70×10		G	$3,900	3/06	ECND	Mechanical swing hopper, hyd. up/down
Farm King	70×10	1996	G	$3,000	4/06	NEND	Hyd. swing hopper, hyd. lift, power swing hopper
Farm King	71×10		G	$2,800	2/06	NWIL	Swing-away PTO hopper
Farm King	841		G	$950	4/06	WCMN	Canadian sale, 41'×8", PTO
Farm King	851		G	$350	11/06	NEND	PTO auger
Feterl	16×10		G	$750	2/06	NCIL	Easi-Roll truck hopper
Feterl	28×8		G	$925	3/06	WCMN	Auger, gas engine
Feterl	28×8		E	$1,100	8/06	NCIA	PTO auger, like new
Feterl	28×8		G	$1,100	2/06	ECMN	
Feterl	30×10		G	$2,600	3/06	SWNE	PTO-driven auger
Feterl	30×7		G	$550	4/06	NEND	20-hp. Briggs
Feterl	30×8		G	$325	3/06	ECNE	
Feterl	32×8		G	$650	3/06	ECNE	5-hp. electric motor
Feterl	34×10		F	$600	2/06	SWNE	540 PTO-driven auger
Feterl	34×10		G	$1,000	3/06	ECIL	Auger, 10-hp. motor
Feterl	34×10		G	$1,100	2/06	NCIL	PTO
Feterl	34×10		G	$1,800	2/06	ECMN	
Feterl	34×10		G	$2,200	11/06	SCSD	Grain auger
Feterl	34×10		E	$2,600	2/06	ECMN	PTO auger, one owner
Feterl	34×8		G	$1,900	6/06	SCMN	Grain auger, 16 hp., Onan gas engine drive
Feterl	44×10		G	$2,100	8/06	SCMN	
Feterl	44×10		E	$2,300	2/06	SWNE	540 PTO-driven auger, like new
Feterl	50'		G	$125	8/06	SCMN	PTO
Feterl	52×7		F	$60	9/06	ECNE	PTO driven, new flighting 2 years ago
Feterl	55×10		G	$2,300	8/06	SEMN	
Feterl	55×8		F	$375	9/06	SCMN	Red
Feterl	55×8		G	$1,750	9/06	SCMN	PTO auger, red
Feterl	60×10		F	$750	3/06	SWNE	PTO drive, swing-away hopper
Feterl	60×8		F	$80	3/06	ECNE	PTO-driven auger
Feterl	60×8		F	$600	2/06	NWSD	
Feterl	60×8		G	$900	12/06	ECNE	PTO-driven auger, crank lift
Feterl	60×8		G	$1,200	3/06	ECNE	Hyd. lift, swing hopper
Feterl	60×8		G	$2,350	8/06	WCMN	Swing hopper, hyd. lift
Feterl	61×10		F	$750	3/06	SWMN	PTO auger
Feterl	61×10		G	$1,350	3/06	SEMN	Grain auger, PTO, like new, flighting
Feterl	61×12		G	$3,150	6/06	SCMN	Hyd. lift, swing hopper, PTO
Feterl	62×10		F	$200	11/06	SCIL	PTO auger
Feterl	62×8		F	$750	1/06	NWIL	
Feterl	66×10		F	$700	3/06	WCMN	Swing hopper
Feterl	66×10		F	$700	3/06	SWNE	PTO-driven auger, fold-out PTO drive hopper, hyd. lift
Feterl	66×10		G	$2,000	3/06	NCIA	PTO auger, mechanical hopper, hyd. raise
Feterl	66×10		G	$2,300	3/06	WCMN	Swing hopper, mechanical drive, hyd. lift
Feterl	66×10		G	$2,300	11/06	SCSD	Grain auger, swing-out hopper
Feterl	66×10		E	$5,000	1/06	NWIA	Direct-drive grain auger, hyd. lift, swing hopper
Feterl	66×8		G	$800	1/06	NWIL	

Augers & Elevators

Make	Model	Year	Cond.	Price	Sale	Location	Comments
Feterl	66×8		G	$950	3/06	SEND	10-hp. electric motor
Feterl	71×10		F	$1,250	6/06	SEND	PTO, mechanical swing
Feterl	72×10		G	$3,300	11/06	NWMN	Swing hopper
Feterl	76×10		G	$2,500	2/06	ECMN	
Feterl	76×10		G	$3,400	12/06	ECNE	PTO-driven auger, hyd. winch
Feterl	76×10	2004	E	$7,000	3/06	ECNE	PTO auger, hyd. lift, like new
Feterl	80×10		G	$7,800	3/06	NENE	Hyd. lift, PTO-driven, used one season, truck hopper
Feterl	86×12		E	$8,600	2/06	ECMN	Grain auger, swing hopper, hyd. lift, PTO drive, one owner
Feterl	NA		G	$1,500	1/06	NECO	Drive-over 8" auger
Feterl	NA		G	$4,000	3/06	SWMN	13" drive-over auger, pit
Flex King	NA		G	$7,000	4/06	WCMN	Canadian sale, 70'×13", swing-away hopper
Grain King	62×10	2002	G	$4,400	2/06	NWIL	PTO auger, swing-away hopper
Grain King	72×10	2003	G	$4,600	2/06	NWIL	PTO auger, swing-away hopper
GSI	62×10		G	$3,700	1/06	WCIL	Swing hopper
Hutchinson	24×6		P	$25	4/06	NWKS	Auger, electric motor
Hutchinson	26×6		G	$275	12/06	WCMN	
Hutchinson	30×10		G	$3,000	1/06	SWOH	
Hutchinson	30×8		G	$350	3/06	NWMN	Briggs 16 hp., electric start
Hutchinson	32×6		F	$150	12/06	NWIL	Top-drive electric mount
Hutchinson	32×8		F	$150	6/06	NCIL	PTO auger
Hutchinson	33×8		E	$2,400	1/06	SCNE	7.5-hp. single-phase motor, like new
Hutchinson	35×6		G	$150	10/06	SWOH	
Hutchinson	36×10		G	$450	9/06	NEIN	
Hutchinson	36×10		G	$3,000	6/06	SCMN	7.5-hp. motor, grain auger, looks new
Hutchinson	36×8		F	$200	12/06	SWMI	3-hp. motor
Hutchinson	41×6		F	$75	4/06	SEND	PTO auger
Hutchinson	48×8		F	$500	3/06	SWNE	10-hp. electric motor
Hutchinson	50×8		F	$450	3/06	WCMN	PTO auger
Hutchinson	50×8		G	$1,900	8/06	NCOH	Top drive PTO
Hutchinson	51×10		G	$1,700	8/06	SCMN	
Hutchinson	52×8		G	$1,150	2/06	SCMI	PTO transport auger
Hutchinson	53×6		P	$25	2/06	SWNE	Belt-driven auger
Hutchinson	53×6		F	$650	8/06	NCOH	
Hutchinson	53×6	1990	F	$250	12/06	NWIL	Top-drive electric mount
Hutchinson	53×8		F	$220	1/06	NWIL	7.5 hp., electric auger
Hutchinson	53×8		G	$650	3/06	NCOH	PTO auger
Hutchinson	53×8		G	$950	3/06	SEND	10 hp., electric
Hutchinson	54×10		G	$750	3/06	NCIL	Hyd. lift
Hutchinson	55×8		G	$1,300	3/06	SEMN	
Hutchinson	56×8		P	$75	3/06	SWNE	PTO-driven auger
Hutchinson	57×8		F	$110	2/06	SWNE	PTO-driven auger
Hutchinson	57×8		F	$250	11/06	SCNE	PTO
Hutchinson	57×8		F	$300	12/06	NCIA	Auger
Hutchinson	57×8		E	$1,300	9/06	NEIN	10-hp. electric motor
Hutchinson	59×8	1993	G	$2,500	12/06	SWMI	PTO-driven transport auger
Hutchinson	60×10		G	$3,700	8/06	NEIL	Swing-away hopper, end PTO drive
Hutchinson	61×8		F	$175	8/06	NCIA	Auger PTO, 110V raise w/ hand control
Hutchinson	61×8		G	$1,300	8/06	SCMN	Auger, 10-hp. electric motor
Hutchinson	61×8	1987	F	$900	2/06	NWIN	Auger

WHAT'S IT WORTH?

Augers & Elevators

Make	Model	Year	Cond.	Price	Sale	Location	Comments
Hutchinson	62×10		F	$800	2/06	ECIL	Swing-away auger
Hutchinson	62×10		G	$2,900	4/06	SWOH	Hyd. swing
Hutchinson	62×8		G	$1,025	1/06	WCIL	Swing hopper
Hutchinson	62×8	2002	G	$3,100	3/06	NEMI	Transport auger, 10-hp. single-phase electric motor
Hutchinson	65×8		F	$500	3/06	ECND	PTO auger
Hutchinson	70×13	2004	G	$7,250	4/06	NWMN	Low Pro hopper
Hutchinson	71×10		G	$1,500	10/06	SEMN	Auger
Hutchinson	81×10		F	$350	4/06	NWMN	PTO auger, hyd. up/down
Hutchinson	92×12		G	$12,000	2/06	SEKS	
Hutchinson	NA		E	$250	3/06	NCOK	30' auger, PTO driven
Hutchinson	NA		F	$300	12/06	WCMI	12' bin sweep auger
Hutchinson	NA		F	$550	12/06	WCMI	15' loadout auger, 2-hp. motor
John Deere	40'		G	$325	8/06	ECNE	Grain elevator, 18" wide, on running gear, shedded
John Deere	428		G	$475	1/06	SCMI	40' PTO-drive flat elevator
Kewanee	40'		G	$1,000	12/06	WCMI	Flat elevator, PTO drive
Kewanee	50'		G	$300	8/06	NEIA	Elevator, PTO raise
Kewanee	50'		G	$350	2/06	NCIN	PTO elevator, drag
Kewanee	500		G	$375	11/06	NEKS	36' PTO elevator
Kewanee	52'		F	$225	10/06	WCWI	All-purpose elevator
Kewanee	52×8		G	$700	8/06	ECNE	Truck hopper, one owner, shedded
Kewanee	56×8		F	$50	9/06	NENE	Fold down auger, 540 PTO
Kewanee	56×8		G	$575	3/06	ECNE	Dolly wheel
Kewanee	600		E	$350	9/06	NEIN	60' elevator, hyd. lift
Kewanee	600		G	$525	8/06	SEMN	52' elevator
Kilbros	14'		F	$675	2/06	SCMI	Steel wagon fertilizer auger
Koyker	NA		G	$650	2/06	SCMI	28'×8.5" transport auger, PTO drive
L. Giant	36'		P	$10	2/06	ECMN	PTO, wide elevator
L. Giant	45'		G	$700	3/06	NCWI	Elevator
Mayrath	19×6		F	$80	2/06	WCIL	Truck auger
Mayrath	27×6		F	$300	1/06	WCNE	5-hp. electric motor
Mayrath	27×8		F	$300	8/06	NWIL	PTO auger
Mayrath	28×8		F	$75	3/06	NWKS	PTO driven
Mayrath	28×8		E	$1,300	8/06	ECNE	PTO-driven auger, like new, shedded
Mayrath	30×6		P	$20	2/06	ECIL	5-hp. electric 220V motor
Mayrath	31×8	2005	E	$2,800	3/06	ECNE	5-hp. electric motor, new – never used
Mayrath	32×10		F	$325	1/06	NWIL	PTO auger
Mayrath	32×10		G	$700	2/06	NCIL	PTO
Mayrath	32×8	2004	G	$1,700	12/06	NWIL	10-hp. electric motor
Mayrath	42×10	1990	G	$1,025	12/06	NWIL	Bottom drive, PTO
Mayrath	42×6		P	$15	11/06	SENE	PTO driven, 540 PTO
Mayrath	50×8		F	$200	8/06	NEKS	PTO-driven auger
Mayrath	50×8		G	$475	8/06	NEIA	Stored inside
Mayrath	50×8		G	$2,200	3/06	NWPA	
Mayrath	50×8		G	$2,700	3/06	NWPA	Swing auger, hyd. lift
Mayrath	51×6		G	$1,025	12/06	NWIL	
Mayrath	53×8		P	$20	9/06	NEND	PTO auger, screens
Mayrath	53×8		G	$775	3/06	NCOH	PTO auger, transport
Mayrath	56×10	1996	F	$150	6/06	NWKS	PTO auger
Mayrath	57×8		P	$70	3/06	NCIA	PTO auger

Augers & Elevators

Make	Model	Year	Cond.	Price	Sale	Location	Comments
Mayrath	58×10		F	$1,000	1/06	NWIL	PTO auger
Mayrath	58×8		F	$175	1/06	NWIL	PTO auger
Mayrath	60×10		G	$800	9/06	NWMN	Swing hopper
Mayrath	60×6		F	$250	4/06	SWSD	PTO
Mayrath	60×8		P	$50	3/06	NWKS	
Mayrath	61×10		G	$650	3/06	NWMN	PTO auger
Mayrath	61×10		F	$750	7/06	NWMN	Swing hopper, auger
Mayrath	61×10		G	$3,250	8/06	WCIL	
Mayrath	61×6		F	$250	12/06	NWIL	Compact PTO or electric mount
Mayrath	61×6	1996	G	$900	12/06	NWIL	Top drive electric mount
Mayrath	61×8		F	$300	2/06	WCIL	Bottom-drive auger
Mayrath	62×10		G	$1,150	4/06	ECND	Hyd. swing hopper
Mayrath	62×10		G	$2,200	1/06	SWOH	Hyd. swing away auger
Mayrath	62×10	2002	G	$4,000	12/06	SEIA	Swing hopper
Mayrath	62×10	2004	G	$4,500	12/06	SEIA	Swing hopper
Mayrath	62×10	2004	E	$5,700	8/06	ECIA	Same as new, swing hopper, hd flighting
Mayrath	62×12		G	$3,500	2/06	NCIL	Swing hopper
Mayrath	62×6		F	$200	2/06	ECIL	PTO auger
Mayrath	62×8		P	$60	11/06	SENE	PTO driven, 540 PTO
Mayrath	62×8		P	$150	1/06	NWIL	PTO auger
Mayrath	62×8		F	$375	3/06	NCIL	Swing-away auger, PTO drive
Mayrath	62×8		G	$700	10/06	WCWI	Auger, hopper, hyd. drive
Mayrath	62×8		G	$1,100	12/06	NWIL	Swing-away hopper
Mayrath	62×8		F	$1,400	3/06	SWOH	PTO auger
Mayrath	62×8		G	$2,450	9/06	NWIL	Used for only 10,000 bu., galvanized
Mayrath	62×8		E	$3,750	3/06	NEIA	Swing hopper, like new
Mayrath	62×8		E	$5,400	11/06	SENE	Unused, direct drive, PTO drive truck hopper w/ screener, hyd. lift, shedded
Mayrath	62×8	1996	G	$2,950	12/06	WCIL	Swing-away auger
Mayrath	64×8		G	$2,300	4/06	SWSD	Hyd. slide away hopper
Mayrath	67×10		G	$2,050	3/06	SESD	Swing hopper, hyd. lift
Mayrath	70×8		G	$3,000	12/06	SEIA	Swing out
Mayrath	71×10		G	$5,700	1/06	NEIA	3 years old
My-D Han-D	NA		E	$205	3/06	NCOK	12V drill fill auger, brand-new
My-D Han-D	NA		G	$700	3/06	NEMI	34' double chain hay/grain transport elevator, hyd. drive
New Idea	177		G	$475	9/06	NEIN	40' elevator, gas engine
Olson	NA		G	$325	2/06	ECMN	40' bale elevator, electric
Owatonna	205		G	$400	5/06	SWWI	50' hay/grain elevator
Peck	31×10		G	$1,700	3/06	NENE	PTO drive auger
Peck	31×8		G	$950	8/06	ECNE	Hyd. drive auger
Peck	56'		F	$100	8/06	NCNE	6" auger
Peck	60×10		F	$425	4/06	NEIA	Auger, swing hopper
Peck	60×6		F	$600	9/06	ECNE	PTO drive
Peck	61×8		F	$200	12/06	NENE	
Peck	61×8		G	$1,075	3/06	ECNE	PTO driven auger
Peck	62×8		G	$3,600	8/06	NCIA	Mechanical swing auger, hyd. lift
Peck	66×10		G	$2,250	1/06	ECNE	Auger, hyd. hopper
Peck	71×10		G	$2,000	3/06	ECNE	PTO auger, hyd. lift
Peck	71×10		G	$4,500	11/06	WCMN	Mechanical swing hopper, hyd. lift, used one season

Augers & Elevators

Make	Model	Year	Cond.	Price	Sale	Location	Comments
Peck	71×10		G	$4,850	8/06	ECNE	Mechanical drive, swinging hopper
Peck	NA		G	$800	11/06	SWIA	30' truck auger, hyd. drive
Peck	NA		G	$1,225	7/06	NWIL	25'×8" truck auger
Sakundiak	33×8	1995	G	$2,300	4/06	NEND	18-hp. engine, hyd. up/down
Sakundiak	37×7		G	$400	7/06	NEND	Auger, 16-hp. Briggs
Sakundiak	45×7		G	$250	4/06	WCMB	Canadian sale, PTO
Scoop-A-Sec	46×8		G	$400	3/06	NWMN	PTO and motor mounts
Snowco	28×8		G	$950	7/06	NCIA	PTO auger
Snowco	40×6		G	$450	1/06	SCMI	PTO
Snowco	54×8		F	$140	9/06	NCIA	PTO auger
Speed King	24×6		F	$200	10/06	SWNE	PTO-driven auger
Speed King	30×6		G	$375	3/06	NCND	Single phase
Speed King	34×6		F	$250	3/06	WCSD	PTO
Speed King	40×6		G	$400	2/06	WCNE	Honda 13-hp. motor
Speed King	40×8		G	$400	4/06	WCSD	PTO auger
Speed King	42×8		P	$60	3/06	NWKS	Auger
Speed King	60×6		F	$200	9/06	SCMN	Electric auger
Speed King	65×8		G	$375	2/06	WCNE	PTO
Speed King	70×10		G	$300	1/06	NECO	PTO
Speed King	71×10		G	$1,500	8/06	NECO	
Sudenga	12×8		G	$500	5/06	SCMI	Transport auger, 2-hp. motor
Sudenga	14×6		G	$1,300	2/06	NCIL	Brush auger, hyd. drive
Sudenga	53×7		F	$550	9/06	SCMN	PTO
Sudenga	54×8		G	$2,000	1/06	NWIA	Truck auger, 5-hp. Baldor motor
Sudenga	61×10		G	$1,100	10/06	SEMN	Auger
Sudenga	61×8		P	$200	1/06	NWIA	PTO drive
Sudenga	61×8		F	$250	8/06	NCIA	Swinging hopper
Sudenga	62×10		G	$1,800	6/06	SCMN	PTO grain auger
Sudenga	66×10		E	$4,800	1/06	NWIA	Direct-drive auger, hyd. lift, dual-auger hopper
Sudenga	71×8		G	$2,600	2/06	NWIA	Hyd. lift auger
Sudenga	NA		G	$225	1/06	ECNE	8' auger, incline bin unload
Unverferth	14×6	2005	E	$900	2/06	NWOH	Plastic seed auger
Versatile	44×8		P	$200	4/06	NESD	Auger
Versatile	45×8		G	$500	8/06	WCMN	New flighting
Versatile	62×8		F	$625	1/06	NEMO	
Versatile	NA		F	$175	11/06	SCNE	63'×8" auger, PTO
Westco	71×10		G	$3,700	8/06	WCMN	Swing hopper
Westfield	100×61		G	$3,900	2/06	NWSD	540 PTO, 10"×61', hyd. lift and slide-away hopper
Westfield	100×71		E	$6,800	1/06	NCCO	Auger, swing out, 2 years old
Westfield	100×61	1999	G	$2,000	11/06	ECND	WR100-61, 20 hp., 3 phase
Westfield	10×8		G	$650	9/06	NECO	Hopper, hyd. drive
Westfield	12×8		G	$900	2/06	SCMI	Auger, 3-hp. motor, wheels & hopper
Westfield	130×91	2005	G	$11,000	11/06	ECND	Auger, hyd. self-propelled swing, gear drive hopper, PTO
Westfield	16×6		G	$625	2/06	NWSD	Drill fill auger
Westfield	20×6		G	$1,000	12/06	WCMN	Drill fill brush auger
Westfield	26×7		G	$900	6/06	NWMN	5-hp. 220V electric motor
Westfield	30×6		G	$300	4/06	SEMN	Canadian sale, Kohler 10-hp. motor
Westfield	30×7		F	$350	3/06	SEND	Loadout hopper auger, 10 hp., single
Westfield	30×8		G	$1,200	11/06	ECNE	PTO, truck auger

Augers & Elevators

Make	Model	Year	Cond.	Price	Sale	Location	Comments
Westfield	31×10		G	$3,700	12/06	NCIA	Truck auger, Kohler 20-hp. gas
Westfield	31×10	2002	G	$2,200	6/06	NWMN	J210-31, 10-hp. 220V electric motor
Westfield	31×7		P	$175	4/06	NESD	Auger, no motor
Westfield	31×7		G	$575	9/06	NEND	5-hp. electric motor
Westfield	31×7		G	$700	4/06	ECND	Loadout auger, Briggs 10-hp. motor
Westfield	31×7	1990	F	$1,300	4/06	NESD	Auger, Honda 13-hp. gas motor, electric start
Westfield	31×7	1993	G	$1,000	6/06	NWMN	5-hp. 220V electric motor
Westfield	31×8		F	$400	3/06	NWMN	Auger, 16-hp. gas engine
Westfield	31×8		G	$950	4/06	NEND	Briggs 16 hp.
Westfield	31×8		G	$1,200	4/06	ECND	Kohler 16 hp., electric start
Westfield	31×8		G	$2,000	2/06	NWMN	10-hp. electric motor, single phase
Westfield	31×8	2002	G	$2,600	1/06	NEIA	Truck auger, 7.5-hp. electric motor
Westfield	36×10		G	$1,650	8/06	NEIL	PTO auger
Westfield	36×14		G	$4,100	11/06	NEND	Belt auger, belt conveyor w/ single-phase motor
Westfield	36×6		F	$300	12/06	WCMN	Electric motor
Westfield	36×7		G	$700	4/06	WCMB	Canadian sale, 16-hp. motor, rope start
Westfield	36×7		G	$1,950	3/06	SEND	J207-36, Honda engine, electric start
Westfield	36×8		G	$850	3/06	SEND	Briggs ES motor
Westfield	36×8		G	$1,250	9/06	NECO	WR8036, PTO
Westfield	36×8		G	$1,400	11/06	NEND	Honda motor and Wheatheart hyd. takeout, J208-36
Westfield	36×8		G	$2,000	3/06	ECND	Kohler 18 hp., electric start
Westfield	36×8		E	$2,700	11/06	ECNE	Truck auger, 5-hp. electric motor, like new
Westfield	41×7		P	$25	7/06	NWMN	Gas engine auger
Westfield	41×7		F	$500	9/06	NWMN	16-hp. gas
Westfield	41×7		G	$600	3/06	NEND	7.5-hp. single phase
Westfield	41×8		G	$450	4/06	NEND	PTO auger
Westfield	41×8		F	$550	3/06	NWMN	PTO
Westfield	41×8		G	$1,250	11/06	NWMN	PTO
Westfield	45×7		G	$350	3/06	NCND	7.5-hp. single phase
Westfield	46×7		G	$2,150	2/06	NWSD	PTO
Westfield	50×8		G	$1,025	8/06	NEIA	
Westfield	51×10		F	$700	4/06	NESD	PTO auger
Westfield	51×10		E	$4,600	8/06	WCMN	MK 1051, low-profile swing hopper, PTO drive, hyd. lift, hyd. power wheel on swing hopper, like new
Westfield	51×10	1992	G	$3,700	3/06	ECND	Swing hopper auger, 540 PTO, one owner
Westfield	51×7	1986	G	$1,500	3/06	ECND	7.5-hp. single phase
Westfield	51×8		G	$500	4/06	NEND	PTO auger
Westfield	51×8		G	$600	3/06	NWKS	PTO driven
Westfield	51×8		F	$625	8/06	NCIA	PTO auger
Westfield	51×8		P	$650	6/06	SCMN	Grain auger, 7.5-hp. electric motor
Westfield	51×8		G	$700	3/06	ECND	PTO
Westfield	51×8		G	$750	8/06	WCMN	PTO drive
Westfield	51×8		F	$850	9/06	NWMN	PTO
Westfield	51×8		G	$1,050	4/06	NWMN	PTO
Westfield	51×8		G	$1,225	4/06	SEND	PTO auger
Westfield	51×8		G	$1,900	4/06	SEND	Swing hopper auger
Westfield	51×8	1978	G	$750	4/06	WCMN	One owner
Westfield	52×8		F	$350	1/06	NEMO	
Westfield	54×8		G	$600	11/06	NEND	7.5 hp., single phase

WHAT'S IT WORTH?

Augers & Elevators

Make	Model	Year	Cond.	Price	Sale	Location	Comments
Westfield	54×8	2003	G	$2,750	1/06	NEIA	7.5-hp. electric motor
Westfield	61×10		F	$500	10/06	NCND	Hyd. lift side hopper
Westfield	61×10		G	$500	11/06	NEND	PTO auger, W100
Westfield	61×10		G	$1,000	2/06	WCIL	Swing-away auger
Westfield	61×10		G	$1,300	9/06	NEND	PTO auger, hyd. swing out
Westfield	61×10		G	$2,000	5/06	SEND	Swing hopper, MK auger
Westfield	61×10		G	$2,100	3/06	SCIA	Swing hopper, 2 years old
Westfield	61×10		G	$2,250	12/06	NWOH	Swing auger
Westfield	61×10		G	$2,350	4/06	NWMN	Mechanical auger
Westfield	61×10		G	$2,400	4/06	WCSD	Grain auger, swing-out hopper
Westfield	61×10	1999	G	$2,900	4/06	NESD	PTO auger, swing hopper
Westfield	61×10		G	$3,500	11/06	NEND	Mechanical swing hopper, MK100-61
Westfield	61×10		G	$4,200	12/06	NCIA	Hyd. lift, swing hopper
Westfield	61×10		G	$5,800	12/06	WCMI	MK100-61, side loader
Westfield	61×10	2001	E	$4,100	1/06	WCIL	MK100, swing out
Westfield	61×8		G	$350	9/06	NWMN	PTO
Westfield	61×8		G	$475	9/06	NECO	W80-61, PTO
Westfield	61×8		F	$650	9/06	SEIA	Auger, swing hopper
Westfield	61×8		F	$700	11/06	WCMN	Hyd. swing hopper, hyd. lift
Westfield	61×8		G	$1,000	12/06	NWIL	MK80, swing hopper
Westfield	61×8		G	$2,100	8/06	WCIL	
Westfield	61×8		G	$3,250	2/06	SEMI	PTO auger
Westfield	61×8	1993	F	$600	12/06	WCMN	Swing hopper
Westfield	61×8	2000	G	$1,350	9/06	SEIA	Auger, swing hopper
Westfield	65×10		F	$700	3/06	NEKS	Hyd. lift swing-away hopper, 540 PTO
Westfield	66×8		E	$3,000	2/06	SENE	Swing away
Westfield	71×10		G	$1,500	11/06	NWKS	PTO, swing-away hopper
Westfield	71×10		G	$2,000	9/06	SCMN	Auger, swing hopper
Westfield	71×10		E	$2,600	9/06	NECO	MK100-71, PTO, swing-out hopper
Westfield	71×10		E	$3,250	1/06	NECO	Hopper auger
Westfield	71×10		G	$3,550	9/06	WCND	MK, PTO, low-profile swing hopper auger
Westfield	71×10		G	$3,600	12/06	NEMO	Swing-away grain auger, new in 2002
Westfield	71×10		G	$3,700	6/06	NWMN	Mechanical-drive swing hopper
Westfield	71×10		G	$4,900	8/06	NCIA	Auger, low-profile mechanical hopper, hyd. raise
Westfield	71×10		E	$6,300	3/06	NWOH	Transport auger, low-profile swing auger, MK100-71
Westfield	71×10	2001	G	$4,500	4/06	NWMN	Mechanical swing low-profile hopper
Westfield	71×10	2002	G	$3,400	2/06	ECMN	PTO auger elevator
Westfield	71×10	2004	E	$6,600	1/06	SWNE	Swing hopper, like new
Westfield	71×13	2001	G	$7,000	4/06	NWMN	Swing hopper, low-profile hopper
Westfield	71×8		E	$2,100	3/06	SEND	PTO
Westfield	80×51	1995	G	$1,700	3/06	NEMI	51'×8" PTO transport auger
Westfield	80×56		G	$300	4/06	NEIA	Auger
Westfield	80×8		F	$800	8/06	WCMN	PTO drive
Westfield	91×13		G	$8,750	8/06	WCMN	
Westfield	J208-31		G	$2,700	4/06	NWMN	Honda engine, 13 hp.
Westfield	J208-36	2002	G	$2,000	11/06	ECND	Kohler gas
Westfield	J208-51		G	$1,600	11/06	NEND	Auger, Vanguard 18-hp. motor
Westfield	J210-31		G	$2,300	11/06	ECND	10 hp., 3 phase
Westfield	J210-31	2006	G	$3,000	12/06	SWIA	Auger, 7.5-hp. single phase, double flight

Augers & Elevators

Make	Model	Year	Cond.	Price	Sale	Location	Comments
Westfield	WR100-61	1999	G	$2,600	11/06	ECND	20 hp., 3 phase
Westfield	WR-31	2005	G	$2,700	12/06	SWIA	31' auger, PTO
Westgo	1210		F	$210	9/06	NEND	Wet grain auger
Westgo	1210		G	$900	5/06	SEND	30×8 auger
Westgo	1305		F	$600	3/06	NEND	61'×10" hyd. swing hopper
Westgo	1305		G	$1,600	4/06	NWMN	60'×10" auger, PTO, hyd. lift & swing hopper
Westgo	1310		F	$900	9/06	NWMN	70'×10" auger, PTO, hyd. swing hopper
Westgo	28×10		G	$1,200	4/06	NWMN	10 hp., single phase
Westgo	40×8		F	$170	5/06	SEND	Wisconsin engine
Westgo	41×8		F	$100	7/06	NWMN	PTO drive
Westgo	54×8		F	$400	9/06	ECNE	Grain auger
Westgo	60×10		G	$2,500	4/06	ECND	Model 1410, mechanical swing hopper
Westgo	60×8		G	$800	4/06	NEND	10-hp. electric with reverse
Westgo	61×10		F	$450	11/06	NWMN	Hyd. swing hopper auger
Westgo	61×10		G	$1,000	11/06	NWMN	PTO
Westgo	61×10		G	$1,100	3/06	NCND	Hyd. swing hopper
Westgo	61×10		G	$2,000	3/06	NWMN	Model 1305, hyd. swing hopper
Westgo	71×10		G	$1,175	7/06	NWMN	Grain auger, side hopper
WIC	626C		G	$1,200	3/06	ECND	Harvester, 6R, hyd. load, Dee row finder
WIC	822C		F	$1,000	7/06	NWMN	Triple-drum rotobeaters, 12R, all rubber
WIC	822C		F	$2,000	7/06	NWMN	Triple-drum rotobeaters, 12R, all rubber
WIC	822C		G	$3,000	7/06	NWMN	Triple-drum rotobeater, 12R, all rubber
WIC	826C		F	$1,000	7/06	NWMN	Harvester, 6R-22, row finder
WIC	826C		F	$1,600	7/06	NWMN	Harvester, 6R-22, row finder
WIC	826C		F	$1,600	7/06	NWMN	Harvester, 6R-22, row finder
WIC	826C	1986	F	$1,000	4/06	NWMN	Lifter, 8R, field-ready
WIC	H2837		G	$17,000	3/06	SWMN	6R sugar beet lifter
WIC	NA		F	$400	7/06	NWMN	24R-22 beet cultivator, cutaways, tunnel shields, lift assist, hyd. fold
WIC	NA		G	$2,000	8/06	WCMN	12R-22 beet topper

Notes

Blades

Grader blades, dozer blades, box scraper blades, three-point back blades, snowplow blades, hydraulic-angle tilt blades. We lump all these various types of blades together into one place. Want to know how much a used blade is worth? Dive right in.

Blades

Make	Model	Year	Cond.	Price	Sale	Location	Comments
Allis-Chalmers	8'		G	$500	11/06	WCIL	
Allis-Chalmers	8'		G	$650	10/06	SWNE	Snap coupler
Arps	8'		G	$400	2/06	SCMI	Back blade, hyd. angle
Big Ox	8'		F	$140	9/06	ECNE	3-pt. blade, swivel no tilt
Big Ox	8'		G	$450	3/06	ECNE	3-pt. hd
Big Ox	9'		F	$150	3/06	NWKS	3 pt.
Big Ox	9'		G	$575	11/06	SCNE	3 pt.
Big Ox	9'		G	$1,900	12/06	NEMO	9' hyd.
Big Ox	S69		G	$900	11/06	SENE	9'
Bush Hog	10'		G	$625	2/06	NECO	Hyd.
Bush Hog	121		G	$2,750	1/06	WCCA	3 pt., 8', hyd. angle blade
Bush Hog	176		G	$2,100	1/06	NCCO	10' 3 pt. rear blade
Bush Hog	176		G	$2,425	1/06	ECIL	3 pt. 10' nice heavy blade, hyd. angle/tilt
Bush Hog	8'		G	$750	12/06	SWIA	3 pt. blade, angle adjacent
Bush Hog	8'		G	$900	2/06	WCIL	3 pt. blade
Caldwell	7'		F	$600	3/06	SEPA	Hercules, 3 pt. 7' hd blade
Case IH	40		F	$450	8/06	NWIL	8' 3 pt. blade
Cline	8'		G	$450	3/06	NWIL	3 pt. hd blade
Command	10'		G	$1,500	3/06	NCCO	Box scraper, pt
Dearborn	6'		F	$200	2/06	SWIN	Grader blade
Degelman	10'		G	$850	1/06	WCNE	Front end, JD mounts
Degelman	10'		G	$900	12/06	NWMO	
Degelman	10'	1995	G	$500	3/06	NWKS	Dozer blade, to fit Case IH tractor
Degelman	12'		G	$800	2/06	NECO	Front, JD 6030 mounts
Degelman	12'		G	$1,200	3/06	NCNE	Hyd. blade, manual tilt, JD 8640 mounts
Degelman	12'		G	$3,750	2/06	SEKS	12-1, 4-ton dozer blade, hyd. tilt & angle, like new
Degelman	12'		G	$4,600	3/06	NCCO	Dozer blade with JD 4560 mounts
Degelman	14'		G	$1,000	2/06	NWSD	Dozer blade, hyd.
Degelman	14'		G	$5,000	3/06	NENE	Front-mount dozer, shop-built brush rack
Degelman	16-1-HA	1999	G	$10,250	11/06	ECND	Hyd. dozer blade, top & side extension, fully hyd. brackets for JD 9400 4WD tractor
Degelman	9'		F	$300	8/06	NCNE	9' for IHC 1586 tractor
Degelman	9'		G	$1,400	3/06	NEMI	9' dozer push blade, underslung, universal fit
Ford	6'		F	$100	8/06	ECNE	3 pt.
Ford	8'	1988	G	$700	12/06	SWMI	Rear blade
Gnuse	8'		G	$1,250	3/06	NCNE	3 pt. hyd.
Grouser	NA		G	$1,200	9/06	ECMN	7' dirt , 10' snow blade attached, 6-way hyd., universal skid steer attach
IHC	300		F	$120	12/06	SEIA	3 pt., 7'
IHC	6'		G	$325	1/06	NWIL	
IHC	7'		F	$175	1/06	NWIL	2 pt.
IHC	8'		F	$250	3/06	NWOH	Back blade
IHC	8'		G	$1,600	4/06	NWMN	6-way hyd. 3 pt., hd, Category III
IMCO	7'		F	$125	3/06	NWKS	3 pt. rear blade
John Deere	10'		F	$650	10/06	NCND	Dozer
John Deere	10'		G	$800	1/06	WCNE	Front mount, manual angle
John Deere	10'		G	$1,500	5/06	SCCA	3 pt., hyd. angle, 2-way hyd.
John Deere	10'		G	$1,600	5/06	SCCA	3 pt, hyd angle , 2-way hyd.
John Deere	10'		G	$1,900	11/06	SCNE	Wheel, hyd. adjustable

Blades

Make	Model	Year	Cond.	Price	Sale	Location	Comments
John Deere	115		G	$800	3/06	ECNE	9', 3 pt., 3 way
John Deere	115		G	$925	3/06	SWMN	8' 3-pt.
John Deere	115		G	$925	3/06	ECNE	6', 3 pt.
John Deere	115		G	$1,025	12/06	WCMI	7' back
John Deere	115		G	$1,200	2/06	NECO	8R, 3 pt., hyd. angle tilt
John Deere	115		G	$1,800	1/06	WCIL	8' hyd.
John Deere	12'		G	$1,500	8/06	SCNE	Dozer blade
John Deere	14'		G	$1,050	2/06	NECO	Heavy pt
John Deere	14'		G	$2,100	8/06	SCFL	Box blade, pt
John Deere	14'		G	$3,250	4/06	NEND	Hyd. dozer, mounts for 40 Series JD tractors
John Deere	155		G	$2,100	2/06	NCIL	9'
John Deere	155		G	$2,300	3/06	NCCO	10' rear hyd.
John Deere	155		E	$3,600	2/06	ECMN	10' rear, 3 pt., hyd. tilt and angle, 1 owner
John Deere	155		G	$3,600	2/06	SWNE	10' hd 3 pt.
John Deere	534		G	$350	1/06	NECO	12' dozer
John Deere	534		G	$1,150	12/06	SCNE	Front dozer
John Deere	6'		G	$250	1/06	NECO	3 pt., manual angler tilt
John Deere	8'		G	$350	2/06	NECO	3 pt., manual angle tilt
John Deere	8'		G	$350	2/06	WCNE	3 pt., manual angle tilt
John Deere	9'		G	$975	11/06	ECNE	3 pt., hyd. cylinder
John Deere	9'		G	$2,200	3/06	SCIN	Grader, 3-way
John Deere	95		G	$675	4/06	WCWI	3 pt.
Kewanee	168		G	$300	10/06	SCMN	8', 3 pt.
Kewanee	189		E	$800	8/06	ECIL	
Kewanee	7'		F	$200	8/06	WCMN	3 pt., manual pivot
Kewanee	8'		F	$50	9/06	ECNE	3 pt.
Kewanee	8'		G	$275	12/06	SEIA	3 pt.
Kewanee	8'		G	$400	5/06	SEWY	3 pt., manual angle tilt
Kewanee	8'		F	$400	9/06	NWIL	3 pt., no cylinder
Kewanee	9'		F	$450	12/06	NWIL	
Kewanee	9'		G	$900	2/06	WCIL	3 pt. hd blade, hyd. angle, tile and moldboard
King Kutter	6'	1997	F	$300	12/06	SWMI	6' box landscraper's grader
Land Pride	3596		G	$850	2/06	SENE	RB3596, hydraulic 8', 3 pt.
Land Pride	7'		G	$550	4/06	SWIN	Grader
Land Pride	NA		G	$3,000	7/06	WCCA	3-pt. hyd.
Land Pride	RB55120		G	$3,500	1/06	WCIL	RB55120, 10' hyd.
Leon	10'		G	$575	1/06	NECO	Front mount, JD mounts
Leon	10'		G	$2,000	11/06	SCNE	3 pt. hyd.
Leon	NA		G	$3,250	3/06	ECNE	Front mount dozer blade, Case IH MX mounts
Leon	NA		G	$6,500	3/06	NCND	Front mount dozer, 6-way, mounts for Cat 75C tractor, used for snow only
Meyer	8'		G	$750	8/06	SCMN	8' snowplow, electric, mounting brackets for 1997 Chevy
Meyer	8'		G	$775	3/06	NWMN	Snowplow, 8', mounts for Ford tractor
MoHawk	8'		G	$300	2/06	NECO	3 pt., mounted axle
Plymouth	8'		G	$650	3/06	NENE	3 pt.
Rhino	1000		G	$800	10/06	NECO	8' 3 pt hyd. angle tilt blade
Rhino	1400		G	$1,600	5/06	SCCA	3 pt., 10', hyd. angle blade
Rhino	1500		G	$2,000	3/06	SWNE	10', 3 pt. blade, hyd. angle, hyd. tilt
Rhino	1540		G	$2,250	8/06	NECO	8', 3 pt.

Blades

Make	Model	Year	Cond.	Price	Sale	Location	Comments
Rhino	1540		G	$2,500	5/06	SCCA	10', 3 pt., hyd. angle blade, 2-way hyd.
Rhino	2500		G	$3,700	2/06	NCCO	3 pt., 12' hyd.
Rhino	7'		F	$450	1/06	NWIL	3 pt.
Rhino	8'		G	$335	6/06	NWKS	R900 model, rear
Rhino	8'		G	$375	12/06	SCNE	3 pt.
Rhino	8'		G	$400	1/06	WCCA	3 pt.
Rhino	900		G	$650	8/06	WCKS	
Rhino	950		G	$1,500	8/06	NECO	8', 3 pt.
Rink	9'		G	$505	8/06	ECNE	Super Brut 9', 3 pt. rear
Servis	6'		F	$120	2/06	WCNE	2 pt.
Servis	8'		G	$425	2/06	NWIL	3 pt.
Sharpe	12'		G	$900	3/06	NWKS	Box
Speeco	7'		F	$150	3/06	SEND	7', 3 pt.
Waldon	9'		G	$125	2/06	WCNE	9' dozer, front unit, wraparound
Westendorf	11'		G	$850	1/06	NWIA	11' front blade for Westendorf TA-45 loader
Westendorf	10'		G	$1,850	8/06	NCIA	10' box scraper
Western	10'		G	$550	3/06	ECMI	
Western	8'		G	$2,200	1/06	NWIL	Snowplow, electric lift
Woods	6'		G	$325	3/06	SWIN	Grader
Woods	RB800		F	$300	9/06	NEND	8', 3 pt.

Notes

WHAT'S IT WORTH?

Chisel Plows

What's that used chisel plow worth? Depends on how big it is, among other factors. Check out these listings on the next few pages. You will see the size listed: 16', 33', 54', and so on. Who would have thought 20 years ago we'd be seeing used chisel plows (Case IH PTX600, JD 2400) bringing $20,000 or more at auction?

Chisel Plows

Make	Model	Year	Cond.	Price	Sale	Location	Comments
Allis-Chalmers	15'		F	$500	5/06	SCCA	3 pt.
Baker	40'		G	$550	2/06	NECO	40' folding
Big Ox	9 shank		F	$100	11/06	SCNE	Deep chisel, 3 pt.
Brady	12'		F	$130	8/06	NCIA	3 pt., springs
Brady	700		G	$575	2/06	NECO	10', 3 pt. spring shank
Brillion	12'		F	$275	12/06	ECNE	
Brillion	12'		G	$650	3/06	ECIA	CP1001, buster bar
Bush Hog	14'		F	$275	8/06	NCIA	Small shanks
Bush Hog	14'		G	$600	9/06	NECO	3 pt., high clearance
Bush Hog	19'		G	$575	8/06	NCIA	Pull chisel plow, springs, hyd. fold, 4 wheels
Case	26'		G	$1,050	2/06	WCNE	Folding spring shank chisel, Flexi-Coil harrow
Case IH	5600		G	$3,100	5/06	SEND	27', tandems on main frame, NH_3, Raymac hitch, adjustable 4-bar harrow
Case IH	5600		G	$3,700	7/06	NEND	41', walking tandems across, 3-bar harrow
Case IH	5600		G	$4,250	3/06	ECND	37', tandems across, Summers 3-bar harrow
Case IH	5600		G	$8,000	11/06	NEND	47', shanks to 51', double fold, walking tandems, 3-bar Summers harrow
Case IH	5800		G	$12,000	4/06	NWMN	29', 3-bar harrow
Case IH	PTX600	2002	E	$20,000	12/06	WCMN	38', hd shanks, Tru-Depth control
Caulkins	NA		G	$3,200	3/06	NCUT	
DMI	12'		F	$150	9/06	NWIL	Buster bar
DMI	Champ		G	$2,000	4/06	SEMI	Coulter Champ, 9 shank
Flexi-Coil	33'		G	$7,750	8/06	WCMN	Harrow
Flexi-Coil	41'		G	$2,000	10/06	NCND	3-bar Degelman harrow
Flexi-Coil	600		G	$3,500	10/06	NCND	50', 4-bar harrow, good teeth, 15 carrier wheels, hd hitch
Flexi-Coil	800		F	$3,250	9/06	WCND	44', tandems across, 3-bar harrow
Flexi-Coil	820	1997	G	$7,000	11/06	NEKS	32' chisel, 1997 model, 7" spacing
Frigstad	3331		G	$4,100	2/06	NWSD	3-tine Morris mulchers, hyd. fold up
Frigstad	42'		G	$1,900	4/06	WCSD	
Frigstad	45'		G	$1,750	4/06	WCSD	
Glencoe	24'		G	$3,300	9/06	NWMN	Walking tandems around
Glencoe	7 shank		G	$2,250	4/06	SCMI	Spike-tooth harrow
Glencoe	9'		F	$150	8/06	NCOH	3 pt.
Geoffry	12'		F	$150	3/06	NENE	12', 3 pt.
Hesston	2310		F	$300	4/06	NENE	13', 3 pt., clod buster
Hesston	2540		G	$1,250	8/06	NEKS	15' pt Conser-Til chisel plow, curved spring shanks
Hinker	1325		F	$1,000	7/06	WCMN	25'
IHC	28'		F	$800	10/06	NCND	Vibra chisel
IHC	55		G	$150	11/06	NEKS	7 shank, pt
IHC	55		G	$400	7/06	NWMN	22'
IHC	55		G	$600	11/06	SENE	Sweeps, extensions
IHC	55		G	$700	4/06	SEND	15', harrow
IHC	55		G	$700	7/06	NWMN	30'
IHC	55		G	$800	2/06	WCNE	17', pt, spring shank, high clearance
IHC	55		G	$1,050	4/06	SEMN	27'
IHC	5500		F	$650	12/06	SEMN	
IHC	5500		F	$700	7/06	NEND	Chisel plow, 37', tandems on main, NH_3, 3-bar harrow
IHC	5500		G	$1,100	3/06	NEND	32', NH_3, rear hitch, Morris 3-bar harrow

WHAT'S IT WORTH?

Chisel Plows

Make	Model	Year	Cond.	Price	Sale	Location	Comments
IHC	5600		G	$850	2/06	WCME	
IHC	645		F	$300	4/06	NESD	20', pt Vibra chisel, spring-fold wings, mulcher
IHC	9'		F	$825	3/06	NWPA	10 shank
IHC	9 shank		G	$550	8/06	SEPA	3 pt.
John Deere	100		G	$200	3/06	WCKS	12', cylinder
John Deere	100		F	$350	9/06	NWMN	21', NH$_3$ reset shanks
John Deere	100		F	$400	4/06	NWSD	New tires & cylinder
John Deere	100		G	$400	2/06	SCKS	Noble 2-bar harrow
John Deere	100		F	$425	2/06	WCNE	16', spring-shank chisel, near new sweeps, hyd. lift
John Deere	100		F	$450	9/06	NWMN	16'
John Deere	100		F	$500	1/06	NECO	24' folding, pt, shop made
John Deere	100		G	$750	1/06	NECO	20', pt
John Deere	100		E	$1,600	3/06	NCOK	15', Degelman harrow on rear
John Deere	1600		F	$110	3/06	WCMN	14' chisel plow frame
John Deere	1600		F	$175	3/06	ECNE	12', pt
John Deere	1600		F	$300	4/06	NESD	16', pt
John Deere	1600		F	$400	3/06	ECNE	16'
John Deere	1600		F	$450	11/06	NEKS	12', pt
John Deere	1600		F	$500	3/06	WCMN	12'
John Deere	1600		G	$550	8/06	WCIA	14'
John Deere	1600		F	$600	5/06	SWWI	12 shank
John Deere	1600		G	$850	1/06	SCMN	14', 3 pt.,1610 tooth conversion
John Deere	1600		G	$1,000	4/06	NWMN	18'
John Deere	1600		F	$1,100	3/06	NESD	18', 3-bar harrow
John Deere	1600		G	$1,300	6/06	NWMN	3 pt., 18', mounted levelers
John Deere	1600		G	$1,500	4/06	NCSD	25'
John Deere	1600		G	$1,500	8/06	NECO	41'
John Deere	1600		F	$1,600	4/06	NEND	35', tandems, 3-bar harrow
John Deere	1600		G	$1,600	5/06	SEND	31', pt, anhydrous attachment, walking tandems
John Deere	1600		G	$1,800	6/06	NWSD	Mulchers, hyd. foldup
John Deere	1610		F	$525	1/06	WCIL	16', REM harrow
John Deere	1610		F	$950	3/06	WCMN	14', 3 pt.
John Deere	1610		G	$1,950	12/06	WCMN	27', tandems, no harrow
John Deere	1610		F	$2,000	4/06	ECND	33', walking tandems, NH3 attachment
John Deere	1610		G	$2,600	4/06	SEND	29', 3-bar harrow
John Deere	1610		G	$3,000	6/06	NWSD	35' chisel, mulchers
John Deere	1610		G	$3,100	4/06	NEND	35', tandems, 3-bar hd harrow
John Deere	1610		G	$3,700	11/06	SCNE	34', pt, mulcher
John Deere	1610		G	$4,500	2/06	SCKS	Hyd. fold, Kasco 1-bar harrow
John Deere	1610		G	$5,500	2/06	NWMN	27', walking tandems, 3-bar harrow
John Deere	1610		G	$5,750	2/06	ECKS	25'
John Deere	1610		G	$8,300	4/06	WCSD	41', Flexi-Coil mulch fertilizer attachment
John Deere	1650		P	$2,750	3/06	WCMN	35', 550-lb. shanks
John Deere	2400		G	$16,500	12/06	SEMN	32'
John Deere	2400		G	$17,000	2/06	SCMI	30', Accu-Depth control, 16" spacing
John Deere	2400		E	$19,000	2/06	ECMN	32.5', Tru-Depth standard, 34', 4-bar mulcher, big gauge wheels, new points, less than 1,000 acres, 1 owner
John Deere	2400	2001	E	$36,000	4/06	NEND	2410 updates, 54' tandems across, full floating hitch, Accu-Depth, 3-bar hd Summers harrow

Chisel Plows

Make	Model	Year	Cond.	Price	Sale	Location	Comments
John Deere	2410	2005	E	$19,800	3/06	SEMN	30', Tru-Depth, gauge wheels
John Deere	610		G	$2,800	6/06	SCMN	Chisel plow
John Deere	610		G	$2,900	10/06	NECO	35', with harrow
John Deere	610		G	$3,500	9/06	NCIA	
John Deere	610		G	$5,000	11/06	NWMN	36', tandems across, single-point depth, 3-bar JD harrow
John Deere	610		G	$6,900	3/06	NEND	33', Summers 3-bar harrow
John Deere	610		G	$7,000	4/06	ECND	25', tandems across, single-point depth, 3-bar harrow
John Deere	610		G	$7,000	6/06	ECND	27', tandems across, 3-bar harrow
John Deere	610		G	$7,200	2/06	ECKS	25'
John Deere	610		G	$7,500	4/06	NESD	27' chisel plow, walking tandems, 3-bar mulchers, 1998 model
John Deere	610	1994	G	$3,000	12/06	SWMI	11', 14 spring shanks, 3 pt., high clearance, gauge wheels
John Deere	610	1994	G	$9,300	6/06	NWMN	30', tandems across, single-point depth control, Summers hd mounted harrow
John Deere	610	1996	G	$8,000	6/06	NWMN	33', tandem across, single-point depth control, Summers hd mounted harrow
John Deere	680		G	$9,500	3/06	NCND	41', tandems across, single-point depth, rear hitch, 3-bar Morris harrow
John Deere	680		G	$11,500	3/06	NEND	37', tandems across, single-point depth, NH3, rear hitch
John Deere	680		G	$12,000	2/06	NWMN	41', JD 3-bar harrow, walking tandems
John Deere	680		G	$12,750	4/06	NWMN	35', tandems across, single-point depth, flotation tires, Summers hd 3-bar harrow
John Deere	680		G	$16,000	6/06	SEND	41', center-point depth, 4 rank, Summers hd 3-bar harrow
John Deere	680	1996	G	$14,250	11/06	ECND	37', Summers 3-bar heavy harrow
John Deere	680	1996	E	$17,000	1/06	SCKS	Hyd. fold, 33 shanks, Waco 2-bar harrow, bought new, shedded, SN 1534
John Deere	680	1997	G	$6,950	4/06	WCMN	15 shank, oscillating tandems, like new, shedded
John Deere	680	1997	G	$16,500	4/06	ECND	41', tandems across, single-point depth, new 4" shovels, Summers 3-bar hd harrow
John Deere	680	2000	E	$15,000	1/06	SCKS	Hyd. fold, 33 shanks, Waco 2-bar harrow, bought new, shedded, SN 3060
John Deere	680	2002	G	$19,000	11/06	ECND	40', Summers 3-bar heavy harrow
Krause	12'		F	$200	2/06	NCKS	3 pt.
Krause	14'		F	$350	9/06	NECO	3 pt., high clearance
Krause	16'		G	$400	9/06	NECO	3 pt., high clearance
Krause	2860		F	$1,600	3/06	SWOH	9 shank
Krause	2889	1987	G	$4,600	2/06	SWOH	9 shank, auto reset & leveler
Krause	30'		G	$2,000	3/06	SEND	Morris 3-bar harrow
Krause	4336		G	$4,750	1/06	NECO	
Krause	730		G	$2,100	3/06	WCKS	730A, 22', extension, some welds
Krause	732A		G	$900	4/06	NCOK	24', 3-bar tine harrows
Krause	790		G	$325	1/06	NEMO	3 pt., 11' chisel plow
Landoll	9 shank		F	$2,800	3/06	NWPA	10'
Leon	4041		P	$750	6/06	SEND	Culti chisel, 44', 3-bar harrow, Valmar 240 applicator
Melroe	25'		F	$850	4/06	NWMN	Chisel plow, 3-bar harrow
Melroe	502		F	$400	6/06	WCMN	13 shank chisel plow, 3 wheel
Melroe	505		G	$1,300	3/06	NWMN	24', 3-bar harrow
Melroe	5505		F	$400	7/06	NWMN	29', 3-bar harrow
Morris	30'		G	$1,250	2/06	NWSD	Fold-up wings, mulchers

Chisel Plows

Make	Model	Year	Cond.	Price	Sale	Location	Comments
Morris	36'		F	$700	2/06	NWSD	Harrows
Morris	631		G	$1,600	4/06	WCSD	Valmar airflow herb applicator
Morris	643		G	$1,900	4/06	WCSD	47', mulchers
Summers	28'	2002	G	$16,500	11/06	ECND	Super chisel, 28' single point depth, fourth twists, 106 Summers, hd 3-bar harrow
Summers	32'	2002	G	$11,000	4/06	NWMN	Chisel plow, 3-bar harrow, 9/16" tines on harrow
Summers	39'		G	$13,000	4/06	NWMN	Tandems across, hd 3-bar harrow
Sunflower	14'		F	$310	11/06	SCNE	3 pt., 3-bar
Sunflower	29'		G	$1,200	3/06	NWKS	Hyd. fold, 1 owner
Sunflower	4210		G	$2,000	3/06	SEND	Coulter chisel, 17', hyd. front disk adjustable, new blades, walking tandems, 5-bar spike tooth harrow
Sunflower	4212	2002	G	$7,500	2/06	SWNE	19', 15-shank stalk slicer/chisel, rolling chopper attachment, ss liquid fertilizer kit, 1 owner
WFE	16'		G	$1,600	3/06	NECO	
White	458		G	$700	3/06	ECMI	12-leg 3-pt, gauge wheels
White	466		F	$375	5/06	SEND	13' chisel plow
White	476		F	$600	3/06	NCND	24', 3-bar harrow
White	11'		G	$1,000	12/06	SWMI	11', 11 shank, 3 pt., high clearance, hd gauge wheels
Wilrich	17'		G	$1,000	3/06	WCMN	Pt
Wilrich	24'		G	$1,500	3/06	NWMN	Farm King 3-bar harrow
Wilrich	28'		F	$500	3/06	SEND	Tandems main frame, 2-bar harrow, NH3 attachment
Wilrich	29'		G	$1,400	4/06	NEND	Walking tandems around, mounted harrow
Wilrich	33'		G	$3,500	3/06	SEND	3-bar harrow
Wilrich	35'		F	$1,500	11/06	NEND	Cold flow, 2-bar harrow
Wilrich	39'		G	$2,700	3/06	ECND	Tandems across, 3-bar harrow
Wilrich	4400		G	$4,700	9/06	NEND	45', 3-bar Summers harrow
Wilrich	4400	1996	G	$6,750	3/06	ECND	26', walking tandems across, hd 3-bar harrow, 1 owner
Wilrich	4830		G	$10,100	9/06	NCIA	35'

Notes

Combine Heads

The rush to plant additional acres of corn in 2007 is having an effect on used corn head values. A big effect. In the first three months of 2007, Case IH 2208 8-row heads were selling for 12.8% more at auction compared to 2006. Sale prices on John Deere 893 8-row heads were up 21.9% over 2006.

Combine Heads

Make	Model	Year	Cond.	Price	Sale	Location	Comments
Case IH	1010		F	$1,000	3/06	NCUT	30'
Case IH	1010		G	$5,100	4/06	NWMN	25' rigid head, finger reel, hyd., fore/aft
Case IH	1010		G	$10,500	12/06	ECKS	30' rigid platform head, 3" cut, hyd., fore/aft
Case IH	1010		G	$11,000	12/06	ECKS	30' rigid platform head, 3" cut, hyd., fore/aft
Case IH	1010	1987	G	$3,600	10/06	NCND	Grain table, 30', fore/aft, bat reel
Case IH	1010	1987	G	$5,350	3/06	ECND	25' straight head, Bonco 9' Sunflower attachment
Case IH	1010	1990	G	$5,000	3/06	NCND	Straight head, 25', Faul 9" pans, bat reel
Case IH	1010	1991	F	$3,400	1/06	NCCO	Grain head, 20' solid pickup
Case IH	1010	1992	G	$4,900	3/06	NWKS	Flex head
Case IH	1010	1995	G	$8,750	3/06	NCND	Straight head, 30', SSR pump, 9" pans, bat reel
Case IH	1010	2004	G	$8,000	8/06	NECO	30' platform, 5-bat reel
Case IH	1010	2004	G	$9,250	8/06	NECO	30' platform, 5-bat reel, lights
Case IH	1015		F	$1,250	7/06	SEND	Pickup head, Rake-Up pickup
Case IH	1015		G	$2,200	4/06	NWMN	Pickup head, 7-belt pickup
Case IH	1015		F	$2,350	7/06	SEND	Pickup head, Melroe 385 7-belt pickup
Case IH	1015		G	$2,400	7/06	ECND	Head, 7-belt pickup
Case IH	1015		G	$2,400	10/06	NCND	Pickup platform, 388 Melroe 7-belt rubber pickup, wind screen
Case IH	1015	1988	G	$2,800	3/06	ECND	Pickup head, IHC 7-belt 12' pickup
Case IH	1020		F	$1,100	12/06	SEMN	20' platform
Case IH	1020		F	$1,200	12/06	SEMN	20' platform
Case IH	1020		F	$1,300	8/06	WCMN	Flex, 20' finger reel, 3" cut
Case IH	1020		F	$2,050	2/06	WCIA	15' platform head
Case IH	1020		F	$2,200	8/06	WCMN	Flex, 20' finger reel, 3" cut
Case IH	1020		G	$2,500	10/06	SEMN	30' platform
Case IH	1020		G	$2,600	11/06	SCIL	20' platform
Case IH	1020		G	$2,650	3/06	SEMN	30' bean head
Case IH	1020		G	$2,800	8/06	SCMN	20' platform
Case IH	1020		G	$3,000	11/06	WCIL	17.5' grain platform, double cut, 1.5" sickle
Case IH	1020		G	$3,000	2/06	NCIL	15' grain platform
Case IH	1020		G	$3,000	3/06	NWIL	17.5' grain platform, 1.5" cut
Case IH	1020		G	$3,600	8/06	SEMN	22.5' platform
Case IH	1020		G	$3,700	9/06	SWIA	20' grain platform
Case IH	1020		G	$3,700	8/06	NWIL	25' platform
Case IH	1020		G	$3,800	3/06	ECND	20' head, finger reel
Case IH	1020		G	$4,000	1/06	ECNE	22.5' platform head, single drive
Case IH	1020		G	$4,600	6/06	NWIL	20' grain head
Case IH	1020		G	$4,750	6/06	ECSD	Flex head
Case IH	1020		G	$4,800	3/06	SWMN	22.5' flex head, Tiger jaw
Case IH	1020		G	$4,900	3/06	SCIA	20' flex
Case IH	1020		G	$4,900	6/06	ECSD	25'
Case IH	1020		G	$5,250	3/06	WCMN	Flex head, header height control
Case IH	1020		G	$5,500	8/06	NEKS	20' flex head
Case IH	1020		G	$6,000	3/06	NENE	15' grain head
Case IH	1020		G	$6,500	2/06	WCIL	25' grain platform
Case IH	1020		G	$7,000	1/06	NWKY	20' grain head
Case IH	1020		G	$7,200	12/06	WCMN	22.5' double-drive flex head
Case IH	1020		G	$7,250	7/06	NWMN	25' flex head
Case IH	1020		G	$8,000	9/06	NCIA	30' platform

Combine Heads

Make	Model	Year	Cond.	Price	Sale	Location	Comments
Case IH	1020		E	$8,000	2/06	NENE	20' flex head
Case IH	1020		G	$8,200	8/06	ECNE	20' flex head
Case IH	1020		G	$8,700	1/06	NWIL	Grain platform, oil bath drive and 3" cut
Case IH	1020		G	$8,750	12/06	SCMN	30' platform
Case IH	1020		G	$9,600	2/06	ECMN	22.5' bean platform, 3" and 1.5" sickles, poly reel
Case IH	1020		G	$10,400	12/06	ECKS	25' flex head, Crary air finger reel, 3" cut
Case IH	1020		E	$12,500	6/06	ECIL	30' flex head, like new, fore/aft, 3" sickle cut
Case IH	1020		G	$15,000	9/06	NCIA	30' platform
Case IH	1020	1987	G	$2,700	7/06	ECND	Flex head, 20' finger reel, new sickle and guards
Case IH	1020	1987	G	$6,000	8/06	NCIA	17.5' flex head, plastic fingers, Tiger jaw style sickle
Case IH	1020	1988	G	$4,000	8/06	NEIA	20' platform, 3" cut
Case IH	1020	1988	G	$4,750	7/06	SEND	25' flex head
Case IH	1020	1990	G	$3,000	4/06	WCWI	15' platform
Case IH	1020	1991	G	$1,400	8/06	NCNE	15' flex, 3" Crary cut
Case IH	1020	1991	G	$4,200	3/06	ECMI	25' flex header
Case IH	1020	1991	F	$5,400	2/06	ECNE	20' flex head
Case IH	1020	1991	G	$6,000	2/06	SEIL	Platform
Case IH	1020	1991	G	$6,900	3/06	NCIA	25' platform, Tiger jaw, Johnson grain saver
Case IH	1020	1992	G	$9,000	3/06	NCND	Flex head, 30', finger reel, 1.5" cut, fore/aft, poly
Case IH	1020	1993	G	$3,700	3/06	NEMI	25' flex platform
Case IH	1020	1993	G	$5,800	12/06	SEIA	20' flex grain table, 3" cut, fore/aft
Case IH	1020	1993	G	$7,000	7/06	SEND	Flex head, 25', fore/aft, Crary cut
Case IH	1020	1994	G	$4,900	3/06	NCIL	Grain platform, homemade head trailer
Case IH	1020	1994	G	$5,500	12/06	SCMN	30' platform
Case IH	1020	1994	G	$6,900	1/06	NWIL	Platform, 20'
Case IH	1020	1995	E	$7,100	2/06	SENE	20' flex head
Case IH	1020	1996	G	$12,750	2/06	NWIA	30' flex bean head, fore/aft, 3" cut
Case IH	1020	1997	G	$5,150	1/06	NWIL	16.5' grain platform
Case IH	1020	1997	E	$6,200	8/06	ECNE	20' flex platform, 1.5" cut, one owner
Case IH	1020	1997	G	$7,750	10/06	NCND	Flex head, 25', fore/aft, poly, AHHC
Case IH	1020	1997	G	$8,000	12/06	NWOH	25' flex grain head, fore/aft reel
Case IH	1020	1997	G	$9,000	5/06	WCMN	Flex head, 25', oil bath, fore/aft, Crary air reel
Case IH	1020	1998	G	$6,600	3/06	SCIA	15' grain head
Case IH	1020	1998	G	$8,000	3/06	NWIL	20' grain platform
Case IH	1020	1998	E	$11,250	1/06	SWOH	25' grain platform, 3" sections, field tracker
Case IH	1020	1998	G	$12,000	3/06	NCND	Flex head, 25', Crary air reel, 3" cut, fore/aft, poly
Case IH	1020	1999	G	$12,250	12/06	SEIA	25' flex grain table, 3" cut, field tracker
Case IH	1020	2001	E	$11,200	1/06	WCIL	20' grain platform, fore/aft, poly skids
Case IH	1020	2001	G	$12,500	3/06	NEKS	25' flex head
Case IH	1020	2001	E	$13,000	11/06	WCIA	20' grain table, 3" cut, tracker
Case IH	1020	2002	E	$11,000	9/06	WCOH	20' grain head
Case IH	1020	2003	E	$17,500	3/06	ECND	Flex head, 30' field tracker, fore/aft, 3" cut, new sickle
Case IH	1020	2005	E	$14,000	12/06	WCIA	20' bean head, field tracker
Case IH	1043		G	$1,600	11/06	SCIL	4RN CH
Case IH	1043		G	$5,000	8/06	SCMN	4RN CH
Case IH	1044		G	$1,200	11/06	WCIL	4RW CH, 36"
Case IH	1044		G	$2,300	2/06	NCIL	4RW CH
Case IH	1044		F	$2,350	1/06	NWIL	4RW CH
Case IH	1044		G	$2,500	8/06	SEMN	4RW CH, new rolls and water pump bags

Combine Heads

Make	Model	Year	Cond.	Price	Sale	Location	Comments
Case IH	1044		G	$2,500	3/06	NWIL	4RW CH, new knives
Case IH	1044		G	$3,100	3/06	NENE	4RW CH
Case IH	1044		G	$3,300	8/06	ECNE	4RW CH, 36"
Case IH	1044		E	$5,600	2/06	NENE	4RW CH, 38", row stomper
Case IH	1044	1987	F	$2,500	5/06	WCMN	4RW CH, 36"
Case IH	1044	1997	G	$3,900	3/06	NCIL	4RW CH, 38"
Case IH	1052	2003	G	$17,000	7/06	SEND	Draper head, 30', fore/aft, AHHC, finger reel
Case IH	1063		F	$2,500	12/06	SEMN	6RN CH
Case IH	1063		G	$3,700	9/06	WCOH	6RN CH, 30"
Case IH	1063		F	$3,700	8/06	NWIL	6RN CH
Case IH	1063		G	$4,200	6/06	ECSD	CH
Case IH	1063		G	$4,200	12/06	ECKS	6RN CH, 30", shedded
Case IH	1063		G	$4,750	12/06	SEMN	6RN CH
Case IH	1063		G	$5,200	3/06	SCIA	6RN CH, poly snouts
Case IH	1063		G	$7,500	1/06	NWKY	6RN CH
Case IH	1063	1989	G	$5,000	8/06	NEKS	6RN CH
Case IH	1063	1989	G	$9,200	8/06	NCIA	6RN CH, 30", new knives last year
Case IH	1063	1990	G	$5,600	7/06	NCIA	6RN CH
Case IH	1063	1991	G	$5,200	3/06	NCIA	6RN CH, 30"
Case IH	1063	1991	F	$6,300	2/06	ECNE	6RN CH
Case IH	1063	1991	G	$7,800	2/06	SEIL	6RN CH, 30"
Case IH	1063	1992	G	$7,500	1/06	SWOH	6RN CH, 30"
Case IH	1063	1996	G	$13,500	11/06	WCIA	6RN CH
Case IH	1063	1998	G	$10,600	3/06	SCIA	6RN CH
Case IH	1063	1999	G	$12,500	3/06	NWIL	6RN CH, 30", poly snouts
Case IH	1063	1999	G	$13,500	8/06	SEMN	6RN CH, poly
Case IH	1063	1999	E	$16,500	12/06	NWIL	6RN CH, 30", plastic snouts AHH
Case IH	1064	1993	G	$3,500	6/06	NWKS	6RW CH
Case IH	1083		G	$5,600	6/06	ECSD	8RN CH
Case IH	1083		G	$6,000	9/06	NCIA	8RN CH
Case IH	1083		F	$6,000	8/06	WCMN	8RN CH
Case IH	1083		G	$6,500	12/06	NWWI	8RN CH
Case IH	1083		F	$6,750	4/06	NCKS	8RN CH
Case IH	1083		G	$7,500	3/06	SEMN	8RN CH, field tracker, poly
Case IH	1083		G	$10,600	8/06	ECNE	8RN CH
Case IH	1083		G	$10,700	12/06	WCMN	8RN CH
Case IH	1083		G	$17,250	2/06	WCIL	8RN CH, poly
Case IH	1083	1990	G	$5,500	3/06	NWKS	8RN CH
Case IH	1083	1991	F	$5,000	8/06	NECO	8RN CH
Case IH	1083	1993	G	$7,750	3/06	NEKS	8RN CH, new sprockets & gathering chains
Case IH	1083	1996	F	$5,600	9/06	SEIA	8RN CH, 30"
Case IH	1083	1996	G	$7,750	3/06	NEMI	8RN CH
Case IH	2015	2002	E	$6,400	3/06	NCND	Pickup platform, 8-belt Rake-Up pickup, hyd. wind guard
Case IH	2206		E	$21,000	7/06	ECIL	6R CH
Case IH	2206	2001	G	$19,500	12/06	SEIA	6R CH, field tracker
Case IH	2206	2001	E	$21,000	1/06	WCIL	6R-30, poly, hyd. deck plates
Case IH	2206	2001	G	$22,500	12/06	WCIA	6RN CH, field tracker, hyd. deck plates
Case IH	2206	2003	G	$18,500	3/06	NEMI	6RN CH, poly, 30" rows
Case IH	2206	2003	G	$18,500	1/06	NWIL	6RN CH, 30", poly, used on 1,300 acres

Combine Heads

Make	Model	Year	Cond.	Price	Sale	Location	Comments
Case IH	2208		G	$20,000	12/06	SCMN	8RN CH
Case IH	2208		G	$22,000	9/06	NCIA	8RN-30 CH, hyd. deck plates
Case IH	2208	2004	E	$27,000	3/06	ECMI	8RN CH, poly, 30" rows, 1,800 acres use
Case IH	2212	2005	E	$39,250	3/06	ECNE	12R-20 poly CH, hyd. deck plates, field tracker, used one season, shedded
Caterpillar	1230	2000	G	$20,000	8/06	NECO	12RN CH, knife rolls, hyd. deck plates, row track
Caterpillar	F30	2001	G	$7,700	8/06	NECO	30' flex platform
Geringhoff	630		G	$27,500	4/06	SEPA	6R, RotoDisc, single point hookup, hyd. deck plates, RD630
Geringhoff	NA		G	$3,500	9/06	NCIA	6R CH
Geringhoff	NA	2004	E	$46,500	3/06	NWMN	8RN CH, 30"
Geringhoff	NA	2004	E	$60,000	12/06	WCMN	12R-22 CH, RotoDisc, poly snouts, auto head control, JD adapted 60 Series, new knives
Geringhoff	NA	2004	E	$62,000	12/06	WCMN	12R-22 CH, RotoDisc, poly snouts, auto head control, JD adapted 60 Series, one season on new knives
Geringhoff	NA	2006	E	$72,500	12/06	SWIA	Northstar 12R-30 folding head, contour master, hyd. deck plates, 3 finger, less than 750 acres
Gleaner	13'		G	$1,900	12/06	SEMN	Platform
Gleaner	15'		F	$1,200	2/06	NWIL	Grain platform, double cut II sickle, see through reel, fly high dividers
Gleaner	15'		G	$1,800	11/06	SCNE	Series II flex head
Gleaner	16'		G	$810	11/06	SCNE	Deutz-Allis rigid grain table
Gleaner	20'		F	$1,100	7/06	NWIL	Grain platform
Gleaner	20'		G	$8,000	2/06	NCIL	Flex head, off R52 combine, mid-1990s
Gleaner	21'		G	$1,750	12/06	WCIL	Deutz-Allis grain platform, off Gleaner L3 combine
Gleaner	24'		G	$800	12/06	WCIL	Grain platform
Gleaner	24'	1993	F	$4,000	9/06	WCND	Flex head
Gleaner	313		G	$600	1/06	WCIL	Grain platform and 4RW CH, black
Gleaner	315		G	$2,900	3/06	ECNE	Flex head, Crary air reel, ss pan, poly skid plates
Gleaner	315		G	$4,250	8/06	SCMI	15' grain head, plastic floor
Gleaner	320	1987	F	$1,100	6/06	NWIL	20' grain platform, quick-cut sickle
Gleaner	320	1987	G	$1,100	6/06	NWIL	20' grain platform
Gleaner	400	1994	F	$1,250	9/06	WCND	Pickup platform, Victory super 8-belt pickup
Gleaner	500		G	$4,200	3/06	NWOH	20' grain head, stainless steel
Gleaner	500	1994	G	$5,000	12/06	NWIL	16' grain platform
Gleaner	500	1995	G	$5,750	3/06	WCKS	30' flex head
Gleaner	520	1994	G	$4,800	3/06	NWOH	20' grain head
Gleaner	630		P	$400	10/06	SEMN	6R-30, orange
Gleaner	630	1985	F	$2,000	6/06	NWIL	6RN CH, 30", 1985 model, black
Gleaner	800		G	$5,400	4/06	SEMI	15' grain head, stainless steel
Gleaner	8000	2002	G	$9,600	12/06	NCIL	20' grain platform
Gleaner	A438		G	$1,900	12/06	SEMN	4R CH
Gleaner	Hugger		E	$9,500	3/06	NEKS	8RN CH, 30"
Gleaner	Hugger	1991	G	$8,500	12/06	NCIL	6R-30 CH
Gleaner	Hugger	1994	G	$2,600	12/06	NWIL	4R-36 CH
Gleaner	LM		G	$550	4/06	NEND	13' head, 11' Sund windrow pickup
Gleaner	LM		G	$1,600	4/06	NEND	Rigid straight head, 20', finger reel and metal bat reel
Gleaner	NA		F	$175	8/06	NCIA	4RN CH, 30"
Gleaner	NA		G	$200	11/06	NEKS	4R-36 CH
Gleaner	NA		P	$600	9/06	WCND	8R-30 CH

WHAT'S IT WORTH?

Combine Heads

Make	Model	Year	Cond.	Price	Sale	Location	Comments
Gleaner	NA		G	$1,000	12/06	WCIL	8RW CH
Gleaner	NA		G	$1,425	7/06	NWIL	8RW CH, low tin, off N5 combine
Gleaner	NA		G	$1,500	3/06	NECO	8R CH
Gleaner	NA		F	$1,500	9/06	WCND	Deutz-Allis pickup head, Rake-Up 7-belt pickup
Gleaner	NA		F	$1,750	2/06	NWIL	6RN CH, 30", stalk slides
Gleaner	NA		G	$2,300	8/06	SCMI	4R CH, low tin
Gleaner	NA		G	$3,200	4/06	SEMI	4R-36 CH
Gleaner	NA		G	$6,000	12/06	NCOH	Grain table, off R42 combine
Gleaner	NA		G	$7,000	12/06	NCOH	6RN CH, 30", off R42 combine
Gleaner	NA		G	$7,700	3/06	ECNE	6RN CH, 30", converted to poly
Gleaner	R320		G	$2,800	8/06	NWIL	
Gleaner	R630	1998	E	$12,000	8/06	ECIL	Hugger 6R CH
Gleaner	R820	1998	E	$13,100	8/06	ECIL	Flex head, quick-cut sickle
Honey Bee	30'	1999	G	$5,000	9/06	WCND	Harvest head, mounts for Gleaner R combine with transport
IHC	810		F	$100	7/06	NWMN	Pickup head
IHC	810		F	$250	6/06	WCMN	Pickup head, 4-belt pickup
IHC	810		G	$400	3/06	ECND	Pickup head, 15', Melroe 388 pickup, orbit drive
IHC	810		F	$400	3/06	ECND	Pickup head, 13', Melroe 378 7-belt pickup, orbit drive
IHC	810		F	$500	3/06	ECND	20' head, finger reel, orbit drive
IHC	810		F	$500	3/06	ECND	30' straight head
IHC	810		F	$500	10/06	NCND	20' head, sunflower pans
IHC	810		F	$700	9/06	NECO	14' Innes pickup
IHC	810		F	$900	7/06	SEND	
IHC	810		G	$1,000	3/06	ECND	Pickup head, 15', Melroe 378 6-belt pickup, orbit drive
IHC	810		G	$1,500	3/06	ECND	Pickup head, 15', Sund 14' pickup, orbit drive
IHC	810	1986	G	$1,800	6/06	NWKS	Wheat head, 24'
IHC	820		G	$550	4/06	NWMN	20' flex head, finger reel
IHC	820		G	$700	12/06	ECKS	20' flex head, Crary air finger reel, 3" cut
IHC	820		G	$1,000	7/06	NCIL	Grain head, 17'
IHC	820		G	$1,125	2/06	SEIA	15' grain platform
IHC	820		F	$1,700	4/06	NEIA	Flex head
IHC	820		G	$1,700	11/06	ECNE	20' flex platform
IHC	820		G	$2,300	3/06	SEMN	Flex bean head, 17.5' new style reel, rock guard
IHC	833		E	$3,900	2/06	SENE	6RN CH, 30"
IHC	843		G	$500	6/06	NWIL	4R CH
IHC	843		F	$500	12/06	SEMN	CH
IHC	843		G	$1,250	2/06	SEIA	4RN CH
IHC	844		F	$275	3/06	NENE	4RW CH
IHC	844		F	$400	2/06	WCIL	4RW CH
IHC	844		F	$575	1/06	SESD	4RW CH
IHC	844		G	$1,500	7/06	NWMN	6RN CH
IHC	863		F	$1,900	3/06	SEIA	6RN CH
IHC	863		G	$2,400	9/06	SEIA	6RN CH, 30"
IHC	863		G	$2,500	8/06	SEMN	6R CH, poly
IHC	863		G	$2,600	9/06	SWIA	6RN CH, 30"
IHC	863		G	$3,600	4/06	NEIA	6RN CH
IHC	863		F	$3,700	3/06	NWOH	6R CH
IHC	863		G	$5,100	3/06	SEMN	6RN CH, 30"
IHC	883		G	$2,250	1/06	SESD	8RN CH

Combine Heads

Make	Model	Year	Cond.	Price	Sale	Location	Comments
IHC	884		G	$1,100	1/06	ECNE	8R-36 CH
IHC	943		G	$1,900	7/06	NCIL	4RN CH, 30"
IHC	944		F	$300	3/06	NCIL	4RN CH
IHC	963		G	$2,500	8/06	SEMN	6R CH
IHC	963		G	$3,000	3/06	WCMN	6RN CH
IHC	963		G	$4,600	4/06	WCWI	6RN CH
IHC	963		G	$5,100	12/06	NWOH	6RN CH, poly snouts
IHC	963	1983	G	$5,900	3/06	ECNE	6RN CH, new Snapper bushings
IHC	963	1984	F	$1,800	1/06	NCCO	6RN CH
IHC	963	1985	G	$2,800	2/06	WCIL	6RN CH
John Deere	100		F	$550	11/06	SCSD	Rubber belt pickup
John Deere	100		G	$1,100	8/06	NECO	Dummy head, 22'
John Deere	1243		P	$7,500	8/06	NECO	12RN CH, rough
John Deere	1243		G	$9,100	2/06	WCMN	12RN CH, 30", oil bath, galvanized poly snouts, universal shafts
John Deere	1243		G	$9,500	12/06	NENE	Metal hoods
John Deere	1243		G	$19,750	6/06	SCMN	12RN CH, 30", all poly snouts
John Deere	1243	1990	F	$10,000	8/06	NECO	12RN CH
John Deere	1243	1993	E	$15,500	3/06	NEKS	12RN CH
John Deere	1253A		G	$11,750	6/06	ECIL	12R-30 row crop bean head, belts at 75%, with optional Bish adapter plate
John Deere	1290		G	$20,000	2/06	SEKS	12RN CH, 20"
John Deere	1290		E	$24,000	2/06	ECMN	12RN CH, 20", all poly, hyd. deck plates, knife rolls, one owner
John Deere	1290		G	$24,000	2/06	SEKS	12RN CH, 20"
John Deere	1290	1998	G	$18,500	12/06	SEND	12R-20 CH, hyd. deck plates
John Deere	1290	1998	G	$21,500	8/06	WCMN	12RN CH, knife rolls
John Deere	1291	1999	G	$24,500	7/06	SEND	12RN CH, 22", fluted rolls
John Deere	1293		G	$31,000	3/06	SEMN	12RN CH, 30", fully poly, like new
John Deere	1293	1994	G	$15,000	12/06	NEKS	12RN CH, always shedded, plastic snouts, 50 Series drive shafts, manual deck plates
John Deere	1293	1995	P	$12,000	8/06	NECO	12RN CH, rough
John Deere	1293	1996	G	$19,000	12/06	SCMN	12RN CH, knife rolls, single point
John Deere	1293	1997	G	$20,000	8/06	NECO	12RN CH, hyd. deck plates, stubble lights, 50 Series
John Deere	1293	1998	G	$22,500	1/06	SESD	12RN CH, hyd. deck plates
John Deere	1293	1999	G	$22,000	12/06	SCMN	12RN CH, knife rolls and hyd. deck plates
John Deere	1293	2000	G	$37,000	3/06	ECND	12RN CH, knife rolls, hyd. deck plates
John Deere	1293	2001	G	$32,000	12/06	NWWI	12RN CH, knife rolls, hyd. deck plates
John Deere	1293	2003	E	$35,000	1/06	NECO	12RN CH
John Deere	1293	2005	E	$45,000	12/06	WCKS	12RN CH, poly snouts, field lights
John Deere	1293	2006	E	$52,000	11/06	SCNE	12R-30, hyd. deck plates
John Deere	200		F	$225	12/06	WCMN	Platform, 6-belt Melroe pickup
John Deere	200	1981	F	$400	12/06	SCMN	Platform
John Deere	212		F	$500	4/06	WCSD	Pickup header
John Deere	212		F	$500	9/06	NWMN	Pickup head, 6-belt pickup
John Deere	212		F	$550	4/06	NWMN	Pickup head, 5-belt pickup
John Deere	212		F	$800	7/06	SEND	Pickup head, JD 5-belt pickups
John Deere	212		G	$1,000	11/06	SCND	Pickup head, 6-belt pickup

Combine Heads

Make	Model	Year	Cond.	Price	Sale	Location	Comments
John Deere	212		G	$1,250	6/06	NWMN	6-belt JD pickup
John Deere	212		F	$1,400	7/06	WCMN	5-belt pickup
John Deere	212		G	$1,500	4/06	NWMN	6-belt pickup
John Deere	212		G	$1,600	4/06	NESD	Dummy head, 6-belt pickup, kept inside
John Deere	212		G	$1,600	4/06	NCSD	Dummy head, JD 7-belt pickup
John Deere	212		G	$1,650	9/06	NECO	5-belt pickup
John Deere	212		G	$1,800	3/06	NWMN	Pickup head, JD 6-belt pickup
John Deere	212		G	$1,800	7/06	WCMN	5-belt pickup
John Deere	212	1982	G	$1,000	4/06	ECND	Pickup head, JD 6-belt pickup
John Deere	212	1983	F	$1,400	11/06	NWMN	Pickup head, JD 6-belt pickup
John Deere	213		F	$50	8/06	ECNE	Rigid head
John Deere	213		F	$50	8/06	ECNE	Rigid head
John Deere	213		G	$1,400	9/06	ECNE	Flex head
John Deere	213		G	$1,650	3/06	ECNE	Flex head
John Deere	213	1978	F	$250	12/06	SEMN	Platform
John Deere	213	1981	F	$150	12/06	SEMN	Platform
John Deere	214		G	$1,100	11/06	SCND	Pickup head, 7-belt
John Deere	214	1982	G	$2,000	7/06	NEND	Pickup head, 7-belt JD pickup
John Deere	215		F	$275	2/06	WCIA	Platform head
John Deere	215		F	$400	3/06	NCIN	Grain head, stainless steel bottom
John Deere	215		F	$500	11/06	NWKS	15' header, 12' pickup attachment
John Deere	215		F	$700	8/06	SEMN	Flex head
John Deere	215		F	$775	3/06	NWPA	15' platform
John Deere	215		G	$1,450	2/06	WCIL	15' grain platform
John Deere	215		G	$2,600	1/06	NEMO	15' grain platform
John Deere	215	1979	F	$1,300	2/06	SCMI	15' grain head, ss
John Deere	216		F	$250	12/06	ECMO	Grain head
John Deere	216		F	$275	12/06	NWWI	Rigid platform
John Deere	216		F	$300	12/06	NWWI	Rigid platform
John Deere	216		F	$900	8/06	SEMN	Flex
John Deere	216		F	$950	8/06	ECNE	Flex head
John Deere	216		F	$1,000	8/06	SEMN	Flex
John Deere	216		F	$1,100	3/06	NWIL	Platform
John Deere	216		G	$1,300	3/06	SCIN	Grain head
John Deere	216		G	$1,700	8/06	ECNE	Flex head
John Deere	216		G	$2,500	8/06	NEIL	Platform
John Deere	216	1981	G	$1,600	11/06	NEKS	Flex head
John Deere	218		P	$150	9/06	NEIA	18' flex head
John Deere	218		F	$300	8/06	WCIL	Table
John Deere	218		F	$850	9/06	SCMN	Flex bean head
John Deere	218		G	$1,000	12/06	NWIL	18' grain platform
John Deere	218		G	$2,100	6/06	NWIL	18' grain platform, black reel
John Deere	218	1983	G	$1,600	3/06	ECND	Flex head stainless, low acres
John Deere	220		F	$200	12/06	NWWI	Poly skid plates
John Deere	220		F	$300	9/06	NEIA	20' flex head
John Deere	220		F	$500	4/06	WCMN	Flex, new wobble box and poly
John Deere	220		P	$500	8/06	ECNE	Flex head, bad reel
John Deere	220		F	$500	8/06	WCMN	Flex, stainless pans, poly skid plates

Combine Heads

Make	Model	Year	Cond.	Price	Sale	Location	Comments
John Deere	220		F	$500	2/06	ECKS	20' head, no reel
John Deere	220		F	$600	6/06	NCIL	Grain table w/ running gear
John Deere	220		P	$600	6/06	SWMN	Flex head, needs repair
John Deere	220		G	$600	8/06	NCNE	24', flex head
John Deere	220		P	$700	7/06	WCMN	Flex head, 20', finger reel
John Deere	220		F	$800	8/06	SCNE	Flex
John Deere	220		F	$1,000	7/06	WCMN	Flex
John Deere	220		F	$1,000	7/06	WCMN	Flex
John Deere	220		F	$1,000	7/06	SEND	Flex head
John Deere	220		G	$1,000	8/06	NCIA	20' black reel flex head, poly, newer style sickle, drive shafts
John Deere	220		G	$1,000	9/06	NWMN	Flex head, 20' finger reel
John Deere	220		G	$1,100	2/06	WCIL	Grain platform
John Deere	220		G	$1,250	8/06	NCIA	20' black reel flex head, stainless steel, Dial-a-Matic, homebuilt head trailer
John Deere	220		G	$1,500	8/06	NCIA	20' black reel flex head
John Deere	220		G	$1,700	8/06	NCIA	20' grain head
John Deere	220		F	$1,750	7/06	WCMN	Flex head, 20' finger reel
John Deere	220		G	$1,800	7/06	WCMN	Flex head, stainless pan
John Deere	220		G	$3,400	8/06	ECNE	Flex head
John Deere	220	1977	G	$950	12/06	NENE	Flex head
John Deere	220	1980	F	$650	12/06	SCMN	Platform
John Deere	220	1982	G	$700	12/06	SCMN	Platform
John Deere	220	1983	G	$800	12/06	SCMN	Platform
John Deere	220	1983	G	$1,000	2/06	WCIL	20' flex platform
John Deere	220	1984	F	$500	11/06	SCSD	Flex head
John Deere	220	1984	G	$4,500	11/06	SENE	Rigid head, full finger reel, milo guards
John Deere	222		F	$110	2/06	WCNE	22' wheat header
John Deere	222		F	$500	3/06	ECKS	Flex head
John Deere	222		P	$500	7/06	SEND	Rigid, bat reel
John Deere	222		P	$600	7/06	SEND	Straight head, bat reel, Lucke 9" pans
John Deere	222		F	$625	2/06	WCIA	Platform head
John Deere	222		F	$900	7/06	SEND	Rigid head, 22', 9" sunflower pans, bat reel
John Deere	222		F	$1,000	1/06	NECO	22', pickup
John Deere	222		F	$1,750	7/06	SEND	(2) 9' Sund pickups and single hyd. motor
John Deere	222		F	$1,800	1/06	SWNE	Platform, Sund bean pickup
John Deere	222		G	$2,050	1/06	NECO	22', pickup
John Deere	222		F	$3,000	7/06	SEND	Flex head
John Deere	222	1979	F	$500	12/06	SCMN	Platform
John Deere	222	1983	G	$1,000	6/06	ECND	Rigid head, Pro plates, bat reel
John Deere	222	1984	G	$1,000	4/06	ECND	Flex head
John Deere	224		F	$250	2/06	WCNE	Wheat platform
John Deere	224		G	$800	9/06	NWMN	Rigid straight head, bat and finger reel
John Deere	224		G	$1,150	2/06	NECO	Pickup
John Deere	224		G	$1,400	4/06	WCSD	Straight head, 24'
John Deere	224		G	$1,500	6/06	NWMN	Straight head, MacDon finger reel
John Deere	224		G	$2,000	2/06	NECO	24', pickup
John Deere	224	1976	G	$1,300	11/06	NEKS	Rigid head
John Deere	224	1981	F	$600	3/06	NWKS	Rigid head, 3" cut

WHAT'S IT WORTH?

Combine Heads

Make	Model	Year	Cond.	Price	Sale	Location	Comments
John Deere	224	1986	G	$4,400	4/06	WCMB	Canadian sale, 24', bat reel, crop lifters
John Deere	224	1988	F	$600	11/06	SCSD	Straight head
John Deere	230		P	$1,300	7/06	SEND	Rigid head, 9" sunflower pans, PTO hookups
John Deere	230		G	$2,500	2/06	NWKS	Rigid head
John Deere	230	1980	F	$2,400	7/06	SEND	Straight head, 30' w/ transport
John Deere	230	1982	G	$1,750	2/06	SCKS	Flex head
John Deere	243		F	$300	9/06	NEIA	2R CH
John Deere	330	1997	G	$4,500	3/06	ECND	Flex
John Deere	343		F	$700	5/06	SEWY	3RN CH, 30"
John Deere	343		F	$825	12/06	NWIL	3RN CH
John Deere	344		G	$2,400	8/06	NECO	3RW CH
John Deere	443		F	$550	3/06	NEMI	4RN CH
John Deere	443		F	$900	9/06	SCMN	4RN CH
John Deere	443		G	$1,150	12/06	SCMN	4RN CH
John Deere	443		G	$1,150	12/06	SCMN	4RN CH
John Deere	443		G	$1,150	12/06	SCMN	4RN CH
John Deere	443		F	$1,200	1/06	SCMI	4RN CH, high tin
John Deere	443		G	$1,400	6/06	ECSD	
John Deere	443		G	$1,400	8/06	SEMN	4RN CH, high tin
John Deere	443		G	$1,950	1/06	SCMN	4RN CH, low tin
John Deere	443	1979	F	$800	2/06	SCMI	4RN CH, low tin
John Deere	444		F	$500	10/06	WCWI	4RW CH
John Deere	444		G	$550	1/06	WCNE	5R-30 CH
John Deere	444		F	$600	9/06	NEIN	4RW CH
John Deere	444		F	$650	9/06	NWIL	4RW CH, 38"
John Deere	444		F	$650	10/06	SEMN	6RW CH, low tin
John Deere	444		F	$675	10/06	SEMN	4RW CH
John Deere	444		F	$750	2/06	WCIA	4RW CH
John Deere	444		F	$800	11/06	ECIL	4RW CH, high tin
John Deere	444		F	$800	12/06	NWWI	4RW CH, low tin
John Deere	444		F	$900	12/06	NWWI	4RW CH, low tin
John Deere	444		G	$1,000	3/06	NCIN	4RW CH, low tin
John Deere	444		G	$1,000	9/06	ECNE	4RW CH, 36"
John Deere	444		G	$1,050	6/06	ECSD	
John Deere	444		G	$1,050	8/06	NWIL	4RW CH, 36"
John Deere	444		G	$1,100	6/06	NWIL	4RW CH, 36"
John Deere	444		G	$1,200	3/06	NENE	4RW CH
John Deere	444		G	$1,200	8/06	SCNE	4RW CH
John Deere	444		G	$1,300	1/06	SESD	4RW CH
John Deere	444		G	$3,500	2/06	WCIL	4RW CH
John Deere	444		G	$5,100	9/06	NCIA	4RW CH
John Deere	444	1977	G	$1,200	9/06	NENE	4RW CH, 36"
John Deere	444	1979	G	$1,600	3/06	ECNE	4RW CH
John Deere	454		P	$25	11/06	ECIL	4-row crop bean head
John Deere	454		F	$400	9/06	NEIA	4R row crop head
John Deere	494		E	$5,800	2/06	SEMI	4RW CH, 36"
John Deere	543	1975	G	$1,900	12/06	NENE	CH, ear saver auger covers
John Deere	620F		G	$17,000	4/06	SEPA	HydraFlex, single-pt. hookup, full finger auger
John Deere	625F	2004	G	$17,500	12/06	WCMN	Flex head, setup for use on JD 9600, used 1½ seasons

Combine Heads

Make	Model	Year	Cond.	Price	Sale	Location	Comments
John Deere	625F	2004	G	$18,000	2/06	NWIL	25' HydraFlex grain platform, full-finger auger, Contour Master, auto header sensors, stubble lights, double-cut sickle, used on fewer than 700 acres
John Deere	625F	2004	G	$19,000	8/06	WCMN	Flex
John Deere	630	2004	G	$16,000	7/06	SEND	Flex head
John Deere	630	2004	G	$16,000	7/06	SEND	Flex head
John Deere	630	2004	G	$16,000	4/06	NWMN	Flex head, fore/aft, stubble lights, 60 Series drive
John Deere	630	2004	G	$16,750	4/06	NWMN	Flex head, fore/aft, stubble lights, 60 Series drive
John Deere	630	2004	G	$16,750	4/06	NWMN	Flex head, fore/aft, stubble lights, 60 Series drive
John Deere	630	2004	G	$18,250	7/06	SEND	Flex head, Contour Master, composite fingers, high stone dam, stubble lights
John Deere	630	2005	G	$16,000	7/06	SEND	Flex head
John Deere	630	2006	E	$22,500	12/06	WCMN	HydraFlex, fore/aft, 60 Series hookups, extra factory sickle
John Deere	630	2006	E	$22,500	12/06	WCMN	HydraFlex, fore/aft, 60 Series hookups, extra factory sickle
John Deere	630F		G	$19,300	3/06	ECND	HydraFlex head
John Deere	630F		G	$19,500	3/06	ECND	HydraFlex head
John Deere	630F		G	$24,000	8/06	WCMN	30' Hydraflex, Crary air system, poly divide, one owner
John Deere	630F	2004	G	$14,500	8/06	WCMN	Flex
John Deere	630F	2004	G	$14,500	12/06	WCMN	Flex head, single point
John Deere	630F	2004	G	$15,250	11/06	ECND	Flex head, fore/aft
John Deere	630F	2004	G	$15,250	11/06	ECND	Flex head, fore/aft
John Deere	630F	2004	G	$15,500	11/06	ECND	Flex head, fore/aft
John Deere	630F	2004	G	$15,750	11/06	SCND	HydraFlex
John Deere	630F	2004	G	$16,000	3/06	SEIA	HydraFlex grain platform, contour sensors, stubble lights, fore/aft
John Deere	630F	2004	E	$16,250	1/06	NECO	
John Deere	630F	2004	G	$16,500	12/06	WCMN	Flex head, single point, Contour Master
John Deere	630F	2005	G	$18,000	12/06	WCKS	HydraFlex platform, fore/aft, contour ready, field lights
John Deere	630F	2005	E	$19,000	12/06	WCKS	HydraFlex platform, fore/aft, contour ready, field lights
John Deere	630F	2005	E	$19,500	12/06	WCKS	HydraFlex platform, fore/aft, contour ready, field lights
John Deere	630F	2005	E	$20,000	12/06	WCKS	HydraFlex platform, fore/aft, contour ready, field lights
John Deere	630F	2006	E	$21,000	12/06	WCKS	HydraFlex platform, fore/aft, contour ready, field lights
John Deere	630F	2006	E	$21,000	12/06	WCKS	HydraFlex platform, fore/aft, contour ready, field lights
John Deere	630F	2006	E	$22,000	12/06	WCMN	New demo unit, single point, Contour Master
John Deere	630F	2006	E	$22,500	12/06	WCKS	HydraFlex platform, fore/aft, contour ready, field lights
John Deere	630R	2005	E	$11,500	12/06	WCKS	Rigid head, contour ready, fore/aft, field lights, bat reels
John Deere	630R	2006	G	$11,500	12/06	WCKS	Rigid head, contour ready, fore/aft, field lights, bat reels
John Deere	630R	2006	E	$12,500	12/06	WCKS	Rigid head, contour ready, fore/aft, field lights, bat reels
John Deere	630R	2006	E	$13,000	12/06	WCKS	Rigid head, contour ready, fore/aft, field lights, bat reels
John Deere	635	2004	G	$16,000	12/06	NWWI	HydraFlex, header height sensing
John Deere	635	2004	G	$20,000	7/06	SEND	Flex head
John Deere	635F		G	$17,000	9/06	NCIA	Flex head
John Deere	635F		G	$18,500	12/06	WCMN	HydraFlex
John Deere	635F		E	$24,000	11/06	SCNE	HydraFlex 35' head
John Deere	635F		E	$24,750	3/06	NESD	HydraFlex
John Deere	635F		E	$24,900	3/06	NESD	HydraFlex
John Deere	635F		E	$25,000	3/06	NESD	HydraFlex, Contour Master
John Deere	635F	2004	G	$15,000	8/06	WCMN	Flex
John Deere	635F	2005	E	$19,000	12/06	WCKS	HydraFlex platform, fore/aft, contour ready, field lights

WHAT'S IT WORTH?

Combine Heads

Make	Model	Year	Cond.	Price	Sale	Location	Comments
John Deere	635F	2005	E	$26,000	3/06	SEMN	Bean head, full finger auger, poly, 2" cut, 35', looks new
John Deere	635F	2006	E	$26,000	12/06	WCMN	New demo unit, HydraFlex, single point, low stone dam
John Deere	643		G	$500	3/06	SCIN	6RN CH
John Deere	643		F	$1,400	2/06	NWOH	6RN CH, high tin
John Deere	643		F	$1,750	7/06	WCMN	6RN CH, high tin
John Deere	643		G	$1,800	5/06	SEWY	6RN CH, 30"
John Deere	643		G	$1,800	5/06	SEWY	6RN CH, 30"
John Deere	643		G	$1,800	12/06	NEMO	6RN CH
John Deere	643		F	$1,825	9/06	SEIL	6RN CH, high tin
John Deere	643		F	$2,000	6/06	SWMN	6RN CH
John Deere	643		F	$2,000	10/06	SEMN	6RN CH
John Deere	643		F	$2,000	2/06	WCOH	6RN CH
John Deere	643		G	$2,300	6/06	NCIL	6RN CH, high tin
John Deere	643		F	$2,300	7/06	WCMN	6RN CH, high tin
John Deere	643		G	$2,400	9/06	NECO	6RN CH, 30"
John Deere	643		G	$2,500	6/06	WCMN	6RN CH, 30"
John Deere	643		F	$2,500	9/06	NCIA	6RN CH
John Deere	643		F	$2,500	8/06	NCIA	6RN CH, 30", high tin
John Deere	643		F	$2,500	9/06	NCIA	6RN CH, knife rolls
John Deere	643		F	$2,500	3/06	NWPA	6RN CH, 30"
John Deere	643		F	$2,600	3/06	NCNE	6RN CH
John Deere	643		G	$2,600	3/06	SWOH	6RN CH, 30"
John Deere	643		G	$2,600	6/06	WCMN	6RN CH, high tin
John Deere	643		F	$2,600	9/06	NEND	6RN CH
John Deere	643		G	$2,800	12/06	SCMN	6RN CH
John Deere	643		F	$3,000	3/06	NESD	6RN CH, older, high tin
John Deere	643		G	$3,000	6/06	ECSD	
John Deere	643		G	$3,000	6/06	ECSD	
John Deere	643		G	$3,000	12/06	NWWI	6RN CH, low tin
John Deere	643		G	$3,100	9/06	NEIA	6RN CH
John Deere	643		G	$3,250	8/06	NCIA	6RN CH
John Deere	643		G	$3,250	8/06	WCMN	6RN CH, low tin
John Deere	643		G	$3,300	2/06	NCIN	6RN CH, high tin, plastic snouts
John Deere	643		G	$3,400	8/06	WCIL	6RN CH
John Deere	643		F	$3,400	2/06	WCIA	6RN CH
John Deere	643		G	$3,500	6/06	ECSD	
John Deere	643		G	$3,500	6/06	ECSD	
John Deere	643		G	$4,000	4/06	SWOH	6RN CH, 30"
John Deere	643		G	$4,000	1/06	WCIL	6RN CH, oil bath, low tin
John Deere	643		G	$4,250	1/06	NEIN	6RN CH
John Deere	643		G	$4,300	3/06	NWOH	6RN CH, low tin, oil
John Deere	643		G	$4,400	8/06	WCMN	6RN CH, 30"
John Deere	643		G	$4,450	1/06	NEIN	6RN CH, low tin, oil bath
John Deere	643		G	$4,500	1/06	WCIL	6RN CH, low tin
John Deere	643		F	$4,700	3/06	NEKS	6RN CH, oil bath
John Deere	643		P	$4,700	2/06	NCIL	6RN CH, very rough
John Deere	643		G	$4,750	4/06	NENE	6RN CH
John Deere	643		G	$4,800	6/06	ECSD	
John Deere	643		G	$4,800	8/06	NEIL	6RN CH, ear saver, low tin, oil bath

Combine Heads

Make	Model	Year	Cond.	Price	Sale	Location	Comments
John Deere	643		G	$4,900	2/06	NWIN	6RN CH, 30"
John Deere	643		G	$5,250	2/06	ECIL	6RN CH, recent oil bath and gathering chains
John Deere	643		G	$5,400	3/06	NWIL	6R, poly
John Deere	643		G	$5,700	8/06	WCMN	6RN CH
John Deere	643		G	$6,100	4/06	WCMN	6RN CH, oil drive, poly snouts
John Deere	643		G	$6,100	3/06	NEIA	6RN CH
John Deere	643		G	$7,400	3/06	SESD	6RN CH, oil drive, low profile, new poly, sprockets and chains last season
John Deere	643		G	$7,500	1/06	NEMO	6RN low tin
John Deere	643		G	$7,900	11/06	SCMN	6RN CH, oil
John Deere	643	1978	G	$2,250	12/06	SEMN	6RN CH
John Deere	643	1979	G	$3,250	11/06	NEKS	6RN CH, 30"
John Deere	643	1979	G	$3,400	3/06	SWKS	6RN CH, 30"
John Deere	643	1979	G	$3,500	4/06	ECND	6RN CH, low tin, non oil
John Deere	643	1982	G	$2,900	12/06	NWWI	6RN CH, low tin
John Deere	643	1982	F	$5,600	1/06	NWIL	6RN CH
John Deere	643	1983	G	$4,800	11/06	NWMN	6RN CH, low tin, oil drive, standard rolls
John Deere	643	1984	G	$5,300	2/06	ECIL	6RN CH, oil bath
John Deere	643	1986	G	$4,800	2/06	SEIN	6RN CH, poly snouts, low tin, oil bath
John Deere	643	1987	G	$5,700	8/06	NCIA	6RN CH, 30", low tin
John Deere	643	1988	F	$2,250	12/06	SEMN	6RN CH
John Deere	643	1988	G	$4,600	12/06	NWWI	6RN CH, low tin
John Deere	643	1989	G	$5,500	12/06	NWWI	6RN CH, low tin
John Deere	643	1990	F	$4,750	3/06	NCNE	6RN CH, low tin, oil drive
John Deere	643	1991	G	$4,500	12/06	NWWI	6RN CH, low tin
John Deere	643	1992	G	$7,500	1/06	WCIL	6RN CH, 30"
John Deere	644		F	$3,100	2/06	WCIA	6RW CH
John Deere	644	1986	G	$12,000	11/06	SENE	6R-36 CH, ear saver, auger covers, oil drive
John Deere	644	1993	G	$4,000	12/06	SCMN	6RW CH, plastic, oil
John Deere	653		F	$200	2/06	NWOH	6R bean head
John Deere	653		F	$400	9/06	NEIA	6R row crop head
John Deere	653		G	$900	12/06	ECKS	6R row crop head, Bish JD to Case IH adapter plate
John Deere	653		F	$1,100	12/06	SCNE	6R row crop head
John Deere	653		G	$2,100	8/06	NEKS	6R row crop head
John Deere	653	1976	F	$650	1/06	NWIL	Bean head, 6R-30, Dial-a-Matic
John Deere	653A		G	$375	4/06	SCKS	6R-30 row head
John Deere	653A		F	$400	11/06	NEKS	6R-30 row crop head
John Deere	653A		G	$650	2/06	WCIA	6R row crop head
John Deere	653A		G	$1,100	3/06	NWMN	6R-30 all crop header
John Deere	653A		G	$1,500	2/06	SCKS	6R row crop head
John Deere	653A	1980	F	$550	11/06	NWMN	6R all crop, factory sides and back
John Deere	653A	1981	F	$700	11/06	NEKS	6R-30 row crop head
John Deere	653A	1982	G	$2,800	11/06	NEKS	6R row crop head, one owner, used on very few acres
John Deere	654A	1983	G	$2,700	11/06	SENE	6R-36 row crop head
John Deere	654A	1990	G	$4,200	6/06	NWKS	6R row crop head, sunflower shields, Bish adapter
John Deere	693		G	$8,400	2/06	NEIN	6RN CH, poly
John Deere	693		G	$9,400	12/06	SEMN	6RN CH
John Deere	693		E	$10,800	3/06	NEKS	6RN CH
John Deere	693		G	$10,900	11/06	NCOH	6RN CH, low profile, poly style snouts

Combine Heads

Make	Model	Year	Cond.	Price	Sale	Location	Comments
John Deere	693		G	$11,900	3/06	NCIL	6RN CH, poly, knife rolls
John Deere	693		G	$12,000	8/06	NWIL	6RN CH
John Deere	693		G	$12,500	3/06	SEMN	6RN CH, all poly, hydraulic deck plates, new chains, sprockets 2 years ago
John Deere	693		G	$13,000	12/06	WCMI	6RN CH, plastic snouts
John Deere	693		G	$14,000	4/06	NESD	6RN CH, knife rolls, ear saver cover, kept inside
John Deere	693		G	$15,500	7/06	ECIL	6RN CH, poly, hyd. stripper plates, ear saver, 1,000 acres total use
John Deere	693	1994	G	$11,000	12/06	NWMO	6RN CH, Contour Master, with shafts, outer snout exterior, rebuilt 9/06
John Deere	693	1995	G	$8,000	7/06	SEND	6RN CH, 30", knife rolls, poly, cob catch, 50 Series drives
John Deere	693	1995	G	$9,400	12/06	NWWI	6RN CH, knife rolls
John Deere	693	1995	G	$11,500	12/06	NWMO	6RN CH, new rolls two seasons ago
John Deere	693	1996	G	$8,500	12/06	SCMN	6RN CH
John Deere	693	1997	G	$12,400	1/06	NEIN	6RN CH, hyd. deck plates
John Deere	693	1998	G	$9,500	3/06	NCOH	6RN CH, poly snout
John Deere	693	1998	G	$9,750	11/06	NEKS	6RN CH, 30", stubble lights, Contour Master drives, straight fluted rolls
John Deere	693	1998	G	$13,250	12/06	NWWI	6RN CH, knife rolls, hyd. deck plates
John Deere	693	2000	G	$10,700	12/06	ECIL	6RN CH
John Deere	693	2002	G	$16,000	2/06	NWIL	6RN CH, Contour Master, hyd. deck plates, header height sensors, fluted rolls and telescoping jack shafts
John Deere	694		G	$16,100	3/06	ECNE	6RW CH, 36", poly
John Deere	843		F	$3,100	2/06	WCIA	8RN CH
John Deere	843		F	$3,400	1/06	SWNE	8RN CH
John Deere	843		G	$3,550	8/06	ECNE	8RN CH, ear saver, 30"
John Deere	843		G	$3,800	8/06	WCMN	8RN CH, 30"
John Deere	843		G	$4,400	8/06	WCMN	8RN CH, 30", high profile
John Deere	843		G	$4,500	12/06	ECMO	8RN CH
John Deere	843		G	$5,000	6/06	ECSD	
John Deere	843		G	$5,750	6/06	ECSD	
John Deere	843		G	$5,900	6/06	ECSD	
John Deere	843		G	$6,000	3/06	ECIL	8RN CH, oil bath
John Deere	843		G	$6,000	2/06	WCIA	8RN CH
John Deere	843		G	$6,300	8/06	SEMN	8RN CH, oil
John Deere	843		G	$6,600	12/06	WCMN	8RN CH, oil bath
John Deere	843		G	$6,700	1/06	SESD	8RN CH, low tin, oil
John Deere	843		G	$6,850	1/06	SESD	8RN CH, low tin, oil
John Deere	843		G	$7,200	2/06	NCIL	8RN CH
John Deere	843		G	$7,300	2/06	WCIL	8RN CH
John Deere	843		G	$7,900	3/06	NWMN	8RN CH, 30", knife rolls
John Deere	843		G	$8,000	1/06	SESD	8RN CH, 1982 model, low tin, oil
John Deere	843		G	$8,900	7/06	WCMN	8RN CH, 30" snouts, knife rolls, new chains and sprockets, all other parts like new
John Deere	843	1977	G	$3,000	12/06	NWMO	8RN CH, high tin, auger cover, ear savers
John Deere	843	1979	F	$3,000	7/06	SEND	8RN CH, 30", high tin
John Deere	843	1980	G	$3,200	12/06	NWMO	8RN CH, non-oil drive, low tin
John Deere	843	1981	G	$6,000	5/06	WCKS	8RN CH
John Deere	843	1985	G	$6,000	11/06	NEKS	8RN CH, 30"

Combine Heads

Make	Model	Year	Cond.	Price	Sale	Location	Comments
John Deere	843	1988	G	$4,600	12/06	NWMO	8RN CH, oil drive, low tin
John Deere	843	1988	G	$6,750	3/06	SEIA	8RN CH, low tin oil-drive CH, Contour Master drive shafts
John Deere	843	1989	G	$8,200	12/06	ECIL	8RN CH
John Deere	843	1993	G	$7,900	3/06	NCIA	8RN CH, 30", low tin, oil
John Deere	843	1998	G	$17,000	12/06	ECNE	8RN CH, poly, hyd. deck plates, ear saver auger covers, head-sight header height sensor, contour shafts
John Deere	844		G	$3,600	9/06	NCIA	8RW CH, high tin
John Deere	853		E	$1,500	4/06	NCSD	8R all crop header
John Deere	853		G	$4,800	3/06	WCKS	8R row crop head
John Deere	853A		F	$500	3/06	NWKS	8R row crop head
John Deere	853A		G	$3,200	3/06	NWMN	8R-30 all crop header
John Deere	853A		G	$3,700	3/06	NWKS	8R row crop head
John Deere	853A		G	$4,700	2/06	ECKS	8R row crop head, sold with header trailer
John Deere	853A		F	$5,900	3/06	ECKS	8R row crop head
John Deere	853A		G	$6,500	11/06	NWKS	8R row crop head
John Deere	853A		G	$7,200	2/06	NWKS	8R row crop head, shedded
John Deere	853A	1980	G	$5,750	3/06	NWKS	8R row crop head
John Deere	853A	1980	G	$5,750	3/06	NWKS	8R row crop head
John Deere	853A	1981	G	$5,750	4/06	ECND	8R all crop head, AHHC, factory sides and back
John Deere	853A	1983	G	$5,200	3/06	SWKS	8 row crop head, rebuilt
John Deere	853A	1986	G	$3,900	11/06	NEKS	8R-30 row crop head
John Deere	853A	1988	G	$4,700	3/06	NEKS	8R row crop head, Bish head adapter plate
John Deere	853A	1990	G	$5,000	5/06	WCKS	8R row crop head
John Deere	854A		F	$1,100	11/06	SCNE	8R-36 row crop head
John Deere	893		F	$9,950	2/06	ECIL	8RN CH, poly snouts
John Deere	893		G	$12,750	11/06	NEKS	8RN CH
John Deere	893		G	$14,750	8/06	WCMN	8RN CH for Contour Master combine
John Deere	893		G	$16,000	2/06	SCMI	8RN CH, knife rolls
John Deere	893		G	$16,500	8/06	WCMN	8RN CH, knife rolls
John Deere	893		G	$16,500	2/06	SCMI	8RN CH, hyd. deck plates
John Deere	893		G	$18,400	3/06	NENE	8RN CH, hyd. deck plates, used one season
John Deere	893		G	$20,000	9/06	NCIA	8RN CH
John Deere	893	1993	G	$8,000	11/06	NWKS	8RN CH
John Deere	893	1995	G	$10,500	12/06	NCIA	8RN CH, trash reel
John Deere	893	1995	G	$13,750	12/06	ECMO	8RN CH
John Deere	893	1996	G	$14,000	12/06	NWMO	8RN CH, Contour Master, with shafts, $10,000 rebuild 12/05
John Deere	893	1996	G	$14,000	1/06	WCIL	8RN CH, poly, hyd. deck plates, knife rolls, Meteer reel
John Deere	893	1996	G	$14,000	2/06	WCIL	8RN CH, 30", poly
John Deere	893	1996	G	$16,000	12/06	NWMO	8RN CH, Contour Master, no shafts, complete rebuild 9/06
John Deere	893	1996	E	$19,500	2/06	NWOH	8RN CH, poly, knife rolls, adj. deck plates
John Deere	893	1997	G	$13,250	8/06	NCIA	8RN CH, poly
John Deere	893	1997	G	$14,000	7/06	SEND	8RN CH, 30", auger cover, telescoping drives
John Deere	893	1997	G	$15,250	8/06	WCMN	8RN CH, knife roll
John Deere	893	1997	E	$15,600	1/06	WCIL	8RN CH, knife rolls, late model drive shafts
John Deere	893	1997	E	$16,500	3/06	ECNE	8RN CH, low profile, 30" spacing
John Deere	893	1998	F	$12,500	12/06	NEKS	8RN CH, poly snouts, manual deck plates, contour shafts
John Deere	893	1998	G	$15,000	11/06	WCMN	8RN CH, 50 Series shafts, knife rolls
John Deere	893	1998	G	$20,000	9/06	NCIA	8RN CH, knife rolls, hyd. deck plates

WHAT'S IT WORTH?

Combine Heads

Make	Model	Year	Cond.	Price	Sale	Location	Comments
John Deere	893	1999	E	$22,000	1/06	NWIA	8RN CH
John Deere	893	2000	G	$18,500	11/06	NCIN	8RN CH, poly, hyd. adj. deck plates
John Deere	893	2002	G	$20,000	2/06	SWNE	8RN CH, hyd. deck plates, one owner, used two seasons
John Deere	893	2002	G	$22,500	1/06	NEIN	8RN CH, hyd. deck plates, knife rolls
John Deere	893	2002	G	$30,000	11/06	WCMN	8RN CH, knife rolls, hyd. deck plate
John Deere	893	2003	G	$22,000	12/06	SWMI	8RN CH, all poly, hyd. deck plates, knife rolls, only used for approximately 4,000 acres
John Deere	893	2003	E	$22,000	3/06	NEKS	8RN CH, hyd. deck plates and Contour Master
John Deere	893	2003	E	$24,500	2/06	NWOH	8RN CH, poly, knife rolls, adj. deck plates
John Deere	893	2004	E	$21,500	12/06	WCKS	8RN CH, poly snouts, field lights
John Deere	893	2004	E	$24,500	12/06	NWWI	8RN CH, hyd. deck plates, single point, 1,200 acres
John Deere	893	2004	G	$25,250	1/06	NEIN	8RN CH, hyd. deck plates, knife rolls
John Deere	893	2005	E	$25,000	12/06	WCKS	8RN CH, poly snouts, field lights
John Deere	893	2005	E	$27,500	2/06	WCIL	8RN CH, poly, flute row units, hyd. adjust deck plates, feeder house cover shield and stubble shoes
John Deere	894	1995	G	$10,800	11/06	SCSD	8RW CH
John Deere	912		G	$5,400	9/06	NECO	6 belt pickup header
John Deere	912	1988	G	$3,350	11/06	NWMN	Pickup head, JD 6-belt pickup
John Deere	912	1990	G	$3,000	3/06	ECND	Pickup platform, JD 6-belt pickup
John Deere	914	1992	G	$5,500	4/06	ECND	Pickup head, 7-belt pickup, AHHC
John Deere	914	1995	G	$4,000	11/06	ECND	Pickup head, 6-belt pickup
John Deere	914	1995	G	$5,000	3/06	ECND	Dummy w/ 7-belt JD pickup
John Deere	914	1995	G	$5,000	3/06	ECND	Dummy w/ 7-belt JD pickup
John Deere	914	1995	G	$6,500	3/06	NEND	Pickup head, DAS, new JD belts, 7-belt pickup
John Deere	914	1997	G	$4,400	11/06	ECND	Pickup head, 6-belt pickup
John Deere	914	1997	G	$6,200	3/06	NWMN	Pickup head, Rake-Up 14' draper pickup
John Deere	914	1997	G	$6,700	3/06	ECND	Dummy w/ 7-belt pickup
John Deere	914	1998	F	$4,300	11/06	NEND	Pickup head, 6-belt pickup, big tires
John Deere	914	1998	G	$6,200	6/06	ECND	Pickup head, 7-belt JD pickup, auto header height
John Deere	914	2003	F	$5,750	12/06	NEKS	Pickup header with Rake-Up
John Deere	914	2003	G	$7,100	12/06	NEKS	Pickup header with Rake-Up
John Deere	914	2003	G	$7,750	12/06	NEKS	Pickup header with Rake-Up
John Deere	915		G	$2,500	12/06	NWWI	Flex
John Deere	915		G	$3,000	12/06	ECMO	Grain head
John Deere	915		G	$3,300	8/06	NWIL	Grain platform, Hume reel
John Deere	915		G	$4,500	1/06	SCMN	Flex
John Deere	915		G	$6,700	12/06	NWWI	Platform
John Deere	915	1993	G	$2,800	3/06	NEKS	Flex head
John Deere	918		G	$5,300	9/06	NEIA	18' flex head
John Deere	918		E	$7,600	2/06	SEMI	Grain head
John Deere	918	1990	G	$1,900	2/06	WCIA	Platform head
John Deere	920		G	$1,750	6/06	ECSD	Flex
John Deere	920		F	$2,500	12/06	WCMN	Flex platform
John Deere	920		G	$2,650	3/06	NEKS	Flex head
John Deere	920		G	$2,800	9/06	NCIA	Platform, fore/aft
John Deere	920		G	$2,900	9/06	SEIL	Platform, Dial-a-Matic
John Deere	920		G	$3,000	8/06	NCNE	Flex hd, 3" Crary cut, stainless steel pan, hyd fore/aft
John Deere	920		G	$3,200	3/06	NCIL	20' grain table

Combine Heads

Make	Model	Year	Cond.	Price	Sale	Location	Comments
John Deere	920		G	$3,250	1/06	WCIL	20' grain platform
John Deere	920		G	$3,300	7/06	WCMN	Flex head, new poly, header height control, field ready
John Deere	920		G	$3,500	2/06	NEIN	Flex head, 20'
John Deere	920		G	$4,200	6/06	ECSD	Flex
John Deere	920		G	$5,000	6/06	ECSD	Flex
John Deere	920		G	$5,200	4/06	NENE	Flex head, poly finger reel
John Deere	920		G	$6,000	12/06	ECMO	Grain head
John Deere	920		G	$6,000	2/06	NCIN	Grain head
John Deere	920		G	$6,700	4/06	SWOH	Poly snouts, poly skids
John Deere	920		G	$6,700	12/06	WCMN	20' grain head, floating cutter bar
John Deere	920	1989	G	$2,750	1/06	SESD	Flex head
John Deere	920	1989	G	$2,800	8/06	WCMN	Flex, platform
John Deere	920	1989	G	$3,000	1/06	WCIL	20' flex head, fore/aft
John Deere	920	1989	G	$3,500	12/06	SEMN	Platform
John Deere	920	1989	G	$5,800	8/06	NCIA	Flex head, 3" sections
John Deere	920	1993	G	$5,200	3/06	ECIL	20' platform, fore/aft, ss, poly
John Deere	920	1994	G	$3,200	3/06	NCNE	20' flex head, stainless steel pan, 3" cut, hyd. fore/aft
John Deere	920	1995	F	$1,900	12/06	NWWI	10 Series drive
John Deere	920	1995	F	$5,300	1/06	NWIL	Platform, fore/aft, poly skids
John Deere	920	1996	P	$550	2/06	WCIA	Flex head
John Deere	920	1996	G	$6,200	2/06	SEIN	20' flex head, fore/aft
John Deere	920	1997	G	$3,500	12/06	NWWI	Flex platform, 50 Series drive, poly points
John Deere	920	1997	G	$7,600	3/06	NCIA	Flex head, poly row dividers, 3" sections
John Deere	920	1998	G	$8,600	2/06	NWIN	Flex head, poly snouts
John Deere	920	1998	G	$8,750	1/06	WCIL	Flex grain platform, poly dividers
John Deere	920F		G	$16,500	12/06	NEMO	20' grain platform, poly, full finger
John Deere	920F	1996	G	$7,500	2/06	WCIL	Platform, poly ends
John Deere	920F	1997	G	$7,900	1/06	WCIL	20' platform, poly dividers, fore/aft
John Deere	922		G	$2,200	12/06	ECIL	Platform, poly
John Deere	922		G	$3,000	3/06	NEOH	Grain table
John Deere	922		G	$3,450	3/06	NESD	Flex, Crary air reel
John Deere	922		G	$3,600	9/06	SWIA	Platform, poly bottom, side hill drives
John Deere	922		G	$5,600	8/06	SCMN	Bean plat, flex head
John Deere	922		G	$6,300	7/06	ECIL	Platform, poly, fore/aft, 1,200 acres total use
John Deere	922	1990	G	$1,950	12/06	NWMO	
John Deere	922	1997	E	$11,500	11/06	SENE	Flex head, poly, 3" cut, used one season on fewer than 200 acres, like new
John Deere	922F	2003	G	$13,100	2/06	ECIL	Platform, fore/aft, 900 acres use
John Deere	924		F	$1,300	9/06	NCIA	Platform
John Deere	924		G	$3,500	3/06	NWMN	Flex head
John Deere	924	1988	G	$1,750	12/06	WCMN	Flex head, Dial-a-Matic, good poly, good sickle
John Deere	924	1988	G	$1,750	12/06	SCMN	Platform
John Deere	925		F	$1,100	3/06	NCUT	Rigid head
John Deere	925		F	$1,500	8/06	WCMN	Flex, air reel and 25' John Deere finger reel
John Deere	925		F	$2,000	12/06	SCMN	Platform
John Deere	925		G	$2,400	12/06	NENE	Plat
John Deere	925		G	$2,500	12/06	SEND	Rigid head
John Deere	925		F	$2,500	2/06	ECIL	25' grain platform
John Deere	925		G	$2,800	8/06	WCMN	Flex

WHAT'S IT WORTH?

Combine Heads

Make	Model	Year	Cond.	Price	Sale	Location	Comments
John Deere	925		G	$3,500	8/06	SCNE	Flex, pickup reel, hyd. fore/aft
John Deere	925		G	$3,500	8/06	WCMN	Flex, poly
John Deere	925		G	$3,600	11/06	NCOH	Grain head, 25', new poly skids and cutter bar, rebuilt in 2006
John Deere	925		G	$3,800	6/06	ECSD	Flex
John Deere	925		G	$3,800	12/06	NENE	Flex head
John Deere	925		G	$4,000	6/06	WCMN	Flex
John Deere	925		G	$4,000	8/06	SCNE	Flex header, pickup reel, hyd. fore/aft, drive lines
John Deere	925		F	$4,100	3/06	SESD	Flex bean head, new sickle last season
John Deere	925		G	$4,250	8/06	WCMN	Flex, Crary air reel
John Deere	925		G	$4,250	8/06	SCNE	Flex, pickup reel, hyd. fore/aft
John Deere	925		G	$5,000	2/06	SEKS	Flex
John Deere	925		G	$6,500	1/06	SCMN	Flex, poly dividers, stainless pan
John Deere	925		F	$7,000	1/06	SWNE	Flex head
John Deere	925		G	$9,250	4/06	NWMN	Flex head, poly snouts
John Deere	925		G	$9,300	12/06	ECMO	Flex platform, converted to full finger auger, poly snouts
John Deere	925		G	$18,300	11/06	SCMN	Box & hoist
John Deere	925	1990	F	$1,900	12/06	SEMN	Platform
John Deere	925	1990	F	$2,700	11/06	NWMN	Flex head, poly bottom
John Deere	925	1991	P	$1,200	12/06	NWMO	Dial-a-Matic, metal, reel bent, fingers cut
John Deere	925	1991	G	$2,250	2/06	WCIA	Platform head
John Deere	925	1991	F	$2,500	12/06	NWMO	Metal, snouts, Dial-a-Matic, tear drop
John Deere	925	1992	G	$8,750	3/06	NEND	Flex head, Crary 4 bat air reel
John Deere	925	1993	F	$2,100	12/06	NWMO	
John Deere	925	1993	F	$3,200	11/06	NWMN	Flex head, poly
John Deere	925	1993	F	$3,600	3/06	NCOH	25' platform w/ cart
John Deere	925	1993	G	$4,750	12/06	SEMN	Platform
John Deere	925	1993	G	$5,400	12/06	NWMO	Metal snouts, Dial-a-Matic
John Deere	925	1994	G	$2,600	8/06	NECO	Rigid platform
John Deere	925	1995	G	$8,500	3/06	NWOH	Grain head fore/aft, poly dividers
John Deere	925	1996	G	$4,700	7/06	SEND	DAS, Dial-a-Matic
John Deere	925	1996	G	$4,900	12/06	NCIA	Flex head
John Deere	925	1996	G	$5,400	2/06	WCIA	Platform head
John Deere	925	1996	G	$5,500	4/06	ECND	Flex head, poly snout, poly bottom, fore/aft
John Deere	925	1996	G	$7,250	4/06	NWMN	Flex head, hyd fore/aft, finger
John Deere	925	1996	G	$8,000	7/06	SEND	Flex head, fore/aft, poly
John Deere	925	1996	G	$8,200	3/06	NWMN	Flex head, fore/aft, stubble lights, poly bottom
John Deere	925	1997	G	$5,500	7/06	SEND	DAS, Dial-a-Matic
John Deere	925	1997	G	$6,000	7/06	SEND	DAS, Dial-a-Matic
John Deere	925	1997	G	$6,000	8/06	SCNE	Flex header, pickup reel, hyd. fore/aft
John Deere	925	1997	G	$11,600	3/06	ECNE	Flex grain platform, poly skids, full-finger auger, hard plastic fingers
John Deere	925	1997	G	$18,000	12/06	ECNE	Flex head, Crary air reel, setup for Contour Master, poly snouts
John Deere	925	1998	F	$3,400	12/06	NWMO	Poly
John Deere	925	1998	G	$4,000	12/06	NWMO	Contour master, poly, poly finger, short reel teeth
John Deere	925	1998	G	$5,500	11/06	NEKS	Flex head, full finger auger, poly skid plates, DAS, Dial-a-Matic, hyd. fore/aft
John Deere	925	1998	G	$6,800	6/06	ECND	Flex head, Contour Master, fore/aft, poly bottom

Combine Heads

Make	Model	Year	Cond.	Price	Sale	Location	Comments
John Deere	925	1998	G	$10,000	8/06	SCNE	Flex header
John Deere	925	2000	G	$6,500	11/06	NEKS	Flex head, full finger auger, poly skid plates, DAS, Dial-a-Matic, hyd. fore/aft
John Deere	925	2001	G	$10,000	4/06	SEND	25' flex cutting head
John Deere	925F		G	$4,800	3/06	NWMN	Flex head
John Deere	925F		E	$12,000	1/06	NWIA	Grain platform, poly snouts and skids, SCH cutting system guards, bean saver
John Deere	925F		E	$12,250	2/06	ECMN	Flex bean head, poly skids, full finger auger, 3" cut, one owner
John Deere	925F		G	$13,500	3/06	NENE	Flex head
John Deere	925F	1999	G	$10,200	11/06	NEKS	25' flex head, poly skid plates, auto header height sensing, hyd. fore/aft, telescoping platform drive shafts, Contour Master terrain tracer, finger/pickup reel, stubble lights
John Deere	925F	2000	G	$11,500	4/06	ECND	Full finger, DAS, fore/aft, poly, stubble lights
John Deere	925F	2001	E	$13,500	4/06	NESD	Flex head, full finger auger, DAS, fore/aft
John Deere	930		F	$1,500	4/06	NCSD	30' flex head
John Deere	930		F	$1,750	7/06	WCMN	Flex
John Deere	930		F	$2,000	7/06	WCMN	Flex
John Deere	930		F	$2,100	7/06	WCMN	Flex
John Deere	930		F	$2,200	9/06	NEND	Straight head
John Deere	930		F	$2,250	7/06	SEND	Rigid platform, fore/aft
John Deere	930		F	$2,500	8/06	NWIL	30' grain platform, needed paint
John Deere	930		F	$2,700	2/06	WCMN	Flex head, SCH cutting system
John Deere	930		G	$3,200	9/06	NCIA	Platform
John Deere	930		F	$3,200	8/06	WCMN	Flex
John Deere	930		F	$3,250	11/06	WCMN	Flex head
John Deere	930		G	$3,250	12/06	SEND	Rigid head, 9" sunflower pans
John Deere	930		G	$3,900	8/06	WCMN	Bean head, fore/aft, new poly, 1 season
John Deere	930		G	$4,000	3/06	SWKS	Rigid head
John Deere	930		G	$4,000	8/06	WCMN	Flex, 30' finger reel, 3" cut
John Deere	930		G	$4,000	9/06	NCIA	Platform, fore/aft
John Deere	930		G	$4,400	3/06	SWKS	Rigid head
John Deere	930		F	$4,500	12/06	NEKS	930D platform, bat reel, fore/aft, field lights
John Deere	930		G	$5,000	3/06	WCMN	Flex, steel snout
John Deere	930		G	$5,100	3/06	WCMN	Flex head, steel snouts
John Deere	930		G	$5,600	9/06	NCIA	Platform, fore/aft
John Deere	930		G	$7,700	2/06	NCIL	Grain table, full finger, flex head
John Deere	930		G	$9,000	7/06	WCMN	Flex
John Deere	930		G	$9,000	1/06	SCKS	30' rigid header, 1 owner, always shedded
John Deere	930		G	$9,750	8/06	WCMN	Flex
John Deere	930	1989	P	$2,500	7/06	SEND	Flex head
John Deere	930	1989	G	$3,100	8/06	NECO	Rigid platform
John Deere	930	1989	G	$3,750	3/06	NEND	Straight head, fore/aft, Pro plates, bat reel, stubble lights
John Deere	930	1989	G	$3,800	8/06	NECO	Rigid platform
John Deere	930	1990	G	$2,500	12/06	NWMO	Contour Master, no shafts, metal snouts, new reel, Dial-a-Matic
John Deere	930	1990	G	$4,200	11/06	NWKS	30' grain platform
John Deere	930	1992	F	$1,200	12/06	SEMN	Platform
John Deere	930	1992	F	$2,500	7/06	WCMN	Flex

Combine Heads

Make	Model	Year	Cond.	Price	Sale	Location	Comments
John Deere	930	1992	G	$4,000	3/06	NEND	Rigid head, 20' skid plates, easy cut, finger reel
John Deere	930	1993	P	$2,700	7/06	SEND	Flex head, stubble lights
John Deere	930	1993	G	$3,000	2/06	WCIA	Platform head
John Deere	930	1995	P	$1,750	7/06	SEND	Flex head, fore/aft
John Deere	930	1995	F	$2,000	12/06	NWWI	Flex head
John Deere	930	1995	F	$2,500	6/06	SEND	Flex head
John Deere	930	1995	P	$2,750	7/06	SEND	Flex head, fore/aft, plastic, stubble lights, 2 sets divider snouts, short/long
John Deere	930	1995	F	$3,000	7/06	SEND	Flex head, DAS, Dial-a-Matic
John Deere	930	1995	G	$5,000	11/06	NEND	Rigid head, bat reel
John Deere	930	1995	G	$5,500	7/06	WCMN	Flex head, 30', finger reel, poly fore/aft, Johnson rock guards, stubble lights
John Deere	930	1996	G	$3,750	2/06	WCIA	Platform head
John Deere	930	1996	F	$5,000	11/06	WCMN	Flex head, 50 Series shafts
John Deere	930	1996	G	$7,000	7/06	SEND	DAS, Dial-a-Matic, fore/aft
John Deere	930	1996	G	$7,000	7/06	SEND	Flex head, DAS, Dial-a-Matic, poly
John Deere	930	1996	G	$12,000	7/06	SEND	Flex head, DAS, Dial-a-Matic, poly
John Deere	930	1997	F	$2,700	12/06	SCMN	Platform
John Deere	930	1997	F	$2,750	7/06	SEND	Rigid head, 9' sunflower pans, bat reel
John Deere	930	1997	F	$2,750	12/06	SCMN	Platform
John Deere	930	1997	G	$4,500	3/06	ECND	Flex
John Deere	930	1997	G	$4,750	2/06	NWMN	Rigid head, fore/aft, stainless steel bottom
John Deere	930	1997	F	$5,000	7/06	SEND	Flex head, fore/aft, poly
John Deere	930	1997	F	$5,000	7/06	SEND	Flexhead, Contour Master, DAS, fore/aft, stubble lights
John Deere	930	1997	G	$8,250	1/06	NECO	Flex head
John Deere	930	1997	G	$9,000	12/06	SCMN	Platform, air reel
John Deere	930	1998	P	$1,000	7/06	SEND	Rigid, fore/aft, bat reel
John Deere	930	1998	P	$1,000	7/06	SEND	Rigid, fore/aft, bat reel
John Deere	930	1998	F	$1,600	12/06	NWMO	
John Deere	930	1998	G	$4,000	8/06	NWIL	30' grain platform
John Deere	930	1998	F	$4,750	7/06	SEND	Flex head, fore/aft, stubble lights, poly, 50 Series hookups
John Deere	930	1998	G	$6,500	7/06	SEND	Flex, DAS, Dial-a-Matic, fore/aft
John Deere	930	1998	F	$6,750	7/06	SEND	DAS, Dial-a-Matic, fore/aft, straight reel & auger
John Deere	930	1998	G	$8,500	7/06	SEND	Flex, DAS, Dial-a-Matic
John Deere	930	1998	G	$12,500	4/06	WCMB	Canadian sale
John Deere	930	1999	G	$4,100	3/06	ECND	Rigid w/ pickup reel
John Deere	930	1999	G	$4,500	7/06	WCMN	Flex
John Deere	930	1999	G	$8,500	3/06	NEKS	Flex head
John Deere	930	1999	G	$11,000	11/06	NEND	Flex head, fore/aft, Dial-a-Matic, poly, Crary air reel
John Deere	930	2000	F	$3,400	12/06	NWWI	Contour Master
John Deere	930	2000	G	$8,100	8/06	WCMN	Flex, full finger auger
John Deere	930	2001	G	$4,500	3/06	ECND	Rigid w/ pickup up reel
John Deere	930	2001	F	$5,500	8/06	SCNE	30' rigid header
John Deere	930	2001	G	$7,500	8/06	SCNE	30' rigid header
John Deere	930	2001	G	$9,500	12/06	NWWI	Contour Master
John Deere	930	2001	G	$13,500	1/06	NEIN	Flex head, poly, full fingered, fore/aft
John Deere	930	2002	G	$9,500	7/06	SEND	Flex head, full finger, Dial-a-Matic, DAS, fore/aft, poly
John Deere	930	2003	G	$11,000	7/06	SEND	Flex head, wedge kit
John Deere	930	2003	G	$11,250	11/06	WCMN	Flex head, 50 Series shafts

Combine Heads

Make	Model	Year	Cond.	Price	Sale	Location	Comments
John Deere	930F		G	$0	6/06	SCMN	No sale at $6,500, bean head, 3" cut, poly skids
John Deere	930F		P	$1,200	8/06	SCNE	Flex header, pickup reel, fore/aft, steel dividers, rough
John Deere	930F		F	$4,750	8/06	WCMN	Flex
John Deere	930F		F	$6,000	12/06	NEKS	30' platform, fore/aft, full finger, contour hookups, field lights
John Deere	930F		F	$6,600	12/06	NEKS	30' platform, fore/aft, full finger, field lights, contour hookups
John Deere	930F		G	$7,300	8/06	SEMN	Flex Contour Master, fore/aft
John Deere	930F		G	$9,250	3/06	SEMN	Bean head, full finger auger, poly rock guard, poly skids, 3" cut
John Deere	930F	1996	G	$9,500	2/06	WCIL	30' grain platform, full finger auger and poly skid plates
John Deere	930F	1997	F	$3,000	7/06	WCMN	Poly, flex
John Deere	930F	1997	G	$6,000	12/06	WCMN	Flex, Dial-a-Matic, full finger
John Deere	930F	1997	G	$9,700	12/06	WCMN	Flex, Dial-a-Matic
John Deere	930F	1998	G	$9,900	12/06	NWMO	Poly, Dial-a-Matic, DAS, stubble lights
John Deere	930F	2000	G	$9,100	11/06	NCIN	Grain head, fore/aft, full finger
John Deere	930F	2000	G	$9,700	12/06	ECMO	Flex platform, poly pads
John Deere	930F	2000	G	$10,250	2/06	SEKS	Flex head, Contour Master
John Deere	930F	2000	G	$11,800	7/06	WCMN	Flex head, 30' finger reel, poly, stubble lights, full finger, Dial-a-Matic, DAS, fore/aft
John Deere	930F	2000	G	$13,000	8/06	NCIA	30' full finger flexhead, fore/aft
John Deere	930F	2000	G	$13,000	12/06	SCMN	Platform
John Deere	930F	2000	G	$13,000	2/06	NWMN	Flex head, full finger, Crary air reel
John Deere	930F	2001	E	$9,500	2/06	NWOH	Grain head, full finger
John Deere	930F	2001	G	$11,000	1/06	SESD	Flex head
John Deere	930F	2002	G	$10,100	12/06	NWMO	Dial-a-Matic, DAS, poly, lights, 50 Series connects
John Deere	930F	2002	G	$13,300	12/06	ECIL	30' platform
John Deere	930F	2003	F	$6,000	12/06	NEKS	30' platform, fore/aft, full finger, field lights, contour hookups
John Deere	930F	2003	G	$12,000	2/06	WCIA	Platform head
John Deere	930F	2003	G	$13,000	2/06	SCMI	Flex head
John Deere	930F	2003	G	$14,500	2/06	SCMI	Flex head
John Deere	930R		G	$8,500	4/06	NWKS	Platform
John Deere	930R	2000	G	$8,000	7/06	SEND	Fore/aft, finger reel, poly bottom, 10 Series hookups
John Deere	930R	2000	G	$15,000	1/06	SCKS	30' rigid header, full finger
John Deere	930R	2001	E	$6,100	12/06	NEKS	30' platform, bat reel, PTO drive, field lights
John Deere	930R	2001	G	$8,000	7/06	SEND	Fore/aft, finger reel, poly bottom, 10 Series hookups
John Deere	930R	2002	F	$4,100	12/06	NEKS	30' platform, PTO drive, bat reel, field lights
John Deere	936	2005	E	$19,500	12/06	WCKS	936D draper head, contour ready, fore/aft, field lights, bat reels
John Deere	936	2005	E	$20,000	12/06	WCKS	936D draper head, contour ready, fore/aft, field lights, bat reels
John Deere	936	2006	E	$20,000	12/06	WCKS	936D draper head, contour ready, fore/aft, field lights, bat reels
John Deere	936	2006	E	$22,000	12/06	WCKS	936D draper head, contour ready, fore/aft, field lights, bat reels
John Deere	936	2006	E	$22,000	12/06	WCKS	936D draper head, contour ready, fore/aft, field lights, bat reels
John Deere	936	2006	E	$22,500	12/06	WCKS	936D draper head, contour ready, fore/aft, field lights, bat reels
Kelderman	NA		G	$850	2/06	SEIN	6R corn saver reel
Kelderman	NA	2002	E	$1,800	8/06	ECIL	Hyd. drive corn reel

Combine Heads

Make	Model	Year	Cond.	Price	Sale	Location	Comments
Leeway	NA		G	$1,250	3/06	ECND	8R row crop head
MacDon	962	1998	G	$5,000	9/06	WCND	Harvest head, 30' w/ transport, bat reel
MacDon	NA		P	$500	9/06	WCND	Finger reel for 30' Honey Bee head
MF	1143		F	$550	3/06	ECIA	4RN CH, 30"
MF	1163		G	$1,350	3/06	NCUT	6R CH
MF	1164		P	$120	3/06	ECNE	CH
MF	1183		G	$3,000	6/06	SEND	8RN CH, 30"
MF	12'		F	$175	2/06	WCNE	Pickup header, 10' pickup
MF	1859		P	$60	3/06	ECNE	Flex head
MF	1859		F	$375	9/06	NEIA	13' platform
MF	1859		F	$500	7/06	NWMN	Pickup, Melroe 351 pickup
MF	1859		F	$550	7/06	NWMN	Flex, finger reel, 20' (for parts)
MF	1859		F	$600	8/06	SEMN	13', 4 reel
MF	1859		F	$600	8/06	WCMN	20' flex
MF	1859		G	$1,400	7/06	NWMN	Flex, U2 finger reel, 20'
MF	1859		G	$1,400	7/06	NWMN	Flex, U2 finger reel, 20'
MF	20'		G	$8,000	1/06	ECIL	Flex platform, aluminum hyd. reel
MF	22'		G	$1,500	7/06	NWMN	Straight head, U2 finger reel
MF	44		F	$100	8/06	NCOH	4RW CH
MF	883		G	$13,000	1/06	ECIL	8R CH
MF	9000		G	$1,900	8/06	NECO	Platform with 9' Rake-Up pickup
MF	9001		F	$400	7/06	NWMN	Pickup, Melroe 388 7-belt pickup
MF	9001		F	$550	7/06	NWMN	Pickup, Melroe 388 7-belt pickup
MF	9022		F	$600	7/06	NWMN	Straight, 22', bat reel
MF	9022		F	$900	7/06	NWMN	Straight, 22', bat reel
MF	9024		G	$700	7/06	NWMN	Straight, 24', bat reel
MF	9120		G	$1,500	7/06	NWMN	Flex head, U2 finger reel, 20'
MF	9463		G	$1,300	3/06	WCMN	6RN CH, 30"
New Holland	30'		G	$15,000	4/06	WCMN	Canadian sale, Honey Bee & converter, steel teeth, new knife
New Holland	73C		G	$10,000	9/06	NCIA	Platform
New Holland	73C	2001	G	$8,500	12/06	SCNE	20' flex platform, hydraulic fore and aft control, lateral float-equipped
New Holland	960		F	$450	8/06	WCMN	20' flex head
New Holland	960		F	$500	4/06	NWMN	Love bar flex head, finger reel
New Holland	960		F	$550	4/06	NWMN	Straight head, 20' top or bottom drive
New Holland	962		F	$400	8/06	WCMN	4RN CH
New Holland	966	1985	F	$800	11/06	WCMN	6RN CH
New Holland	96C		G	$21,000	9/06	NCIA	CH
New Holland	96C	2001	G	$20,000	12/06	SCNE	8R-30 CH, all plastic
New Holland	970		P	$600	7/06	SEND	Pickup head, Melroe 378 pickup
New Holland	971		F	$600	10/06	NCND	Pickup header
New Holland	971	1992	P	$50	11/06	SCND	Pickup head
New Holland	971	1995	F	$200	11/06	SCND	Pickup head
New Holland	972		G	$2,750	4/06	NWMN	Flex head, 22', finger reel
New Holland	972		G	$3,600	4/06	NWMN	Flex head, 20', finger reel
New Holland	972	1982	G	$1,800	3/06	SEND	Flex head, 20', finger reel
New Holland	973		G	$1,000	12/06	SEMN	16' platform
New Holland	973		G	$2,000	8/06	ECIA	Grain table with stainless deck
New Holland	973		G	$4,750	6/06	ECSD	Flex, 25'

Combine Heads

Make	Model	Year	Cond.	Price	Sale	Location	Comments
New Holland	973		G	$12,300	2/06	ECNE	25' platform, Crary cut, air system, poly plates
New Holland	973	1997	G	$5,400	9/06	NCIA	30', Crary air reel
New Holland	973	1998	G	$6,800	12/06	WCMN	30' flex head
New Holland	974		G	$2,000	12/06	SEMN	6RN CH, 30"
New Holland	974		G	$3,500	8/06	ECIA	CH, used on fewer than 1,000 acres
New Holland	974		G	$3,600	10/06	SEMN	8RN CH, 30"
New Holland	974	1982	G	$1,600	3/06	SEND	6RN CH, 30"
New Holland	974	1991	G	$2,250	9/06	NCIA	8RN CH, 30"
New Holland	994		G	$15,000	4/06	SWMB	Canadian sale, Honey Bee & converter, 30' cut header, Ull pickup reel, steel teeth, new knife, factory transport
New Holland	996		G	$11,500	9/06	NCIA	CH
New Holland	996		G	$14,100	2/06	ECNE	6RN CH, 30", adj. stripper plates
Pickett	NA	1997	G	$6,000	8/06	WCMN	Edible bean cutter, 6R-30 or 8R-22

Notes

WHAT'S IT WORTH?

Combines

Used combine values jumped 10% to 15% in late November 2006. Hmm, I wonder why? You know why. The surging price of corn didn't hurt any. One price that really caught my eye: a 1992 JD 9500 with 1,334 engine hours that sold for $67,000 in southeast Nebraska just after Thanksgiving 2006. High demand for harvesters 10-plus years old with low hours.

Combines

Make	Model	Year	Hrs.	Cond.	Price	Sale	Location	Comments
Amadas	2105H	2002	192	G	$70,000	3/06	ECND	Edible bean combine, pt, cylinder disk sep, 14' adjustable pickup, single owner, never in rocks, never outside
Bidwell	666	1993		G	$24,000	8/06	WCMN	Edible bean combine, Pickett pickup, Dickey-john monitor
Case IH	1620	1993	1,844	E	$20,500	3/06	NENE	Axial flow, no heads
Case IH	1640		2,200	G	$19,750	3/06	SCIA	
Case IH	1640	1987	2,573	G	$21,500	5/06	SCMI	Case IH 1063 corn head, spreader
Case IH	1640	1988	2,330	E	$23,500	8/06	NEIA	
Case IH	1640	1988	1,724	E	$28,500	8/06	NCIA	Chopper, side adjustable sieves, shaft speed monitor
Case IH	1640	1990	3,000	G	$15,900	3/06	NCIL	Rock trap, chaff spreader
Case IH	1640	1990	2,204	G	$26,500	8/06	SCMN	
Case IH	1640	1990	1,575	G	$29,000	8/06	SEMN	
Case IH	1640	1992	2,208	E	$26,500	8/06	ECNE	No chopper, been through shop, new vinyl discharge auger, new unloading auger, 24.5-32 tires
Case IH	1644		1,363	G	$39,500	3/06	WCMN	Axial flow, specialty rotor, chopper
Case IH	1644	1993	2,918	G	$36,000	3/06	SEIA	RW drive, specialty rotor, Cummins, chaff spreader, 30.5×32 front, 16.9×26 rear Ag Leader, 2000 yield monitor
Case IH	1660			F	$8,000	8/06	SEMN	
Case IH	1660			F	$10,500	3/06	NCMN	
Case IH	1660		3,200	G	$14,250	8/06	NWIL	Diesel
Case IH	1660		1,200	G	$24,500	9/06	NWIL	Grain loss monitor
Case IH	1660	1987	3,240	F	$10,300	8/06	NWIL	Grain monitor, chopper
Case IH	1660	1987	3,508	G	$13,700	9/06	NCIA	AHH, chopper, rock trap, hd finals, one season on rotor and concave
Case IH	1660	1987	3,658	G	$14,900	3/06	NWIL	Fully-equipped cab, grain loss monitor, hydro, feeder reverser, Vittetoe chaff spreader
Case IH	1660	1988	2,978	G	$11,750	4/06	WCWI	4WD, chopper
Case IH	1660	1989	2,281	F	$27,500	1/06	NWIL	Specialty rotor, Ag Leader 2000 w/ NorthStar yield monitor, oil bath gear, Case on unload auger
Case IH	1660	1991	3,100	G	$16,000	11/06	WCIL	Cummins engine, chaff spreader, 30.5-32 tires, diesel
Case IH	1660	1991	2,660	G	$18,250	9/06	SWIA	Cummins engine, chopper, chaff spreader, rock trap
Case IH	1660	1991	3,299	G	$21,000	11/06	ECNE	Cummins engine, grain loss monitor, machine monitor, very clean
Case IH	1660	1991	3,400	F	$26,250	2/06	ECNE	Straw chopper
Case IH	1660	1991	1,531	G	$38,000	2/06	SEIL	Axial flow, 4WD, chaff spreader, bin extension, 30.5-32 tires, clean
Case IH	1660	1992	3,834	F	$16,000	1/06	NWIL	Cummins engine, 24.5-32, 14.9-24 rears
Case IH	1660	1992	2,741	G	$25,500	3/06	NCIA	Grain loss monitor, yield monitor, tank extension, chopper, swing-away Vittetoe chaffer
Case IH	1660	1992	1,710	E	$37,250	2/06	NENE	
Case IH	1660	1992	2,379	E	$38,000	2/06	SENE	New tires, reconditioned, no heads
Case IH	1660	1993	3,410	G	$17,000	6/06	NWKS	Axial flow
Case IH	1666		1,387	F	$40,500	2/06	NCIL	
Case IH	1680			F	$9,500	3/06	NCUT	
Case IH	1680		3,433	G	$26,500	3/06	SWMN	Axial flow, RWA, hydro, CAH
Case IH	1680			G	$31,000	4/06	NEND	Rotary, auto height, rock trap, bin extension, chopper, 30.5-32, DAS, grain scan

Combines

Make	Model	Year	Hrs.	Cond.	Price	Sale	Location	Comments
Case IH	1680	1986	4,500	G	$18,000	10/06	NCND	Axial flow, AHH, chopper, chaff spreader, rock trap, reverser, fore/aft, near new cones & Bison rotor
Case IH	1680	1987		F	$10,250	1/06	SESD	
Case IH	1680	1987	3,550	G	$13,000	7/06	ECND	AHH, rock trap, chopper, feeder reverser, airflow sieve
Case IH	1680	1988	3,000	G	$18,250	7/06	NWMN	Axial flow
Case IH	1680	1989	4,300	F	$20,000	5/06	WCMN	Cummins engine, AHHC, reverse, chopper, spreader, 3-stand feeder house chain, long auger, oil bath unload auger drive
Case IH	1680	1990	3,000	G	$31,000	7/06	WCMN	Cummins engine, specialty rotor, rock trap, chopper, chaff spreader, bin extension, long shoe
Case IH	1680	1991		G	$22,500	4/06	NCKS	
Case IH	1680	1992	3,670	G	$18,000	3/06	NWKS	30.5-32 front, 14.9-24 rear tires, third cylinder on feeder house, chaff spreader
Case IH	1680	1992	1,637	G	$43,500	4/06	NWMN	Cummins engine, AHHC, specialty rotor, chopper, rock trap, auto reel speed control, grain scan monitor, big-top hopper extension, 30.5-32 drive tires
Case IH	1680	1992	1,865	E	$46,000	3/06	ECND	CAH, Cummins, AHH, RS, fore/aft, rock trap, chopper, specialty rotor, reverser, cross flow fan, bin extension, long auger, 30.5-32 singles, 14.9-24 rears
Case IH	1688		2,339	G	$42,000	4/06	NEND	18.4-38 duals, specialty rotor, rock trap, air foil chopper, chopper, monitors
Case IH	1688	1994	3,684	G	$37,000	3/06	NCND	Axial flow, AFX rotor, rock trap, chopper, fore/aft, long unload, large and small wire concaves, many updates
Case IH	1688	1994	2,893	G	$37,500	3/06	NCND	Axial flow, auto header height, fore/aft, rock trap, chopper, Makeeff specialty rotor, large and small wire concaves, long unload auger, straddle duals, one owner
Case IH	1688	1994		G	$40,000	3/06	NEMI	4×4, 260 hp., field tracker, rock trap, specialty rotor, 1,700 sep hours
Case IH	1688	1994	2,407	G	$50,500	2/06	WCIA	RWA, chopper, standard rotor, 30.5-32, long auger, recently spent $10K over three years on it
Case IH	2166		1,884	E	$49,500	8/06	WCIA	1,378 sep hours, yield monitor, bin extension, chopper, specialty rotor, rock trap
Case IH	2166	1995	1,642	G	$62,000	1/06	NWIL	Specialty rotor, external chaffer, sieve and chopper adjustments, 1,321 sep hours
Case IH	2166	1995	1,426	E	$72,000	11/06	WCIA	891 hours on rotor, field tracker, chopper, rock trap, grain loss monitor, specialty rotor, one owner, 24.5-32 drive tires, long unload auger, bin extension
Case IH	2166	1996	2,425	G	$47,750	8/06	ECNE	1,691 sep hours, 18.4-38 duals, 14.9-24, chaff spreader, field tracker, grain monitor, bin extension
Case IH	2166	1997	2,021	G	$47,000	1/06	NWKY	1,510 sep hours, (combined w/ Case 1063 corn head & 1020 20' grain head - package sold together for $63,000)
Case IH	2166	1997	1,458	G	$52,750	8/06	NEKS	1,144 sep hours, 30.5L-32 tires, wheat concaves, one owner
Case IH	2166	1997	2,252	G	$55,500	12/06	NWOH	Rock trap, grain loss monitor, Maurer grain bin extension, 1,848 sep hours
Case IH	2166	1997	1,937	G	$70,000	12/06	WCIA	1,449 rotor hours, field tracker, GPS, new 30.5-32 tires
Case IH	2166	1997	1,387	E	$73,000	1/06	SWMN	941 sep hours
Case IH	2166			F	$25,000	8/06	SWWI	

Combines

Make	Model	Year	Hrs.	Cond.	Price	Sale	Location	Comments
Case IH	2188		3,003	G	$39,500	12/06	NWIL	2,353 sep hours, AFS monitor, bin and auger extension, 1997 model
Case IH	2188	1995	3,470	G	$34,000	1/06	ECNE	2-speed hydro, specialty rotor, 655 sep hours, Ag Leader monitor, 30.5L-32 tires, AHH, AM/FM/cassette radio
Case IH	2188	1995	3,271	G	$40,000	7/06	SEND	Specialty rotor, rock trap, chopper, yield and moisture monitor, bin extension, RWD, 2,418 sep hours
Case IH	2188	1996		G	$35,000	8/06	WCMN	Axial flow, AFS, specialty rotor, rock trap, chopper, duals, bin extension w/ bubble auger, AHH
Case IH	2188	1997	6,028	F	$16,000	4/06	NEND	4,549 sep hours, axial flow, deluxe cab, AHHC, specialty rotor, long auger, rock trap, chopper
Case IH	2188	1997	6,146	F	$20,000	4/06	NEND	4,618 sep hours, axial flow, deluxe cab, AHHC, specialty rotor, long auger, rock trap, chopper
Case IH	2188	1997	3,860	F	$28,500	12/06	SEMN	2,677 sep hours, 30.5L-32, AFS
Case IH	2188	1997	3,545	G	$33,000	3/06	NWKS	2,721 sep hours, straw chopper, rock trap, bin extension, AHH
Case IH	2188	1997	3,545	G	$34,500	3/06	NWKS	2,705 sep hours, straw chopper, rock trap, bin extension, AHH
Case IH	2188	1997	2,374	G	$44,500	9/06	NCIA	1,754 sep hours, AHH, 2-speed hydro, chopper, rock trap, 20' auger, duals
Case IH	2188	1997		G	$53,000	4/06	NEND	1,970 sep hours, axial flow, auto height, chaff spreader, rock trap, chopper, 30.5-32
Case IH	2188	1997	1,655	G	$59,000	3/06	ECMI	4WD, 18.4R-42 duals, deluxe options, 280 hp., straw chopper, 1,119 sep hours
Case IH	2188	1997	2,732	G	$64,250	3/06	SEMN	Axial flow combine, 1,912 sep hours, rock trap, AFX rotor updates, duals, straw chopper, field tracker, Maurer bin extension, AFS monitor
Case IH	2366		1,344	G	$69,000	12/06	WCMN	Axial flow, 18.4R-42 straddle duals, Crary tank extension
Case IH	2366	1998	1,894	E	$57,500	3/06	NWIL	Fully-equipped cab, monitors, specialty rotor, chopper, Maurer grain tank extension, 1,516 sep hours
Case IH	2366	1998	911	G	$69,000	3/06	SCIA	676 sep hours, chopper, rock trap, spec. rotor
Case IH	2366	1998	1,055	E	$87,000	12/06	NWIL	Axial flow specialty rotary combine, chopper, Maurer, folding bin extension, 670 sep hours, bought when one year old
Case IH	2366	1999	1,079	G	$84,000	2/06	NWIA	773 sep hours, AFS, spec. rotor, chopper, field tracker, Maurer bin extension, 208" unload auger
Case IH	2366	2001	550	E	$88,000	7/06	ECIL	
Case IH	2366	2001	485	E	$93,000	9/06	WCOH	Axial flow, CAH, field tracker, rock trap, moisture monitor, special rotor, 377 sep hours
Case IH	2366	2002	711	G	$100,000	2/06	ECMN	Axial flow, w/ hyd. reverse, field tracker, large fuel tank, Maurer tank extension, 456 sep hours, 30.5L-32 fronts, 14.9-24 rears, used three seasons, sharp
Case IH	2366	2004	158	E	$116,750	1/06	WCIL	Yield monitor, AFX rock trap, 2 spd. hyd, chopper, spreader, 125 sep hours, used one season, 30.5 tires
Case IH	2388	1998	5,897	G	$20,500	5/06	SEWY	Hopper extension, diesel
Case IH	2388	1998	4,484	G	$54,000	3/06	NWKS	3,484 sep hours, specialty rotor w/ Gordon rasp bars, straw chopper, rock trap, bin extension, AHH

Combines

Make	Model	Year	Hrs.	Cond.	Price	Sale	Location	Comments
Case IH	2388	1998	3,000	G	$66,000	3/06	NEKS	Axial flow, 2,187 sep hours, Cummins diesel engine, 30.5L-32 front tires, 14.9-24 rear, contour field tracker, fore/aft, standard grain loss monitor, straw chopper, bin extension, specialty rotor
Case IH	2388	1999	3,300	G	$55,000	3/06	NWKS	2,650 sep hours, straw chopper, rock trap, bin extension, AHH
Case IH	2388	1999	1,762	G	$85,000	2/06	WCMN	Axial flow, duals, RWA, yield monitor, 1,373 sep hours
Case IH	2388	2000		G	$60,000	11/06	ECND	Chopper, 18.4-42 duals, 1,821 sep hours, specialty rotor, field tracker, AFS
Case IH	2388	2000	1,174	G	$67,000	11/06	ECND	863 sep hours, specialty rotor, field tracker, chopper, 30.5-32 singles
Case IH	2388	2000		G	$78,250	1/06	SESD	Chopper, tracker, AFS, 880 sep hours
Case IH	2388	2000	1,414	F	$80,000	2/06	WCIL	4WD, Maurer bin extension, AFS yield monitor chopper, 1,098 sep, rotor worn/damaged, looked nice
Case IH	2388	2001	1,382	G	$71,500	6/06	ECSD	Chopper, loaded
Case IH	2388	2001	1,566	G	$77,000	8/06	SCNE	Axial flow, AHHC, DAS, field tracker, bin extension, specialty rotor, rock trap, chopper, duals, 1,360 sep hours
Case IH	2388	2001	1,628	G	$80,000	12/06	WCMN	Axial flow
Case IH	2388	2001	1,345	G	$85,000	12/06	SEIA	1,074 sep hours, axial flow, GPS, AFS yield monitor, specialty rotor, field tracker, rock trap, Maurer bin extension, chopper
Case IH	2388	2001	1,231	G	$88,000	12/06	SCMN	904 sep hours
Case IH	2388	2002	2,511	G	$79,500	7/06	SEND	1,912 sep hours, CAH, AHH, AFX rotor, rock trap, chopper, rear wheel drive, 20' auger, yield monitor, hopper extension, hd drive
Case IH	2388	2002		G	$86,500	12/06	WCMN	1,077 sep hours, 4WD, spec. rotor, yield & moisture, stone trap
Case IH	2388	2002	424	E	$130,000	1/06	SWOH	Axial flow, chopper, field tracker, 288 sep hours
Case IH	2388	2003	2,063	G	$79,000	11/06	ECND	CAH, GPS-AFS yield monitor, rock trap, specialty rotor, reverser, field tracker, 17' auger, chaff spreader, hd finals, 2-spd. rear assist, rear weight pkg., straddle duals, 1,334 sep hours
Case IH	2388	2003		G	$92,000	3/06	ECNE	728 sep hours, duals, AFX rotor, field tracker
Case IH	2388	2003	1,298	G	$92,000	12/06	ECKS	1,036 sep hours, 20.5I-32 front tires, chaff spreader, Crary big top bin extension, AHHC, fore/aft, reel speed, long unload auger, small & large grain grates, wheat concaves
Case IH	2388	2003	1,345	G	$94,000	12/06	ECKS	1,067 sep hours, 20.5I-32 front tires, chaff spreader, Crary big top bin extension, AHHC, fore/aft, reel speed, long unload auger, small & large grain grates, wheat concaves
Case IH	2388	2004	820	G	$91,000	9/06	NCIA	624 sep, field tracker, Ag Leader, AHH, chopper, 2-spd. hydro, rock trap, 20' auger
Case IH	2388	2004		G	$117,000	11/06	ECND	608 sep hours, rear-wheel drive, rotor, rock trap, chopper, reverser, heavy lift, field tracker, AFX, yield monitor, 420×46 duals, 22" space
Case IH	2388	2005	409	E	$107,000	8/06	NECO	298 sep hours, AFS rotor, field tracker, fore/aft, Bish bin extension, 18.4R-42 w/ duals

Combines

Make	Model	Year	Hrs.	Cond.	Price	Sale	Location	Comments
Case IH	2388	2005	356	E	$112,000	8/06	NECO	251 sep hours, AFS rotor, field tracker, fore/aft, Bish bin extension, chaff spreader, 18.4R-42 w/ duals
Case IH	2388	2005	308	E	$130,000	9/06	NCIA	263 sep hours, field tracker, AFX rotor, duals
Caterpillar	465	1999	2,059	G	$50,000	12/06	SCMN	1,690 sep hours
Caterpillar	470	2001		F	$29,500	11/06	SCND	Lexion, 1,573 sep hours, 4WD, auto Contour Master, chopper, spreader, 200 hours on new chain
Caterpillar	480	2000	1,700	G	$53,000	8/06	NECO	CAH, long unload auger, 20.8-42 duals
Caterpillar	485	1998	3,050	G	$42,000	11/06	ECND	CAH, dual ranger, reverser, rock trap, variable speed feeder house, 24' auger, chopper, chaff spreader, hopper extension, field contour, yield monitor, 1,847 sep hours
Gleaner	F2			F	$800	8/06	NCIA	Corn soybean special, cab, chopper
Gleaner	F2			G	$1,400	11/06	NEKS	
Gleaner	F2			G	$1,600	12/06	WCIL	Diesel, no heads
Gleaner	F2			G	$4,000	3/06	WCMI	Gleaner 430N CH (black stripe), hydro, 1,218 sep hours, rasp bar, straw chopper, diesel
Gleaner	F2	1978		F	$1,000	8/06	NWOH	Gas, chopper, 13' grain head
Gleaner	F2	1978		G	$2,100	3/06	NEKS	Diesel
Gleaner	F2	1978		F	$4,700	3/06	NWOH	15' grain head, tach says 1,952 hours
Gleaner	F2	1982	1,640	G	$7,000	3/06	NENE	980 sep hours, always shedded, 433 diesel engine, one owner
Gleaner	F2	1983	3,188	G	$5,500	1/06	WCIL	2,488 sep hours
Gleaner	F3	1983	1,590	G	$12,000	8/06	SCMI	Chopper, no heads
Gleaner	F3	1986	3,600	G	$9,000	8/06	SCMI	RWA, no heads
Gleaner	L2		3,177	G	$1,700	9/06	NWMN	Hydro, Tattletale monitor system, chopper, 2,531 sep hours
Gleaner	L2		2,810	G	$5,300	4/06	NEND	One owner, CAH, hydro, Tattletale monitor, long shoe
Gleaner	L2	1978		G	$7,500	4/06	NCOK	24' header, big engine, 400 hours on overhaul, hydro, chopper, diesel
Gleaner	L2	1979		F	$5,800	2/06	NCCO	24' grain head
Gleaner	L2	1980	2,119	G	$7,100	2/06	NCKS	Hydro, 24' platform, 1,866 sep hours, good 23.1-34 rubber
Gleaner	L2	1981	1,200	G	$5,700	1/06	SESD	Hydro
Gleaner	L2	1981	1,318	E	$13,000	3/06	NCOK	24' header, 1,131 sep hours, hydro, new tires
Gleaner	L3		2,649	G	$4,000	12/06	WCIL	
Gleaner	L3		3,230	F	$8,750	2/06	NWIL	Corn/soybean special, modified cylinder bars, many new parts, 1,931 sep hours
Gleaner	L3	1985	3,263	G	$10,000	4/06	WCSD	158 hp., corn/soybean combine w/ 24' dummy header, 2,764 sep hours, pickup trailer
Gleaner	M2			F	$1,300	8/06	SEMN	
Gleaner	M2			G	$1,900	12/06	SEMN	
Gleaner	M2	1979		G	$9,100	12/06	SCNE	Corn/soybean special, hydro, low hours, one owner, 20' platform
Gleaner	M2	1981		F	$2,450	8/06	WCIL	Hydro, diesel
Gleaner	M3	1983	1,900	G	$14,750	11/06	SCNE	Diesel, 23.1-30 tires, used only on wheat, grain sorghum, and soybeans, no corn
Gleaner	N5			P	$700	6/06	NWIL	As is, not running
Gleaner	N5		2,000	G	$5,000	7/06	NWIL	Diesel
Gleaner	N6	1980	4,128	G	$2,750	12/06	WCIL	RWA, chopper and spreader, 2,654 sep hours
Gleaner	N6	1980	1,186	G	$7,500	3/06	NECO	611 sep hours
Gleaner	N6	1981		F	$3,500	6/06	NWIL	Cab, air, monitor, hydro jack, engine overhaul
Gleaner	N6	1984	2,500	F	$3,750	7/06	SEND	CAH, corn/soybean special, 1,750 sep hours

WHAT'S IT WORTH?

Combines

Make	Model	Year	Hrs.	Cond.	Price	Sale	Location	Comments
Gleaner	N7	1984	3,828	F	$5,500	7/06	SEND	One owner, 30.5-32 singles
Gleaner	N7	1984	3,504	G	$7,500	7/06	SEND	30.5-32 singles
Gleaner	R42	1998	1,600	E	$41,000	4/06	SEMI	1,200 sep hours, lateral tilt, spreader
Gleaner	R42	2001	800	G	$56,500	12/06	NCOH	612 sep hours, diesel, CAH, Fieldstar, 30.5-32 rubber front & 14.9-28 rear cleats
Gleaner	R50		2,582	G	$10,000	3/06	ECNE	1,753 sep hours, Ag Leader 2000 yield monitor, 24.5-32 front tires, 12.4-24 rear, Duetz air-cooled engine
Gleaner	R50		2,850	G	$11,500	7/06	SEND	Head and Melrose 7-belt pickup
Gleaner	R50	1988	4,028	G	$19,000	3/06	NWOH	2,888 sep hours, monitor, spreader
Gleaner	R50	1989	2,600	F	$8,750	8/06	NWIL	
Gleaner	R52		2,710	F	$16,200	8/06	NCOH	Hydro, chopper, chaff spreader, new unloader auger, 1,957 sep hours, no heads
Gleaner	R52	1993	1,475	G	$28,000	12/06	NWIL	Fully-equipped cab, monitors, electric ladder lift, Cummins engine, hd final drives, 30.5-32 drive tires, 14.9-24 steering tires, bought new in 1994, 1,055 sep hours, sharp
Gleaner	R52	1994	2,233	G	$24,250	2/06	NCIL	Ag Leader Model 3000 monitor, GPS, 1,591 sep hours
Gleaner	R52	1998	1,125	E	$46,000	8/06	ECIL	CAH, chopper, spreader bin extension, 818 sep hours
Gleaner	R52	2002	560	G	$64,000	12/06	NCIL	384 sep hours, bin extension, 24.5-32 tires, chopper, spreader
Gleaner	R60	1989	4,390	F	$6,400	8/06	NWIL	3,106 sep hours
Gleaner	R62	1994	1,840	G	$30,500	8/06	SEMN	1,200 sep hours, chopper
Gleaner	R70	1993	2,537	F	$17,500	9/06	WCND	1,912 sep hours, custom harvest special, Duetz air cooled, fore/aft, 330-bu. hopper, acre counter, Tattletale monitor, rock trap, unload auger extension, 30.5-32 singles
Gleaner	R72	1992		G	$39,500	3/06	WCKS	1,335 sep hours, $20,000 in repairs last two years
IHC	1420	1978		G	$4,500	2/06	SEIA	Chopper, always shedded, field ready
IHC	1420	1981	3,436	G	$4,750	3/06	NCIL	
IHC	1420	1981	2,783	G	$5,000	7/06	NCIL	Major overhaul at 2,637 hours, chaff spreader
IHC	1440		3,248	G	$5,200	2/06	WCIL	
IHC	1440			F	$6,000	3/06	SEPA	Axial flow, no heads, electric over hydraulics, fair rubber
IHC	1440	1978	3,790	F	$4,000	3/06	NWOH	Spreader
IHC	1440	1979	3,939	G	$2,400	7/06	NCIA	Hydro, tank extension, 15' IHC 820 platform, Jamison header control
IHC	1440	1985	2,000	G	$9,000	11/06	SCIL	Clean, no heads
IHC	1460			F	$2,200	3/06	SEND	CAH, shedded
IHC	1460		3,503	F	$2,300	3/06	ECND	Chopper
IHC	1460		5,051	G	$3,250	3/06	ECND	Rock trap, chopper
IHC	1460			F	$3,600	3/06	NWIL	Diesel
IHC	1460			E	$4,000	3/06	NEKS	12' grain head
IHC	1460		3,000	G	$5,600	4/06	NEIA	
IHC	1460			G	$7,000	3/06	SEND	CAH, shedded
IHC	1460		2,713	G	$10,500	6/06	NWIL	No heads
IHC	1460	1977	3,986	F	$3,400	3/06	SEIA	
IHC	1460	1978		F	$4,000	1/06	SESD	
IHC	1460	1978	3,122	G	$14,500	3/06	NWOH	IHC 820 20' grain head, rock trap, straw chopper
IHC	1460	1980	3,677	G	$4,600	9/06	SEIA	
IHC	1460	1980	3,400	F	$8,200	1/06	NCCO	3,400 hours
IHC	1460	1981	3,406	G	$5,400	3/06	ECNE	Axial flow, 23.1-26 tires, AHH, hyd. fore/aft
IHC	1460	1982	3,702	G	$4,300	4/06	NWMN	Hydro, grain loss monitor, shedded

Combines

Make	Model	Year	Hrs.	Cond.	Price	Sale	Location	Comments
IHC	1460	1983	3,748	G	$14,500	3/06	SEMN	Electric over hyd., new style fan, new style unload auger, rock trap
IHC	1460	1985	3,665	F	$4,000	2/06	WCIL	Chopper, spreader
IHC	1480			F	$3,250	8/06	SEMN	
IHC	1480		4,000	F	$3,600	8/06	NEKS	Early model, 4,000+ hours
IHC	1480		1,347	G	$4,550	2/06	NECO	Bin extension
IHC	1480		6,368	G	$8,250	10/06	NCKS	24' IHC 810 platform, 2 seasons on engine overhaul and new hydro
IHC	1480		3,081	G	$12,500	3/06	ECND	AHH, rock trap, chopper
IHC	1480	1980		G	$3,250	6/06	NECO	Diesel
John Deere	4420	1985	2,381	G	$6,800	8/06	NWOH	Chopper
John Deere	6620			G	$7,400	4/06	NENE	Hydro turbo, straw chopper, Dial-a-Matic, shedded
John Deere	6620		1,857	G	$16,250	6/06	NWIL	Turbo, RWA
John Deere	6620	1979	4,200	F	$3,800	4/06	WCMN	Diesel, clutch drive, 23.1-26 tires, straw chopper
John Deere	6620	1979	4,689	F	$4,000	2/06	WCIA	Hydro
John Deere	6620	1979	3,977	F	$4,600	2/06	WCIA	Hydro
John Deere	6620	1979	3,745	G	$5,000	8/06	WCIL	New air
John Deere	6620	1979		G	$8,000	8/06	NEIL	One owner, 28L-26 tires, chopper
John Deere	6620	1979	5,854	G	$11,000	2/06	SWOH	Sold with John Deere 444 4R-36" CH, hydroic, recent front tires, exceptionally clean for age
John Deere	6620	1980	1,800	G	$15,000	2/06	WCOH	Turbo, John Deere 216 grain table, 643 hi tin 6-30" CH
John Deere	6620	1981		G	$3,250	5/06	SEWY	Cab, straw chopper, diesel
John Deere	6620	1981	3,328	G	$5,900	8/06	NWOH	Chopper
John Deere	6620	1981		G	$11,700	1/06	NEIN	Hydro, one owner
John Deere	6620	1981	2,033	G	$15,000	1/06	NEMO	4WD
John Deere	6620	1982		G	$4,000	5/06	SEWY	Cab, straw chopper, diesel
John Deere	6620	1982	2,914	G	$7,100	3/06	NCIN	Turbo hydroic, chopper, 28L-26 tires
John Deere	6620	1982	3,462	G	$12,500	8/06	NWIA	Nice
John Deere	6620	1983		G	$5,000	12/06	NWWI	Very clean
John Deere	6620	1983	2,334	G	$14,250	3/06	ECNE	30.5-32 front tires, 11.2-24 rear tires, straw chopper
John Deere	6620	1984	4,160	E	$9,500	8/06	WCIL	Hydro, lot of work done on this combine
John Deere	6620 II		2,680	G	$14,300	11/06	ECIL	Titan II, Dial-a-Matic, Acu-Grain yield monitor
John Deere	6620 II	1985		G	$11,000	12/06	ECMO	Titan II, 4WD, 24.5-32 front, 14.9-24 rear
John Deere	6620 II	1986		G	$10,500	12/06	ECMO	Titan II, 2WD, grain loss monitor, chopper
John Deere	6620 II	1988	3,354	G	$15,000	12/06	NENE	Titan II, sidehill, 23.1-26 front tires, 11.2-24 rear tires, Vittetoe chaff spreader, chopper
John Deere	6620 SH			F	$2,500	12/06	NWIL	Sidehill, 4WD
John Deere	6620 SH			F	$3,500	8/06	NWIL	Sidehill, hydro, diesel
John Deere	6620 SH	1982	4,200	F	$4,250	2/06	WCIA	Sidehill
John Deere	6620 SH	1983	2,782	E	$27,000	3/06	NEIA	Sidehill, hydro., diesel, no heads
John Deere	7720		2,073	F	$4,000	9/06	SEIL	Factory 4×4, turbo, chopper, grain loss monitor
John Deere	7720		4,939	F	$5,250	7/06	WCMN	24.5-32
John Deere	7720			G	$5,500	12/06	NWIL	Turbo, diesel
John Deere	7720		4,282	G	$9,000	7/06	WCMN	24.5-32, one owner
John Deere	7720	1979	3,072	G	$4,400	3/06	NWKS	Turbo hydro, 30.5L-32 front tires, chopper, AM/FM radio
John Deere	7720	1979		G	$4,400	6/06	NECO	Bin extension, diesel
John Deere	7720	1979	4,200	G	$5,500	8/06	WCMN	18.4-38 duals, chopper, header height, Dial-a-Matic, long auger
John Deere	7720	1979	3,700	F	$7,100	6/06	SWMN	Needs throat work, turbo

WHAT'S IT WORTH?

Combines

Make	Model	Year	Hrs.	Cond.	Price	Sale	Location	Comments
John Deere	7720	1980	3,706	G	$11,500	2/06	NCIN	Turbo-hydro, chopper
John Deere	7720	1981	4,614	G	$6,500	8/06	WCMN	AHH, 30.5-32 tires
John Deere	7720	1981		G	$8,750	2/06	WCIL	30.5-32 tires
John Deere	7720	1982	3,408	F	$6,000	2/06	WCIA	
John Deere	7720	1982	4,290	G	$6,500	9/06	NWMN	Turbo hydro, JD monitor, chopper, 24.5-32 drive tires, 14.9-24 rear traction tires, field ready, over $7,000 in recent repairs
John Deere	7720	1982	4,000	G	$7,000	8/06	ECNE	Turbo, hydro, 24.5-32 front tires, 14.9-24 rear, straw chopper, long unloading auger, hd rear end, big shaver header control
John Deere	7720	1982	3,724	G	$14,500	3/06	NWOH	218 grain head, spreader, chopper
John Deere	7720	1982	2,466	E	$19,750	2/06	SCMN	Turbo hydro, tank extension, chopper, 30.5-32, 16.5L-16.1 rear
John Deere	7720	1983		G	$4,000	3/06	NEKS	Hydro chopper
John Deere	7720	1983	5,121	G	$6,500	4/06	ECND	Turbo hydro, corn/grain, hopper extension
John Deere	7720	1983	4,700	G	$9,800	2/06	NWOH	220 grain head, RWA, chopper, bin extension
John Deere	7720	1984	3,651	G	$10,900	4/06	WCMN	Rebalanced chopper, 660 hours on rasp bars, concave, all belts, all chains, Dial-a-Matic
John Deere	7720 II			F	$10,900	9/06	NCIA	Titan II
John Deere	7720 II		3,288	F	$11,750	3/06	NCKS	Titan II, John Deere 220 20' head, 24' header
John Deere	7720 II			G	$15,100	12/06	SEMN	Titan II
John Deere	7720 II	1985	3,850	G	$10,500	8/06	WCMN	Titan II, 24.5-32 tires, AHH
John Deere	7720 II	1986		F	$10,900	1/06	SESD	Titan II
John Deere	7720 II	1987	3,218	F	$12,500	8/06	NCIA	Titan II, cab, air, Maurer tank extension, chopper w/ slow down kit, Dial-a-Matic
John Deere	7720 II	1987	3,100	G	$14,400	8/06	NCIA	Titan II
John Deere	7720 II	1987	2,010	G	$20,000	2/06	WCIL	Titan II, hydro, chopper, chaff spreader, Dial-a-Matic, bin extension
John Deere	7720 II	1987	2,606	G	$27,500	8/06	NCIA	Titan II, grain loss monitor, extra fuel tank, chopper, grain tank extension
John Deere	7720 II	1988	3,421	G	$12,000	7/06	WCMN	Titan II, 18.4-38 duals
John Deere	7720 II	1988		G	$15,000	12/06	WCMN	Titan II, Dial-a-Matic, tank extension
John Deere	7720 II	1988	2,440	G	$28,000	4/06	WCMB	Canadian sale, hopper top extension
John Deere	7721	1979		G	$2,250	4/06	NEND	212 pickup head, 6-belt pickup, pt, hopper extension, roll tarp, hyd. swing pole
John Deere	7721	1982		G	$1,700	7/06	NEND	212, pt, Melroe 388 7-belt pickup
John Deere	8820			F	$3,000	9/06	SEIL	Factory 4×4, chopper
John Deere	8820			F	$4,250	9/06	NCIA	18.4R-42 duals
John Deere	8820			G	$7,000	12/06	NENE	
John Deere	8820			G	$8,000	4/06	WCSD	Turbo, hydro w/ all crop 213 header, 8R, sunflower pans
John Deere	8820		2,972	G	$9,500	7/06	ECIL	4×4, updated, fore/aft, Dial-a-Matic, hydro, chopper
John Deere	8820		3,520	G	$10,000	3/06	NWMN	AHHC, 2-speed cylinder, grain loss monitor, chopper
John Deere	8820	1979		G	$3,000	3/06	NEKS	No heads
John Deere	8820	1979	3,477	F	$5,000	7/06	WCMN	Straw chopper
John Deere	8820	1979		G	$5,100	7/06	NEND	Hydro, reverser, chopper
John Deere	8820	1979		G	$10,500	6/06	WCMN	Straddle duals, grain tank extension, Dial-a-Matic
John Deere	8820	1980		G	$5,000	12/06	ECMO	Turbo, RWA, 30.5-32 drive tires
John Deere	8820	1980	5,148	F	$8,000	7/06	WCMN	Chaff spreader, long unloading auger, AHH, straw chopper
John Deere	8820	1981	3,598	G	$6,500	11/06	SCND	All-wheel drive

Combines

Make	Model	Year	Hrs.	Cond.	Price	Sale	Location	Comments
John Deere	8820	1981	3,900	G	$9,500	4/06	SCKS	Turbo, hydro, RWA w/ 230 header
John Deere	8820	1982		F	$6,500	7/06	ECND	Turbo, CAH, air foil sieve
John Deere	8820	1982	4,266	G	$10,000	6/06	NWMN	CAH, chopper, air foil chaffer
John Deere	8820	1982		G	$15,500	2/06	SCKS	Turbo, 30.5L-32 front tires, 14.9-24 rear tires, clamp on duals, harvested 1,000 acres since meter quit
John Deere	8820	1982	4,097	G	$23,500	2/06	NWKS	Long unloading auger, bin extension, chopper, cyclone chaff spreader, new feeder house chain, sprockets, chaffer, clean grain elevator, chain, bearings, housing, boot head, loading tube, sump auger in grain tank
John Deere	8820	1983	2,716	G	$11,500	7/06	ECND	Turbo, air foil sieves
John Deere	8820 II		4,860	G	$21,000	2/06	WCMN	Titan II, hydro, RWA, Vittetoe chaff spreader, Crary big top hopper extension, long unloading auger, bubble-up auger in tank
John Deere	8820 II	1985	2,333	G	$17,500	4/06	NWMN	Titan II, 2-speed cylinder, fore/aft
John Deere	8820 II	1986	3,550	F	$8,000	9/06	NEND	Titan II, CAH, reversible feeder house
John Deere	8820 II	1986	4,963	F	$8,750	7/06	SEND	Titan II, DHH, 20' auger
John Deere	8820 II	1987	3,842	F	$8,500	7/06	SEND	Titan II, 20' auger, Dial-a-Matic
John Deere	8820 II	1987	3,406	F	$13,000	11/06	SCSD	Titan II, 4WD
John Deere	8820 II	1988	3,600	F	$7,750	11/06	SCND	Titan II, AH
John Deere	8820 II	1988	3,742	G	$24,000	11/06	NWMN	Titan II, DHH, 2-speed cyl., 20' auger, mud hog rear-wheel drive, Maurer bin extension, Harvestrak monitor
John Deere	9400			G	$40,000	8/06	WCIL	
John Deere	9400	1989	3,140	G	$26,000	2/06	WCIA	2,188 sep hours, Dial-a-Matic, DAS, chopper
John Deere	9400	1989		G	$27,000	9/06	NEIA	1,666 sep hours, Dial-a-Matic, DAS, fore/aft
John Deere	9400	1991	3,341	G	$27,750	4/06	SWOH	2,492 sep hours
John Deere	9400	1991	2,900	G	$31,000	2/06	NWIN	1,800 sep hours
John Deere	9400	1992		F	$18,000	9/06	NEIA	1,703 sep hours, big engine, Dial-a-Matic, DAS, fore/aft
John Deere	9400	1993	1,806	G	$49,000	12/06	WCMI	1,295 sep hours, RWA, bin extension
John Deere	9400	1994	2,250	G	$34,000	3/06	SESD	1,603 sep hours, big top grain extension
John Deere	9400	1995		E	$42,100	3/06	NCIL	1,100 sep hours, chopper, bin extension
John Deere	9500			G	$39,750	11/06	SCMN	1,700 sep hours
John Deere	9500		2,153	G	$45,500	11/06	NCOH	Big engine, chaff spreader, 1,601 sep hours
John Deere	9500		1,650	E	$54,000	4/06	NESD	1,241 sep hours, Dial-a-Matic, DAS, fore/aft, Crary big top hopper extension, Cyclone chaff spreader, variable-speed reel, micro track, kept inside
John Deere	9500	1989	4,047	G	$22,000	12/06	SCMN	2,700 sep hours, 24.5-32 tires
John Deere	9500	1989	3,150	G	$24,000	1/06	NEIN	2,194 sep hours
John Deere	9500	1989	5,000	G	$27,500	7/06	WCMN	AHH, yield monitor, hyd fore/aft, grain loss monitor, 4,200 sep hours
John Deere	9500	1989		G	$31,000	2/06	NEIN	Bish bin extension chopper, hydra spreader, 2,118 sep hours, RWA, chopper
John Deere	9500	1990	8,263	F	$9,600	8/06	NECO	Chopper
John Deere	9500	1990		F	$17,000	12/06	NWWI	2,900 sep hours, chopper, 24.5-32
John Deere	9500	1990		F	$21,000	12/06	WCMN	Chopper, grain extension
John Deere	9500	1990	2,820	G	$22,000	12/06	WCMN	1,985 sep hours, new motor, new feeder house chain, Dial-a-Matic, DAS, chopper
John Deere	9500	1990	4,228	G	$25,000	11/06	NEKS	Hydro, 2,964 sep hours, chopper, rock trap, hyd. fore/aft, AHHC, auto reel speed, grain loss monitor, field ready

Combines

Make	Model	Year	Hrs.	Cond.	Price	Sale	Location	Comments
John Deere	9500	1990	4,276	G	$26,000	7/06	WCMN	Chopper, Dial-a-Matic, 2,691 sep hours
John Deere	9500	1990	3,884	G	$29,000	12/06	NWMO	2,594 sep hours, 4×4, DAS, 30.5-32 front tires, $10,000 in repairs
John Deere	9500	1990	2,922	G	$38,000	1/06	NWIA	1,986 sep hours, easy view dust eliminator, updated Kuchar concave kit and sep grate, chopper, Vittetoe chaff spreader, grain tank
John Deere	9500	1990	1,475	G	$41,750	3/06	ECND	DAS, chaff spreader, hopper extension, 1,169 sep hours, 30.5-32 singles, 14.9-24 rears
John Deere	9500	1991		F	$20,000	12/06	SCMN	Diesel, hydro, 20.83-38 tires
John Deere	9500	1991	4,012	G	$27,000	4/06	ECND	DHH, DAS, fore/aft, 20' unload auger, chaff spreader, big top hopper extension, 3,171 sep hours
John Deere	9500	1991	3,000	G	$28,000	2/06	NEMO	920 grain table & JD 643 grain head, Vittetoe chaff spreader, 30.5L-32 tires, pusher
John Deere	9500	1991	3,181	G	$32,250	2/06	ECIL	Spreader, Bish bin extension, 2,357 sep hours
John Deere	9500	1991	3,695	G	$33,000	6/06	WCMN	2,528 sep hours, DAS, Dial-a-Matic, fore/aft, chopper, grain loss monitor
John Deere	9500	1992		F	$16,000	3/06	ECKS	2,393 sep hours
John Deere	9500	1992		F	$23,750	11/06	NEKS	Chopper, chaff spreader, hyd. fore/aft, Dial-a-Speed
John Deere	9500	1992	2,500	G	$29,500	8/06	WCIL	1,500 sep hours, DAS, Dial-a-Matic, fore/aft, 17' auger
John Deere	9500	1992	2,765	G	$34,500	3/06	NWMN	1,943 sep hours, CAH, Dial-a-Matic, DAS, fore/aft, big engine, Maurer bin extension, 30.5-32 singles, 14.9-42 rears
John Deere	9500	1992	2,015	G	$38,000	1/06	WCIL	1,404 sep hours, 17' auger, new 30" tires
John Deere	9500	1992	2,117	G	$40,000	3/06	ECNE	1,460 sep hours, chopper, AHH, Ag Leader, Maurer bin extension
John Deere	9500	1992	1,334	E	$67,000	11/06	SENE	730 sep hours, 30.5-32 front, 14.9-24 rear tires, chopper, bin extension, AHH, axle extensions, DAS, Harvestrak monitor, AM/FM
John Deere	9500	1993		F	$26,000	12/06	NWWI	2,000 sep hours, 10 Series updates, chopper
John Deere	9500	1993	2,940	G	$29,100	2/06	SEIN	2,170 sep hours, Ag Leader yield monitor, chaff spreader
John Deere	9500	1993	1,940	G	$38,000	2/06	ECIL	1,406 sep hours, Maurer bin extension, 30.5-32 tires
John Deere	9500	1993	1,940	G	$39,000	12/06	ECIL	1,406 sep hours, 30.5L-32, bin extension, chopper, Harvestrak monitor, updated, good maintenance
John Deere	9500	1993	2,707	G	$40,000	1/06	WCIL	1,740 sep hours, 4WD, big engine, 17' auger, Harvestrak monitor
John Deere	9500	1993		G	$40,000	1/06	SCMN	2,100 sep hours, 10 Series updates
John Deere	9500	1993	2,439	G	$44,250	1/06	NWIL	Big engine, rebuilt injectors and pump, 17' unload, bin extension, chaff spreader, mud hog, 4WD, digital concave, sieve and chaffer updates, 1,561 sep hours
John Deere	9500	1993	951	E	$69,000	8/06	WCKS	703 sep hours, hydro, 25' platform
John Deere	9500	1994	2,662	G	$38,000	3/06	NESD	Hydro, Harvestrak monitor, DAS, Dial-a-Matic, fore/aft, full-view wiper w/ washer, Crary big top hopper, extension and chaff spreader
John Deere	9500	1994	2,206	G	$40,000	2/06	WCIL	1,507 sep hours, 30.5-32 tires
John Deere	9500	1995	2,710	G	$30,000	12/06	NWMO	1,850 sep hours, 4×4, 18.4-26 rear tires (no duals), Dial-a-Matic
John Deere	9500	1995		G	$33,000	12/06	NWMO	4×4, 30.5×32 front tires, 18.4×26 rear tires, big engine, Dial-a-Matic, DAS, chopper

Combines

Make	Model	Year	Hrs.	Cond.	Price	Sale	Location	Comments
John Deere	9500	1995	2,736	G	$34,000	3/06	NCOH	1,914 sep hours
John Deere	9500	1995	1,724	G	$43,750	1/06	WCIL	1,223 sep hours, Maurer bin extension, Ag Leader monitor, 30" tires, Vittetoe spreader
John Deere	9500	1996		F	$15,500	3/06	ECKS	3,069 sep hours
John Deere	9500	1996	2,663	G	$34,000	12/06	WCMN	1,885 sep hours, tank extension, small engine, chopper, 20' auger, fore/aft, DAS, Dial-a-Matic
John Deere	9500	1996	1,491	G	$53,000	3/06	NCIA	Vittetoe dual spreader, Maurer tank extension, 1,008 sep hours, 18.4-38 duals
John Deere	9500	1997	2,160	G	$44,500	12/06	ECMO	RWA, Contour Master, chopper, chaff spreader, big engine, 1,604 sep hours
John Deere	9500	1997	2,259	G	$45,000	4/06	SEND	CAH, monitor, big engine, 1,705 sep hours
John Deere	9500	1997	1,740	G	$49,000	12/06	NEMO	Harvestrak monitor, bin extension, 1,215 sep hours
John Deere	9500 SH	1996	2,200	G	$62,500	1/06	SWIA	Sidehill, tires not good
John Deere	9510	1998		F	$25,500	3/06	ECKS	2,314 sep hours
John Deere	9510	1998		G	$55,500	11/06	NEKS	1,163 sep hours, chopper, chaff spreader, hyd. fore/aft, Dial-a-Speed, grain bin extension
John Deere	9510	1998	1,680	G	$61,000	2/06	WCIA	1,104 sep hours, Dial-a-Matic, DAS, fore/aft, chopper, Vittetoe chaff spreader, Maurer bin ext, duals
John Deere	9510	1998	1,470	E	$70,000	2/06	SEMI	Maximizer, RWA, yield monitor, 1,034 sep hours.
John Deere	9510	1999		F	$41,000	12/06	NWWI	1,850 sep hours, Dial-a-Matic, chopper, 30.5-32
John Deere	9510	1999	2,485	E	$54,000	3/06	NWOH	New cylinder bars, chaff spreader, monitors, 1,705 sep hours
John Deere	9510	1999	1,650	G	$62,500	12/06	NCIA	1,250 sep hours, GreenStar
John Deere	9510 SH	1998		G	$69,000	9/06	NEIA	Sidehill, 997 sep hours, Dial-a-Matic, DAS, fore/aft, chopper
John Deere	9510 SH	1999		G	$67,500	9/06	SWIA	Sidehill, 1,250 sep hours, fully loaded, GreenStar mapping, turbo tube, Vittetoe chaff spreader, Maurer hopper, long unloading auger, rear weights
John Deere	9550			G	$75,000	12/06	WCMN	800 sep hours, chopper, 18.4-38 duals
John Deere	9550	2000		G	$65,000	12/06	NWWI	1,750 sep hours, deluxe header, chopper, chaff spreader, 30.5-32
John Deere	9550	2000	1,631	G	$73,000	3/06	SWMI	1,135 sep hours, 20.8-38 duals, chopper, chaff spreader, long auger, Maurer bin extension, yield monitor, deluxe cab, stubble lights
John Deere	9550	2002	1,034	G	$73,500	9/06	NCIA	697 sep hours, deluxe header package, chopper, duals
John Deere	9550	2002	699	G	$81,000	8/06	WCMN	459 sep hours, hydro, big engine, yield monitor, grain loss monitor, long auger, Maurer bin extension, 24.5-32 front, 14.9-24 rear, fore/aft, set up for air reel, one owner, sharp
John Deere	9550	2002	706	G	$81,000	8/06	SCNE	Walker, DAS, Dial-a-Matic, AHHC, hyd. fore/aft, 17" auger, chaff spreader, chopper, 439 sep hours
John Deere	9550	2002	1,427	E	$85,000	2/06	NWOH	1,117 sep hours, Maurer bin extension, 4WD, chopper, spreader, GreenStar
John Deere	9550	2003	1,061	G	$74,500	8/06	SCNE	Walker, 240-hp. engine, deluxe header control, GreenStar ready, hopper extension, duals, 753 sep hours
John Deere	9560	2004	445	E	$122,000	9/06	NEIA	Sidehill, 318 sep hours, one owner, deluxe head package, fore/aft, chopper, 30.5-32 tires
John Deere	9560	2005	623	G	$105,000	12/06	SCMN	Walker, 469 sep hours, 18.4-38 tires
John Deere	9560 STS		327	G	$157,000	4/06	SEPA	2004 model, GreenStar mapping, mapping monitoring, slope dividers, Maurer bin extension, RWA

WHAT'S IT WORTH?

Combines

Make	Model	Year	Hrs.	Cond.	Price	Sale	Location	Comments
John Deere	9560 STS	2004	407	E	$135,000	2/06	NWIL	250 sep hours, fully-equipped cab, Ag Leader PF 3000 monitor, Northstar GPS system, Contour Master, premium header control pkg, chopper, hd rear axle, Maurer grain tank extension, 21.5' unloading auger
John Deere	9560 STS	2005	377	G	$119,000	8/06	SCNE	265-hp. engine, DAS, AHHC, yield and moisture monitor, GreenStar ready, hopper extension, 316 sep hours
John Deere	9600			P	$15,000	3/06	NCUT	
John Deere	9600		5,045	F	$17,500	8/06	SCNE	Dial-a-Matic, hyd. fore/aft, hopper extension, chopper, 3,313 sep hours
John Deere	9600		5,009	F	$18,000	8/06	SCNE	Dual chaff spreader, chopper, 3,382 sep hours
John Deere	9600			F	$27,000	3/06	WCMN	Big top hopper, straddle duals
John Deere	9600		2,755	G	$35,000	8/06	SCNE	DAS, AHHC, hyd. fore/aft, hopper extension, chopper, duals, 2,259 sep hours
John Deere	9600	1989	3,882	F	$17,250	11/06	NEKS	2,616 sep hours, chopper, chaff spreader
John Deere	9600	1989	2,494	G	$28,300	3/06	ECIL	1,699 sep hours, 20' unloading auger, grain loss monitor, chopper, 18.4R-38 tires w/ factory duals
John Deere	9600	1990		F	$19,000	12/06	SCMN	30.5-32 tires
John Deere	9600	1990	3,621	G	$22,000	2/06	SEKS	3,621 sep hours, Contour Master, 4WD, Ag Leader, Dial-a-Matic, DAS, fore/aft, chopper, double fan chaff spreader, 10 Series updates
John Deere	9600	1990	3,100	G	$23,750	12/06	WCMN	Duals, long auger, tank extension, fore/aft, Dial-a-Matic, DAS, chopper
John Deere	9600	1990	3,074	G	$26,000	11/06	ECND	CAH, DHH, DAS, fore/aft, 20' unload auger, 2,164 sep hours
John Deere	9600	1991		F	$24,900	2/06	ECIL	Maurer bin extension, 20' auger, trash spreader
John Deere	9600	1991		G	$27,000	5/06	WCKS	Chopper
John Deere	9600	1991	2,378	G	$35,500	3/06	NEND	1,716 sep hours, DHH, DAS, fore/aft, single chaff spreader, 20' auger, straddle duals
John Deere	9600	1991		E	$40,000	2/06	NCIL	1,853 sep hours, bin extension, long auger, 18.4R-38 duals
John Deere	9600	1992	3,253	F	$20,000	7/06	SEND	Dial-a-Matic, DAS, fore/aft, 20' auger
John Deere	9600	1992	2,613	E	$26,000	9/06	NECO	3,200 sep hours, diesel
John Deere	9600	1992	2,760	G	$26,000	6/06	NECO	Had JD inspection, diesel
John Deere	9600	1992	6,510	F	$29,750	11/06	NEKS	4,337 sep hours, 4WD, chopper, chaff spreader, rock trap, hyd. fore/aft, AHHC, grain loss monitor, totally reconditioned
John Deere	9600	1992		G	$44,000	2/06	ECKS	Sold with JD 224 grain head
John Deere	9600	1992	2,827	G	$47,000	4/06	ECND	DAS, Dial-a-Matic, fore/aft, long auger, twin-chaff spreader, 2,113 sep hours
John Deere	9600	1993	3,972	G	$36,500	6/06	SCMN	Duals, GreenStar monitor, straw chopper, bin extension, long auger, many updates, 2,560 sep hours
John Deere	9600	1993	3,398	G	$47,000	3/06	NEND	Corn and bean, hopper extension, perforated auger, bean screens, spreader, 2,522 sep hours
John Deere	9600	1994	5,937	F	$19,600	12/06	NWMO	3,748 sep hours, Dial-a-Matic, DAS
John Deere	9600	1994	3,226	F	$20,000	8/06	SEMN	2,092 sep hours, Dial-a-Matic, DAS, fore/aft, chopper, duals
John Deere	9600	1994	4,381	F	$23,000	11/06	ECND	CAH, DAS, Dial-a-Matic, fore/aft, yield monitor, variable speed feeder house, 20' auger, chaff spreader, bin extension, 2,797 sep hours
John Deere	9600	1994	2,809	G	$26,000	8/06	SEMN	1,851 sep hours, Dial-a-Matic, DAS, fore/aft, duals
John Deere	9600	1994	4,400	G	$28,000	3/06	NWMN	DAS, Dial-a-Matic, AHHC, grain loss monitor, big top hopper, 3,100 sep hours

Combines

Make	Model	Year	Hrs.	Cond.	Price	Sale	Location	Comments
John Deere	9600	1994	2,829	F	$29,750	12/06	NWMO	1,773 sep hours, 4×4, Dial-a-Matic, DAS
John Deere	9600	1994	2,164	G	$32,500	12/06	SCMN	42" duals
John Deere	9600	1994	3,146	G	$34,000	7/06	SEND	Dial-a-Matic, DAS, fore/aft, 20' auger, JD chaff spreader, 2,187 sep hours.
John Deere	9600	1994		G	$40,000	2/06	WCKS	Sold with 1998 JD 930 platform, 2,100 sep hours, new tires, bin extension
John Deere	9600	1994		G	$49,000	11/06	WCMN	DAS, AHHC, fore/aft, 20' auger, duals
John Deere	9600	1995	6,691	F	$22,000	7/06	SEND	Dial-a-Matic, fore/aft, harvest stroke, Maurer big top, new Vittetoe chaff spreader, duals, 4,334 sep hours
John Deere	9600	1995	1,650	G	$38,500	6/06	ECSD	Duals, chopper
John Deere	9600	1996	3,500	F	$19,000	7/06	SEND	Dial-a-Matic, DAS, fore/aft, 20' auger, JD chaff spreader
John Deere	9600	1996		F	$22,500	3/06	NCUT	2,960 sep hours, 38" duals
John Deere	9600	1996	3,097	G	$31,000	4/06	NEND	2,137 sep hours, 4WD, auto height, Dial-a-Matic, DAS, fore/aft, 30.5-32 rice tires
John Deere	9600	1996	2,479	G	$57,000	6/06	ECND	Contour Master, CAH, DHH, DAS, fore/aft, JD chaff spreader, JD rear-wheel drive, 20' unload auger, 1,927 sep hours
John Deere	9600	1996	2,103	G	$72,500	4/06	SEMN	Canadian sale, diesel, chopper, 1,447 sep hours
John Deere	9600	1997	3,090	G	$4,200	2/06	SEKS	2,057 sep hours, Contour Master, 4WD, Ag Leader, Dial-a-Matic, DAS, fore/aft, chopper, double fan chaff spreader
John Deere	9600	1997	2,474	F	$32,500	3/06	ECNE	1,840 sep hours
John Deere	9600	1997	2,060	G	$35,000	8/06	NECO	1,530 sep hours, chopper, chaff spreader, 18.4-38 duals
John Deere	9600	1997	2,298	G	$37,000	8/06	NECO	1,671 sep hours, chopper, chaff spreader, 18.4-38, duals
John Deere	9600	1997	2,969	G	$38,000	11/06	ECND	CAH, DHH, DAS, fore/aft, 20' unload auger, JD chaff spreader, data center, JD yield and moisture, straddle duals, 2,048 sep hours
John Deere	9600	1997		F	$38,000	12/06	WCMN	2,138 sep hours, duals, Maurer extension
John Deere	9600	1997	2,904	G	$41,000	8/06	SCNE	DAS, yield and moisture monitor, duals, 2,119 sep hours
John Deere	9600	1997	2,925	G	$46,000	4/06	NCSD	2,222 sep hours, flare top and bin extension, concave bearings
John Deere	9600	1997		G	$47,500	12/06	WCMN	Straddle duals, fore/aft, grain extension
John Deere	9600	1997		G	$49,000	12/06	SEMN	2,020 sep hours, 4WD, Contour Master, Dial-a-Matic, DAS, fore/aft, chopper, JD chaff spreader
John Deere	9600	1997	1,782	G	$52,000	11/06	NWMN	1,330 sep hours, DHH, fore/aft, DAS, 20' auger, hd adjustable rear axle
John Deere	9600	1997	1,348	E	$54,500	1/06	WCIL	Fore/aft, duals, 20' unloading auger, Ag Leader yield monitor, Maurer bin extension, Cyclone chaff spreader, 1,017 sep hours
John Deere	9600	1997	1,389	E	$67,000	7/06	SEMN	844 sep hours, duals, JD monitor
John Deere	9600	1997	2,085	G	$70,000	12/06	ECNE	9610 updates, 1,420 sep hours, feeder house updates, 30.5-32 new front tires, 14.9-24 rear, chopper, chaff spreader, long unload auger, Contour Master, Dial-a-Matic, DAS, Ag Leader GPS monitor w/ mapping
John Deere	9610			P	$30,000	8/06	NECO	Very rough
John Deere	9610			G	$46,000	3/06	WCMN	Big top hopper extension
John Deere	9610	1998		G	$40,500	7/06	WCMN	Dial-a-Matic, DAS, 20' auger, spreader, chopper, bin extension
John Deere	9610	1998	3,119	G	$46,000	8/06	SCNE	DAS, hopper ext, chopper, dual chaff spreader, duals, 2,151 sep hours
John Deere	9610	1998	2,532	G	$46,000	12/06	SEMN	1,846 sep hours, 30.5L-32, Ag Leader

WHAT'S IT WORTH?

Combines

Make	Model	Year	Hrs.	Cond.	Price	Sale	Location	Comments
John Deere	9610	1998	3,635	G	$47,000	12/06	NWMO	2,293 sep hours, 4×4, 18.4-26 rear tires, 30.5-32 front tires, Dial-a-Matic, DAS, Contour Master, yield monitor, $10,000 in recent repairs
John Deere	9610	1998	2,200	F	$47,250	1/06	SESD	38" duals, chopper, GreenStar
John Deere	9610	1998	2,870	G	$47,500	1/06	NEIN	2,243 sep hours, 4WD, 20.8-42 duals
John Deere	9610	1998	2,174	G	$50,000	8/06	NCIA	1,448 sep hours, Contour Master, long auger, fore/aft, Maurer extension, swing-away Vittetoe spreader, chopper
John Deere	9610	1998		G	$50,500	9/06	NCIA	1,483 sep hours, 1997 engine, Dial-a-Matic, DAS, fore/aft, chopper, chaff spreader, 20' auger, duals
John Deere	9610	1998	2,855	G	$52,500	3/06	SWKS	2,109 sep hours, maximizer, chopper, chaff spreader, long auger, 30.5-32 front, 14.9-24 rear
John Deere	9610	1998	2,344	E	$58,000	1/06	SCNE	Maximizer, CAH, loaded w/ monitors, straw chopper, 1,769 sep hours, shedded
John Deere	9610	1998	1,828	G	$60,000	11/06	NWKS	1,262 sep hours
John Deere	9610	1998	2,382	G	$60,000	3/06	NWMN	GreenStar yield and moisture, no mapping, no bulb, straddle duals, big top hopper extension, chaff spreader, 50 Series reverser and direct drive, 1,775 sep hours
John Deere	9610	1998	1,380	E	$62,000	3/06	NEOH	Maximizer, 4WD, GreenStar, Vittetoe chaff spreader, dust diverter, 1,020 sep hours
John Deere	9610	1998	1,839	G	$65,000	2/06	NWMN	1,358 sep hours, hopper extension, straddle duals, straw spreader
John Deere	9610	1998	1,506	G	$77,000	11/06	NEKS	4WD, 1,087 sep hours, grain bin extensions, Contour Master, chopper, chaff spreader
John Deere	9610	1998	935	E	$96,000	1/06	SCKS	790 sep hours, 28R-26 tires on JD 1600-cc hyd. rear WD, chaff spreader, chopper, long auger, fore/aft, reel spd., monitor, 20.8-38 tires, JD duals, new cyl. & concave 90 hours ago, AM/FM SN 677698, bought new, always shedded
John Deere	9610	1999		F	$39,500	12/06	SEMN	2,544 sep hours
John Deere	9610	1999	2,107	G	$46,000	3/06	NCNE	1,491 sep hours, maximizer, 30.5L-32 front tires, 14.9-24 rear, GreenStar, yield/moisture monitor, Maurer bin extension, 20' unloading auger, chaff spreader, chopper
John Deere	9610	1999	2,308	F	$50,000	7/06	SEND	Dial-a-Matic, DAS, fore/aft, 20' auger, power RWD, bin extension, 1,863 sep hours
John Deere	9610	1999	2,946	G	$51,000	11/06	NEND	Dial-a-Matic, header height, DAS, fore/aft, yield pkg, JD factory double chaff spreader, bin ext, air suspension seat, 20' perforated auger, 1,891 sep hours
John Deere	9610	1999	2,443	G	$59,000	2/06	SCMI	4WD, 1,512 sep hours, yield monitor, Ag Leader yield monitor, GPS mapping, bin extension, 18.4-38 tires
John Deere	9610	1999	1,648	G	$63,500	1/06	NEIN	1,160 sep hours, Contour Master, GreenStar ready, duals
John Deere	9610	1999	1,926	G	$65,000	2/06	SCMI	1,242 sep hours, Contour Master, yield monitor, GreenStar yield monitor, chaff spreader, bin extension, 20.8-42 tires
John Deere	9610	1999	1,345	E	$86,500	2/06	ECMN	894 sep hours, duals, planetaries, GreenStar monitor, straw chopper, bin extension, Dial-a-Speed, fore/aft, one owner
John Deere	9610	1999	1,210	G	$98,500	4/06	WCMB	Canadian sale, 888 sep hours, diesel, Vittetoe chaff spreader, hopper topper
John Deere	9650	2000		G	$57,000	11/06	ECND	Walker, deluxe controls, 20' auger, chaff spreader, rear WD, bin extension, 1,946 sep hours

Combines

Make	Model	Year	Hrs.	Cond.	Price	Sale	Location	Comments
John Deere	9650	2000	2,961	G	$58,000	11/06	ECND	Walker, 2,003 sep hours, Contour Master, deluxe controls, 20' auger, chaff spreader, GreenStar yield & moisture, 30.5-32 singles
John Deere	9650	2000	2,100	G	$67,500	11/06	ECND	Walker, GreenStar ready yield and moisture, long auger, Crary big top hopper, 1,600 sep hours
John Deere	9650	2000	2,720	G	$70,000	7/06	WCMN	Walker, Contour Master, GreenStar, 1,877 sep hours
John Deere	9650	2000	1,865	G	$70,000	11/06	SCND	Walker, GreenStar, duals, JD chaff spreader
John Deere	9650	2000		G	$70,000	12/06	NWMO	1,433 sep hours, 4×4, 30.5-32 front tires, 18.4-26 rear tires, deluxe hydro package
John Deere	9650	2000	2,584	G	$72,000	12/06	SCMN	Walker, 2,584 sep hours, duals
John Deere	9650	2000	2,079	G	$76,000	12/06	SEMN	Walker, 1,433 sep hours, 4×4, Contour Master, chopper, chaff spreader, Ag Leader
John Deere	9650	2000	1,345	G	$79,000	8/06	SCNE	Walker, GreenStar ready, deluxe header control, hopper extension, chopper, duals, 1,001 sep hours
John Deere	9650	2000	587	E	$124,000	1/06	SCKS	466 sep hours, 18.4R42 tires w/ Kirchner Straddle duals, 28R-26 rear tires on JD 1600-cc hyd. rear WD, chaff spreader, chopper, long unloader auger, AHHC, DAS, GPS wire equipped, AM/FM, air, SN 686448, always shedded
John Deere	9650	2002	1,065	G	$87,500	4/06	NEND	Walker, 744 sep hours, Dial-a-Matic, DAS, fore/aft, level land, yield & moisture GreenStar, Maurer bin extension, 30.5-32
John Deere	9650	2002	901	E	$88,500	4/06	NWMN	Walker level land deluxe controls, 60 Series, single point, 20' unload auger, hd adjustable rear axle, 680 sep hours
John Deere	9650	2003	1,466	G	$89,000	11/06	ECND	Walker, 1,105 sep hours, Maurer extension, double chaff spreader, 30.5-32, 20.8-38, GreenStar
John Deere	9650	2003	878	E	$94,000	4/06	NWMN	Walker, deluxe controls, 60 Series, single pt, hd adjustable rear axle, 20' unload auger, 640 sep hours
John Deere	9650	2003	1,286	G	$96,000	11/06	ECND	Walker, 996 sep hours, Maurer extension, double-chaff spreader, 30.5-32, 20.8-38, GreenStar
John Deere	9650 STS	2000	4,452	F	$41,000	12/06	NEKS	3,035 rotor hours, GreenStar, yield monitor, AHHC, chopper, bin extension, rock trap, 20' auger, 800/65R32 fronts, 18.4-26 rear tires, RWA
John Deere	9650 STS	2000	4,986	F	$51,000	12/06	NEKS	3,317 rotor hours, GreenStar, yield monitor, AHHC, chopper, bin extension, rock trap, 20' auger, 800/65R32 fronts, 18.4-26 rear tires, RWA
John Deere	9650 STS	2000		F	$52,000	12/06	NEKS	Meter replaced - hours not known, GreenStar display, AHHC, yield monitor, chopper, bin extension, rock trap, 20-foot unload auger, 800/65R 32 fronts, 18.4×26 rear tires, RWA
John Deere	9650 STS	2000	4,234	F	$53,500	12/06	NEKS	2,811 rotor hours, GreenStar, yield monitor, AHHC, chopper, bin extension, rock trap, 20' auger, 800/65R32 fronts, 18.4-26 rear tires, RWA
John Deere	9650 STS	2000	2,658	F	$57,000	12/06	SCMN	
John Deere	9650 STS	2000	2,771	G	$62,500	11/06	ECND	Contour Master, deluxe header pkg., 20' unloading auger, GreenStar yield and moisture, custom cutter pkg, final cut chopper, straddle duals, hd adjustable rear axle 1,932 sep hours

Combines

Make	Model	Year	Hrs.	Cond.	Price	Sale	Location	Comments
John Deere	9650 STS	2000	2,950	G	$63,000	11/06	ECND	Contour Master high-capability lift cycle, deluxe header pkg., 20' unloading auger, GreenStar yield and moisture, custom cutter pkg., fine cut chopper, straddle duals, hd adjustable rear axle, 2,152 sep hours.
John Deere	9650 STS	2000	3,819	G	$70,000	3/06	ECND	2,120 sep hours, GreenStar, chopper, loaded
John Deere	9650 STS	2000	2,263	G	$72,000	2/06	WCMN	Contour Master, deluxe controls, hyd. rear wheel drive, hd adjustable rear axle, fine-cut chopper, 20' auger, Maurer bin extension, 1,504 sep hours
John Deere	9650 STS	2000	1,200	G	$75,500	11/06	NCIN	1,000 sep hours, Maurer bin extension, 30.5L-32, 20' auger, no contour
John Deere	9650 STS	2000	2,920	G	$76,000	8/06	SCNE	GreenStar, deluxe control, hopper extension, chopper, 1,903 sep hours
John Deere	9650 STS	2000	1,285	G	$82,000	6/06	ECSD	Contour duals
John Deere	9650 STS	2000	1,674	G	$83,000	8/06	SCNE	Dial-a-Matic, DAS, AHHC, GreenStar, Contour Master, hopper extension, chaff spreader, duals, 1,167 sep hours
John Deere	9650 STS	2000	1,763	G	$87,500	12/06	WCMN	John Deere GreenStar monitor, straddle duals
John Deere	9650 STS	2000	1,064	G	$88,000	4/06	NWKS	GreenStar wiring harness only, chaff spreader, 738 sep hours, chaff spreader, 20' unloading auger, 800/65R-32-R1W front, 18.4R26 rear
John Deere	9650 STS	2000	1,430	G	$90,500	12/06	ECMO	RWA, chopper, duals, deluxe cab, 20' unloading auger, 930 sep hours
John Deere	9650 STS	2000	1,033	G	$109,500	3/06	SEMN	580 sep hours, duals, straw chopper, big top bin extension, GreenStar monitor
John Deere	9650 STS	2001	3,182	G	$60,500	12/06	NWMO	2,021 sep hours, Dial-a-Matic, DAS
John Deere	9650 STS	2001	2,850	G	$64,000	11/06	ECND	Contour Master, high capability lift cyl., deluxe header package, 20' unloading auger, GreenStar yield and moisture, straddle duals, 1,981 sep hours
John Deere	9650 STS	2001	2,317	G	$71,500	12/06	WCMN	1,685 sep hours, 18.4×42 duals, big lift cyl., Maurer tank extension, Contour Master, yield & moisture monitors, service lights
John Deere	9650 STS	2001	1,183	G	$81,000	9/06	NCIA	812 sep hours, deluxe header package, chopper, duals
John Deere	9650 STS	2001	886	G	$87,000	8/06	NECO	685 sep hours, chopper, 20.8-38 duals
John Deere	9650 STS	2001		G	$88,000	12/06	SCMN	
John Deere	9650 STS	2001	1,530	G	$103,000	3/06	ECNE	496T turbo 6-cyl., hydro trans., CAH, deluxe AHHC, Contour Master, hd rear axle, grain loss and field monitors, 1,062 sep hours
John Deere	9650 STS	2002	3,495	F	$56,500	11/06	ECND	Contour Master, high-capability lift cylinder, deluxe header pkg., yield and moisture monitor, custom cutter pkg., 20' auger, fine cut chopper, straddle duals, 2,550 sep hours
John Deere	9650 STS	2002	3,122	G	$61,000	11/06	ECND	Contour Master, high-capability lift cylinder, deluxe header pkg., yield and moisture monitor, custom cutter pkg., 20' auger, fine cut chopper, straddle duals, 2,210 sep hours
John Deere	9650 STS	2002	2,899	G	$70,000	11/06	WCMN	Contour Master, deluxe controls, custom cutter pkg., 20' auger, Ag Leader monitor, GreenStar ready, duals, 2,096 sep hours

Combines

Make	Model	Year	Hrs.	Cond.	Price	Sale	Location	Comments
John Deere	9650 STS	2002	2,330	G	$75,000	11/06	WCMN	Contour Master, deluxe controls, custom cutter pkg., 20' auger, Ag Leader monitor, GreenStar ready, duals, 1,651 sep hours
John Deere	9650 STS	2002	2,710	G	$78,000	2/06	WCMN	Contour Master, deluxe controls, straddle duals, hd adjustable. rear axle, fine cut chopper, 20' auger, Crary bin extension, Ag Leader yield and moisture, 1,939 sep hours
John Deere	9650 STS	2002	2,503	G	$78,000	2/06	WCMN	Contour Master, deluxe controls, straddle duals, 20' auger, Crary bin extension, Ag Leader yield and moisture, 1,841 sep hours
John Deere	9650 STS	2002		G	$78,250	2/06	WCMN	Contour Master, deluxe controls, straddle duals, fine cut chopper, 20' auger, Crary bin extension, Ag Leader yield and moisture, 2,040 sep hours
John Deere	9650 STS	2002	1,675	G	$94,000	12/06	SWMI	1,150 sep hours, 20.8-42 duals, RWA, 20L-26 rear tires, Maurer bin extension, yield & moisture monitors
John Deere	9650 STS	2002	1,103	G	$97,500	12/06	NWMO	726 sep hours, 4×4, 30.5-32 front tires, 28-26 rear tires, Contour Master, Dial-a-Matic, DAS, AHC
John Deere	9650 STS	2002	1,298	G	$101,000	3/06	SEMN	865 sep hours, 30.5L-32R tires, straw chopper, GreenStar, bin extension, long auger, bought new
John Deere	9650 STS	2002	912	G	$101,000	12/06	NWMO	625 sep hours, 4×4, 800/65-32 front tires, Contour Master, yield monitor, chopper, wiper, service lights, hd alternator
John Deere	9650 STS	2003	2,273	G	$93,000	3/06	NWKS	4WD, 1,556 sep hours, Contour Master, Maurer bin extension, GreenStar, 30.5L-32 front & 16.9R-26 rear tires, straw chopper
John Deere	9650 STS	2003	970	E	$120,000	3/06	SEIA	4WD, Contour Master, hd reverser, high-capability lift cylinders, GreenStar monitor w/ display, high-wear augers, chopper, duals, 721 sep hours
John Deere	9660 STS	2003	750	E	$131,000	1/06	NECO	GreenStar, loaded, 500 sep hours
John Deere	9660 STS	2004	1,304	G	$107,500	3/06	ECND	985 sep hours, GreenStar, chopper, loaded
John Deere	9660 STS	2004	1,315	G	$107,500	3/06	ECND	990 sep hours, GreenStar ready, chopper, loaded
John Deere	9660 STS	2004	1,925	G	$112,000	3/06	NWKS	1,269 sep hours, 2×4, GreenStar, straw chopper, Maurer bin extension., 18.4R-42 front & 18.4R-26 front tires
John Deere	9660 STS	2004		G	$115,000	12/06	WCMN	831 sep hours, hd final drive, high-capability
John Deere	9660 STS	2004	1,073	G	$117,500	2/06	WCMN	Level land, deluxe controls, TouchSet, fine cut chopper, bin extension, GreenStar yield and moisture, 729 sep hours
John Deere	9660 STS	2004	400	E	$118,500	4/06	NWMN	Level land, deluxe controls, fine cut chopper, 20' unload auger, 2WD, adjustable rear axle, 297 sep hours
John Deere	9660 STS	2004		G	$122,000	12/06	NWWI	750 sep hours, 20.8-42 duals, Contour Master, deluxe header fore/aft, chopper, hd final drives, hd rear axles, long auger, field office
John Deere	9660 STS	2004	700	E	$129,000	9/06	NCIA	482 sep hours, Contour Master, GreenStar, deluxe header pkg., fore/aft, chopper, single point hose hookup, 20' auger, duals
John Deere	9660 STS	2004	597	E	$136,000	12/06	NWMO	358 sep hours, 4×4, 800/65-32 front, 600/65-28 rear tires, Contour Master, deluxe hydro control, roundbar concave, monitor, service lights, high-capacity auger
John Deere	9660 STS	2005	1,357	G	$118,000	12/06	WCKS	1,143 sep hours, speed hydro trans., bullet rotor, GreenStar, yield monitor, Contour Master, fore/aft, AHHC, variable reel speed, bin extension, 20' unload auger, rock trap

WHAT'S IT WORTH?

Combines

Make	Model	Year	Hrs.	Cond.	Price	Sale	Location	Comments
John Deere	9660 STS	2005	1,140	G	$124,000	8/06	SCNE	Contour Master, deluxe header package, chopper, light pkg., 913 sep hours, yield, high-capacity unloading auger, 800/65R32 drive tires, 18.4-26 front
John Deere	9660 STS	2005	358	G	$151,500	12/06	NWMO	243 sep hours, 4×4, Dial-a-Matic, DAS
John Deere	9660 STS	2005	370	G	$159,000	12/06	NWMO	279 sep hours, 4×4, 18.4-42 front duals, 28L-26 rear tires, deluxe hyd. control
John Deere	9660 STS	2005	480	E	$168,750	12/06	ECIL	296 sep hours, 4WD, deluxe factory options, Contour Master, GreenStar, 20.8R-42 w/ duals & 28L-26 rear tires, 2-speed 4×4, 140-bu. Maurer fold-down bin extension, hi-unload, GPS wired, wheat concave & inserts
John Deere	9660 STS	2006	682	G	$143,000	12/06	WCKS	452 sep hours, speed hydro trans., bullet rotor, GreenStar, yield monitor, Contour Master, fore/aft, AHHC, variable reel speed, bin extension, 20' unload auger, rock trap
John Deere	9660 STS	2006	600	G	$144,000	12/06	WCKS	447 sep hours, speed hydro trans., bullet rotor, GreenStar, yield monitor, Contour Master, fore/aft, AHHC, variable reel speed, bin extension, 20' unload auger, rock trap
John Deere	9660 STS	2006	594	G	$152,000	12/06	WCKS	393 sep hours, speed hydro trans., bullet rotor, GreenStar, yield monitor, Contour Master, fore/aft, AHHC, variable reel speed, bin extension, 20' unload auger, rock trap
John Deere	9660 STS	2006	380	E	$165,000	12/06	WCKS	260 sep hours, speed hydro trans., bullet rotor, GreenStar, yield monitor, Contour Master, fore/aft, AHHC, variable reel speed, bin extension, 20' unload auger, rock trap
John Deere	9660 STS	2006	223	E	$176,000	12/06	WCKS	151 sep hours, speed hydro trans., bullet rotor, GreenStar, yield monitor, Contour Master, fore/aft, AHHC, variable reel speed, bin extension, 20' unload auger, rock trap
John Deere	9660 STS	2006	0	E	$193,000	12/06	WCKS	New, speed hydro trans., bullet rotor, GreenStar, yield monitor, Contour Master, fore/aft, AHHC, variable reel speed, bin extension, 20' unload auger, rock trap
John Deere	9750 STS	2000	2,476	G	$69,500	3/06	NWKS	1,919 sep hours, GreenStar
John Deere	9750 STS	2000	2,278	E	$96,000	2/06	WCIL	GreenStar/yield mapping capability, 20' auger, chopper, duals, Maurer bin extension, 1,473 sep hours, has had JD inspection program every year, field ready
John Deere	9750 STS	2000	2,150	G	$106,000	12/06	SCMN	1,670 sep hours, 20.8-42 duals, one owner
John Deere	9750 STS	2001	2,402	G	$69,500	3/06	NWKS	4×2, 1,707 sep hours
John Deere	9750 STS	2001	2,318	G	$72,000	3/06	NWKS	1,633 sep hours, 2×4
John Deere	9750 STS	2001	2,645	G	$85,000	3/06	NWKS	4×4, 1,836 sep hours, GreenStar, straddle duals
John Deere	9750 STS	2001	962	G	$95,000	8/06	SCNE	DAS, Dial-a-Matic, AHHC, hyd. fore/aft, chopper, duals, 557 sep hours
John Deere	9750 STS	2002		G	$80,000	12/06	WCMN	1,623 sep hours, duals, Contour Master, tank extension
John Deere	9750 STS	2002		G	$91,000	12/06	WCMN	Duals, Crary big top, long auger, Contour Master
John Deere	9750 STS	2002	1,171	G	$102,000	8/06	SCNE	RWA, DAS, Dial-a-Matic, auto header height control, hyd. fore/aft, Contour Master, GreenStar yield, duals, 877 sep hours
John Deere	9750 STS	2002	1,218	G	$114,000	4/06	NEND	893 sep hours, deluxe cab, DAS, Dial-a-Matic, fore/aft, Maurer hopper extension, chopper, wired for GreenStar, 20.8-42 duals
John Deere	9750 STS	2003	2,031	G	$80,000	12/06	WCMN	John Deere GreenStar monitor
John Deere	9750 STS	2003		G	$97,000	11/06	SCND	1,144 sep hours, GreenStar, hopper extensions

Combines

Make	Model	Year	Hrs.	Cond.	Price	Sale	Location	Comments
John Deere	9760 STS	2003		G	$102,000	12/06	NWWI	900 sep hours, 20.8-42 duals, Contour Master, no chopper, deluxe header fore/aft, long auger
John Deere	9760 STS	2004		G	$107,500	12/06	WCMN	1,281 sep hours
John Deere	9760 STS	2004	1,955	G	$120,000	12/06	WCKS	1,282 sep hours, speed hydro trans., GreenStar, yield monitor, Contour Master, fore/aft, AHHC, variable reel speed, bin extension, 20' unload auger, rock trap
John Deere	9760 STS	2004	1,200	G	$140,000	11/06	ECND	CAH, TouchSet controls, Contour Master, high capacity unload, GreenStar yield and moisture, less mapping, RWA, chopper, 970 sep hours
John Deere	9760 STS	2004	591	G	$151,000	7/06	SEND	Deluxe controls, high unload pkg., 22 1/4' auger, fine cut chopper, GreenStar yield and moisture, straddle duals, 391 sep hours
John Deere	9760 STS	2005	1,164	E	$141,000	12/06	WCKS	814 sep hours, speed hydro trans., GreenStar, yield monitor, Contour Master, fore/aft, AHHC, variable reel speed, bin extension, 20' unload auger, rock trap
John Deere	9760 STS	2005	1,093	G	$147,000	12/06	WCKS	681 sep hours, RWA, speed hydro trans., bullet rotor, GreenStar, yield monitor, Contour Master, fore/aft, AHHC, variable reel speed, bin extension, 20' unload auger, rock trap
John Deere	9760 STS	2005	515	G	$162,000	12/06	WCMN	407 sep hours, bullet rotor
John Deere	9760 STS	2005		E	$162,000	3/06	NESD	318 sep hours, 2-wheel drive, high rate unload system, long auger, chopper, 800/65R32
John Deere	9760 STS	2005		E	$167,500	3/06	NESD	357 sep hours, 4WD, long auger, 800/65R32
John Deere	9760 STS	2005		E	$178,000	3/06	NESD	381 sep hours, Contour Master, 4WD, high rate unload system, long auger, 800/65R32
John Deere	9760 STS	2005		E	$180,000	12/06	WCMN	130 sep hours, bullet rotor, Contour Master, GreenStar monitor, yield & moisture, Zenon lighting, TouchSet, hi-cap unload, 20.8-42 duals, long augers, tank extension
John Deere	9760 STS	2005		E	$180,000	3/06	NESD	340 sep hours, Contour Master, 4WD, high rate unload system, long auger, chopper, 800/65R32
John Deere	9760 STS	2006	711	G	$145,000	12/06	WCKS	476 sep hours, speed hydro trans., bullet rotor, GreenStar, yield monitor, Contour Master, fore/aft, AHHC, variable reel speed, bin extension, 20' unload auger, rock trap, Lincoln automatic greasers
John Deere	9760 STS	2006	654	G	$162,000	12/06	WCKS	487 sep hours, speed hydro trans., bullet rotor, GreenStar, yield monitor, Contour Master, fore/aft, AHHC, variable reel speed, bin extension, 20' unload auger, rock trap
John Deere	9760 STS	2006	700	E	$171,000	12/06	WCKS	452 sep hours, RWA, speed hydro trans., bullet rotor, GreenStar, yield monitor, Contour Master, fore/aft, AHHC, variable reel speed, bin extension, 20' unload auger, rock trap, Lincoln automatic greasers
John Deere	9760 STS	2006	422	E	$173,000	12/06	WCKS	277 sep hours, speed hydro trans., bullet rotor, GreenStar, yield monitor, Contour Master, fore/aft, ACCH, variable reel speed, bin extension, 20' unload auger, rock trap
John Deere	9760 STS	2006	245	E	$176,000	12/06	WCKS	162 sep hours, speed hydro trans., bullet rotor, GreenStar, yield monitor, Contour Master, fore/aft, AHHC, variable reel speed, bin extension, 20' unload auger, rock trap

Combines

Make	Model	Year	Hrs.	Cond.	Price	Sale	Location	Comments
John Deere	9760 STS	2006	225	E	$190,000	12/06	WCMN	4WD, GreenStar w/ mapping, Contour Master, variable speed feeder house, hi unload, Crary big top w/ bubble augers, Dial-a-Matic, DAS, warranty
John Deere	9760 STS	2006	225	E	$191,000	12/06	WCMN	4WD, GreenStar w/ mapping, Contour Master, variable speed feeder house, hi unload, Crary big top w/ bubble augers, Dial-a-Matic, DAS, warranty
John Deere	9760 STS	2006	135	E	$195,000	12/06	WCKS	95 sep hours, speed hydro trans., bullet rotor, GreenStar, yield monitor, Contour Master, fore/aft, AHHC, variable reel speed, bin extension, 20' unload auger, rock trap
John Deere	9860 STS	2004		G	$128,000	12/06	WCMN	1,140 sep hours, 2WD, autosteer
John Deere	9860 STS	2006	330	E	$185,000	11/06	SCNE	357 rotor hours, bullet rotor, field monitor, GreenStar ready, service lights, long unloading auger, 18.4-42 straddle duals, 18.4R-26 rear tires
Lilliston	6200			G	$2,700	3/06	WCMI	High-capacity bean, bucket elevator, Sund pickup
Lilliston	6200			G	$3,250	3/06	SEND	Edible bean combine, belted return, hyd. Sund pickup, 5 bar
Lilliston	6200			G	$3,250	3/06	SEND	Edible bean combine, hyd. Sund pickup, 5 bar
MF	540	1978		G	$3,500	3/06	NWIL	Perkins 318 diesel engine, with 4R corn head & platform
MF	760	1972		G	$1,150	9/06	NWOH	Gear drive w/ chopper, Massey 16' grain head w/ U2 reel
MF	760	1978		P	$425	11/06	WCMN	24.5-32 tires
MF	760	1978	2,790	G	$1,500	7/06	NWMN	Chopper, tank extension, auger extension
MF	850	1984		G	$5,800	1/06	SCNE	Diesel
MF	8560		3,684	G	$14,750	3/06	WCMN	Rotary combine, hydro, straddle duals
MF	8570	1993	1,714	G	$37,000	1/06	ECIL	Rotary, 30.5L-32, 14.9-24 rear, bin extension, long out auger, grain loss monitor
MF	860		2,650	F	$0	7/06	ECND	Couldn't even get a starting bid, CAH
MF	860			F	$1,250	7/06	WCMN	Hydro, 540 V-8, corn/soybean, hyd. reel drive, hyd. header height, duals
MF	860			G	$4,500	3/06	NEKS	No heads
MF	860	1981	3,953	G	$1,900	7/06	NWMN	6-cyl. gear, CAH, chopper, tank and auger extension
MF	860	1981	3,796	G	$2,600	7/06	NWMN	6-cyl. gear, CAH, chopper, tank and auger extension
MF	860	1981		G	$3,750	8/06	ECIA	Turbo, diesel
MF	860	1982		G	$3,300	7/06	NWMN	6-cyl. gear, CAH, chopper, tank and auger extension
MF	860	1983	2,336	G	$2,500	7/06	NWMN	6-cyl. gear, CAH, chopper, tank and auger extension
MF	860	1983	4,300	G	$6,000	6/06	SEND	V-8, hydro, 24.5-32 fronts
MF	860	1984		F	$3,250	7/06	SEND	V-8, hydro, bean and corn
MF	860	1985	2,224	G	$8,500	7/06	NWMN	V-8, hydro, CAH, chopper, tank and auger extension
MF	860	1987	3,008	G	$9,500	6/06	SEND	Gear drive, Perkins 6-cyl. intercooled, 24.5-32 fronts
New Holland	CR960	2004	1,108	G	$93,000	4/06	NEND	792 sep hours, twin rotor, Dial-a-Matic, DAS, fore/aft, yield & moisture monitor, self-leveling sieve, electric rock trap, chopper, 800/38 tires
New Holland	CX840	2003	680	E	$152,500	4/06	WCMN	Canadian sale, Swathmaster pickup, yield & moisture monitors
New Holland	CX840	2003	680	E	$152,500	4/06	SWMB	Canadian sale, Swathmaster pick-up, yield & moisture monitors, 900 tires, shedded, like new, SN 301324026
New Holland	TR 75	1983	3,106	G	$2,000	3/06	SEND	Cat 3208, S cube rotor, rock trap, 28L-26 singles
New Holland	TR 85		2,871	F	$2,000	9/06	NEIN	2 heads, diesel

Combines

Make	Model	Year	Hrs.	Cond.	Price	Sale	Location	Comments
New Holland	TR 85	1981	4,670	F	$1,400	4/06	NWMN	CAH, posi-torque, 3208 Cat, torque-sensing drive, rock trap, chopper, NH 970 pickup head w/ Melroe pickup
New Holland	TR 86	1988	2,700	P	$2,100	11/06	WCMN	Hydro, Ford diesel, Contour Master
New Holland	TR 86	1991		G	$12,750	9/06	NCIA	1,693 sep hours, rear WD, AHHC
New Holland	TR 89	2002	713	E	$101,000	2/06	ECNE	427 sep hours, 2-speed rotor, long auger, straw chopper, Maurer grain bin extension
New Holland	TR 95	1981	4,791	G	$3,400	4/06	NWMN	CAH, hydro, AHHC, 3208 Cat, S cube rotors, torque-sensing drive, rock trap, chopper w/ NH 970 pickup head, Melroe pickup
New Holland	TR 96		4,519	F	$5,600	8/06	WCMN	Cube rotor, hopper topper, rock trap, 30.5-32 tires
New Holland	TR 96		3,000	F	$8,000	7/06	SEND	CAH, S cube rotor, Ford engine, hydro, terrain tracer, reverser
New Holland	TR 96	1990	1,953	F	$5,100	10/06	NCND	RWA
New Holland	TR 96	1991	2,970	G	$22,000	8/06	ECIA	Nearly completely updated including rotor, housing, concave, chopper, fountain auger, and more ($20K in last two years), diesel
New Holland	TR 97	1995	2,905	G	$16,500	12/06	WCMN	Chaff spreader
New Holland	TR 98		2,076	G	$32,000	9/06	NCIA	1,435 sep hours, terrain tracer, chopper, stone trap, chaff spreader, duals
New Holland	TR 99	2001	1,322	G	$91,000	12/06	SCNE	822 sep hours, terrain tracer lateral float equipment, chopper, Crary chaff spreader, big top extension, one owner, always shedded
New Idea	804		3,000	G	$7,100	3/06	NEMI	Uniharvester, 4×4, hydro, late model, 858 combine unit, 839 Husking bed, 846N 6-RCH
New Idea	UNI 800C		1,707	F	$1,500	3/06	NWOH	NI 818 combine & 815 grain head
White	8600	1977	1,200	G	$5,600	3/06	ECMI	Harvest Boss 2WD, hydro, White 15' floating cutter bar grain platform & White 704N 4-RCH

Notes

_____

_____

_____

_____

_____

_____

_____

_____

_____

_____

WHAT'S IT WORTH?

Construction Equipment

Heavy equipment has been finding more and varied uses on the farm for years now. Rather than break this equipment into a million separate categories, we list all types of construction equipment together. Crawlers, dozers, payloaders, backhoes, road graders, forklifts, excavators, even telehandlers. We do list skid steers separately beginning on page 254.

Construction Equipment

Make	Model	Year	Hrs.	Cond.	Price	Sale	Location	Comments
Allis-Chalmers	M100			G	$8,400	1/06	NWIA	M100 road grader, 12' blade, double snow blade, nice
Allis-Chalmers	545			G	$7,000	11/06	SWCA	Rubber-tired loader
Allis-Chalmers	705			G	$1,500	10/06	WCFL	Rough terrain forklift
Allis-Chalmers	840C		7,847	G	$3,250	5/06	SWCA	Rubber-tired loader, canopy
Allis-Chalmers	D			G	$3,200	9/06	NEIN	Grader, 4-cyl. gas, 12' moldboard
Allis-Chalmers	D			G	$3,400	3/06	ECIN	Grader, scarifier, hyd. side shift, tilting wheels
Allis-Chalmers	D			G	$7,000	6/06	NEIN	Cab, scarifier, PS side shift
Allis-Chalmers	G6			G	$6,250	8/06	WCMN	Crawler/loader, 13" tracks, 6.5' bucket
Allis-Chalmers	HD11			G	$3,100	9/06	NEIN	Crawler, canopy, straight blade, tilt
Allis-Chalmers	I600			G	$4,600	2/06	WCMN	Forklift, side shift, triple mast
Ag Krane	NA			G	$1,300	2/06	SEKS	3-point high lift, pallet forks
Ag Krane	NA			G	$2,000	11/06	NEND	3-point forklift
Ag Krane	NA			G	$2,400	3/06	NENE	3-point hyd. boom crane
Ag Krane	NA			G	$3,500	3/06	NCNE	3-point hyd. boom, feed bag carrier, shop built platform
Airman	NA	2000	2,565	G	$7,250	8/06	SETN	Mini excavator, rubber tracks
Allied	NA	2000		G	$1,100	4/06	NWMN	Hot water power washer steamer
Arps	730			G	$3,100	3/06	SWIN	Backhoe attachment w/ 3-point height, 12" & 24" buckets, stabilizer pads
ASV	RC30		713	G	$9,000	9/06	ECMN	R Series, track machine
ASV	RC30			G	$15,600	8/06	SETN	Backhoe, sod roller, trencher, posthole digger, grapple bucket
Baker	B40PL			F	$300	11/06	ECNE	Forklift, charger
BLH	Type 25			F	$3,500	8/06	SCMI	Baldwin/Lima/Hamilton 40' crane
Bobcat	225		1,800	F	$8,200	3/06	SEPA	Mini excavator, rubber track
Bobcat	2410	1992		G	$10,500	3/06	WCWA	Wheel loader, 4WD, gp bucket, cab
Bobcat	325			F	$10,750	8/06	SEPA	Mini excavator, average track
Bobcat	325	2002	2,101	G	$9,000	10/06	WCMA	Mini hyd. excavator, Kubota diesel, backfill blade, rubber tracks
Bobcat	331			G	$15,750	12/06	SWWI	Mini excavator
Bobcat	331	1997	2,931	G	$8,250	10/06	WCMA	Mini hyd. excavator, Kubota diesel, backfill blade
Bobcat	331	1999		G	$14,500	3/06	WCWA	Mini excavator, gp bucket, thumb, OROPS
Bobcat	331	1999		G	$14,500	3/06	WCWA	Mini excavator, gp bucket, thumb, OROPS
Bobcat	334	2002	1,486	G	$17,000	10/06	WCMA	Mini hyd. excavator, Kubota diesel, hydrostatic, backfill blade, rubber tracks
Bobcat	B250			G	$16,500	5/06	SWCA	Loader backhoe, all-wheel steer, diesel, hyd. drive
Bobcat	B250	2003	142	G	$13,500	11/06	WCMN	Loader backhoe, front aux. hyd., Bob-Tach
Bobcat	NA			E	$1,400	9/06	NEIN	Trencher, skid steer attachment
Bobcat	NA			G	$1,500	7/06	WCCA	Hyd. auger
Bobcat	NA			G	$1,500	12/06	ECMN	Sweeper, hyd. drive, parking lot sweeper, pick-up hopper
Bobcat	NA			G	$5,500	2/06	WCSD	Sheepsfoot attachment
Bobcat	T200		1,695	G	$21,500	8/06	SETN	Track loader, gp bucket
Bobcat	X325			G	$5,700	10/06	WCFL	Mini track excavator
Bobcat	X331-C			G	$11,500	10/06	SWOH	Hyd. excavator, Kubota diesel, cab, swing boom, standard stick
Bomag	BW120AD		2,137	G	$6,250	9/06	SECA	2-double drum roller
Bomag	BW120AD	2002	850	G	$17,000	9/06	SECA	3-double drum roller
Bomag	BW142PD	1999		G	$25,000	9/06	WCTX	Vibratory roller, diesel, 54" smooth drum
Bomag	BW172-D2	1999		G	$19,500	9/06	WCTX	Vibratory roller, diesel, ROPS, 66" padsfoot drum
Bomag	BW213	1998		G	$52,000	1/06	WCPA	Vibratory roller, Cummins diesel, 84" smooth drum

Construction Equipment

Make	Model	Year	Hrs.	Cond.	Price	Sale	Location	Comments
Bomag	BW213D2			G	$22,500	7/06	ECNY	Vibratory roller, Deutz diesel, OROPS, 84" smooth drum
Bomag	BW213D2	1994		G	$29,500	1/06	WCPA	Vibratory roller, 84" smooth drum, vibratory drum drive, OROPS
Bomag	BW213D2	1997		G	$29,000	10/06	SWOH	Vibratory roller, diesel
Bomag	BW213PDB			G	$26,000	9/06	WCTX	Vibratory roller, diesel, 84" pads
Bradco	NA			E	$5,800	6/06	SCMN	213 9 hd 3-point tractor mount backhoe attachment w/ outriggers, 24" bucket, like new
Broce	RJ300			G	$6,000	3/06	ECIN	Broom, JD diesel, canopy
Bucyrus Erie	NA			G	$4,900	10/06	SENJ	Crane, 54B
Case	1085C			G	$10,000	1/06	WCOH	Rubber-tired excavator, Cummins diesel, cab
Case	1088	1990		G	$18,500	10/06	NCND	Track hoe
Case	1150			G	$9,500	6/06	NEIN	ROPS, sweeps, 6-way blade
Case	1150			G	$23,000	3/06	ECIN	Crawler, canopy, ripper
Case	1150	2003		G	$52,000	10/06	WCFL	Crawler, diesel, EROPS, air engine enclosures
Case	1150B			G	$10,000	6/06	NEIN	Dozer, sweeps, 6-way blade
Case	1150G			G	$37,000	1/06	WCOH	Crawler, diesel, cab, air, 6-way blade
Case	1150G	1997		G	$41,000	9/06	NEIN	Crawler, long track, 6-way blade, 22" pads
Case	1150G	1999		G	$37,500	10/06	SWOH	Crawler, diesel, ROPS, 6-way blade
Case	1155			G	$13,000	10/06	ECMO	ROPS, powershift
Case	1155E			G	$18,000	11/06	NCKY	High lift
Case	1450			G	$11,000	6/06	NEIN	Crawler loader, gp bucket
Case	1450	1976		G	$13,500	9/06	ECMN	24" pads, 119" blade, power tilt, OROPS
Case	1450B			G	$11,500	6/06	NEIN	ROPS, sweeps, straight blade, tilt
Case	1450B			G	$21,000	3/06	ECIN	Crawler, canopy
Case	1550			G	$17,000	6/06	NEIN	Dozer
Case	170C			G	$17,000	5/06	SWCA	Hyd. excavator, standard undercarriage, medium stick, cab
Case	1825B			G	$6,500	11/06	SCCA	
Case	1835C		2,195	G	$5,750	9/06	ECMN	Gas, OROPS, 5' bucket
Case	1850	2002		G	$120,500	1/06	WCOH	Crawler, diesel, cab, air, 24" pads
Case	1850	2003		G	$122,500	1/06	WCOH	Crawler, diesel, cab, air, 24" pads
Case	1850	2003		G	$129,500	1/06	WCOH	Crawler, diesel, cab, air, 24' pads
Case	330	2002		E	$67,500	10/06	NCWI	Articulated haul truck, 6×6, diesel, cab, air, 30-ton capacity
Case	330	2002		G	$99,000	1/06	WCOH	Articulated haul truck, 6×6, Cummins QS11 diesel, cab, front suspension semi-independent, nitrogen-oil suspension
Case	330	2003		G	$99,000	1/06	WCOH	Articulated haul truck, 6×6, Cummins QSM11 diesel
Case	350	1979		G	$6,600	3/06	SWOH	Bulldozer, diesel, torque converter drive scoop bucket, homemade blade, rear weights
Case	350B			G	$5,500	8/06	SETN	Crawler loader, 4-in-1 bucket
Case	380B			G	$6,000	11/06	NCKY	Industrial tractor, loader
Case	450			G	$5,200	11/06	SEIA	Dozer, 4-way blade
Case	450			G	$5,500	9/06	NEIN	Crawler, canopy, 16" pads
Case	450			G	$5,750	6/06	NEIN	Crawler loader
Case	450		1,622	G	$6,500	12/06	NEMN	
Case	450			G	$6,600	6/06	NEIN	Canopy, 6-way blade
Case	450			G	$7,000	3/06	SCIN	6-way blade
Case	450			F	$8,250	3/06	NWIL	6' bucket
Case	450			G	$8,250	3/06	ECIN	Crawler loader, JD 207 turbo diesel, new sprockets, rails, starter

Construction Equipment

Make	Model	Year	Hrs.	Cond.	Price	Sale	Location	Comments
Case	450B			F	$7,400	9/06	SEIA	Crawler loader
Case	450C			G	$9,750	9/06	NEIN	Crawler, canopy, 6-way blade
Case	450C			G	$11,000	3/06	ECMI	Long track, 28" pads, 6-way blade, ROPS
Case	450C			G	$13,000	10/06	SWOH	Crawler, Case diesel, front sweeps, 6-way blade
Case	450C			G	$18,000	3/06	ECIN	Crawler, diesel, canopy, sweeps, 6-way blade
Case	450C	1991		G	$13,000	3/06	ECMI	Long track, ROPS, sweeps, 6-way blade
Case	455C			G	$11,500	3/06	SCIN	Crawler loader, 4-in-1 bucket
Case	480D			G	$5,900	10/06	WCFL	Box blade
Case	480E			G	$8,000	11/06	SWCA	4WD, Gannon 5-valve rear scraper
Case	480F			G	$11,500	11/06	SWCA	4WD, Gannon 3-valve rear scraper, canopy
Case	480F			G	$12,000	11/06	SWCA	4WD, Gannon 4-valve rear scraper, canopy
Case	480F			G	$15,000	11/06	SECA	4WD, 4-in-1 bucket, canopy, Gannon scraper
Case	480L			G	$2,800	11/06	SETN	Front end blade
Case	530			F	$4,000	9/06	NWIL	530B, backhoe, loader, gas
Case	530			F	$5,000	8/06	SCMI	Backhoe/loader, 24" backhoe, Construction King, gas, 6' bucket, #32 loader
Case	530			G	$6,000	4/06	WCMT	Backhoe tractor, gas engine, loader with 5' bucket, backhoe has 16' reach and a 24" bucket
Case	550	1994		G	$4,600	10/06	ECMO	Vibrator plow
Case	550	2000		G	$27,000	1/06	WCOH	LGP crawler, diesel, canopy
Case	550E			G	$13,000	7/06	ECNY	Crawler, diesel, OROPS, 6-way blade, long track
Case	550E			G	$19,500	7/06	ECNY	Crawler, diesel, OROPS, long track
Case	550G			G	$20,000	10/06	NCWI	Crawler, diesel, ROPS, long track, 6-way blade
Case	550G		2,800	F	$25,500	1/06	SEPA	Dozer, long track, ROPS, power angle
Case	550G	1997	3,850	G	$24,000	9/06	NEIN	Crawler, canopy, 6-way blade
Case	550G	1998	3,296	G	$24,000	11/06	SWCA	Crawler loader, 6-way blade, long track, canopy
Case	550G	1999		G	$25,500	9/06	SECA	Dozer
Case	570			F	$0	3/06	SEPA	No sale at $21,000, backhoe/loader, MFWD, CAH, turbo, fair rubber, Model 570 MXT
Case	570		3,707	G	$17,500	9/06	SECA	
Case	570		2,275	G	$18,500	9/06	SECA	
Case	570		2,275	G	$18,500	9/06	SECA	
Case	570		2,275	G	$19,000	9/06	SECA	
Case	570		2,275	G	$19,500	9/06	SECA	
Case	570	1999		G	$16,000	9/06	WCTX	TLB, diesel, ROPS
Case	570	1999		G	$23,500	1/06	WCCA	4WD loader/scraper
Case	570	1999		G	$23,500	8/06	WCTX	Diesel
Case	570	2000		G	$16,000	9/06	ECMN	3 pt., 85" box blade on rear, enclosed cab, loader, quick-tach
Case	570	2000		G	$18,000	9/06	WCTX	TLB, 4WD, diesel, ROPS
Case	570	2001	1,718	G	$17,500	9/06	WCTX	ROPS, diesel
Case	570	2003		G	$33,000	8/06	SECA	4×4 loader/scraper
Case	570	2004		E	$37,000	1/06	WCCA	4WD, loader/scraper
Case	570L			F	$12,000	3/06	NCUT	570LXT loader tractor
Case	570L	1996	3,592	G	$20,000	11/06	SWCA	4×4, 4-in-1 bucket
Case	570L	1997		G	$16,000	11/06	SWCA	4×4, Gannon 5-valve rear scraper
Case	570L	1997		G	$16,500	11/06	SWCA	4×4, Gannon 5-valve rear scraper
Case	570L	1999		G	$19,000	7/06	WCCA	Series II, 4WD, skip loader, bucket, canopy, Gannon scraper
Case	580			G	$9,000	7/06	WCCA	4-in-1 bucket, canopy, Gannon scraper

WHAT'S IT WORTH?

Construction Equipment

Make	Model	Year	Hrs.	Cond.	Price	Sale	Location	Comments
Case	580			G	$13,500	10/06	ECMO	Extendahoe
Case	580			G	$14,000	10/06	ECMO	Extendahoe
Case	580			G	$28,500	3/06	NWIL	Diesel
Case	580B			G	$6,750	3/06	SCIN	Backhoe, canopy, OROPS
Case	580B			G	$42,500	11/06	SCCA	ROPS, 30" bucket
Case	580C			G	$6,000	11/06	SCCA	Loader, EROPS, 12"
Case	580C		5,740	G	$7,500	11/06	SETN	24" bucket
Case	580C			G	$8,500	3/06	SCIN	Standard hoe
Case	580C			G	$8,500	9/06	NEIN	Forklift, diesel, cab
Case	580C			G	$9,000	7/06	WCCA	Bucket, canopy, 24" hoe bucket
Case	580C		5,822	F	$9,100	8/06	NWOH	Backhoe, cab
Case	580C			G	$9,500	11/06	SWCA	Canopy
Case	580C			G	$13,000	3/06	WCWA	Loader backhoe, 80" gp bucket, OROPS
Case	580D			G	$5,500	7/06	ECNY	TLB, diesel, OROPS, digging bucket
Case	580D		622	G	$9,500	3/06	ECIN	Loader backhoe, canopy
Case	580E			G	$7,750	9/06	WCTX	TLB, diesel, EROPS, Extendahoe, gp bucket
Case	580E			G	$14,250	5/06	SWCA	4-in-1 bucket, center mounted leveler blade, Gannon rear scraper, canopy
Case	580K			G	$9,500	11/06	SWCA	4-in-1 bucket, canopy
Case	580K			F	$10,500	3/06	NCMN	
Case	580K			G	$10,500	8/06	WCTX	TLB, diesel, EROPS, digging bucket
Case	580K		5,284	G	$11,000	9/06	SECA	
Case	580K			G	$11,000	11/06	SWCA	Canopy
Case	580K			G	$11,500	3/06	ECMI	2×4, cab, Extendacab, fresh paint
Case	580K			G	$12,500	9/06	NEIN	2WD, loader backhoe
Case	580K			G	$13,000	5/06	SWCA	Loader backhoe
Case	580K			G	$13,500	9/06	NEIN	Cab
Case	580K			G	$13,800	3/06	SCIN	4WD, backhoe, loader, canopy, OROPS
Case	580K			G	$14,500	9/06	NEIN	TLB, cab/heat, Extendahoe, 4WD
Case	580K			G	$15,500	9/06	SWCA	Loader backhoe, canopy
Case	580K		3,550	G	$16,500	12/06	ECMN	4WD, Extendahoe, EROPS, 30' bucket, rear rack
Case	580K	1993		G	$12,000	9/06	NCMI	2WD diesel backhoe, Extendahoe, enclosed cab
Case	580L			G	$22,500	8/06	WCTX	TLB, diesel, EROPS, digging bucket
Case	580L		3,643	G	$23,500	8/06	SETN	Loader backhoe, cab, 4WD, Extendahoe
Case	580L			G	$26,000	9/06	SECA	
Case	580L		1,900	G	$31,000	3/06	ECIN	4WD, e-stick, cab
Case	580L	1997		G	$21,500	8/06	WCTX	TLB, diesel, ROPS, 18" digging bucket
Case	580L	1998		G	$20,500	9/06	WCTX	TLB, diesel, OROPS, standard hoe, digging bucket
Case	580L	1999	2,288	G	$22,500	9/06	NEIN	Series 2 TLB, standard hoe, canopy, gp bucket
Case	580L	2000		G	$24,000	8/06	WCTX	TLB, 4WD, diesel, OROPS, standard hoe
Case	580L	2000		G	$24,500	9/06	WCTX	TLB, diesel, OROPS, standard hoe, digging bucket
Case	580L	2000		G	$25,000	1/06	WCOH	Series II, 4WD diesel, gp bucket
Case	580L	2000		G	$25,000	1/06	WCOH	TLB, 4WD, diesel, EROPS, gp bucket, digging bucket
Case	580L	2000		G	$25,500	7/06	WCPA	TLB, diesel, EROPS, digging bucket
Case	580L	2000		G	$29,000	7/06	ECNY	TLB, 4WD, diesel, EROPS
Case	580L	2000		G	$29,000	1/06	WCOH	Series II, 4WD diesel, gp bucket
Case	580L	2000		G	$29,000	1/06	WCOH	TLB, 4WD, diesel, EROPS, gp bucket, digging bucket
Case	580L	2000		G	$30,000	10/06	WCFL	TLB, 4WD, diesel, EROPS, gp bucket, digging bucket
Case	580M			G	$36,000	8/06	WCTX	OROPS, digging bucket, TLB, 4WD, diesel

Construction Equipment

Make	Model	Year	Hrs.	Cond.	Price	Sale	Location	Comments
Case	580M			G	$37,000	7/06	ECNY	TLB, 4WD, diesel, EROPS, Extendahoe
Case	580M	2003	800	G	$27,000	8/06	SEPA	Loader/backhoe, MFWD, CAH, turbo, Extendahoe
Case	580M	2004		G	$40,000	7/06	ECNY	TLB, 4WD, diesel, EROPS, Extendahoe
Case	580SK			G	$20,000	9/06	SECA	Enclosed cab
Case	580SK	1993		G	$16,000	3/06	WCWA	Turbo loader backhoe, 4WD, Extendahoe, gp bucket, OROPS
Case	580SL	1997		G	$9,000	11/06	SECA	4WD, 4-in-1 bucket, canopy, Extendahoe
Case	580SL	1999		G	$29,000	3/06	WCWA	Loader backhoe, 4WD, Extendahoe
Case	580 Super E			G	$8,500	9/06	NEIN	Cab, 2WD
Case	580 Super E		3,283	G	$8,500	11/06	SWCA	4-in-1 bucket, Gannon rear scraper
Case	580 Super E			G	$11,000	5/06	SWCA	Loader backhoe, Extendahoe, canopy
Case	580 Super E		4,822	G	$11,200	11/06	ECIL	Backhoe
Case	580 Super E			G	$12,500	11/06	SECA	4-in-1 bucket, canopy, Gannon scraper
Case	580 Super E			G	$15,000	5/06	SWCA	Loader backhoe, Extendahoe, canopy
Case	580 Super E			G	$15,000	11/06	SECA	Canopy, 4-in-1 bucket, Gannon scraper
Case	580 Super E	1983	3,850	G	$16,900	3/06	NCIA	Backhoe w/ cab & loader, 22" backhoe bucket
Case	580 Super K			G	$14,000	9/06	WCTX	TLB, diesel, OROPS
Case	580 Super K			G	$14,500	9/06	NEIN	TLB, cab, 2WD, standard hoe
Case	580 Super K			G	$15,000	8/06	WCTX	TLB, 4WD, diesel, OROPS
Case	580 Super K		3,361	G	$15,000	5/06	SWCA	Loader backhoe, canopy
Case	580 Super K			G	$15,500	3/06	SCIN	Backhoe, cab, 36" & 18" buckets
Case	580 Super K		5,741	G	$15,500	5/06	SWCA	Loader backhoe, canopy
Case	580 Super K			G	$19,000	11/06	SCCA	Loader, 4WD, Extendahoe, turbo
Case	580 Super K			G	$19,750	3/06	ECIN	4WD, e-stick, cab
Case	580 Super K		3,400	G	$20,250	9/06	NEIN	TLB, 4WD, cab, Extendahoe
Case	580 Super K			G	$22,000	11/06	SCCA	4WD, Extendahoe
Case	580 Super L		5,501	G	$18,000	11/06	SETN	4WD, OROPS, 24" rear bucket
Case	580 Super L			G	$19,500	9/06	WCTX	TLB, diesel, OROPS, street pads, digging bucket
Case	580 Super L			G	$21,500	10/06	SWOH	TLB, 4WD, diesel, EROPS, Extendahoe
Case	580 Super L			G	$22,000	8/06	WCTX	TLB, EROPS, digging bucket, ride control
Case	580 Super L			G	$22,000	12/06	NEMN	Extendahoe
Case	580 Super L			G	$23,000	9/06	WCTX	TLB, diesel, ROPS, digging bucket
Case	580 Super L			G	$23,500	8/06	WCTX	TLB, EROPS, digging bucket, ride control
Case	580 Super L			G	$24,000	1/06	WCOH	Loader backhoe, 4WD, diesel, EROPS
Case	580 Super L			G	$24,000	8/06	WCTX	TLB, EROPS, digging bucket, ride control
Case	580 Super L			G	$24,000	9/06	NEIN	TLB, Extendahoe, cab, 4WD
Case	580 Super L			G	$24,000	1/06	WCOH	TLB, 4WD, diesel, EROPS, Extendahoe
Case	580 Super L			G	$25,000	8/06	WCTX	TLB, EROPS, digging bucket, ride control
Case	580 Super L			G	$25,500	1/06	WCOH	TLB, 4WD, diesel
Case	580 Super L			G	$25,500	8/06	WCTX	TLB, diesel, EROPS, ride control, digging bucket
Case	580 Super L			G	$25,500	1/06	WCOH	TLB, 4WD, diesel, EROPS, Extendahoe
Case	580 Super L		3,290	G	$26,500	9/06	SECA	
Case	580 Super L		3,700	G	$27,000	9/06	NEIN	TLB, 4WD, Extendahoe
Case	580 Super L		2,103	G	$30,500	8/06	WCTX	TLB, 4WD, diesel, OROPS
Case	580 Super L			G	$32,000	1/06	WCOH	TLB, 4WD, diesel, EROPS
Case	580 Super L			G	$32,000	1/06	WCOH	TLB, 4WD, diesel, EROPS, 4-in-1 bucket
Case	580 Super L	1996	3,469	G	$20,000	5/06	SWCA	Loader backhoe, canopy
Case	580 Super L	1996		G	$20,000	10/06	NCWI	TLB, 4WD, diesel, EROPS, Extendahoe, digging bucket
Case	580 Super L	1998		G	$22,000	8/06	WCTX	TLB, 4WD, diesel, OROPS

Construction Equipment

Make	Model	Year	Hrs.	Cond.	Price	Sale	Location	Comments
Case	580 Super L	1998		G	$23,000	3/06	ECIN	Extendahoe, ride control
Case	580 Super L	1998		G	$24,000	8/06	WCTX	TLB, 4WD, diesel, OROPS
Case	580 Super L	1998		G	$24,000	9/06	WCTX	TLB, 4×4, diesel, OROPS
Case	580 Super L	1998		G	$25,000	8/06	WCTX	TLB, diesel, ROPS
Case	580 Super L	1998		G	$26,000	8/06	WCTX	TLB, diesel, ROPS
Case	580 Super L	1999		G	$24,500	8/06	WCTX	TLB, 4WD, diesel, OROPS
Case	580 Super L	1999	4,440	G	$24,500	9/06	SECA	
Case	580 Super L	1999		G	$24,500	9/06	WCTX	TLB, 4×4, diesel, ride control, gp bucket
Case	580 Super L	1999		G	$25,500	9/06	WCTX	TLB, 4×4, diesel, ride control, gp bucket
Case	580 Super L	1999		G	$28,500	1/06	WCOH	TLB, 4WD, diesel, EROPS
Case	580 Super L	1999		G	$28,500	1/06	WCOH	TLB, 4WD, EROPS, Extendahoe, 24" digging bucket
Case	580 Super L	2000		G	$26,500	7/06	ECNY	TLB, 4WD, diesel, EROPS, digging bucket
Case	580 Super L	2000	1,538	E	$40,500	1/06	ECIL	Backhoe, Series 2, Extendahoe, 4×4, comfort cab, heat, ride control, 7' hyd. bucket on front, 24" backhoe bucket, one owner, shedded
Case	580 Super L	2001	2,561	G	$27,500	11/06	SCCA	4W, EROPS
Case	580 Super M			G	$29,500	9/06	WCTX	TLB, diesel, EROPS, digging bucket
Case	580 Super M	2001		G	$33,000	11/06	SCCA	4WD, aux. hyd.
Case	580 Super M	2001	1,946	G	$41,000	9/06	SECA	
Case	580 Super M	2002		G	$30,000	10/06	SWOH	TLB, 4WD, diesel, EROPS
Case	580 Super M	2002	1,737	G	$34,000	9/06	WCTX	TLB, 4×4, diesel, OROPS
Case	580 Super M	2002	1,737	G	$34,000	9/06	WCTX	TLB, 4×4, diesel, OROPS
Case	580 Super M	2002	1,440	G	$36,000	9/06	WCTX	TLB, 4×4, diesel, OROPS
Case	580 Super M	2002		G	$45,500	1/06	WCOH	Loader backhoe, 4WD, diesel, EROPS
Case	580 Super M	2003		G	$36,000	10/06	NCWI	TLB, 4WD, diesel, EROPS, digging bucket, Extendahoe, 4-in-1 bucket
Case	580 Super M	2003		G	$37,500	9/06	WCTX	TLB, 4×4, diesel, EROPS
Case	580 Super M	2004		G	$35,000	10/06	WCFL	TLB, 4WD, diesel
Case	580 Super M	2004		G	$36,000	10/06	WCFL	TLB, 4WD, turbo diesel, EROPS, gp bucket, digging bucket
Case	585E			G	$11,000	1/06	WCCA	48" forks, 2 stage
Case	586			G	$13,500	8/06	SEPA	Diesel, forklift, ROPS, 6,000-lb. capacity, 21' lift, 3-stage mast
Case	586E			G	$9,250	1/06	WCOH	Forklift, 4WD, ROPS, 21' mast
Case	586E			G	$9,250	1/06	WCOH	Forklift, 4WD, diesel, ROPS, 21' mast
Case	586E			G	$12,500	10/06	WCFL	Diesel, forklift, OROPS
Case	586E		2,921	G	$14,500	9/06	SECA	RT forklift
Case	586E			G	$15,500	1/06	WCOH	Forklift, 4WD, ROPS, 21' mast
Case	586E			G	$15,500	1/06	WCOH	Forklift, 4WD, diesel, ROPS, 21' mast
Case	586E	1998		G	$13,500	10/06	WCFL	4×4, diesel, forklift, ROPS, 3-stage mast
Case	586G	2000	2,081	G	$18,000	9/06	WCTX	Forklift, diesel, OROPS, 6,000-lb. capacity, 21.5' mast, forks
Case	590			G	$15,000	9/06	SECA	
Case	590			G	$17,000	9/06	WCTX	TLB, OROPS, Extendahoe, digging bucket
Case	590			G	$20,500	7/06	ECNY	TLB, 4WD, turbo, EROPS, standard hoe, digging bucket
Case	590	1998		G	$19,500	10/06	SWOH	TLB, 4WD, diesel, EROPS, digging bucket
Case	590	2003		G	$36,000	10/06	WCFL	TLB, 4WD, turbo diesel, EROPS, aux. hyd., ride control, digging bucket
Case	590 Super L			G	$17,500	9/06	WCTX	TLB, diesel, ROPS, digging bucket
Case	590 Super L			G	$25,000	7/06	ECNY	Loader backhoe, 4WD, diesel, EROPS, Extendahoe
Case	590 Super L			F	$27,000	9/06	NEIN	TLB, 4WD, cab, Extendahoe

Construction Equipment

Make	Model	Year	Hrs.	Cond.	Price	Sale	Location	Comments
Case	590 Super L			G	$28,000	10/06	NCWI	TLB
Case	590 Super L	1998		F	$25,000	1/06	SEPA	Backhoe loader, MFWD, Series II, Extendahoe, CAH, fair rubber
Case	590 Super L	1998		G	$30,500	10/06	WCFL	TLB, 4WD, diesel, EROPS, Extendahoe, gp bucket, digging bucket
Case	590 Super L	2000		G	$17,000	8/06	WCTX	TLB, diesel, EROPS
Case	590 Super L	2000		G	$28,500	7/06	ECNY	EROPS, TLB, 4WD, diesel, Extendahoe
Case	621		3,000	G	$44,000	8/06	SEPA	Wheel loader, CAH, average rubber
Case	621			G	$46,000	9/06	NEIN	Tool carrier, cab, radial tires, hyd. coupler, gp bucket
Case	621	2001	875	G	$53,000	7/06	ECNY	Rubber-tired loader, diesel, EROPS, third valve, air
Case	621	2004		G	$77,500	1/06	WCOH	Rubber-tired loader, diesel
Case	621	2004		G	$77,500	1/06	WCOH	Rubber-tired loader, diesel, cab, air, gp bucket
Case	621C	2001		G	$50,000	1/06	WCOH	Rubber-tired loader, diesel, EROPS, ride control, third valve hyd., forks
Case	680C			G	$4,000	7/06	WCCA	Loader backhoe, canopy, 24" hoe bucket
Case	721			G	$25,000	9/06	NEIN	Cab
Case	750			G	$4,000	12/06	WCIL	Crawler w/ bucket, street pads, uses some oil
Case	750	2003		G	$54,500	1/06	WCOH	Crawler, diesel, OROPS, 6-way blade
Case	750	2004		G	$70,500	1/06	WCOH	Crawler, diesel, cab, air
Case	760			G	$1,700	11/06	SETN	Leveling blade
Case	760			G	$8,250	9/06	WCTX	Trencher, 4WD, diesel, backhoe cable plow
Case	821			G	$38,000	1/06	WCOH	Rubber-tired loader, diesel, cab, air, 4-cubic-yard bucket
Case	821	1992		G	$25,500	3/06	ECMI	Cab, 3.5-yard gp bucket, fresh paint, needs minor trans. work
Case	821	2000		G	$56,000	1/06	WCOH	Rubber-tired loader, diesel, EROPS, third valve
Case	821	2000		G	$56,000	1/06	WCOH	Rubber-tired loader, diesel, EROPS, third valve, gp bucket
Case	821	2000		G	$60,000	1/06	WCOH	Rubber-tired loader, diesel, EROPS, third valve
Case	821	2000		G	$60,000	1/06	WCOH	Rubber-tired loader, diesel, EROPS, third valve, gp bucket
Case	821B			G	$38,000	1/06	WCOH	Rubber-tired loader, diesel, cab, air, 4-cubic-yard gp bucket
Case	850			G	$9,250	9/06	NWTN	Crawler dozer
Case	850			G	$15,500	6/06	NEIN	6-way blade
Case	850	2003		G	$58,500	1/06	WCOH	Diesel, EROPS, 6-way blade
Case	850	2003		G	$74,000	1/06	WCOH	Crawler, diesel, EROPS, air, 6-way blade
Case	850B			G	$5,000	12/06	NEMN	Excavator
Case	850B			G	$16,500	9/06	NWTN	Crawler dozer, 6-way blade, OROPS, brush guard
Case	850B	1978		G	$15,500	7/06	NWOH	Dozer, powershift trans., 6-way blade, newer undercarriage & trans.
Case	850D			G	$13,000	7/06	ECNY	Crawler, diesel, OROPS, 6-way blade
Case	850D			G	$17,000	9/06	NEIN	Crawler, canopy, sweeps, 6-way blade
Case	850D	1987		G	$15,750	3/06	ECMI	82 hp., Cummins diesel, ROPS
Case	850G			G	$35,000	9/06	NEIN	Crawler, canopy, sweeps, long track
Case	855D			G	$14,500	3/06	ECIN	Crawler, diesel, canopy, sweeps, gp bucket
Case	85XT			G	$12,500	8/06	WCTX	Diesel, roll cage, aux. hyd., gp bucket
Case	880B		4,000	G	$19,500	9/06	NEIN	Excavator, table leveler, Cat controls, 2 buckets, Cummins diesel
Case	880C			G	$6,500	1/06	WCOH	New diesel engine, cab, digging bucket
Case	880D			G	$10,000	1/06	WCOH	Hyd. excavator, Cummins diesel, cab, hyd. cab leveler
Case	9010B	1995		G	$31,000	3/06	SCIN	Excavator
Case	9020B			G	$25,000	3/06	ECIN	30" bucket

Construction Equipment

Make	Model	Year	Hrs.	Cond.	Price	Sale	Location	Comments
Case	9030B			G	$32,000	11/06	SWCA	Hyd. excavator
Case	9030B		6,567	G	$33,000	7/06	WCTN	Excavator
Case	9030B	1995		G	$39,000	3/06	ECIN	Excavator, diesel, pilot controls
Case	9030B	1997		G	$45,500	1/06	WCOH	Hyd. excavator, diesel
Case	9030B	1999		G	$25,500	8/06	WCTX	Hyd. excavator, diesel, cab, digging bucket
Case	9030B	1999		G	$25,500	8/06	WCTX	Hyd. excavator, diesel, cab, digging bucket
Case	921C			G	$40,000	10/06	NCWI	Rubber-tired loader, diesel, EROPS, gp bucket
Case	921C	1999		G	$85,000	1/06	WCOH	Rubber-tired loader, diesel, EROPS, heat, third valve hyd.
Case	921C	1999		G	$85,000	1/06	WCOH	Rubber-tired loader, diesel, EROPS, heat, third valve hyd. gp bucket
Case	DH7			G	$6,500	5/06	SEWY	Trencher, 6' bar, D130 hoe, 20" bucket
Case	Super K	1992		G	$23,500	3/06	SCIN	Backhoe, cab, 4-in-1 bucket, Extendahoe
Case	W14	1980		G	$12,500	5/06	SEND	Feedlot special, cab, heat, 1½-yard bucket, grapple
Case	W14B			G	$10,000	1/06	WCOH	Rubber-tired loader, diesel, EROPS, gp bucket
Case	W14B			G	$13,500	10/06	NCWI	Rubber-tired loader, diesel, EROPS, gp bucket, forks
Case	W18			G	$7,700	1/06	WCOH	Rubber-tired loader, diesel, EROPS, gp bucket
Case	W20			G	$14,000	7/06	ECNY	Rubber-tired loader, diesel, ROPS, gp bucket
Case	W20			G	$19,000	7/06	WCCA	Tink rollout bucket, canopy
Case	W20C			G	$8,750	1/06	WCOH	Rubber-tired loader, diesel, EROPS, gp bucket
Case	W20C			G	$19,500	12/06	WCMN	Payloader, diesel, 3-yard bucket
Case	W24C		2,187	F	$8,200	9/06	NECO	Payloader, clam shell bucket, diesel
Case	W24C			F	$9,200	10/06	NECO	Payloader, diesel, 2.5-yard clam shell bucket
Case	W26B			F	$4,500	3/06	ECIN	Rubber-tired loader, diesel, cab
Case	W26B			G	$7,000	9/06	NEIN	Rubber-tired loader, cab, gp bucket
Case	W36			F	$6,000	6/06	NECO	Payloader, cab, 3.5-yard bucket, diesel
Case	W7			G	$6,000	8/06	WCMN	Loader, all WD, 1½- to 2-yard bucket, cab heat, locally owned, 15.5 rubber
Caterpillar	112			G	$4,000	8/06	WCTX	Motor grader, diesel, EROPS
Caterpillar	112			G	$14,000	8/06	WCTX	Motor grader, EROPS
Caterpillar	112E			G	$9,000	8/06	WCTX	Motor grader, diesel, EROPS, sliding moldboard
Caterpillar	12			F	$1,500	2/06	WCSD	Road grader, yellow
Caterpillar	12			P	$2,000	3/06	SWNE	Motor grader, needs work, 12' blade, 13:00-24 tires
Caterpillar	12			G	$5,500	8/06	WCTX	Motor grader, diesel, cab, air, scarifier
Caterpillar	120	1977		G	$13,000	1/06	NECO	14' boards
Caterpillar	120G			G	$49,500	8/06	WCTX	Motor grader, diesel, EROPS, Low Pro cab, 12' sliding moldboard
Caterpillar	12E			F	$2,000	3/06	SEIA	Motor grader
Caterpillar	12E			G	$5,800	12/06	ECMN	12' blade
Caterpillar	12E			G	$9,000	9/06	NEIN	Grader
Caterpillar	12F			G	$8,500	11/06	SETN	EROPS
Caterpillar	12F			G	$11,000	5/06	ECNE	Motor grader, powershift, 14' blade, 14:00-24TG, 10-ply tires
Caterpillar	12F			G	$13,500	11/06	SETN	EROPS
Caterpillar	12F			G	$16,500	8/06	WCTX	EROPS, diesel, motor grader
Caterpillar	12G			G	$42,000	5/06	SWCA	Motor grader, 14' moldboard, side shift, push block, canopy
Caterpillar	12G			G	$44,000	9/06	WCTX	Motor grader, Cat diesel, EROPS, front scarifier
Caterpillar	12G			G	$49,000	5/06	SWCA	Motor grader, 14' moldboard, side shift, push block, canopy
Caterpillar	14	2000		G	$170,000	9/06	WCTX	Motor grader, diesel, push block, rear-mounted ripper
Caterpillar	14	2000		G	$170,000	9/06	WCTX	Motor grader, diesel, push block, rear-mounted ripper

Construction Equipment

Make	Model	Year	Hrs.	Cond.	Price	Sale	Location	Comments
Caterpillar	14	2000		G	$175,000	10/06	WCFL	Motor grader, diesel, ROPS
Caterpillar	140G			G	$30,500	4/06	WCSD	Road grader, runs
Caterpillar	140G			G	$40,000	11/06	SECA	14', cab, heat
Caterpillar	140G		1,635	G	$48,000	11/06	SWCA	Motor grader, 14' moldboard, ripper, cab
Caterpillar	140G		21,731	G	$75,000	11/06	SWCA	Motor grader, 14' moldboard, ripper, cab
Caterpillar	140G		8,412	G	$83,000	5/06	SWCA	Motor grader, 14' moldboard, side shift, push block, cab, air
Caterpillar	140H		4,837	G	$103,000	7/06	WCTN	Road grader, cab, blade Pro Specta physics motor grader control system
Caterpillar	140H		12,239	G	$125,000	5/06	SWCA	Motor grader, 14' moldboard, side shift, accumulator, push block, laser, cab, ripper
Caterpillar	140H	1995	13,288	G	$80,000	11/06	SCCA	Motor grader
Caterpillar	140H	1995	13,288	G	$82,500	11/06	SCCA	Motor grader
Caterpillar	140H	1995	13,288	G	$90,000	11/06	SCCA	Motor grader
Caterpillar	140H	1995	13,288	G	$92,500	11/06	SCCA	Motor grader
Caterpillar	140H	2000	8,416	G	$134,000	11/06	SWCA	Motor grader
Caterpillar	14D			P	$1,600	12/06	WCMN	Road grader, needs repair & tires
Caterpillar	14G			G	$40,000	3/06	WCWA	Motor grader, 14' snow wing, front dozer blade, accumulators, articulating steering
Caterpillar	14G			G	$51,000	1/06	WCPA	EROPS, grader, 14' moldboard, hyd. sideshift
Caterpillar	14G			G	$52,000	7/06	WCCA	Grader, 14' moldboard, accumulator, cab, air
Caterpillar	212			F	$800	9/06	NEIN	Grader, diesel, pony motor, cab
Caterpillar	215			G	$14,500	9/06	NEIN	Excavator, plumbed
Caterpillar	22			F	$750	8/06	SCIL	
Caterpillar	22			G	$19,500	8/06	SCIL	
Caterpillar	225			G	$12,500	3/06	SCIN	48" dirt bucket
Caterpillar	225			G	$14,000	9/06	NEIN	Excavator
Caterpillar	225			G	$16,000	6/06	NEIN	48" bucket
Caterpillar	225			G	$21,500	9/06	NEIN	Excavator, pilot controls
Caterpillar	225B		11,222	G	$18,000	5/06	SWCA	Hyd. excavator, standard undercarriage, medium stick
Caterpillar	225BLC			G	$33,500	10/06	WCFL	Hyd. excavator, diesel, cab, long undercarriage
Caterpillar	225BLC			G	$33,500	10/06	WCFL	Hyd. excavator, diesel, cab, long undercarriage
Caterpillar	226	2003		G	$12,500	11/06	SECA	Bucket, canopy, aux. hyd.
Caterpillar	226	2003		G	$12,500	11/06	SECA	Bucket, canopy, aux. hyd.
Caterpillar	226	2004		G	$12,500	10/06	SCPA	Diesel
Caterpillar	226	2004		G	$13,000	10/06	SCPA	Diesel
Caterpillar	229		12,591	G	$25,000	12/06	WCIL	Trackhoe, 3208 Cat motor
Caterpillar	231D			G	$22,500	6/06	NEIN	60" bucket
Caterpillar	235			G	$62,500	1/06	WCNH	Hyd. excavator, diesel, cab, 44" bucket
Caterpillar	250E			G	$58,000	11/06	SETN	Off-road dump track, articulating
Caterpillar	257	2003	1,400	G	$16,500	9/06	NEIN	Track loader
Caterpillar	257	2003	1,500	G	$17,500	9/06	NEIN	Track loader
Caterpillar	257	2003		G	$18,500	9/06	NEIN	Track loader
Caterpillar	257	2003	2,669	G	$19,500	3/06	ECIN	Tracks, cab, air
Caterpillar	257	2004		G	$20,000	10/06	WCFL	Rubber-tired loader, diesel, roll cage, aux. hyd.
Caterpillar	257	2005	1,100	G	$22,500	10/06	WCFL	Rubber-tired loader, diesel, roll cage, aux. hyd.
Caterpillar	277			G	$14,500	9/06	WCTX	Diesel, roll cage, aux. hyd.
Caterpillar	277	2003		G	$22,000	7/06	ECNY	Rubber track, roll cage, aux. hyd.
Caterpillar	302.5	2003		G	$12,000	11/06	SECA	Mini excavator, S dozer

WHAT'S IT WORTH?

Construction Equipment

Make	Model	Year	Hrs.	Cond.	Price	Sale	Location	Comments
Caterpillar	302.5	2003		G	$12,000	11/06	SECA	Mini excavator, S dozer
Caterpillar	307			G	$14,000	9/06	WCTX	Hyd. excavator, diesel, canopy, blade
Caterpillar	307			G	$17,000	10/06	NCWI	Hyd. excavator, diesel, cab, blade, aux. hyd.
Caterpillar	307			G	$18,000	10/06	WCFL	Hyd. excavator, diesel
Caterpillar	307			G	$18,500	7/06	ECNY	Hyd. excavator, diesel, cab, air, blade, offset boom
Caterpillar	307			G	$18,500	1/06	WCOH	Hyd. excavator, diesel, cab, blade, offset boom
Caterpillar	307			G	$19,000	7/06	WCPA	Hyd. excavator, diesel, cab, blade, offset boom, rubber tracks
Caterpillar	307	2001		G	$36,000	1/06	WCNH	Hyd. excavator, diesel
Caterpillar	307	2001		G	$36,000	1/06	WCNH	Excavator, diesel, cab, air, blade
Caterpillar	311			G	$30,000	9/06	WCTX	Hyd. excavator, diesel, cab, air, 20" pads, 34" digging bucket
Caterpillar	311			G	$30,500	7/06	ECNY	Hyd. excavator, diesel, cab, long stick, digging bucket
Caterpillar	311	2001		G	$42,500	10/06	WCFL	Hyd. excavator
Caterpillar	311	2001		G	$47,500	7/06	ECNY	Hyd. excavator, Cat 3064, 80-hp. diesel, cab, air
Caterpillar	311	2002		G	$45,000	1/06	WCNH	Hyd. excavator, diesel, cab, air, 20" pads
Caterpillar	311	2002		G	$45,000	1/06	WCNH	Hyd. excavator, diesel, cab, air, 20" pads, third valve
Caterpillar	311B	1996		G	$36,500	7/06	WCPA	Hyd excavator, diesel, cab, air, third valve
Caterpillar	311B	2000		G	$39,000	1/06	WCNH	Hyd. excavator, diesel, cab, air
Caterpillar	311B	2000		G	$39,000	1/06	WCNH	Hyd. excavator, diesel, cab, air, 20" pads
Caterpillar	312			G	$27,000	3/06	ECIN	Manual thumb
Caterpillar	312		5,501	G	$28,000	11/06	SWCA	Hyd. excavator
Caterpillar	312			G	$29,500	9/06	NEIN	Excavator
Caterpillar	312			G	$30,000	10/06	SWOH	Hyd. excavator, diesel, air, third valve
Caterpillar	312			G	$31,000	9/06	NEIN	Excavator
Caterpillar	312			G	$31,500	1/06	WCOH	Hyd. excavator, diesel, cab, air, 36" digging bucket
Caterpillar	312	1996		G	$32,500	7/06	WCPA	Hyd. excavator, cab
Caterpillar	312	2001		G	$48,500	10/06	WCFL	Hyd. excavator, diesel
Caterpillar	312	2001		G	$55,500	1/06	WCNH	Hyd. excavator, diesel, air, 20" pads
Caterpillar	312	2001		G	$55,500	1/06	WCNH	Hyd. excavator, diesel, cab, air, 20" pads
Caterpillar	312	2001		G	$56,500	7/06	ECNY	Hyd. excavator, Cat 3064T diesel
Caterpillar	312	2002		G	$53,000	8/06	WCTX	Hyd. excavator
Caterpillar	312	2002		G	$53,000	8/06	WCTX	Hyd. excavator, diesel, cab, air, 20" pads
Caterpillar	312	2005		G	$61,500	10/06	WCFL	Hyd. excavator, diesel
Caterpillar	312B			G	$37,000	9/06	NEIN	Excavator
Caterpillar	312B			G	$38,500	1/06	WCNH	Hyd. excavator, diesel, cab
Caterpillar	312B			G	$38,500	1/06	WCNH	Hyd. excavator, diesel, cab, digging bucket
Caterpillar	312B	1996	5,500	G	$32,000	12/06	ECMN	36" bucket, 28" pads, 8' stick w/ thumb
Caterpillar	312B	1997		G	$37,500	10/06	NCWI	Hyd. excavator, diesel, cab, air, 24" pads, 36" digging bucket
Caterpillar	312B	1997		G	$41,000	7/06	ECNY	Hyd. excavator, Cat 3064T diesel, 84 hp., cab, air, digging bucket
Caterpillar	312B	1999		G	$42,500	10/06	WCFL	Hyd. excavator
Caterpillar	312B	2000		G	$41,000	8/06	SEPA	Diesel, hyd. excavator, cab, air, 20" pads
Caterpillar	312B	2001		G	$40,000	1/06	WCNH	Hyd. excavator, diesel, cab, digging bucket
Caterpillar	312B	2001		G	$40,000	1/06	WCNH	Hyd. excavator, diesel, cab, digging bucket
Caterpillar	315L			G	$28,000	10/06	WCFL	Hyd. excavator, diesel, cab, air
Caterpillar	315L			G	$30,000	11/06	ECND	Excavator, standard stick, good undercarriage

Construction Equipment

Make	Model	Year	Hrs.	Cond.	Price	Sale	Location	Comments
Caterpillar	315L			G	$35,000	7/06	ECNY	Hyd. excavator, diesel, cab, long undercarriage, reach boom
Caterpillar	315L	1999		E	$43,000	8/06	WCTX	Hyd excavator, diesel, long undercarriage
Caterpillar	315L	1999		E	$43,000	8/06	WCTX	Hyd. excavator, diesel, cab, long undercarriage
Caterpillar	320	2001		G	$81,000	1/06	WCNH	Hyd. excavator, diesel, cab, air, long undercarriage
Caterpillar	320	2002		G	$85,000	10/06	WCFL	Hyd. excavator, diesel
Caterpillar	320	2002	2,586	G	$89,000	11/06	SWCA	Hyd. excavator
Caterpillar	320	2002		G	$130,000	3/06	WCWA	Log loader, Cat front w/ grapple, elevated cab
Caterpillar	320	2004		G	$108,500	1/06	WCNH	Hyd. excavator, diesel, cab, long undercarriage, Cat high-capacity bucket
Caterpillar	320B	2000		G	$90,000	3/06	WCWA	Log loader, Cat front w/ grapple. elevated cab
Caterpillar	320BL	1997		G	$54,000	1/06	WCNH	Hyd. excavator, diesel, cab, long undercarriage, digging bucket
Caterpillar	320BL	1999		G	$56,500	1/06	WCNH	Hyd. excavator, diesel, cab, long undercarriage, digging bucket
Caterpillar	320BL	2000	7,170	G	$56,000	9/06	NEIN	Excavator, plumbed w/ third valve, 54" bucket, 32" pads
Caterpillar	320BL	2001		G	$56,500	1/06	WCNH	Hyd. excavator, diesel, cab, long undercarriage, digging bucket
Caterpillar	320L			G	$39,500	1/06	WCPA	Hyd. excavator, diesel, cab
Caterpillar	320L			G	$42,500	7/06	ECNY	Hyd. excavator, diesel, cab, standard stick, reach boom
Caterpillar	322BL	1999		E	$65,000	8/06	WCTX	Hyd. excavator, diesel, long undercarriage
Caterpillar	322BL	1999		E	$65,000	8/06	WCTX	Hyd. excavator, diesel, cab, long undercarriage
Caterpillar	322L			G	$41,000	9/06	WCTX	Hyd. excavator, diesel, enclosed cab, long undercarriage
Caterpillar	322L	2004		G	$112,500	1/06	WCNH	Hyd. excavator, diesel, cab, air, long undercarriage, Cat high-capacity bucket, side cutters
Caterpillar	325			E	$350	10/06	NCWI	Ripper to fit Cat 325
Caterpillar	325B			G	$50,000	8/06	SEPA	Hyd. excavator, diesel, cab, long undercarriage
Caterpillar	325B	1999		E	$70,000	8/06	WCTX	Hyd. excavator, diesel, cab
Caterpillar	325L			G	$49,000	10/06	WCFL	Hyd. excavator, diesel
Caterpillar	325L	1999		E	$70,000	8/06	WCTX	Hyd. excavator, diesel, long undercarriage
Caterpillar	325L	2003		G	$122,500	10/06	WCFL	Hyd. excavator, diesel
Caterpillar	330BL		7,209	G	$70,000	7/06	WCTN	Excavator, new undercarriage
Caterpillar	330BL	1998		G	$62,000	9/06	NEIN	Excavator, quick coupler
Caterpillar	330BL	1999		G	$82,500	1/06	WCNH	Hyd. excavator, diesel, cab, air, long undercarriage, 34" digging bucket
Caterpillar	330BL	2000	6,700	G	$86,500	3/06	ECIN	Excavator, pilot controls
Caterpillar	330L			G	$46,000	9/06	WCTX	Hyd. excavator, diesel, enclosed cab, long undercarriage
Caterpillar	330L	1994		G	$70,000	9/06	NEIN	Excavator, quick attach, plumbed for third valve, 213 hydro hammer
Caterpillar	35			G	$300	8/06	SCIL	Crawler
Caterpillar	350L			G	$78,500	7/06	WCPA	Hyd. excavator, diesel, cab, long undercarriage
Caterpillar	40			P	$300	8/06	SCIL	Parts unit, dozer
Caterpillar	416			G	$10,000	3/06	ECIN	Canopy, loader backhoe
Caterpillar	416			P	$10,000	2/06	WCIL	Extendahoe backhoe, EROPS
Caterpillar	416			G	$10,700	10/06	WCFL	TLB
Caterpillar	416			G	$14,000	7/06	ECNY	TLB, gp bucket, diesel, 4WD, EROPS
Caterpillar	416			G	$15,000	9/06	SECA	
Caterpillar	416			G	$21,000	9/06	NEIN	Loader backhoe, 4WD, cab, Extendahoe, gp bucket
Caterpillar	416B			G	$15,500	11/06	SETN	24" bucket, Extendaboom

WHAT'S IT WORTH?

Construction Equipment

Make	Model	Year	Hrs.	Cond.	Price	Sale	Location	Comments
Caterpillar	416B			G	$16,500	11/06	SWCA	Extendahoe
Caterpillar	416B			G	$19,500	3/06	ECIN	Backhoe, cab, 4WD
Caterpillar	416B		5,154	G	$21,000	5/06	SWCA	Extendahoe, air
Caterpillar	416C		4,555	G	$27,250	7/06	WCTN	Backhoe loader, cab, 4WD, Extendahoe
Caterpillar	416C			G	$27,500	11/06	SWCA	4WD
Caterpillar	416C			G	$28,500	11/06	SWCA	4WD
Caterpillar	416C			G	$28,500	11/06	SWCA	4WD
Caterpillar	416C			G	$29,500	10/06	WCFL	4WD, diesel, EROPS, Extendahoe
Caterpillar	416C	1997		G	$29,500	10/06	WCFL	TLB, 4WD, turbo diesel, OROPS, standard stick, counterweight, digging bucket
Caterpillar	416C	1998		G	$26,000	7/06	ECNY	TLB, 4WD, diesel, EROPS, digging bucket
Caterpillar	416C	1999		G	$28,000	7/06	ECNY	TLB, 4WD, diesel, EROPS, Extendahoe, gp bucket
Caterpillar	416C	1999		G	$32,000	7/06	ECNY	TLB, 4WD, diesel, EROPS, Extendahoe
Caterpillar	416C	2000	5,638	G	$27,500	11/06	SWCA	4-in-1 bucket
Caterpillar	416C	2000		G	$30,000	7/06	ECNY	TLB, 4WD, diesel, EROPS, ride control, digging bucket
Caterpillar	416C	2000		G	$31,000	1/06	WCNH	TLB, 4WD, diesel, EROPS, quick coupler, Extendahoe, 24" rear-digging bucket, forks
Caterpillar	416C	2001		G	$32,000	5/06	SWCA	Loader backhoe, 4WD, 4-in-1 bucket, Extendahoe, cab, air
Caterpillar	420D	2001		G	$30,000	11/06	SWCA	Extendahoe
Caterpillar	420D	2002	2,794	G	$35,500	5/06	SWCA	Loader backhoe, 4-in-1 bucket, cab, air
Caterpillar	420D	2002		G	$36,000	10/06	WCFL	TLB, 4WD, diesel, OROPS, Extendahoe, gp bucket
Caterpillar	420D	2003		G	$42,000	8/06	WCTX	TLB, 4WD, diesel, EROPS, air, ride control
Caterpillar	420D	2003		G	$45,000	5/06	SWCA	Loader backhoe, 4WD, 4-in-1 bucket, canopy, Extendahoe
Caterpillar	420D	2003		G	$46,000	9/06	NEIN	TLB, cab, 4WD, Extendahoe
Caterpillar	420D	2004		G	$49,000	5/06	SWCA	Loader backhoe, 4WD, bucket, Extendahoe, canopy
Caterpillar	420D	2005		E	$52,500	7/06	ECNY	TLB, 4WD, diesel, EROPS, Extendahoe, digging bucket
Caterpillar	426			G	$10,750	11/06	SWCA	Canopy
Caterpillar	426B			G	$27,000	9/06	SECA	
Caterpillar	426B	1993		G	$17,000	3/06	WCWA	Turbo loader backhoe, gp bucket, Extendahoe, cab
Caterpillar	426B	1993		G	$17,500	3/06	WCWA	Turbo diesel, loader backhoe, gp bucket, Extendahoe, cab
Caterpillar	426B	1994		G	$17,000	3/06	WCWA	Turbo loader backhoe, gp bucket, Extendahoe, cab
Caterpillar	426B	1994		G	$20,000	10/06	WCMA	4WD, TLB, Cat diesel, EROPS, third valve
Caterpillar	426C		3,968	G	$26,000	9/06	SECA	Turbo, 4×4
Caterpillar	426C			G	$27,000	11/06	SETN	4WD, OROPS, 24" bucket, 36" bucket, 12" trench bucket
Caterpillar	426C	1997		G	$26,000	9/06	NEIN	TLB, 4WD, cab, Extendahoe
Caterpillar	426C	1998		G	$27,000	9/06	SECA	
Caterpillar	426C	2000	6,373	G	$22,000	12/06	ECMN	4×4 excavator, 89" loader bucket, EROPS, heat
Caterpillar	436B			G	$27,500	10/06	WCFL	4WD TLB
Caterpillar	44			F	$225	8/06	SCIL	Pt road grader
Caterpillar	44			F	$325	8/06	SCIL	Pt road grader
Caterpillar	446B		4,389	G	$24,000	11/06	SWCA	4WD
Caterpillar	446B			G	$55,500	5/06	SWCA	Loader backhoe, 4WD, 4-in-1 bucket, Extendahoe, canopy
Caterpillar	446B	1998	5,716	G	$26,500	11/06	SWCA	Backhoe, 4WD, 4-in-1
Caterpillar	50		3,751	G	$1,300	8/06	NECO	50B forklift, 40" forks
Caterpillar	50	2000	2,620	E	$13,750	12/06	WCMN	Forklift, 50', triple mast
Caterpillar	55			G	$7,350	8/06	SETN	Mini excavator, rubber tracks, front blade
Caterpillar	60			G	$900	8/06	SCIL	
Caterpillar	60			G	$12,000	11/06	NWMN	Scraper, 15 yard, hyd. conversion, diamond tires, hyd. push off

Construction Equipment

Make	Model	Year	Hrs.	Cond.	Price	Sale	Location	Comments
Caterpillar	60	1997		G	$4,500	7/06	ECNY	Forklift, diesel, 6,000-lb. capacity
Caterpillar	613			G	$6,250	7/06	ECNY	Motor scraper, Cat diesel, open canopy, elevated
Caterpillar	613			G	$9,500	3/06	ECIN	Canopy
Caterpillar	613			G	$10,000	3/06	ECIN	Scraper, canopy, diesel
Caterpillar	613C			G	$10,500	9/06	WCTX	Motor scraper, diesel, self-loading
Caterpillar	613C			G	$25,000	1/06	WCOH	Motor scraper, diesel, OROPS, open bowl
Caterpillar	613C			G	$25,000	1/06	WCOH	Motor scraper, diesel, OROPS, open bowl
Caterpillar	613C			G	$30,000	9/06	WCTX	Motor scraper, diesel, self-loading
Caterpillar	613C	1997	6,225	G	$102,000	8/06	WCNC	
Caterpillar	615			G	$35,000	3/06	ECIN	Scraper, canopy
Caterpillar	621			F	$6,500	3/06	SEIA	Scraper, 3306 6-cyl. engine conversion, powershift, 23H Series, good rubber
Caterpillar	631B		3,137	G	$9,000	12/06	NEMN	Scraper
Caterpillar	631B		3,137	G	$13,000	12/06	NEMN	Scraper
Caterpillar	70	1993		G	$14,500	3/06	ECIN	Excavator, 24" & 36" buckets
Caterpillar	824B			G	$10,500	11/06	SWCA	
Caterpillar	826C			G	$80,000	1/06	WCPA	Wheel compactor, 825 conversion, Cat diesel, EROPS
Caterpillar	826C			G	$110,000	1/06	WCPA	Wheel compactor, 825 conversion, Cat diesel, EROPS
Caterpillar	850	1986		G	$20,000	3/06	SCIN	Dozer, new trans., new engine
Caterpillar	892E	1996		G	$36,500	7/06	ECNY	Hyd. excavator, diesel, cab, long undercarriage, wide pads
Caterpillar	910		1,773	G	$8,000	5/06	SWCA	Rubber-tired loader, cab
Caterpillar	910		683	G	$12,750	5/06	SWCA	Rubber-tired loader, grapple bucket, canopy
Caterpillar	920			G	$14,000	5/06	SWCA	Rubber-tired loader, cab
Caterpillar	922B			G	$3,000	10/06	SENJ	Front end loader
Caterpillar	924F	1994	12,000	G	$26,000	12/06	NWIL	Wheel loader
Caterpillar	926		3,009	G	$25,000	11/06	SWCA	Rubber-tired loader, cab, air
Caterpillar	926E			G	$27,000	8/06	WCTX	Rubber-tired loader, diesel, EROPS, gp bucket
Caterpillar	926E			G	$27,000	8/06	WCTX	Rubber-tired loader, diesel, EROPS, gp bucket
Caterpillar	928F			G	$25,000	9/06	WCTX	Rubber-tired loader, diesel, EROPS, forks
Caterpillar	928F			G	$28,500	10/06	WCFL	Rubber-tired loader, diesel, EROPS, AIR forks
Caterpillar	928F	1998		G	$32,000	9/06	WCTX	Rubber-tired loader, diesel, EROPS, gp bucket
Caterpillar	928G	1997		G	$48,000	11/06	SWCA	Rubber-tired loader
Caterpillar	928G	2003		G	$71,000	8/06	WCTX	Gp bucket, rubber-tired loader
Caterpillar	928G	2003		H	$71,000	8/06	WCTX	Rubber-tired loader, diesel, EROPS, gp bucket
Caterpillar	928G	2004		G	$49,500	9/06	WCTX	Rubber-tired loader, diesel, EROPS, gp bucket
Caterpillar	928G	2004		G	$60,000	10/06	WCFL	Rubber-tired, diesel, EROPS
Caterpillar	930			G	$13,500	7/06	ECNY	Rubber-tired loader, diesel, EROPS, gp bucket
Caterpillar	930			G	$15,000	5/06	SWCA	Rubber-tired loader, canopy
Caterpillar	930			G	$15,500	5/06	SWCA	Rubber-tired loader, canopy
Caterpillar	930			G	$20,000	9/06	WCTX	Rubber-tired loader, diesel, EROPS, gp bucket
Caterpillar	930			G	$20,500	1/06	WCPA	Rubber-tired loader, diesel, EROPS, gp bucket
Caterpillar	930	2005		G	$125,000	7/06	ECNY	Rubber-tired loader, diesel, EROPS, air ride control, 3-yard gp bucket
Caterpillar	931	1994	3,200	F	$16,600	3/06	SEPA	931C, track loader, Series II, cab, air, heat, 3-way bucket
Caterpillar	931B			G	$15,000	11/06	SWCA	Crawler loader, canopy
Caterpillar	933			F	$4,900	6/06	NCIA	Track end loader, 1¼-yard bucket
Caterpillar	933			G	$8,300	6/06	NWIL	Loader bucket and shuttle clutch
Caterpillar	935C			G	$17,000	11/06	SWCA	Series II crawler loader, ripper
Caterpillar	936			G	$22,250	9/06	ECMN	EROPS

Construction Equipment

Make	Model	Year	Hrs.	Cond.	Price	Sale	Location	Comments
Caterpillar	936			G	$30,000	11/06	SWCA	Rubber-tired loader
Caterpillar	936	2001		G	$69,500	1/06	WCNH	Rubber-tired loader, diesel, EROPS, 3.65-cubic-yard gp bucket
Caterpillar	936E			G	$33,000	1/06	WCPA	Rubber-tired loader, diesel, EROPS, gp bucket
Caterpillar	938F	1997		G	$35,000	10/06	WCFL	Rubber-tired loader, diesel, EROPS
Caterpillar	938G	2005		G	$112,500	10/06	WCFL	Rubber-tired loader, EROPS
Caterpillar	939C			G	$21,000	8/06	SETN	Crawler loader, EROPS
Caterpillar	941			G	$5,400	6/06	ECSD	Crawler/loader
Caterpillar	950			G	$24,500	3/06	ECIN	Rubber-tired loader
Caterpillar	950B			G	$37,000	1/06	WCNH	Rubber-tired loader, diesel, EROPS, 4-cubic-yard gp bucket
Caterpillar	950B		10,876	G	$38,000	5/06	SWCA	Rubber-tired loader, cab
Caterpillar	950E		9,951	G	$40,000	5/06	SWCA	Rubber-tired loader, cab, air
Caterpillar	950E			G	$41,000	5/06	SWCA	Rubber-tired loader, cab, air
Caterpillar	950F			G	$39,500	7/06	ECNY	Rubber-tired loader, diesel, EROPS, gp bucket
Caterpillar	950F			G	$58,000	5/06	SWCA	Series II rubber-tired loader, cab, air
Caterpillar	950G			G	$160,000	7/06	ECNY	Rubber-tired loader, Cat 3126B 183 hp. diesel, EROPS, third valve hyd., gp bucket
Caterpillar	950G	1998	10,111	G	$61,000	11/06	SWCA	Rubber-tired loader, cab, air
Caterpillar	950G	1998	10,107	G	$87,000	5/06	SWCA	Rubber-tired loader, cab, air
Caterpillar	950G	2002		G	$107,000	8/06	WCTX	Rubber-tired loader, diesel, EROPS, gp bucket, air
Caterpillar	950G	2004		G	$120,000	8/06	WCTX	Rubber-tired loader, diesel, EROPS, gp bucket
Caterpillar	950G	2004	1,800	G	$139,500	7/06	ECNY	Rubber-tired loader, Cat 3126B 183-hp. diesel, EROPS, ride control
Caterpillar	951C		9,251	G	$6,000	12/06	NEMN	
Caterpillar	953			G	$15,500	10/06	SWOH	Crawler, Cat diesel, Remco rake, hyd. grapple, rear bumper guard, 3 hyd.
Caterpillar	953			G	$17,000	11/06	SETN	
Caterpillar	953			G	$21,000	8/06	SETN	
Caterpillar	953	1987		G	$9,750	12/06	ECMN	EROPS, ripper
Caterpillar	953C	1998		G	$56,500	1/06	WCOH	Crawler loader, diesel, ROPS, 4-in-1 bucket
Caterpillar	953C	2002		G	$75,000	9/06	WCTX	Crawler, loader, diesel, EROPS, gp bucket, 2-lever hyd. controls
Caterpillar	955			G	$3,700	6/06	NEIN	Crawler loader
Caterpillar	955H			G	$2,250	11/06	SCCA	Crawler
Caterpillar	955L			G	$4,500	7/06	WCPA	Crawler loader, Cat diesel, gp bucket, recent engine work
Caterpillar	955L			G	$9,000	8/06	SETN	Crawler loader, OROPS
Caterpillar	955L		6,253	G	$21,000	9/06	NEIN	Crawler loader, canopy, 4-in-1 bucket
Caterpillar	963			G	$23,000	10/06	SWOH	Crawler loader, Cat diesel, EROPS, gp bucket, bolt-on teeth
Caterpillar	963			G	$35,500	1/06	WCPA	Crawler, diesel, EROPS
Caterpillar	963		5,647	G	$49,000	11/06	SWCA	Crawler, loader, ripper, cab, air
Caterpillar	966A			g	$10,500	11/06	SWCA	Rubber-tired loader, canopy
Caterpillar	966B			G	$20,000	10/06	WCFL	Rubber-tired loader
Caterpillar	966C			G	$14,750	3/06	ECIN	Cab, gp bucket
Caterpillar	966C			G	$19,000	3/06	SCIN	Rubber-tired loader, 3.5-yard bucket
Caterpillar	966C			G	$19,000	12/06	ECMN	Cat 3306 engine, 170 hp.
Caterpillar	966C		3,875	G	$23,000	5/06	SWCA	Rubber-tired loader
Caterpillar	966C			G	$30,000	12/06	NEMN	Rubber-tired loader
Caterpillar	966D		13,515	G	$42,500	12/06	NEMN	Rubber-tired loader
Caterpillar	966F			G	$77,000	7/06	ECNY	Rubber-tired loader, diesel, EROPS, gp bucket

Construction Equipment

Make	Model	Year	Hrs.	Cond.	Price	Sale	Location	Comments
Caterpillar	977K			G	$5,100	9/06	NEIN	Crawler, 46 hp., gp bucket
Caterpillar	977L			G	$10,000	11/06	SWCA	
Caterpillar	977L			G	$10,000	11/06	SWCA	Crawler loader, canopy
Caterpillar	977L			G	$16,500	9/06	NEIN	Crawler loader, canopy
Caterpillar	980			G	$13,500	12/06	NEMN	
Caterpillar	980	1997		G	$92,500	10/06	WCFL	Rubber-tired loader
Caterpillar	980	1999		G	$156,500	1/06	WCNH	Rubber-tired loader, diesel, EROPS, ride control
Caterpillar	980B			G	$14,000	3/06	ECIN	Rubber-tired loader, diesel, 5-yard bucket, gp bucket
Caterpillar	980C			G	$39,000	7/06	ECNY	Rubber-tired loader, diesel, EROPS, gp bucket
Caterpillar	988A			G	$3,750	3/06	SCIN	Rubber-tired loader, 5-yard bucket
Caterpillar	99E			G	$9,500	9/06	ECMN	EROPS
Caterpillar	D1300			G	$1,200	4/06	WCSD	Gravel crusher power unit on trailer
Caterpillar	D2			G	$600	8/06	SCIL	Loader, bucket & blade
Caterpillar	D3			G	$14,500	7/06	WCPA	Crawler, diesel, OROPS, 6-way blade
Caterpillar	D3		623	G	$50,000	8/06	SETN	Dozer, OROPS, 6-way blade
Caterpillar	D3	2004		G	$57,500	1/06	WCNH	Crawler, diesel, OROPS, 6-way blade
Caterpillar	D3B			G	$9,750	9/06	NEIN	Crawler, 6-way blade
Caterpillar	D3B			G	$10,000	7/06	ECNY	Crawler, diesel, ROPS, 6-way blade
Caterpillar	D3B			G	$10,750	12/06	ECMN	6-way blade
Caterpillar	D3B			G	$11,000	9/06	NEIN	Crawler, canopy, 6-way blade
Caterpillar	D3B			G	$15,000	9/06	NEIN	Crawler, canopy, 6-way blade
Caterpillar	D3B	1980	4,500	G	$15,000	2/06	WCIL	Dozer, ROPS, 6-way bucket
Caterpillar	D3C			G	$17,000	3/06	SCIN	Dozer
Caterpillar	D3C			G	$19,000	9/06	NWTN	Crawler, Series II, 6-way blade, OROPS
Caterpillar	D3C		5,000	F	$23,750	3/06	SEPA	Dozer, average undercarriage, cab
Caterpillar	D3C		1,387	G	$34,250	8/06	SETN	Crawler dozer, 6-way blade
Caterpillar	D3C	1994		G	$22,000	8/06	ECMN	Series III, 6-way, OROPS
Caterpillar	D3C	1997		G	$27,500	1/06	WCNH	Crawler, diesel, OROPS, 20" pads, 6-way blade
Caterpillar	D3C	1998	2,793	G	$26,000	8/06	SETN	Crawler dozer, 6-way blade, pedal steer
Caterpillar	D3C	2000		G	$34,000	1/06	WCNH	Crawler, diesel, OROPS, 16" pads
Caterpillar	D3G		2,859	G	$36,500	8/06	SETN	Crawler/dozer, 6-way blade, OROPS
Caterpillar	D4			G	$650	8/06	SCIL	
Caterpillar	D4			G	$1,250	8/06	SCIL	Crawler loader, tracks on, 4-cable loader
Caterpillar	D4			G	$2,250	9/06	NEIN	Crawler loader, pony motor, diesel
Caterpillar	D4	2002		G	$43,000	7/06	ECNY	Crawler, diesel, EROPS, 6-way blade, air
Caterpillar	D4	2002		G	$50,000	1/06	WCNH	Crawler, diesel, OROPS, hystat, long track, 18" pads
Caterpillar	D4	2004		G	$42,500	10/06	WCFL	Crawler, diesel, ROPS, 6-way blade
Caterpillar	D4C			F	$3,000	1/06	WCCA	3 hyd.
Caterpillar	D4C		4,082	G	$26,000	8/06	SETN	Series II crawler, 6-way blade, ROPS
Caterpillar	D4C	1990		G	$16,500	3/06	ECMI	78 hp., 3204 Cat diesel
Caterpillar	D4CXL		2,100	G	$37,000	9/06	SECA	Crawler
Caterpillar	D4D			G	$6,000	2/06	WCME	Crawler dozer
Caterpillar	D4D			G	$7,750	9/06	NEIN	Crawler, canopy, straight blade, powershift trans., tilt
Caterpillar	D4H			G	$18,500	10/06	WCFL	Crawler, diesel, ROPS, 6-way blade
Caterpillar	D4H			G	$24,000	9/06	WCTX	Crawler, diesel, OROPS, 6-way blade
Caterpillar	D4H			G	$25,000	12/06	NEMN	LGP
Caterpillar	D4H			G	$28,000	9/06	NEIN	Crawler, canopy, 6-way blade, rear drawbar
Caterpillar	D4H		5,928	G	$29,000	5/06	SWCA	Crawler, 6-way dozer, slope board, canopy
Caterpillar	D4H			G	$32,500	7/06	ECNY	Crawler, diesel, ROPS, 6-way blade

Construction Equipment

Make	Model	Year	Hrs.	Cond.	Price	Sale	Location	Comments
Caterpillar	D4H		9,326	G	$33,000	11/06	SWCA	Crawler, 6-way blade
Caterpillar	D5	2004		G	$73,000	9/06	NEIN	Crawler, canopy, 6-way blade
Caterpillar	D5B			G	$22,500	9/06	NEIN	Crawler, canopy, straight w/ tilt, powershift
Caterpillar	D5C			G	$15,000	9/06	WCTX	Crawler, diesel, ROPS, 6-way blade
Caterpillar	D5C			G	$27,500	8/06	WCTX	Crawler, ROPS, 6-way blade
Caterpillar	D5C			G	$28,500	7/06	ECNY	Crawler, Series III, diesel, OROPS, 6-way blade
Caterpillar	D5C		2,600	G	$36,000	8/06	SEPA	Dozer, hydro, ROPS, good undercarriage
Caterpillar	D5C	1995		G	$34,000	1/06	WCOH	Diesel, OROPS
Caterpillar	D5C	1999		G	$35,000	8/06	SETN	LGP crawler, dozer, Series III, 6-way blade, OROPS, rippers
Caterpillar	D5CXL			G	$29,500	7/06	ECNY	Crawler, Series III, diesel, ROPS, long undercarriage, 6-way blade
Caterpillar	D5CXL	1996		G	$28,000	5/06	SWCA	Series 2 crawler, Dual slope boards, canopy, rippers
Caterpillar	D5CXL	2001		G	$34,000	7/06	WCPA	Hystat crawler diesel, OROPS, PS, 6-way blade
Caterpillar	D5H		8,635	G	$47,500	7/06	WCTN	LGP dozer, new motor & fuel system
Caterpillar	D5HXL	1998		G	$62,000	3/06	ECIN	Crawler, canopy
Caterpillar	D5M			G	$33,000	9/06	WCTX	Crawler, diesel, ROPS, 6-way blade
Caterpillar	D5M			G	$46,000	9/06	WCTX	Crawler, diesel, ROPS, 6-way blade
Caterpillar	D5M	1998	250	G	$45,000	9/06	NEIN	Crawler, finger-tip controls, new oil pump
Caterpillar	D5X			F	$3,200	4/06	WCMN	Straight cable dozer
Caterpillar	D6			F	$3,200	4/06	SWMB	Canadian sale, straight cable dozer, likely running
Caterpillar	D6	1998		G	$78,000	1/06	WCNH	Crawler, diesel, EROPS, 28" pads, 6-way blade
Caterpillar	D6B			G	$5,000	10/06	NCWI	Crawler, Cat diesel, ROPS, hyd. straight blade
Caterpillar	D6C			G	$9,500	7/06	ECNY	Crawler, diesel, OROPS, angle blade, twin tilt
Caterpillar	D6C			G	$12,000	3/06	ECMI	LGP, wide track, 140 hp.
Caterpillar	D6C			G	$15,750	3/06	ECIN	Crawler, turbo diesel, new rollers, canopy
Caterpillar	D6C			G	$24,000	12/06	NEMN	Dozer
Caterpillar	D6C	1978		G	$26,000	12/06	WCIL	Crawler, 1,400 hours on OH, 3-way blade, winch, diesel
Caterpillar	D-6C			G	$20,000	11/06	SETN	Sweeps, OROPS
Caterpillar	D6D			G	$27,500	3/06	SEIA	Dozer, powershift, ROPS, 24" pads, undercarriage 50%
Caterpillar	D6D			G	$35,000	10/06	WCFL	Crawler, diesel, EROPS, heat, tandem axle, hyd. tilt blade
Caterpillar	D6D LGP			G	$22,500	9/06	WCTX	Crawler, diesel, ROPS
Caterpillar	D6H		4,732	G	$47,500	9/06	NEIN	Crawler, canopy, semi-U blade, different steer, rear drawbar
Caterpillar	D6H		16,200	G	$64,000	9/06	SECA	Crawler
Caterpillar	D6H	1987	16,200	G	$67,000	5/06	ECNE	Dozer, Cat 3306 diesel, sweeps, straight blade w/ hyd. tilt, 3 hyd. scrapers, cab, air, radio, new Cat undercarriage
Caterpillar	D6H	1992	10,635	G	$36,000	9/06	ECMN	EROPS, 39" pads, new paint
Caterpillar	D6H LGP			G	$41,000	9/06	WCTX	Series II, Cat diesel, EROPS
Caterpillar	D6HXL			G	$75,000	1/06	WCPA	Crawler, Cat 3306 diesel, EROPS
Caterpillar	D6M		5,018	G	$95,000	7/06	WCTN	LGP dozer, cab
Caterpillar	D6M	1999	8,796	G	$68,500	12/06	ECMN	Cab, air, 34" pads, 13.5" blade, 6 way
Caterpillar	D6R	1997		G	$71,000	8/06	WCTX	Crawler, diesel, EROPS, air
Caterpillar	D6R	1998		G	$60,000	11/06	SWCA	Crawler, ripper, canopy
Caterpillar	D6RXL	1997		G	$86,000	5/06	SWCA	Crawler, semi-U blade, slope board ripper, cab
Caterpillar	D6RXL	1999	8,750	G	$87,500	5/06	ECNE	Dozer, Cat 3306 diesel engine, sweeps, straight blade w/ hyd. tilt, cab, air, radio
Caterpillar	D7			G	$2,750	6/06	NEIN	Brush cab, cable 10' blade
Caterpillar	D7			G	$3,200	1/06	WCOH	Crawler, diesel, canopy, 122" straight blade

Construction Equipment

Make	Model	Year	Hrs.	Cond.	Price	Sale	Location	Comments
Caterpillar	D7			F	$3,500	4/06	WCMT	Dozer, electric-start pony motor, 12' cable angle dozer with a 2-spool Cat cable control, main OH 3,622 hours ago, sells with new grouser bars, pins turned once
Caterpillar	D7			G	$3,500	9/06	NEIN	Crawler, diesel, hyd. brakes, hyd. blade
Caterpillar	D7E			G	$13,000	6/06	NEIN	ROPS, sweeps, straight blade, new trans.
Caterpillar	D7F			G	$15,000	11/06	SETN	Hyd. tilt blade
Caterpillar	D7F			G	$21,000	3/06	SCIN	Straight blade, tilt, ROPS
Caterpillar	D7G			G	$27,000	6/06	NEIN	Dozer, cab, straight blade, tilt, LP
Caterpillar	D7G			G	$28,000	3/06	SCIN	Dozer, ROPS
Caterpillar	D7G	1986		G	$49,000	11/06	ECND	Dozer, ROPS, brush canopy, Carco 80 winch
Caterpillar	D8			G	$5,250	8/06	SCIL	
Caterpillar	D8			G	$5,900	3/06	NENE	Dozer, Cat 10' blade, tree guard, OROPS
Caterpillar	D8			G	$21,000	2/06	WCME	Crawler dozer, ripper
Caterpillar	D8H			G	$11,000	12/06	NEMN	Dozer
Caterpillar	D8R	2001		G	$280,000	1/06	WCPA	Crawler, Series II, EROPS
Caterpillar	D9H	1980		G	$44,000	11/06	SCCA	Dozer, 15' blade
Caterpillar	E110B			G	$20,000	7/06	ECNY	Hyd. excavator, diesel, canopy, 20" pads, 34" digging bucket
Caterpillar	E120B			G	$28,000	7/06	WCPA	Hyd. excavator, diesel, cab, third valve hyd., 20" pads
Caterpillar	E120B	1992		G	$22,500	3/06	SCIN	Excavator
Caterpillar	E120B	1993		G	$23,000	3/06	ECMI	84 hp., long stick, 36" bucket
Caterpillar	E70B			G	$18,500	10/06	SWOH	Hyd. excavator, diesel, cab, blade, 18" pads
Caterpillar	E70B	1989		G	$7,700	10/06	SENJ	Excavator
Caterpillar	EL240			G	$17,000	8/06	WCTX	Hyd. excavator, diesel, EROPS
Caterpillar	EL240			G	$17,500	7/06	ECNY	Hyd. excavator, diesel, cab, long stick
Caterpillar	EL240			G	$28,500	8/06	WCTX	Yard excavator, diesel, cab, front blade, swing boom
Caterpillar	EL240			G	$28,500	8/06	WCTX	Hyd. excavator, diesel, cab, 30" triple grouser pads, 48" bucket
Caterpillar	GP25			G	$7,000	5/06	SWCA	Industrial forklift, 5,000 lb., LP engine, canopy
Caterpillar	GP25			G	$7,250	5/06	SWCA	Industrial forklift, 5,000 lb., LP engine, canopy
Caterpillar	GP25	1997		G	$6,500	5/06	SWCA	Industrial forklift, 5,000-lb. capacity, 11' lift, side shift, dual fuel, canopy
Caterpillar	GP25	2003		G	$12,000	11/06	SECA	5,000-lb. forklift, 42" forks
Caterpillar	GP25	2003		G	$12,000	11/06	SECA	5,000-lb. forklift, 42" forks
Caterpillar	IT28-B	1992		G	$26,000	3/06	ECMI	Cab, quick-tach bucket, forks
Caterpillar	IT28F			G	$27,000	3/06	ECIN	Diesel, bucket & forks, canopy
Caterpillar	IT28F			G	$29,000	10/06	SWOH	Tool carrier, diesel, EROPS, third valve hyd., bucket
Caterpillar	IT28F			G	$35,000	3/06	ECIN	Integrated tool carrier, quick coupler, 2.6-yard bucket, cab
Caterpillar	IT28G	1999	8,603	G	$51,000	9/06	NEIN	Integrated tool carrier, bucket & forks, cab, air, heat
Caterpillar	IT28G	2004		G	$66,000	10/06	WCFL	Tool carrier, OROPS
Caterpillar	IT38F	1997		G	$26,500	7/06	ECNY	Tool carrier, diesel, EROPS, attach, third valve
Caterpillar	IT38F	1997		G	$42,000	7/06	ECNY	Tool carrier, diesel, EROPS, attach, third valve
Caterpillar	IT38F	1997		G	$51,000	10/06	WCFL	Tool carrier
Caterpillar	M30			G	$500	12/06	ECMN	Forklift, 3 stage, single-phase charger
Caterpillar	RD4			G	$425	8/06	SCIL	
Caterpillar	RD4			G	$450	8/06	SCIL	Crawler
Caterpillar	RD4			G	$750	8/06	SCIL	
Caterpillar	T30			G	$1,600	12/06	ECMN	3,000-lb. capacity, 2-stage mast, side shift, LP
Caterpillar	T30			G	$2,350	11/06	NCKY	TC 30-tow motor, propane

WHAT'S IT WORTH?

Construction Equipment

Make	Model	Year	Hrs.	Cond.	Price	Sale	Location	Comments
Caterpillar	TH62			G	$23,000	1/06	WCOH	Telescoping forklift, 4WD, diesel, EROPS, 25' lift, 6,000-lb. capacity
Caterpillar	TH62	2001		G	$27,500	1/06	WCNH	Telescoping forklift, 4WD, diesel, EROPS, 6,000-lb. capacity
Caterpillar	TH63		1,777	G	$35,000	8/06	SETN	Telehandler, 6,000-lb. lift capacity
Caterpillar	TH63	1997		G	$32,000	8/06	SETN	Telescoping lift, 6,000-lb. lift capacity, stabilizer
Caterpillar	TH63	2000		G	$41,500	8/06	WCMN	Telehandler, 41" reach
Caterpillar	TH63	2001		G	$37,500	1/06	WCNH	Telescoping forklift, 4WD, diesel, EROPS, 6,000-lb. capacity
Caterpillar	TH63	2002		G	$43,000	1/06	WCPA	Telescopic forklift, 4WD, diesel, EROPS
Caterpillar	TH83	1996	7,500	G	$21,250	12/06	ECMN	8,000-lb. lift
Caterpillar	V80C			G	$3,000	6/06	NEIN	Forklift, air tires
Cedar Rapids	CR451	2002		G	$49,500	7/06	ECNY	Asphalt paver, diesel, ST20 stretch screed, all new fluids
Clark	125			G	$2,000	1/06	SETN	Rubber-tired loader
Clark	C40			G	$2,200	5/06	SWCA	Forklift, 4,000-lb. capacity, 14' lift, gas engine
Clark	C500			G	$3,250	3/06	SEMN	Forklift, LP gas, hard tires, shuttle shift
Clark	C500	1984		G	$5,000	2/06	NECO	
Clark	C-500Y			G	$4,000	5/06	SWCA	Construction forklift, 10,000-lb. capacity, 24' lift, LP engine, canopy
Clark	CFY 40B-675			g	$1,600	9/06	NEIN	4,000 lb., LP, standard tires, 2-stage
Clark	CGP25			G	$4,250	8/06	SEPA	Forklift, gas/propane, 5,000-lb. capacity
Clark	CY40B			G	$3,500	2/06	SWNE	Forklift, 4-cylinder continental gas engine, pneumatic tires, 9' lift, 27×10×12 tires
Clark	NA			F	$400	12/06	SEMN	Forklift, 4,000-lb. capacity
Clark	NA			G	$1,850	3/06	ECMI	Forklift, 6-cyl., gas
Clark	NA			G	$2,000	6/06	NEIN	10-ton forklift, gas
Clark	NA			G	$2,100	8/06	NECO	Forklift
Clark	NA			G	$2,200	2/06	WCME	3,000-lb. capacity forklift
Clark	NA			G	$2,500	10/06	NECO	Forklift, 4,000 lb., 2-stage, gas
Clark	NA			G	$2,900	9/06	NECO	Forklift, 4,000 lb., gas, 2-stage mast
Clark	NA			G	$6,500	11/06	WCMN	Forklift, 6,000 lb., 3-stage, side shift, tires, recently serviced
Crown	NA			P	$25	10/06	NCWI	Diesel, ROPS, forklift
Daewoo	200	2004	700	G	$66,000	7/06	ECNY	Rubber-tired loader, diesel, EROPS, air, light package, third valve
Daewoo	G30E	2002		G	$4,000	10/06	NCWI	Forklift, LP, ROPS, 6,000-lb. capacity
Daewoo	Mega 200	1998		G	$19,500	10/06	WCFL	Rubber-tired loader, diesel, ROPS, gp bucket, rake
Datsun	NA			G	$1,650	4/06	SEIA	Forklift, gas, single stage
Ditch Witch	1020			G	$1,900	9/06	SECA	Trencher
Ditch Witch	1030H			G	$1,000	11/06	SCCA	
Ditch Witch	1030H			F	$2,000	9/06	SECA	Trencher
Ditch Witch	1030H			G	$2,200	1/06	SCTN	Walk-behind trencher
Ditch Witch	1030H			G	$2,200	1/06	SCTN	Walk-behind trencher
Ditch Witch	1030H			G	$2,500	1/06	SCTN	Walk-behind trencher
Ditch Witch	1820	2002	469	G	$4,500	10/06	WCGA	Walk-behind trencher
Ditch Witch	1820	2002		G	$4,500	10/06	WCGA	Walk-behind trencher
Ditch Witch	2200			G	$350	11/06	SCCA	Ride-on trencher
Ditch Witch	2310D			G	$450	11/06	SCCA	
Ditch Witch	2310D			G	$2,500	9/06	NEIN	Trencher, diesel, backhoe, leveling blade, boring attach.
Ditch Witch	3500			G	$1,400	10/06	ECMO	Backfill, 6' dirt blade
Ditch Witch	3500			G	$3,500	9/06	NEIN	Trencher, backhoe combo, leveling blade, A222 backhoe

Construction Equipment

Make	Model	Year	Hrs.	Cond.	Price	Sale	Location	Comments
Ditch Witch	3500				$4,000	11/06	SCCA	Ride-on trencher
Ditch Witch	3500		1,862	G	$5,200	9/06	SECA	Ride-on trencher
Ditch Witch	3700	1999		g	$7,500	5/06	SWCA	Trencher, 4WD, diesel, 4' digging depth, backfill blade
Ditch Witch	3700	2000		G	$6,000	11/06	SECA	Trencher, H314 trencher
Ditch Witch	3700	2000		G	$6,500	3/06	WCWA	Trencher, 4WD, Deutz 3-cyl. engine, backfill blade, 6' trenching bar
Ditch Witch	3700	2000		G	$8,000	11/06	SECA	Trencher
Ditch Witch	3700	2002		G	$9,500	11/06	SECA	Trencher, H314 trencher
Ditch Witch	3700	2003		G	$11,000	10/06	WCGA	Ride-on trencher, canopy
Ditch Witch	3700	2003		G	$14,000	10/06	WCGA	Ride-on trencher, canopy
Ditch Witch	4010		2,217	F	$13,250	1/06	NWIL	Trencher, A321 backhoe, Deutz engine
Ditch Witch	5010		219	G	$7,600	12/06	NENE	A450 plow, A420 backhoe, dig depth 5'
Ditch Witch	5110			G	$1,500	10/06	ECMO	Trencher, diesel
Ditch Witch	5110	2001		G	$11,000	10/06	WCGA	Ride-on trencher, backhoe attach
Ditch Witch	6510			G	$3,000	10/06	ECMO	Trencher, 7' diesel
Ditch Witch	6510			G	$3,500	3/06	WCWA	Trencher, cable plow, spool mount, backfill blade
Ditch Witch	6510			G	$9,750	9/06	NEMO	4WD trencher, Deutz diesel engine, front hyd. 17" bucket, 10' rear trencher, outriggers, front blade
Ditch Witch	7510			G	$1,500	10/06	ECMO	Trencher
Ditch Witch	7510		3,326	G	$6,500	12/06	ECMN	Cable plow, backhoe combo, Deutz diesel
Ditch Witch	R100			G	$10,000	5/06	ECNE	R100D trencher, Detroit 453 diesel, T100A trencher attach., new chain, 6-way front blade, 18 front-end weights, extra chain
Ditch Witch	R40			F	$1,000	5/06	ECNE	Trencher, VP 40 vibrating plow, 4-cyl. gas engine, shop built reel carrier
Ditch Witch	R40			F	$2,600	5/06	ECNE	4WD trencher, Detroit diesel engine, 8' rear trencher, front angle blade
Ditch Witch	R60		2,655	P	$1,000	2/06	NECO	Gas, 6' bar, 18" bucket
Ditch Witch	V30			G	$900	7/06	WCCA	Trencher, S-dozer
Dresser	125E			G	$9,300	1/06	WCOH	Crawler loader, Cummins diesel
Dresser	175			G	$8,000	6/06	NEIN	Crawler loader
Dresser	510			G	$10,000	3/06	SCIN	Articulated rubber-tired loader, 2-yard bucket, forks
Dresser	510	1985		G	$6,100	10/06	SENJ	Front end loader
Dresser	515			G	$14,500	3/06	ECIN	Rubber-tired loader
Dresser	515B			G	$7,500	11/06	SWCA	Rubber-tired loader, Cummins diesel
Dresser	530			G	$15,500	11/06	SWCA	4-in-1 bucket
Dresser	530	1992		G	$19,000	3/06	ECMI	165 hp., cab
Dresser	540		5,000	G	$14,000	3/06	ECIN	Rubber-tired loader, diesel, 4-in-1 bucket
Dresser	560B			G	$11,500	9/06	ECMN	7¼-yard bucket, 25 hours on complete OH
Dresser	TD12C	1993		E	$23,000	2/06	NEIN	Bulldozer, 11.5' 6-way blade
Dresser	TD15C			G	$7,750	3/06	ECMI	120 hp., blade, ROPS, sweeps, engine & torque rebuilt
Dresser	TD15C			G	$22,000	6/06	NEIN	Straight blade, tilt
Dresser	TD15C			G	$26,500	3/06	SCIN	Dozer, sweeps, tilt, ROPS
Dresser	TD7E			G	$6,750	3/06	ECMI	6-way blade
Dresser	TD-7H			G	$20,000	9/06	NEIN	Crawler, rear screens, canopy, sweeps, 6-way blade
Dresser	TD8E			G	$8,500	3/06	ECMI	Crawler tractor, 6-way
Drott	40			G	$21,000	3/06	ECMI	Rubber hyd. excavator, diesel, outriggers, ditching bucket
Dual	NA			G	$925	1/06	NEIN	Forklift

WHAT'S IT WORTH?

Construction Equipment

Make	Model	Year	Hrs.	Cond.	Price	Sale	Location	Comments
Dynolift	D4			G	$11,500	5/06	SWCA	Forward reach 5,000-lb. capacity forklift, 20' reach, canopy
Dynolift	D4P60			G	$10,500	7/06	ECNY	Telescopic forklift, 4WD, diesel, ROPS
Eagle	NA			G	$550	3/06	NEND	Air compressor, 9 hp., Honda hose reel
Eagle Picher	NA	1996	3,382	G	$9,000	5/06	SWCA	Construction forklift, diesel, canopy
Economy	NA			G	$1,500	1/06	WCCA	Platform lift
Elgin	NA			G	$2,750	5/06	SWCA	Street sweeper, dual gutter brooms, 5' rear broom, diesel, auto
Essick	NA			F	$400	3/06	WCWA	30" tandem smooth drum roller, gas engine
Fiat Allis	125C	1986	4,100	G	$12,000	2/06	NEIN	4×4 backhoe, 3-spd. power shift, 24" hoe bucket, 7' bucket, rollover bar
Fiat Allis	14C	1983		G	$13,250	3/06	SEIA	Dozer, 10' semi U-blade, ROPS & sweeps
Fiat Allis	21B			F	$5,000	11/06	ECND	Hyd. blade dozer, powershift, ROPS canopy
Fiat Allis	545B			G	$7,500	6/06	NEIN	Cab, 2-yard bucket
Fiat Allis	545B		5,500	G	$15,000	1/06	NECO	1¾-yard bucket, grapple, articulating
Fiat Allis	545B	1982		G	$9,000	3/06	ECMI	2-yard bucket, 100 hp.
Fiat Allis	645B			G	$9,000	3/06	ECIN	Rubber-tired loader
Fiat Allis	645B			G	$13,000	11/06	SCCA	7-8 yard
Fiat Allis	645B	1976		G	$20,500	2/06	NCCO	4WD loader, 4 years on engine & trans. OH
Fiat Allis	7GB			G	$6,500	11/06	SETN	OROPS, crawler
Fiat Allis	FR10			G	$7,000	11/06	SCCA	
Fiat Allis	FR10			G	$10,000	11/06	SCCA	
Fiat Allis	FR10			G	$14,500	5/06	SWCA	Rubber-tired loader, cab
Fiat Allis	FR20			G	$5,500	7/06	WCCA	Front end loader, bucket, cab, 270 hp. Cummins
Fiat Allis	NA		4,405		$13,250	8/06	WCNC	Tired loader
Fisher	NA			F	$19,000	4/06	WCSD	80' gravel stacker conveyor, 30" wide belt
Ford	445			G	$4,250	8/06	WCTX	4WD, box blade, front loader
Ford	445A			G	$4,000	7/06	WCCA	Bucket, canopy, box scraper
Ford	445A			G	$6,500	11/06	SECA	Bucket, canopy, scraper
Ford	445D		3,137	G	$14,750	5/06	SWCA	3-valve rear scraper, canopy
Ford	445D	1996		G	$7,250	8/06	WCTX	TLB, diesel, Gannon box, gp bucket
Ford	4500			G	$3,250	9/06	NEIN	Gas
Ford	4500			G	$3,900	3/06	SCIN	Standard hoe
Ford	540B		778	G	$8,250	2/06	WCIL	Trencher, loader
Ford	545			G	$3,500	11/06	SWCA	Rear scraper, canopy
Ford	545	1996	2,788	G	$9,000	11/06	SWCA	4WD
Ford	545	1996	2,788	G	$13,500	11/06	SWCA	4WD
Ford	545A			G	$6,800	9/06	NCMI	Industrial loader tractor, diesel, shuttle shift, 3 pt., PTO
Ford	545A			G	$7,000	5/06	SWCA	Gannon 3-valve rear scraper, canopy
Ford	545A			G	$8,750	11/06	SWCA	4WD, 4 valve, rear scraper
Ford	545A		2,613	G	$9,000	5/06	SWCA	Gannon 3-valve scraper, canopy
Ford	545C		2,633	G	$8,500	11/06	SWCA	4WD, Gannon 3 valve
Ford	545C		2,633	G	$9,250	11/06	SWCA	4WD, Gannon 3 valve
Ford	545C	1989		G	$9,900	8/06	NCOH	Industrial tractor, loader, FWA, 3-pt., shuttle clutch PTO, 3-pt. box scraper
Ford	555			G	$6,400	3/06	SCIN	Backhoe
Ford	555			G	$10,200	3/06	SCIN	Backhoe, Extendahoe, 4-in-1 bucket
Ford	5550			F	$8,500	3/06	NEOH	Backhoe/loader
Ford	555A			G	$9,500	10/06	SENJ	Backhoe, 4WD
Ford	555B			G	$7,500	5/06	SWCA	Loader backhoe, Extendahoe, canopy

Construction Equipment

Make	Model	Year	Hrs.	Cond.	Price	Sale	Location	Comments
Ford	555B			G	$8,500	9/06	NEIN	Diesel, Extendahoe, Wain Ray quick coupler, Wrist-a-Twist attachment, cab
Ford	555C			G	$10,500	7/06	ECNY	TLB, diesel, ROPS, digging bucket
Ford	555C			G	$12,750	8/06	NWIL	Backhoe, 4×4, with loader, diesel
Ford	555D			G	$8,550	6/06	NECO	Backhoe, cab, 20" bucket, diesel, tach shows 1,924 hours
Ford	555D			G	$14,100	9/06	NWTN	TLB, 4WD, OROPS, Extendahoe
Ford	555D			G	$15,500	10/06	WCFL	TLB, 4WD, diesel, OROPS, digging bucket
Ford	555E	1999		G	$18,000	8/06	WCTX	TLB, OROPS, 18" digging bucket
Ford	655		7,751	G	$12,500	11/06	SWCA	Canopy
Ford	750			G	$1,200	8/06	SWCA	Backhoe loader
Ford	755			G	$3,750	7/06	ECNY	TLB, diesel, EROPS, digging bucket
Ford	755	1981		G	$12,500	8/06	WCMN	Loader backhoe, cab, heat, 30" hoe bucket, new rear tires and hyd. pump
Ford	755A			G	$9,000	10/06	WCFL	TLB, diesel, EROPS, gp bucket, digging bucket
Ford	755A	1984		G	$11,000	8/06	WCMN	Backhoe loader, rock guard top
Ford	755B				$14,000	11/06	SWCA	
Ford	A62			G	$5,750	9/06	NEIN	Rubber-tired loader, cab, diesel
Ford	L8000	1995		G	$65,000	5/06	ECMI	Simon boom truck crane, 29,038 miles, 5,579 hours
Ford	Louisville	1997		G	$52,500	5/06	ECMI	Simon Model TC3067 15-ton hyd. boom truck crane, 13,568 miles
Ford	NA			G	$2,300	9/06	NCMI	Ford Marshall hi/lo forklift, 12' mast, rough terrain, large tires, side shift
Freightliner	NA	1999	4,387	G	$100,000	5/06	ECMI	31,377 miles, 4,387 engine hours, boom truck crane
Galion	118		1,522	G	$4,600	8/06	WCTX	Motor grader, diesel, EROPS, 12' moldboard
Galion	118B			G	$2,250	9/06	NEIN	Grader, diesel, scarifier
Galion	150			G	$1,500	11/06	SCCA	15 ton, Detroit diesel
Galion	500			G	$3,750	6/06	NEIN	Powershift, grader
Galion	503			G	$12,500	7/06	ECNY	Motor grader, diesel, EROPS, hyd. side shift
Galion	NA			G	$6,000	6/06	NEIN	18-ton truck crane, 70' boom
Galion	T600			G	$6,600	3/06	SEIA	T600C road grader
Gehl	883	1997		G	$25,500	1/06	WCOH	Telescoping forklift, JD diesel engine, ROPS, 8,000-lb. capacity
Genie	Z45			G	$5,000	11/06	SCCA	Knuckleboom, 4WD, gas
Genie	Z45			G	$10,500	10/06	WCGA	45' lift
Genie	Z45			G	$11,000	9/06	SECA	Boom lift
Genie	Z45			G	$12,500	10/06	WCGA	45' lift
Genie	Z45			G	$12,500	9/06	SECA	Boom lift
Genie	Z45			G	$12,500	9/06	SECA	Boom lift
Genie	Z45			G	$13,000	9/06	SECA	Boom lift
Genie	Z45			G	$23,000	10/06	WCGA	45' lift
Genie	Z45	1998	814	G	$14,000	10/06	WCFL	Boom lift, Ford gas engine, 45' lift
Genie	Z45	1998	814	G	$15,000	10/06	WCFL	Boom lift, Ford gas engine, 45' lift
Genie	Z45	1999		G	$9,500	10/06	WCFL	Boom lift, diesel, 45' lift
Genie	Z45	1999		G	$20,000	9/06	SECA	Articulating boom lift
Genie	Z45	1999		G	$26,000	9/06	SECA	Articulating boom lift
Genie	Z45	1999		G	$26,000	10/06	WCFL	Boom lift, diesel, 45' lift
Genie	Z45	2001		G	$15,500	9/06	WCTX	Boom lift, 4×4, dual fuel powered, 45' lift, articulating boom

Construction Equipment

Make	Model	Year	Hrs.	Cond.	Price	Sale	Location	Comments
Gradall	534			G	$23,000	5/06	SWCA	Forward reach forklift, 4×4, 9,000-lb. capacity, 34' reach, 3-stage diesel, canopy
Gradall	534	1998		G	$29,000	1/06	WCOH	Telescoping forklift, 4WD, diesel, ROPS
Gradall	534	2000		G	$38,500	10/06	WCFL	Telescoping forklift
Gradall	534C-6			G	$23,750	5/06	SWCA	Forward reach forklift, 4WD, 6,000-lb. capacity, 36' reach, diesel, canopy
Gradall	534C-9			G	$18,000	9/06	SECA	Telescoping forklift
Gradall	534C-9	1997		G	$16,000	7/06	ECNY	Telescopic forklift, 4WD, diesel, OROPS, 42' lift, 9,000-lb. capacity
Gradall	544D		2,902	G	$47,000	9/06	SECA	
Gradall	G660C			G	$3,750	11/06	SWCA	Hyd. excavator
Grizzly	NA			G	$3,400	8/06	NWIL	Backhoe, 3 pt., 16" bucket
Grove	AMX 66XT	1995	8,485	F	$4,500	7/06	SEND	Aerial lift, 60'
Grove	AMX 66XT	1996	3,182	G	$7,500	7/06	SEND	Aerial lift, 60'
Grove	MZ46C			G	$6,750	8/06	SEPA	Electric-powered boom lift
Grove	MZ66		5,618	G	$5,500	5/06	SWCA	500-lb. capacity boom lift, 66' reach, dual fuel
Grove	NA	1978		G	$10,500	3/06	WCMN	18-ton truck crane, gas engines front and back, out and downriggers, all WD assist
Hamm	2210		2,467	G	$14,000	9/06	SECA	Compactor
Harlo	NA			G	$2,750	10/06	NCWI	Forklift, diesel, ROPS, 21' 3-stage mast
Hein Warner	C14			G	$2,500	9/06	NEIN	Excavator, Detroit diesel, 36" bucket
Hitachi	EX100			G	$23,000	3/06	ECIN	Excavator, diesel, pilot controls
Hitachi	EX100			G	$25,000	7/06	WCPA	Hyd. excavator, diesel, cab, 10' stick
Hitachi	EX100			G	$26,500	10/06	NCWI	Hyd. excavator, diesel, 20" pads, 34" digging bucket
Hitachi	EX100	1997		G	$32,500	10/06	WCFL	Hyd. excavator, diesel, cab, 20" pads
Hitachi	EX120			G	$22,000	8/06	SETN	Excavator
Hitachi	EX120			G	$29,000	8/06	SEPA	Hyd. excavator, diesel, cab, air, 20" pads
Hitachi	EX200			G	$33,500	8/06	WCTX	Hyd. excavator, diesel, cab, digging bucket
Hitachi	EX200			G	$33,500	8/06	WCTX	Hyd. excavator, diesel, cab
Hitachi	EX400LC		2,513	G	$30,500	5/06	SWCA	Hyd. excavator, long undercarriage, medium stick, cab
Hitachi	EX400LC		2,513	G	$34,000	5/06	SWCA	Hyd. excavator, long undercarriage, medium stick, canopy
Hitachi	EX60			G	$12,500	3/06	ECIN	Excavator, diesel, plumbed
Hitachi	EX60			G	$13,500	10/06	SWOH	Hyd. excavator, diesel, cab, blade
Hitachi	EX60			G	$14,000	7/06	WCPA	Hyd. excavator, diesel, cab, blade, offset boom, digging bucket
Hitachi	EX60			G	$14,000	10/06	NCWI	Hyd. excavator, diesel, canopy, 18" pads
Hitachi	EX60			G	$15,000	7/06	ECNY	Hyd. excavator, diesel, canopy, blade
Hitachi	EX-60			G	$13,750	3/06	ECMI	38 hp., steel tracks, dozer blade, 18' reach
Hough	60		7,144	G	$8,400	1/06	NECO	Articulating
Hough	90			F	$2,500	8/06	SCMI	Payloader, 12' front blade
Hough	90			G	$4,500	11/06	SCCA	Wheel loader
Hough	H90C			G	$8,000	5/06	ECMI	Articulation front end loader, Detroit diesel
Hy-Hoe	680			F	$4,300	8/06	SCMI	Hydro hoe, 36" bucket
Hypac	C832B			G	$16,500	9/06	WCTX	Vibratory roller, diesel, OROPS
Hyster	40			F	$750	7/06	NECO	5,000-lb. forklift
Hyster	50			G	$2,800	10/06	SEMN	Forklift, 50XL, 5,000 lb., gas, 14' mast
Hyster	50		2,900	G	$13,500	12/06	NENE	Forklift
Hyster	60			G	$1,600	12/06	SCMN	XA60 forklift
Hyster	60			G	$13,100	12/06	NENE	6,000-lb. capacity forklift

Construction Equipment

Make	Model	Year	Hrs.	Cond.	Price	Sale	Location	Comments
Hyster	60	2000		G	$9,500	9/06	SECA	Forklift
Hyster	60	2000		G	$10,000	9/06	SECA	Forklift
Hyster	60	2000		G	$11,000	9/06	SECA	Forklift
Hyster	80			G	$6,700	9/06	SCNE	Challenger, 8,000-lb. forklift, 12' lift, 6-cyl. gas engine, dual front wheels, 7.50-15 tires
Hyster	8000			G	$3,500	3/06	ECMI	Pneumatic tire, gas
Hyster	C530A			G	$750	12/06	ECMN	9-wheel rubber tire, General Motors gas engine
Hyster	C612B			G	$8,000	9/06	NEIN	Padfoot compactor, Detroit diesel, 84" drum drive, canopy
Hyster	H50C			F	$750	9/06	NEIN	5,000 lb., gas, 3 stage
Hyster	H50C	1996		G	$4,750	3/06	WCWA	5,000-lb. forklift, LP power
Hyster	H50XM			G	$5,400	10/06	WCFL	5,000-lb. forklift
Hyster	H50XM			g	$8,500	9/06	SECA	Forklift
Hyster	H50XM	1999		G	$8,250	11/06	SCCA	Forklift, dual fuel, sideshift
Hyster	NA	1990		G	$3,500	3/06	WCWA	4,000-lb. forklift, LP power
Hyster	NA	2000		G	$7,500	5/06	SWCA	Industrial forklift, 5,000 lb., sideshift, LP engine
IHC	3082			G	$3,250	3/06	NWIL	Series A backhoe, 3 pt.
IHC	3400A			F	$5,000	10/06	NECO	Backhoe/loader, cab, 18" backhoe, diesel
IHC	412			G	$8,000	3/06	ECIN	Scraper, 466DT diesel, self-loading, canopy
IHC	412			G	$9,750	3/06	ECIN	Diesel, rebuilt machine, ps
IHC	80			G	$35,000	10/06	WCGA	Excavator
IHC	TD15B			G	$5,000	8/06	WCNC	Bulldozer
IHC	TD15B			G	$13,000	9/06	NEIN	Crawler, canopy, straight blade, tilt
IHC	TD15C			G	$23,500	3/06	SEIA	Dozer, ROPS, sweeps
IHC	TD18			F	$1,350	3/06	SEIA	Crawler tractor, no blade
IHC	TD25		1,004	G	$15,500	12/06	NEMN	Dozer
IHC	TD25C			G	$8,000	3/06	ECIN	Crawler, single shank ripper, sweeps, straight blade
IHC	TD7			F	$4,750	3/06	ECMI	6-way blade, ROPS, sweeps, weak steering
IHC	TD7			G	$10,000	3/06	ECMI	6-way blade, powershift
IHC	TD8	1978		G	$9,100	8/06	SETN	Crawler, 6-way blade, ROPS
IHC	TD9			F	$3,250	6/06	NWMN	Crawler, dozer
IHC	TD9			G	$4,200	4/06	NWMN	Crawler, hyd. dozer
Ingersoll	SD100D			G	$25,000	7/06	ECNY	Vibratory roller, Cummins diesel, 84" smooth drum
Ingersoll	SD100D			E	$67,500	10/06	WCFL	Vibratory roller, new, Cummins turbo diesel, canopy, 2-spd. drum
Ingersoll	SD100D	2002		G	$55,000	10/06	WCFL	Vibratory roller
Ingersoll	SD100F	1999		G	$47,000	9/06	WCTX	Vibratory roller, diesel, canopy
Ingersoll	SD40D		719	G	$34,000	7/06	WCTN	Cleated shell kit
Ingersoll	SD40D	1997		G	$27,500	3/06	ECIN	Vibratory roller, JD diesel
Ingersoll	SD70	2002		G	$39,500	10/06	WCFL	Vibratory roller
Ingram	NA			G	$3,100	1/06	NEIN	12-ton roller
JCB	1400B			G	$14,000	1/06	WCNH	TLB, 4WD, diesel, EROPS, Extendahoe, 4-in-1 bucket
JCB	210-S			G	$13,250	9/06	NEIN	Landscape loader, quick-tach bucket, 3-point hitch, cab
JCB	214			G	$18,000	10/06	WCFL	TLB, 4WD, diesel, EROPS, digging bucket
JCB	214			G	$19,500	10/06	SWOH	TLB, Series III, 4WD, EROPS, 3 hyd., bucket, standard hoe, Wain Roy mechanical quick coupler, 12" bucket, street pads, 2-lever control
JCB	214	2000		G	$19,000	10/06	WCFL	TLB, 4WD, diesel
JCB	214	2000		G	$19,500	10/06	WCFL	TLB, 4WD, diesel, EROPS, digging bucket
JCB	214	2000		G	$22,000	10/06	WCFL	TLB, 4WD, diesel, EROPS, digging bucket

WHAT'S IT WORTH?

Construction Equipment

Make	Model	Year	Hrs.	Cond.	Price	Sale	Location	Comments
JCB	214	2000		G	$22,000	10/06	WCFL	TLB, 4WD, diesel, EROPS, digging bucket
JCB	214	2001		G	$18,500	11/06	SWCA	4WD
JCB	214E			G	$21,000	10/06	WCFL	TLB, diesel, EROPS, gp bucket, digging bucket
JCB	214E	1999		G	$20,000	10/06	WCFL	TLB, 4WD, diesel, EROPS, standard hoe
JCB	214E	2000		G	$18,500	10/06	WCFL	TLB, 4WD, diesel, EROPS, standard hoe
JCB	214E	2000		G	$20,000	10/06	WCFL	TLB, 4WD, diesel
JCB	214E	2000		G	$21,000	10/06	WCFL	TLB, 4WD, diesel, EROPS, standard hoe
JCB	214E	2000		G	$21,000	10/06	WCFL	TLB, 4WD, diesel, EROPS, standard hoe
JCB	214E	2001		G	$21,000	10/06	WCFL	TLB, 4WD, diesel, EROPS, standard hoe, digging bucket
JCB	214E	2001		G	$21,500	10/06	WCFL	TLB, 4WD, diesel, EROPS, digging bucket
JCB	214S	2000		G	$25,000	7/06	ECNY	TLB, 4WD, diesel, EROPS, Extendahoe, front forks, digging bucket
JCB	506B			G	$24,000	5/06	ECMI	Shooting boom forklift, 6,000-lb. capacity, diesel, 4WD
JCB	506C	1999	2,600	G	$17,000	8/06	WCTX	Telescopic forklift, 4WD, diesel, ROPS
JCB	506C	1999	2,600	G	$17,000	9/06	WCTX	Telescoping forklift, 4×4, diesel, ROPS
JCB	506C	1999		G	$22,000	10/06	WCFL	4WD, diesel, ROPS
JCB	520		1,994	G	$15,100	8/06	SETN	Shoot boom forklift
JCB	926			G	$6,500	8/06	WCTX	Forklift, 4WD, EROPS, 5,200-lb. capacity, triple mast
JCB	930			G	$5,000	1/06	WCCA	48" forks, 3-stage mast
JCB	930			G	$10,000	10/06	ECMO	Forklift, diesel
JCB	930	1999		G	$15,500	9/06	SECA	Forklift
John Deere	110		900	F	$26,000	3/06	SEPA	Backhoe/loader, mechanical front-wheel drive, ROPS, hydro, average rubber
John Deere	110	2003	868	G	$21,000	11/06	SCCA	4WD
John Deere	120		3,600	G	$37,500	8/06	SETN	Excavator, EROPS, aux. hyd.
John Deere	120	2003		G	$48,000	10/06	WCFL	Hyd. excavator
John Deere	120	2003		G	$49,000	10/06	WCFL	Hyd. excavator, diesel, digging bucket
John Deere	120	2003		G	$50,000	10/06	WCFL	Hyd. excavator
John Deere	120	2003		G	$51,000	10/06	WCFL	Hyd. excavator
John Deere	120	2003		G	$52,000	10/06	WCFL	Hyd. excavator, diesel
John Deere	160	1999		G	$51,500	1/06	WCOH	Hyd. excavator, diesel, cab, long stick
John Deere	160	2000		G	$38,500	9/06	NEIN	Excavator, plumbed quick coupler, 2 buckets
John Deere	160	2001		G	$47,500	7/06	ECNY	Hyd. excavator, diesel, cab, air
John Deere	200	1997	5,545	H	$34,000	11/06	SWCA	Hyd. excavator, long undercarriage
John Deere	200	1998	7,091	G	$31,000	11/06	SWCA	Hyd. excavator, long undercarriage
John Deere	200	1998	7,091	G	$39,000	11/06	SWCA	Hyd. excavator, long undercarriage
John Deere	200	1998		G	$58,000	5/06	SWCA	Hyd. excavator, long undercarriage, med. stick, cab
John Deere	2010			G	$3,000	10/06	SCMN	Crawler/loader, original w/ hyd., 60" bucket, low hours on engine
John Deere	2010			G	$5,700	6/06	NEIN	Track loader, backhoe attach
John Deere	210			G	$13,500	9/06	WCTX	Landscape tractor, diesel, ROPS, loader
John Deere	210	2002		G	$25,000	11/06	SECA	4WD, 4-in-1 bucket, canopy, scraper
John Deere	210C			G	$5,750	12/06	ECMN	Loader, 3-point, leveler, 2WD
John Deere	210C			G	$8,500	8/06	NWIL	Backhoe, loader, diesel
John Deere	210C				$13,500	9/06	SECA	
John Deere	210L			G	$14,000	8/06	WCTX	TLB
John Deere	210L			G	$16,500	9/06	WCTX	4×4, diesel, ROPS, loader bucket, rear-box blade
John Deere	210L	2002		G	$30,000	11/06	SECA	4WD, 4-in-1 bucket, canopy, scraper
John Deere	210L	2002	1,828	G	$30,000	9/06	SECA	

Construction Equipment

Make	Model	Year	Hrs.	Cond.	Price	Sale	Location	Comments
John Deere	210L	2002	1,817	G	$30,000	9/06	SECA	
John Deere	210L	2003		G	$25,000	11/06	SECA	4WD, canopy, scraper
John Deere	210L	2003		G	$25,000	11/06	SECA	4WD, canopy, scraper
John Deere	210L	2003		G	$25,000	11/06	SECA	4-in-1 bucket, canopy, scraper
John Deere	210L	2003		G	$32,500	11/06	SECA	4WD, 4-in-1 bucket, canopy, scraper
John Deere	230LC	1998	8,222	G	$28,000	11/06	SWCA	Hyd. excavator
John Deere	230LC	2000		G	$50,000	10/06	WCFL	Hyd. excavator, diesel
John Deere	230LC	2002	2,832	G	$125,000	4/06	ECND	Excavator, 30" pads, 40" bucket w/ thumb, air radio, one owner
John Deere	244E		3,178	G	$26,500	12/06	NEMN	Attachment
John Deere	27	2003	1,356	g	$18,500	9/06	WCTX	Hyd. excavator, diesel, canopy, rubber track
John Deere	290			G	$11,000	7/06	ECNY	Hyd. excavator, diesel, 28" pads, digging bucket
John Deere	300B			G	$4,700	12/06	ECMN	Loader, PTO, 3 pt., 8' back blade
John Deere	300D			G	$16,500	10/06	WCFL	TLB, 4WD, diesel, OROPS, standard hoe
John Deere	310			G	$26,000	3/06	NWIL	Diesel, 4WD
John Deere	310	1999		G	$26,000	8/06	WCTX	TLB, 4WD, diesel, EROPS, digging bucket
John Deere	310	2003		G	$26,500	9/06	WCTX	TLB, diesel, OROPS, standard hoe
John Deere	310A			G	$6,750	11/06	SWCA	Extendahoe
John Deere	310A			G	$6,750	9/06	NEIN	Loader backhoe, canopy
John Deere	310B			G	$23,500	3/06	ECIN	4WD, cab, clip-on forks
John Deere	310C			G	$5,500	7/06	ECNY	TLB, diesel, OROPS, Extendahoe, gp bucket
John Deere	310C			G	$8,350	7/06	WCPA	TLB, diesel, EROPS, standard bucket, digging bucket
John Deere	310C			G	$9,250	1/06	WCPA	TLB, diesel, EROPS
John Deere	310C			G	$10,250	9/06	NEIN	2WD, loader backhoe, canopy
John Deere	310C			G	$11,500	1/06	WCOH	TLB, diesel, EROPS, digging bucket
John Deere	310C			G	$11,500	1/06	WCOH	TLB, diesel, EROPS, digging bucket
John Deere	310C			G	$12,500	1/06	WCOH	TLB, diesel, EROPS
John Deere	310C			G	$12,500	1/06	WCOH	TLB, diesel, EROPS, digging bucket
John Deere	310D		4,000	G	$21,000	9/06	NEIN	TLB, cab, 4-in-1 bucket, 4WD, Extendahoe
John Deere	310D	1991	3,866	E	$26,500	4/06	NWMN	TLB, 4WD, Extendahoe, turbo diesel, cab, heat, shuttle trans., 24" bucket
John Deere	310D	1992	4,200	G	$19,000	9/06	NEIN	TLB, 4WD, cab, Extendahoe
John Deere	310D	1995		G	$15,000	8/06	WCTX	Turbo, TLB, diesel, OROPS
John Deere	310D	1996	4,476	G	$37,250	2/06	NCCO	Backhoe & loader, 4×4, Extendahoe
John Deere	310E			G	$21,000	9/06	WCTX	TLB, diesel, EROPS, digging bucket
John Deere	310E			G	$21,000	9/06	WCTX	TLB, diesel, EROPS
John Deere	310E			G	$21,000	9/06	WCTX	TLB, diesel, EROPS
John Deere	310E			G	$21,500	9/06	WCTX	TLB, diesel, EROPS, digging bucket
John Deere	310E			G	$22,500	9/06	WCTX	TLB, diesel, EROPS, digging bucket
John Deere	310E			G	$22,500	9/06	WCTX	TLB, diesel, EROPS, digging bucket
John Deere	310E			G	$22,500	9/06	WCTX	TLB, diesel, EROPS, digging bucket
John Deere	310E		4,400	G	$23,500	8/06	SEPA	Loader/backhoe, mechanical front-wheel drive, CAH, fair rubber
John Deere	310E			G	$24,500	7/06	ECNY	TLB, 4WD, turbo diesel, EROPS
John Deere	310E	1997		G	$23,000	8/06	WCTX	TLB, 4WD, diesel, EROPS
John Deere	310E	1997		G	$24,000	8/06	WCTX	TLB, 4WD, diesel, OROPS
John Deere	310E	1997	4,335	F	$33,000	1/06	NWIL	Extendahoe, MFWD
John Deere	310E	1998		G	$21,000	8/06	WCTX	TLB, 4WD, diesel, ROPS
John Deere	310E	1998	4,100	G	$23,500	9/06	SECA	4WD

WHAT'S IT WORTH?

Construction Equipment

Make	Model	Year	Hrs.	Cond.	Price	Sale	Location	Comments
John Deere	310E	1998		G	$24,000	7/06	ECNY	TLB, 4WD, diesel, EROPS, Extendahoe, digging bucket
John Deere	310E	1998	3,765	G	$24,000	5/06	SWCA	Loader backhoe, quick disconnects, canopy
John Deere	310E	1999		G	$21,500	5/06	SWCA	Loader backhoe, Extendahoe, canopy
John Deere	310E	1999		G	$21,500	8/06	WCTX	TLB, diesel, OROPS, digging bucket
John Deere	310E	2000		G	$22,500	8/06	WCTX	TLB, diesel, OROPS, digging bucket
John Deere	310E	2000		G	$23,000	8/06	WCTX	TLB, diesel, OROPS, digging bucket
John Deere	310E	2000		G	$23,500	8/06	WCTX	TLB, diesel, OROPS, digging bucket
John Deere	310E	2000		G	$23,500	8/06	WCTX	TLB, diesel, OROPS, digging bucket
John Deere	310E	2000		G	$23,500	8/06	WCTX	ROPS, TLB, digging bucket
John Deere	310E	2000		G	$23,500	8/06	WCTX	TLB, diesel, OROPS, digging bucket
John Deere	310E	2000		G	$23,500	8/06	WCTX	TLB, diesel, OROPS, digging bucket
John Deere	310E	2000		G	$26,000	10/06	WCFL	TLB, diesel, OROPS, standard hoe, digging bucket
John Deere	310E	2000		G	$26,000	9/06	SECA	
John Deere	310E	2000		G	$26,500	7/06	ECNY	EROPS, TLB, 4WD, diesel, Extendahoe
John Deere	310E	2000		G	$26,500	9/06	SECA	
John Deere	310E	2000		G	$27,000	9/06	SECA	
John Deere	310E	2000		G	$27,500	7/06	ECNY	EROPS, TLB, 4WD, diesel, Extendahoe
John Deere	310E	2000		G	$28,500	10/06	WCFL	TLB, 4WD, diesel, OROPS, digging bucket
John Deere	310E	2000		G	$28,500	10/06	WCFL	TLB, 4WD, diesel, OROPS, digging bucket
John Deere	310G		1,546	G	$29,000	10/06	WCGA	4WD TLB
John Deere	310G			G	$31,000	7/06	ECNY	TLB, 4WD, diesel, EROPS, digging bucket
John Deere	310G		1,485	G	$32,000	10/06	WCGA	4WD, backhoe loader
John Deere	310G		1,759	G	$32,000	10/06	WCGA	4WD, TLB
John Deere	310G	2001		G	$29,000	9/06	SECA	
John Deere	310G	2001	2,097	G	$30,000	9/06	SECA	
John Deere	310G	2001	4,037	G	$34,000	5/06	SWCA	Loader backhoe, 4-in-1 bucket, canopy
John Deere	310G	2001	2,059	G	$36,000	9/06	SECA	
John Deere	310G	2003		G	$36,000	1/06	WCCA	4WD, loader backhoe
John Deere	310G	2005	500	G	$42,500	9/06	WCTX	TLB, 4×4, diesel, ROPS, Extendahoe
John Deere	310SE			G	$21,500	8/06	WCTX	TLB, diesel, OROPS, gp bucket
John Deere	310SE			G	$21,500	8/06	WCTX	TLB, diesel, OROPS, gp bucket
John Deere	310SE	1998		G	$28,000	8/06	SETN	4WD, loader backhoe, cab, Extendahoe
John Deere	310SE	1999		G	$23,500	9/06	WCTX	TLB, diesel, ROPS, digging bucket
John Deere	310SE	1999		G	$26,000	7/06	WCCA	4WD, 4-in-1 bucket, canopy, Extendahoe, Wain Roy coupler, 24" bucket
John Deere	310SE	2000		G	$27,500	10/06	WCFL	TLB, 4WD, diesel, OROPS
John Deere	310SE	2000		G	$29,500	9/06	NEIN	TLB, 4WD, cab, Extendahoe
John Deere	310SE	2000	2,995	G	$30,000	11/06	SWCA	4WD, 4-in-1 bucket
John Deere	310SE	2001		G	$24,000	8/06	WCTX	TLB, diesel, EROPS, digging bucket, flip pads, quick coupler
John Deere	310SE	2001		G	$26,000	8/06	WCTX	TLB, diesel, EROPS, digging bucket, flip pads, quick coupler
John Deere	310SG			G	$34,500	8/06	WCTX	TLB, 4WD, diesel, EROPS, digging bucket
John Deere	310SG	2001		G	$36,500	10/06	WCFL	TLB, 4WD, diesel, EROPS
John Deere	317	2005	3,000	G	$17,500	9/06	WCTX	Diesel, enclosed cab, air aux. hyd.
John Deere	317	2005	3,000	G	$17,500	9/06	WCTX	Diesel, enclosed cab, air aux. hyd.
John Deere	320	2004	1,050	G	$13,000	9/06	WCTX	Diesel, roll cage, hand controls, aux. hyd.
John Deere	3400	2003	1,500	G	$44,500	11/06	ECND	Telehandler, 100 hp., 4-spd. shuttle shift
John Deere	3800	2003	2,100	E	$36,500	11/06	SCSD	Telehandler, scoop w/ grapple
John Deere	400			F	$1,400	12/06	WCMN	Industrial loader, 7' bucket
John Deere	410		4,428	G	$5,000	9/06	SECA	

Construction Equipment

Make	Model	Year	Hrs.	Cond.	Price	Sale	Location	Comments
John Deere	410		7,232	G	$6,750	12/06	NEMN	
John Deere	410		7,232	G	$14,000	12/06	NEMN	
John Deere	410	2002		G	$39,000	10/06	WCFL	TLB, diesel, EROPS, diesel, 24" bucket
John Deere	410	2002		G	$39,000	10/06	WCFL	TLB, diesel, EROPS, diesel, 24" bucket
John Deere	410	2003		G	$47,500	11/06	SCCA	4WD, Extendahoe
John Deere	410B			G	$7,500	11/06	SETN	24" bucket, OROPS
John Deere	410B			G	$9,500	11/06	SCCA	EROPS
John Deere	410D			G	$15,000	5/06	SWCA	Loader backhoe, canopy
John Deere	410D			G	$18,000	9/06	NEIN	TLB, 4WD, Extendahoe, cab
John Deere	410E			G	$21,000	9/06	WCTX	TLB, diesel, OROPS, Extendahoe
John Deere	410E			G	$25,500	8/06	WCTX	TLB, 4WD, diesel, OROPS, digging bucket
John Deere	410E	1998	9,200	G	$20,000	9/06	NEIN	TLB, cab, heat, 4WD, Extendahoe, JD quick-tach
John Deere	410E	1999		G	$33,000	7/06	ECNY	TLB, 4WD, diesel, EROPS, Extendahoe, digging bucket
John Deere	420			F	$6,500	3/06	SEPA	Dozer, rebuilt undercarriage
John Deere	440C		3,746	G	$5,750	12/06	NEMN	Cable skidder
John Deere	444			G	$14,000	12/06	ECMN	Closed cab, new crate motor
John Deere	444	2005	6,000	G	$80,000	10/06	WCFL	Rubber-tired loader, diesel, OROPS, pin on bucket, front & rear fenders, engine enclosure
John Deere	444E		17,642	G	$17,000	5/06	SWCA	Rubber-tired loader, canopy
John Deere	444H			G	$33,500	10/06	WCFL	Rubber-tired loader, diesel, ROPS, hyd. quick attach
John Deere	444H			G	$35,000	8/06	SETN	Wheel loader, cab
John Deere	444H	1998		G	$55,000	11/06	SCCA	
John Deere	450			G	$13,000	8/06	WCIL	Crawler with bucket & forks
John Deere	450C			F	$7,850	3/06	SEPA	Dozer, ROPS, tilt blade
John Deere	450C			E	$16,500	12/06	SWWI	Dozer, undercarriage like new
John Deere	450E		6,718	G	$16,000	9/06	ECMN	6-way blade, 24" pads, 9' blade
John Deere	450G			G	$20,500	7/06	ECNY	Crawler, diesel, OROPS, 6-way blade
John Deere	450G	1989		G	$17,000	10/06	SENJ	Dozer
John Deere	450G	1996	3,000	G	$27,000	11/06	ECND	Crawler, LGP, 6-way blade, new undercarriage
John Deere	450G	1998		G	$25,500	10/06	WCFL	Crawler, diesel, ROPS, 6-way blade
John Deere	450G	1999		G	$26,000	10/06	WCFL	Crawler, diesel, ROPS, 6-way blade
John Deere	450G	1999		G	$26,000	10/06	WCFL	Crawler, diesel, ROPS, 6-way blade
John Deere	450H	2000		G	$30,000	9/06	WCTX	Crawler, diesel, ROPS, 6-way
John Deere	450H	2000		G	$32,500	10/06	WCFL	Crawler, diesel, ROPS, 6-way blade
John Deere	450H	2000		G	$39,000	9/06	SECA	Dozer
John Deere	450H	2001		G	$29,500	10/06	WCFL	Crawler, diesel, OROPS, sweeps, engine enclosure, long track, 6-way blade
John Deere	450H	2001		G	$30,000	9/06	WCTX	Crawler, diesel, OROPS, 6-way blade
John Deere	450H	2001		g	$31,000	10/06	WCFL	Crawler, diesel, OROPS, 6-way blade
John Deere	455D		2,300	G	$13,250	3/06	ECIN	Crawler, canopy, 4-in-1 bucket
John Deere	455E			G	$15,800	12/06	ECMO	
John Deere	455G			F	$19,500	3/06	SEPA	Track loader, new undercarriage
John Deere	480A			G	$3,500	3/06	ECMI	Rough terrain forklift
John Deere	486E	1999		G	$21,500	9/06	SECA	4×4 forklift
John Deere	490D			G	$15,000	3/06	SCIN	Excavator, 36" dirt bucket, thumb
John Deere	490E			G	$18,000	8/06	WCTX	Hyd. excavator, diesel, cab, digging bucket
John Deere	490E			G	$18,000	8/06	WCTX	Hyd. excavator, diesel, digging bucket
John Deere	490E	1994		G	$23,000	9/06	ECMN	27½" track, 3' bucket w/ thumb
John Deere	490E	1995		G	$22,000	2/06	WCSD	Excavator, cab, heat, steel track, 42" bucket

WHAT'S IT WORTH?

Construction Equipment

Make	Model	Year	Hrs.	Cond.	Price	Sale	Location	Comments
John Deere	50	2000	4,358	G	$21,000	11/06	SWCA	Mini excavator
John Deere	500C			G	$6,250	3/06	SCIN	Backhoe, cab
John Deere	510			G	$13,500	5/06	SWCA	4-in-1 bucket, canopy
John Deere	510	1982		G	$12,000	12/06	WCMN	Backhoe loader, 8' front. bucket, 35" hoe bucket, cab, heat, new rear tires, rebuilt hyd. pumps
John Deere	510C	1986	4,400	G	$20,000	3/06	WCMN	TLB, Extendahoe
John Deere	544			G	$8,500	11/06	SECA	ROPS
John Deere	544			F	$15,000	8/06	NECO	Wheel loader
John Deere	544	2005		G	$82,000	10/06	WCFL	Rubber-tired loader, diesel, OROPS, front windshield, gp bucket
John Deere	544A			G	$2,500	10/06	WCFL	Rubber-tired loader, diesel, OROPS, pin-on bucket
John Deere	544B			G	$11,000	12/06	ECMN	Closed cab, 8' bucket
John Deere	544D			G	$19,000	10/06	WCFL	Wheel loader
John Deere	544E			G	$26,000	10/06	WCFL	Wheel loader
John Deere	544E			G	$27,500	10/06	WCFL	Wheel loader
John Deere	544E			G	$34,000	10/06	WCFL	Wheel loader, cab
John Deere	544G			G	$23,000	7/06	WCCA	Bucket, third valve, cab, air
John Deere	544G			G	$27,000	9/06	WCTX	Rubber-tired loader, gp bucket, EROPS
John Deere	544GTC			G	$34,500	3/06	ECIN	Intergrated tool carrier, quick coupler, bucket & forks, cab
John Deere	544H			G	$50,000	7/06	ECNY	Rubber-tired loader, diesel, EROPS, gp bucket
John Deere	544H	1999	5,100	G	$60,000	11/06	ECND	End loader, standard material bucket, near new rubber
John Deere	544H	2000		G	$39,000	10/06	WCFL	Rubber-tired loader, diesel, ROPS, gp bucket
John Deere	550			G	$12,500	3/06	SCIN	6-way blade
John Deere	550			G	$13,500	3/06	ECIN	Crawler, diesel, 6-way blade, lever steer, PS
John Deere	550	2004	400	E	$70,000	3/06	ECIN	Crawler tractor, 105" blade, 18" pads, canopy, 6-way blade
John Deere	550A			G	$11,500	9/06	NEIN	Crawler, canopy, 300 hours on rebuilt engine, sweeps, 6-way blade
John Deere	550C			G	$13,000	6/06	NEIN	Angle blade
John Deere	550C			G	$17,500	8/06	NCMI	Dozer, 6-way blade, recent OH, 90% tracks, ROPS, sweeps
John Deere	550G			G	$20,000	3/06	ECIN	Crawler, diesel canopy, 6-way blade
John Deere	550G			G	$21,000	9/06	WCTX	Crawler, diesel, ROPS, 6-way blade
John Deere	550G	1993	10,880	G	$19,500	9/06	NEIN	Crawler, grade control, canopy, 6-way blade
John Deere	550G	1995	4,800	G	$25,500	12/06	ECMN	24" pads, lever steer, new paint
John Deere	550G	1997	6,400	G	$26,500	9/06	ECMN	LGP Series, 6 way, OROPS, undercarriage 75%
John Deere	550G	1997	6,400	G	$26,500	9/06	ECMN	LGP Series, 6 way, OROPS
John Deere	550H	2001		G	$35,000	9/06	WCTX	Crawler, diesel, OROPS, 6-way blade
John Deere	550H	2001		G	$35,000	9/06	WCTX	Crawler, diesel, OROPS, 6-way blade
John Deere	550H	2001		G	$39,000	7/06	ECNY	Crawler, diesel, EROPS, air, limb risers
John Deere	550H	2002		G	$42,500	10/06	WCFL	Crawler, diesel, 75/84 hp., OROPS, engine enclosure
John Deere	570A			G	$16,500	3/06	ECIN	Grader, hyd. tip control, hyd. sliding moldboard, front-mounted scarifier
John Deere	624E		17,755	G	$27,500	5/06	SEWY	Payloader, 3-yard bucket, Schlagel grapple, third valve
John Deere	624H	1999		G	$40,000	10/06	WCFL	Rubber-tired loader, 160-hp. diesel, ROPS
John Deere	624H	2000		G	$42,500	10/06	WCFL	Rubber-tired loader, diesel, EROPS, gp bucket
John Deere	624H	2000		G	$42,500	10/06	WCFL	Rubber-tired loader, diesel, EROPS, gp bucket
John Deere	624H	2000		G	$56,000	10/06	WCFL	Rubber-tired loader, diesel, EROPS, gp bucket
John Deere	644			G	$5,500	7/06	ECNY	Rubber-tired loader, diesel, EROPS, gp bucket
John Deere	644B	1977		G	$16,500	4/06	SEND	Wheel loader, cab, heater, 2½-yard bucket
John Deere	644B	1978	5,635	G	$34,000	11/06	ECND	Payloader, 4-in-1 bucket, one owner, always farm loader

Construction Equipment

Make	Model	Year	Hrs.	Cond.	Price	Sale	Location	Comments
John Deere	644E	1992	6,883	G	$45,000	11/06	SCCA	
John Deere	644G			G	$30,000	8/06	WCTX	Rubber-tired loader, diesel, EROPS, gp bucket, digging bucket
John Deere	644G			G	$30,000	8/06	WCTX	Rubber-tired loader, diesel, EROPS
John Deere	644G	1995	4,500	G	$55,000	11/06	ECND	Payloader, CAH, shuttle shift, rear weights, 3-yard bucket
John Deere	644G	1998		G	$55,000	11/06	SECA	Cab, air, gp bucket
John Deere	644H	1999		G	$50,000	10/06	WCFL	Rubber-tired loader, 170 hp. diesel, ROPS, 3.5-4 cubic yard gp bucket
John Deere	644H	2000	7,654	G	$61,000	11/06	SWCA	Rubber-tired loader
John Deere	648	2005		E	$137,500	3/06	WCWA	Grapple skidder, dual function grapple, clearing blade, cab
John Deere	648D	1986		G	$9,750	12/06	ECMN	4×4 sweeps, brush guards, dual function grapple, stacking blade
John Deere	650	1999		G	$40,000	1/06	WCOH	Crawler, diesel, ROPS
John Deere	650G			G	$21,500	10/06	WCFL	Crawler, diesel, ROPS, 6-way blade
John Deere	650G			G	$24,500	7/06	ECNY	Crawler, diesel, OROPS, 6-way blade
John Deere	650G	1997		G	$24,500	3/06	ECIN	Crawler, lever steer, canopy, 6-way blade
John Deere	650G	1998		G	$33,000	11/06	SCCA	Loader, rear ripper
John Deere	650G	1999		G	$33,000	8/06	WCTX	Crawler, diesel, OROPS, 6-way blade
John Deere	650H			F	$48,000	10/06	WCFL	Crawler, damaged by rollover
John Deere	650H	2000		G	$32,500	10/06	WCFL	Crawler, diesel, ROPS, 6-way blade
John Deere	650H	2000		G	$37,000	10/06	WCFL	Crawler, diesel, ROPS, 6-way blade
John Deere	650H LGP	1999		G	$40,000	1/06	WCOH	Crawler tractor, diesel, ROPS
John Deere	650H LGP	2000		G	$40,000	10/06	WCFL	Crawler, diesel, ROPS, 6-way blade
John Deere	655B			F	$15,000	2/06	WCIL	Crawler/loader, EROPS, hydro, 4-in-1 bucket, hyd. leak
John Deere	670			G	$14,000	9/06	WCTX	Motor grader, JD diesel, EROPS, front scarifier
John Deere	670A			G	$18,500	1/06	WCOH	EROPS, motor grader, diesel, hyd. tip & sideshift moldboard, trans. rebuilt by JD
John Deere	670A			G	$18,500	1/06	WCOH	Motor grader, diesel, EROPS
John Deere	690		8,463	G	$18,500	12/06	NEMN	Excavator
John Deere	690A			G	$11,000	4/06	SEND	Track excavator, 36" bucket
John Deere	690B			G	$12,000	9/06	NEIN	Excavator, 41,000 lb.
John Deere	690C	1986		G	$27,500	4/06	SEND	Track excavator, 36" bucket
John Deere	70			G	$12,000	9/06	NEIN	Excavator, front-leveling blade, cab
John Deere	710B		699	G	$12,000	3/06	ECIN	Diesel, soundguard cab, ps
John Deere	710B	1999	218	G	$31,000	9/06	SECA	Turbo, backhoe loader
John Deere	710D			G	$17,000	9/06	SECA	
John Deere	710D	1995		G	$19,000	7/06	ECNY	TLB, turbo diesel, EROPS, gp bucket, digging bucket
John Deere	710D	1996		G	$27,500	7/06	ECNY	TLB, 4WD, turbo, 6 cyl., rear aux. hyd. powershift trans., gp bucket
John Deere	710D	1998		G	$17,000	9/06	SECA	
John Deere	744E			G	$34,000	7/06	ECNY	Rubber-tired loader, EROPS, coupler, front hyd.
John Deere	750B			G	$24,000	3/06	SCIN	Dozer, 6-way blade, ROPS
John Deere	750B	1988	2,481	G	$20,250	4/06	WCWI	Crawler dozer
John Deere	762			G	$8,500	1/06	WCOH	Motor scraper, diesel, ROPS
John Deere	762	1981		G	$13,250	3/06	ECMI	ROPS, powershift, 11 yard, 175 hp., fresh paint
John Deere	762A	1986		G	$14,000	3/06	ECMI	Cab, powershift, 11 yard
John Deere	770	1987		F	$32,500	2/06	WCSD	770B motor grader, rear ripper, front scarifier, heater, air, 12,000 hours, no guarantee
John Deere	770A			G	$26,000	9/06	ECMN	Wing

WHAT'S IT WORTH?

Construction Equipment

Make	Model	Year	Hrs.	Cond.	Price	Sale	Location	Comments
John Deere	770B			G	$40,500	9/06	WCTX	Motor grader, JD diesel, EROPS, front scarifier
John Deere	772	1996		G	$31,000	11/06	SCCA	Motor grader, 6WD, 14'
John Deere	790E			G	$35,000	9/06	WCTX	Hyd. excavator, diesel, enclosed cab, long undercarriage
John Deere	850			G	$12,000	12/06	NEMN	Dozer
John Deere	850	1990	11,240	F	$19,500	11/06	ECND	Dozer, CAH, 10½' dozer, undercarriage 20%, new sprockets
John Deere	850B	1992	6,500	G	$18,000	11/06	ECND	Hyd. tilt dozer, ROPS canopy
John Deere	850C	1995		G	$39,000	5/06	ECNE	Dozer, cab, air, sweeps
John Deere	850C	1997	2,500	G	$29,000	11/06	ECND	Series 1 LGP dozer, CAH, hyd. tilt blade
John Deere	855			G	$32,000	11/06	SWCA	Crawler loader
John Deere	860A			G	$3,250	11/06	SWCA	Self-elevating motor scraper, cab
John Deere	862			G	$7,500	9/06	NEIN	Scraper, canopy
John Deere	892D-LC			F	$16,000	9/06	NEIN	Excavator, one track locks up, boom ROPS on its own
John Deere	892ELC			G	$35,000	7/06	ECNY	Hyd. excavator, diesel, cab, wide pads
John Deere	892ELC	1996		G	$33,000	9/06	NEIN	Excavator, rebuilt engine, hyd. pump, swing motor
John Deere	9300			G	$13,000	6/06	NEIN	Backhoe attachment fits JD 550 dozer
John Deere	PR72			G	$2,500	5/06	ECMI	72" power landscape rake
JLG	2030	2005		G	$7,700	7/06	SEND	2030ES, scissor lift, 20'×30", low hours
JLG	2033	1998		G	$1,250	10/06	WCFL	
JLG	2033	1998		G	$1,250	10/06	WCFL	
JLG	2033	1998		G	$1,750	10/06	WCFL	Scissors lift, electric powered, 20' lift
JLG	2033	1998		G	$1,750	10/06	WCFL	Scissors lift, electric powered, 20' lift
JLG	2033	1998		G	$2,000	10/06	WCFL	Scissors, electric
JLG	2033	1998		G	$2,200	10/06	WCFL	Scissors lift, electric powered, 20' lift
JLG	2033	1998		G	$2,700	10/06	WCFL	Scissors, electric
JLG	2646			G	$2,100	9/06	SECA	
JLG	2646			G	$2,700	9/06	SECA	
JLG	2646			G	$3,250	10/06	SCPA	Scissors lift, electric
JLG	2646			G	$3,250	10/06	SCPA	Scissors lift, electric
JLG	2646			G	$3,250	10/06	SCPA	Scissors lift, electric
JLG	2646	1998		G	$2,500	10/06	WCFL	Scissors lift, electric
JLG	2646	1998		G	$2,750	10/06	WCFL	Scissors lift, electric
JLG	2646	1998		G	$2,750	10/06	WCFL	Scissors lift, electric, 26' lift
JLG	2646	1998		G	$3,000	9/06	WCTX	Scissors lift, electric, 26' lift
JLG	2646	1998		G	$3,000	10/06	WCFL	Scissors lift, electric, 26' lift
JLG	2646	1998		G	$3,200	10/06	WCFL	Scissors lift, electric
JLG	2646	1998		G	$3,200	10/06	WCFL	Scissors lift, electric
JLG	2646	1998		G	$3,350	10/06	WCFL	Scissors lift, electric
JLG	2646	1999	397	G	$3,400	10/06	WCFL	Scissors lift, electric powered, 26' lift
JLG	2646	1999	397	G	$3,500	10/06	WCFL	Scissors lift, electric powered, 26' lift
JLG	2646	1999	397	G	$3,500	10/06	WCFL	Scissors lift, electric powered, 26' lift
JLG	35	1997		G	$3,250	9/06	WCTX	Boom lift, 35' lift
JLG	40	1998		G	$6,750	1/06	WCOH	Scissors lift, dual fuel, 40' lift, rough terrain
JLG	45			G	$4,000	9/06	SECA	Boom lift
JLG	60H			G	$6,500	5/06	SWCA	66' lift, boom lift, 500-lb. capacity, diesel
JLG	60H			G	$8,000	5/06	SWCA	60' lift, boom lift, 500-lb. capacity, dual fuel
Kelly	55			G	$1,500	5/06	SEWY	Backhoe, 3 point, 14" bucket
Kelly	55			G	$1,950	3/06	NCOH	3-point backhoe
Kelly	55			G	$2,400	1/06	WCCA	Backhoe attach

Construction Equipment

Make	Model	Year	Hrs.	Cond.	Price	Sale	Location	Comments
Kelly	NA			G	$0	8/06	WCMN	No sale at $4,000, 3-point backhoe
Kobelco	K907D-LC			G	$16,000	9/06	NEIN	Excavator
Kobelco	SK200	1998		G	$35,000	6/06	NEIN	Excavator
Kobelco	SK200LC			G	$22,000	9/06	NEIN	Excavator, diesel, pilot control, 44,500 lb.
Kobelco	SK200LC	1998		G	$34,500	8/06	WCTX	Hyd. excavator, diesel, long undercarriage
Kobelco	SK200LC	1998		G	$34,500	8/06	WCTX	Hyd. excavator, diesel, cab, long undercarriage
Kobelco	SK210LC	2005		G	$106,000	1/06	WCOH	Hyd. excavator, diesel, cab, air, digging bucket
Kobelco	SK210LC	2005	400	E	$106,000	1/06	WCOH	Hyd. excavator, diesel, cab, air, digging bucket
Kobelco	SK220LC	1998		G	$36,000	9/06	WCTX	Hyd. excavator, diesel, cab, air, long stick
Kobelco	SK300	1998		G	$105,000	3/06	WCWA	Swing yarder, excavator, Jewell yarder package, Acme carriage, gp bucket, cab
Kobelco	SK300LC			G	$29,000	9/06	WCTX	Hyd. excavator, diesel, digging bucket
Kobelco	SK300LC	1998		G	$36,000	10/06	WCFL	Hyd. excavator, Cummins diesel
Kobelco	SK300LC	1998		G	$39,000	10/06	NCWI	Hyd. excavator, diesel, cab, air, long undercarriage, smooth lip bucket
Kobelco	SK300LC	1999		G	$65,000	1/06	WCOH	Hyd. excavator, diesel, cab, air, 54" digging bucket
Kobelco	SK330LC	1999		G	$65,000	1/06	WCOH	Hyd. excavator, diesel, cab, air, medium stick, 54" digging bucket
Kobelco	SK330LC	2002		G	$53,500	10/06	WCFL	Hyd. excavator, diesel, cab, digging bucket
Kobelco	SK330LC	2002		G	$66,000	10/06	WCFL	Hyd. excavator, diesel, cab, digging bucket
Koehring	405			G	$2,500	10/06	SENJ	Crane
Koehring	6608			G	$9,750	3/06	ECMI	Hyd. excavator, dozer blade, steel tracks
Koehring	6608	1985		G	$13,500	9/06	ECMN	Blade
Koehring	6625			G	$4,000	9/06	NEIN	Excavator
Koehring	6644			G	$7,000	12/06	NEMN	Excavator
Komatsu	D20			G	$4,000	8/06	SETN	Crawler, OROPS
Komatsu	D20P			G	$3,250	3/06	ECMI	6-way blade, ROPS
Komatsu	D21P-7	1997		G	$14,500	7/06	ECNY	Crawler, diesel, EROPS, 6-way blade
Komatsu	D31			G	$15,250	3/06	NCMN	D31A, 6-way dozer
Komatsu	D31A			G	$11,000	10/06	SWOH	Crawler, diesel, OROPS, 6-way blade
Komatsu	D31A	1977		G	$12,500	7/06	SEND	Dozer, fresh OH out of frame, nice tight machine
Komatsu	D31E	2003	2,758	G	$37,250	9/06	NEIN	Crawler, new undercarriage, 6-way blade
Komatsu	D31E	2003	2,758	G	$39,000	9/06	NEIN	Crawler, new undercarriage, 6-way blade
Komatsu	D31P	1981		G	$9,250	3/06	ECMI	Long track, foot steer, 6-way blade
Komatsu	D31P	1993		G	$18,000	3/06	WCWA	Crawler tractor, 6-way blade, canopy
Komatsu	D31P	1999		G	$18,250	11/06	ECND	Crawler, 6-way dozer
Komatsu	D31P-20	1997	4,456	G	$21,000	12/06	ECMN	80% undercarriage, OROPS, 6-way blade
Komatsu	D31P-20A	1999	908	G	$22,000	11/06	ECND	Dozer, open station, 6-way blade, 24" tracks
Komatsu	D-31S	1983		G	$12,500	9/06	ECMN	New undercarriage
Komatsu	D37E			G	$9,000	6/06	NEIN	Dozer, 6-way blade
Komatsu	D37E			G	$28,500	3/06	ECIN	Crawler, canopy, 6-way blade
Komatsu	D39P		4,100	G	$26,000	7/06	WCTN	Dozer, 6-way blade
Komatsu	D41E			G	$29,000	10/06	SWOH	Crawler, Komatsu diesel, OROPS, 6-way blade, single lever trans.
Komatsu	D41E	1998		G	$32,500	8/06	WCTX	Crawler, diesel, ROPS, 6-way blade
Komatsu	D41P			G	$14,500	9/06	ECMN	EROPS, Turbo II, wide pad, tilt blade, 9'9" blade
Komatsu	D41P		4,900	G	$21,000	9/06	NEIN	Crawler, canopy, 28" pads
Komatsu	D41P			G	$28,000	9/06	WCTX	Crawler, diesel, OROPS, 6-way blade
Komatsu	D41P		4,900	G	$32,500	9/06	NEIN	Crawler, canopy, 28" pads

Construction Equipment

Make	Model	Year	Hrs.	Cond.	Price	Sale	Location	Comments
Komatsu	D41P	1985		G	$12,000	3/06	ECMI	28" pads, 4-way blade, 95 hp.
Komatsu	D65E			G	$22,500	12/06	WCIL	6" dozer, 4-way 11' hyd. blade, ROPS, 24' pads
Komatsu	D65EX-12	1994		G	$50,000	2/06	WCIL	Dozer, EROPS, air, recent undercarriage, 1,400 hours on major OH, undercarriage good, cab, appearance average
Komatsu	D65P-6			G	$14,000	3/06	ECIN	Diesel
Komatsu	D65PX	2000		G	$41,000	10/06	WCFL	Crawler, diesel, ROPS, torque converter
Komatsu	FG25C			G	$3,500	8/06	SEPA	Forklift, gas/propane, 5,000-lb. capacity
Komatsu	FG25C			G	$4,500	8/06	SEPA	Forklift, gas/propane, 5,000-lb. capacity
Komatsu	FG25C			G	$4,500	8/06	SEPA	Forklift, gas/propane, 5,000-lb. capacity
Komatsu	PC100	1996	5,392	G	$21,750	9/06	ECMN	Diesel, 20" pads, 33" bucket, thumb, 8' stick, air, heat, radio
Komatsu	PC128US	1999		G	$37,500	3/06	WCWA	Hyd. excavator
Komatsu	PC150LC	1997		G	$47,500	1/06	WCPA	Hyd. excavator, diesel, cab
Komatsu	PC200			G	$10,500	3/06	SCIN	Excavator
Komatsu	PC200	1997		G	$32,000	7/06	WCPA	Hyd. excavator, diesel, cab, digging bucket
Komatsu	PC200LC			G	$13,750	3/06	SCIN	Excavator
Komatsu	PC200LC			G	$16,000	3/06	SCIN	Excavator
Komatsu	PC200LC	2003		G	$72,500	10/06	WCFL	Long reach excavator, diesel, cab, 50' long reach arm, 60" digging bucket
Komatsu	PC200LC	2005	1,400	G	$102,500	8/06	WCTX	Hyd. excavator, diesel, cab, air, 32" pads, digging bucket
Komatsu	PC200LC	2005	1,400	G	$102,500	8/06	WCTX	Hyd. excavator, diesel, cab, air digging bucket
Komatsu	PC200LC-3	1989		G	$6,100	10/06	SENJ	Excavator
Komatsu	PC200LC-6	1997		G	$41,000	9/06	WCTX	Hyd. excavator, diesel, enclosed cab, long undercarriage
Komatsu	PC200LC-6	1999		G	$55,000	1/06	WCNH	Hyd. excavator, diesel, cab, long undercarriage, new bottom
Komatsu	PC220			G	$14,000	6/06	NEIN	Excavator
Komatsu	PC220LC			G	$19,500	7/06	ECNY	Hyd. excavator, diesel, cab, long undercarriage, digging bucket
Komatsu	PC220LC			G	$27,000	3/06	ECIN	Excavator, diesel, plumbed
Komatsu	PC220LC	2001		G	$51,000	9/06	WCTX	Hyd. excavator, diesel, cab, reach boom, long undercarriage, digging bucket
Komatsu	PC220LC	2001		G	$66,500	1/06	WCNH	Hyd. excavator, diesel, cab, air, long undercarriage, Esco bucket
Komatsu	PC300	1994		F	$25,000	11/06	ECND	Excavator, Cummins engine, long stick, good undercarriage, recent new hyd. pump & engine OH, new injectors & pump
Komatsu	PC300	1998		G	$43,500	10/06	WCFL	Hyd. excavator, diesel, cab, digging bucket
Komatsu	PC300LC-3	1996		G	$37,000	1/06	WCPA	Hyd. excavator, diesel, cab
Komatsu	PC300LC5			G	$30,000	1/06	WCPA	Hyd. excavator, diesel, cab
Komatsu	PC35	1998		G	$11,500	1/06	WCOH	Hyd. excavator
Komatsu	PC400LC-6			G	$35,500	10/06	SWOH	Hyd. excavator, Komatsu diesel, cab, reach boom, standard stick, Esco 48" bucket
Komatsu	PC400LC-6	1998		G	$85,000	1/06	WCNH	Hyd. excavator, diesel, cab, long undercarriage, digging bucket
Komatsu	PC400LC-6	2002		G	$60,000	10/06	WCFL	Hyd. excavator
Komatsu	PC400LC-6	2002		G	$83,000	10/06	WCFL	Hyd. excavator
Komatsu	PC50		3,808	G	$10,600	8/06	SETN	Mini excavator, swivel boom, rubber tracks, front blade
Komatsu	PC50	1994		G	$8,500	3/06	WCWA	Mini excavator, gp bucket, rubber tracks
Komatsu	PC50UUU	1990	1,042	G	$10,750	11/06	ECND	Excavator, offset boom

Construction Equipment

Make	Model	Year	Hrs.	Cond.	Price	Sale	Location	Comments
Komatsu	PC60			G	$28,500	1/06	WCNH	Hyd. excavator
Komatsu	PC75UU-2			F	$14,600	3/06	SEPA	Track excavator, ROPS, rubber track
Komatsu	WA180-1			G	$39,000	3/06	ECIN	Rubber-tired loader, cab, third valve, bucket, forks
Komatsu	WA180-1	2003		G	$42,500	11/06	SWCA	Rubber-tired loader
Komatsu	WA250		5,400	G	$45,000	11/06	SETN	Cab
Komatsu	WA320	1989		G	$27,000	3/06	ECMI	150 hp., cab, 3.5 gp bucket
Komatsu	WA350			F	$8,000	4/06	WCSD	Loader, no engine, tire size 23.5-25
Komatsu	WA350			G	$20,500	1/06	WCOH	Rubber-tired loader, diesel, ROPS, gp bucket
Komatsu	WA350			G	$27,000	9/06	NEIN	Rubber-tired loader
Komatsu	WA420			F	$18,000	4/06	WCSD	Loader, runs, 26.5-25 tires
Komatsu	WA420	1994		G	$33,000	8/06	WCTX	Rubber-tired loader, diesel, EROPS, gp bucket
Komatsu	WA450			G	$35,250	2/06	SCNY	Nice machine
Komatsu	WB140	1999		G	$18,500	11/06	SWCA	4WD
Komatsu	WB140	1999		G	$21,000	11/06	SWCA	Canopy
Komatsu	WB140	2000		G	$21,500	7/06	ECNY	TLB, 4WD, diesel, EROPS, air, heat, hazard lights, engine enclosure
Komatsu	WB140	2000		G	$22,000	7/06	ECNY	TLB, 4WD, diesel, EROPS, front & rear wipers
Komatsu	WB140	2000		G	$22,500	7/06	WCPA	4WD, diesel, EROPS, hazard lights, rear wipers, engine enclosure, gp bucket, digging bucket
Komatsu	WB140	2000	1,980	G	$25,000	3/06	ECIN	Loader backhoe, diesel, 4WD, Extendahoe
Kubota	B20			G	$7,200	8/06	WCTX	TLB, 4WD, diesel, OROPS, digging bucket
Kubota	B20			G	$8,000	9/06	WCTX	TLB, diesel, EROPS, digging bucket
Kubota	B21			G	$12,000	9/06	WCTX	TLB, diesel, EROPS
Kubota	B2410	2004		G	$4,500	1/06	WCOH	Diesel, utility, ROPS, hydro drive
Kubota	B2910			G	$7,500	8/06	WCTX	TLB, 4WD, diesel, front loader, 3-point hitch
Kubota	KX71		160	G	$21,300	3/06	SEPA	Mini excavator, rubber track, warranty
Kubota	KX91-2S			G	$10,100	3/06	NWTN	Excavator, OROPS, front blade, rubber tracks
Kubota	KX91-2S			G	$12,100	9/06	NWTN	Excavator, OROPS, front blade, rubber tracks
Kubota	L35			F	$14,400	3/06	SEPA	Backhoe/loader, MFWD, ROPS, average rubber
Kubota	L35		650	F	$19,500	3/06	SEPA	Backhoe/loader, MFWD, ROPS
Link-Belt	2700			G	$35,000	9/06	NEIN	Quantum excavator, pilot controls
Link-Belt	LS2800	1987		G	$19,000	9/06	SECA	Excavator
Link-Belt	LS3400			G	$20,000	11/06	SWCA	Hyd. excavator
Link-Belt	NA			F	$2,000	8/06	NCMI	30' dragline, diesel engine, 1.5-yard bucket, travel gears just went but good running condition
Loadall	NA			G	$33,500	9/06	SECA	
Long	1199B			G	$2,400	5/06	SEWY	Backhoe, 3 point, 16" bucket
Long	510			F	$200	1/06	WCCA	(2) ss tanks, front fold spray boom
Lull	1044			G	$1,999	7/06	WCPA	Telescopic forklift, 4WD, diesel, ROPS
Lull	1044	2000		G	$42,000	10/06	WCFL	Telescoping forklift
Lull	644		3,378	G	$25,000	8/06	SETN	Telescoping boom lift, 34' reach
Lull	644	1999		G	$21,000	10/06	WCFL	Telescoping forklift
Lull	644	1999		G	$21,000	10/06	WCFL	Telescoping forklift
Lull	644	1999		G	$22,000	10/06	WCFL	Telescoping forklift
Lull	644	1999		G	$22,000	10/06	WCFL	Telescoping forklift
Lull	644	1999		G	$22,000	10/06	WCFL	Telescoping forklift
Lull	644	1999		G	$22,000	10/06	WCFL	Telescoping forklift, 4WD, diesel, ROPS
Lull	644	1999		G	$22,500	10/06	WCFL	Telescoping forklift, 4WD, diesel, ROPS
Lull	644	1999		G	$22,500	10/06	WCFL	Telescoping forklift

WHAT'S IT WORTH?

Construction Equipment

Make	Model	Year	Hrs.	Cond.	Price	Sale	Location	Comments
Lull	644	1999		G	$23,500	8/06	WCTX	Telescoping forklift, 4WD, diesel, ROPS
Lull	644	1999		G	$24,000	10/06	WCFL	Telescoping forklift
Lull	644	1999		G	$24,000	10/06	WCFL	Telescoping forklift
Lull	644	1999		G	$24,000	9/06	WCTX	Telescoping forklift, 4×4, diesel, ROPS
Lull	644	1999		G	$24,500	9/06	WCTX	Telescoping forklift, 4×4, diesel, ROPS, 34' lift, 6,000 lb.
Lull	644	1999		G	$29,500	1/06	WCOH	Telescoping forklift, 4WD, diesel, ROPS
Lull	644	2000		G	$31,500	10/06	SWOH	Telescoping forklift, diesel, ROPS
Lull	644B	1998		G	$25,000	10/06	WCFL	Telescoping forklift, 4WD, diesel
Lull	644B	1998		G	$25,500	12/06	WCMN	37' telescopic shooter boom, 6,000 lb., 37' reach, 4WD, 4-wheel steer, JD diesel engine
Lull	644B	1999		G	$24,000	10/06	WCFL	Telescoping forklift, 4WD, diesel
Lull	644B	1999		G	$24,000	10/06	WCFL	Telescoping forklift, 4WD, diesel
Lull	644B	1999		G	$24,000	10/06	WCFL	Telescoping forklift, 4WD, diesel
Lull	644B	1999		G	$25,000	10/06	WCFL	Telescoping forklift, 4WD, diesel
Lull	644TT-34			G	$20,000	5/06	ECMI	Shooting boom forklift, diesel, 6,000-lb. capacity, 4×4
Lull	844B			G	$11,500	9/06	NEIN	Telescoping forklift, diesel
Lull	844C-42	1999		G	$32,500	8/06	WCTX	Telescoping forklift, 4WD, diesel, ROPS
Lull	844C-42	1999		G	$32,500	8/06	WCTX	Telescoping forklift, 4WD, diesel, ROPS
Lull	844TT-34	1989		G	$11,100	10/06	SENJ	Highlander forklift
Lull	NA	2004		G	$53,000	1/06	WCNH	Telescoping forklift
Manitou	MLT 629		3,416	G	$21,000	11/06	WCMN	Telehandler
MEC	2033			G	$1,600	5/06	ECMI	Scissors lift, electric, 20' lift
MEC	2033			G	$2,000	5/06	ECMI	Scissors lift, electric, 20' lift
Melroe	320			G	$8,800	3/06	NWIL	Diesel
Melroe	322			G	$8,000	11/06	SWCA	Mini excavator
Melroe	322			G	$9,500	11/06	SWCA	Mini excavator
Melroe	322			G	$11,750	11/06	SWCA	Mini excavator
Melroe	322	2000		G	$7,250	11/06	SWCA	Poly tracks
Melroe	325			G	$6,500	9/06	SECA	Mini excavator
Melroe	325			F	$9,800	3/06	SEPA	Mini excavator, Bobcat
Melroe	325		3,415	G	$10,750	8/06	SETN	Excavator, diesel, front blade
Melroe	325	1999		G	$5,500	9/06	WCTX	Hyd. excavator, diesel, canopy, rubber track
Melroe	331			G	$7,000	9/06	WCTX	Hyd. excavator, diesel
Melroe	331		1,649	G	$13,000	8/06	SETN	ROPS, rubber tracks
Melroe	331	1999		G	$12,000	11/06	SWCA	Mini excavator, poly tracks, canopy
Melroe	331	1999		G	$15,000	11/06	SWCA	Mini excavator, poly tracks, canopy
Melroe	331E	2004	900	G	$24,500	9/06	NEIN	
Melroe	337	2003		G	$29,000	9/06	NEIN	Excavator, cab, air, aux. hyd., quick 4-change bucket
Melroe	811			G	$2,250	11/06	SWCA	Backhoe attach.
Melroe	909			G	$2,800	3/06	SCIN	Backhoe attach, 12" & 16" buckets
Melroe	911			G	$4,000	11/06	SWCA	Backhoe attach.
MF	24			G	$7,500	5/06	SWCA	Forward reach forklift, 4WD, Perkins diesel, canopy
MF	2500			G	$18,000	10/06	WCFL	Rough terrain forklift
MF	40		4,100	G	$6,400	8/06	NWIL	Forklift, side shift, engine OH, 16.9-24 drive tires
MF	40B			G	$3,500	11/06	SWCA	4WD, rear counterweight
MF	50			G	$10,500	11/06	SWCA	4WD, 3 valve, rear scraper
MF	50C		3,200	G	$8,500	11/06	WCMN	TLB, one owner
MF	50E		1,549	G	$4,100	11/06	SWCA	4WD, loader bucket
MF	50E		1,549	G	$5,500	11/06	SWCA	4WD, loader bucket

Construction Equipment

Make	Model	Year	Hrs.	Cond.	Price	Sale	Location	Comments
MF	55			G	$800	3/06	SCIN	Backhoe attach.
MF	6500			G	$4,000	1/06	WCCA	4WD, 48" forks
MF	6500H			G	$7,500	1/06	WCCA	48" forks, 15012 stage
MF	708			G	$5,600	10/06	NCND	Loader backhoe
Michigan	125B			G	$5,250	9/06	NEIN	Rubber-tired loader, diesel, cab, gp bucket
Michigan	175			G	$4,500	9/06	NEIN	Rubber-tired loader, Detroit diesel, cab, gp bucket
Michigan	175B			G	$4,800	3/06	SCIN	Articulated loader, 4-yard bucket
Michigan	175B			G	$5,500	3/06	ECIN	Rubber-tired loader, diesel, 5-yard bucket
Michigan	175B			G	$6,500	3/06	ECIN	Rubber-tired loader, diesel, 5-yard bucket
Michigan	210H			G	$2,600	10/06	SWOH	Motor scraper, Cummins diesel, Hancock self-loading rear scraper
Michigan	35			G	$3,100	9/06	ECMN	Front end loader, Detroit diesel, all-wheel steer, 4WD
Michigan	55B			G	$9,000	3/06	ECIN	Rubber-tired loader
Michigan	75			G	$4,500	12/06	ECMN	Front end loader, 8.5' bucket, closed cab
Michigan	75A			F	$2,900	8/06	WCMN	Waukesha diesel engine, 1⅓-yard with round bale attachment, 14:00×24 rubber
Michigan	L160V			G	$15,500	9/06	NEIN	Rubber-tired loader
Mitsubishi	BD 2G			G	$7,750	1/06	WCOH	Crawler tractor, diesel, canopy, 6-way blade
Mitsubishi	BD 2G			G	$9,000	6/06	NEIN	6-way blade
Mitsubishi	FG20			G	$4,750	3/06	WCWA	Forklift, 3 stage, 188" lift, LP power
Mitsubishi	FG25			G	$9,850	2/06	WCIL	FG25F17B gas fork truck with 700-12 pneumatic tires, 5,000 lb., 2-stage mast, completely reconditioned 41.6 hours ago, sold separate: 2 extra sets of pallet tines ($450 & $150)
Mitsubishi	FGC25	1997		G	$3,250	9/06	WCTX	Forklift, diesel, 5,000-lb. capacity
National	NA			G	$700	12/06	ECMN	Teleboom for truck or trailer
New Holland	435		400	E	$43,000	12/06	SWWI	435A Telehandler
New Holland	445	1996		G	$9,500	11/06	SWCA	4WD, Gannon 4-valve, rear scraper
New Holland	555E			G	$13,500	10/06	WCFL	TLB, diesel, OROPS, digging bucket
New Holland	555E		1,935	G	$17,500	7/06	ECNY	TLB, 4WD, diesel, OROPS, gp bucket, Extendahoe, thumb
New Holland	555E		1,847	G	$23,000	1/06	WCOH	Loader backhoe, 4WD, diesel
New Holland	555E		1,847	G	$23,000	1/06	WCOH	TLB, 4WD, diesel, OROPS, standard hoe
New Holland	555E	1999		G	$13,000	11/06	SWCA	Extendahoe
New Holland	555E	1999		G	$17,000	9/06	WCTX	TLB, diesel, OROPS, gp bucket
New Holland	555E	1999		G	$23,000	7/06	ECNY	TLB, 4WD, diesel, EROPS, Extendahoe, gp bucket, digging bucket
New Holland	555E	2000	1,778	G	$21,500	8/06	WCTX	TLB, 4WD, diesel, ROPS, third valve, gp bucket, digging bucket
New Holland	555E	2000	2,110	G	$24,500	8/06	WCTX	TLB, 4WD, diesel, ROPS, third valve, gp bucket, digging bucket
New Holland	575			G	$14,500	11/06	SCCA	Turbo, 4WD, EROPS
New Holland	575E	2000	3,586	G	$24,000	7/06	SEND	TLB, 4WD, cab, heat, Extendahoe, 85 hp., 2 lever, 84" bucket, 24" backhoe bucket
New Holland	575E	2000		G	$37,000	11/06	SCCA	4WD, Extendahoe
New Holland	655E TLB			G	$22,000	7/06	ECNY	4WD, diesel, EROPS, Extendahoe, digging bucket
New Holland	655E TLB	1996		G	$14,000	11/06	SWCA	Extendahoe
New Holland	LB75			G	$20,000	9/06	WCTX	TLB, ROPS, digging bucket
New Holland	LB75		275	G	$28,000	10/06	WCFL	TLB

WHAT'S IT WORTH?

Construction Equipment

Make	Model	Year	Hrs.	Cond.	Price	Sale	Location	Comments
New Holland	LM430	1999	3,056	G	$26,000	8/06	WCMN	Telescopic 4×4 loader, 6,000-lb. lift, 21' reach, big pallet forks, large bucket, 4-wheel steer
OMC	770	1981		G	$10,900	4/06	SEIA	Articulated 4WD forklift, 14' mast, hydro, gas
Pettibone	636			G	$10,250	8/06	SETN	Telescoping forklift
Pettibone	B-66C			G	$15,000	12/06	NEMN	
Pettibone	MC6000RTL			G	$6,500	5/06	SWCA	Rough terrain forklift, 4WD, 6,000-lb. 116" lift, diesel, canopy
Pettibone	SUPER 4			G	$3,100	12/06	ECMN	4WD, gas, 19'8" lift height
Rammax	P33/24 HMR	1998		G	$3,000	10/06	WCFL	Trench roller
Raygo	320A			G	$8,000	12/06	ECMN	60" pad foot drum, JD diesel, push blade
Raygo	400A			G	$16,500	7/06	ECNY	Vibratory roller, diesel
Reynolds	14C	1996		G	$17,500	5/06	ECNE	Pt scraper, 6 rear tires
Reynolds	14C	1996		G	$17,500	5/06	ECNE	Pt scraper, 4 rear tires
Samsung	SL120-2		4,700	G	$22,000	3/06	ECIN	Rubber-tired loader, cab
Samsung	SL120-2	1996	4,662	G	$20,500	2/06	NWOH	Payloader, 4-spd. automatic, cab, 2¼-yard bucket
Schaff	HR-12		2,766	G	$8,000	8/06	SETN	Excavator, rubber tracks
Simon	2515			F	$3,000	11/06	WCMN	Right scissor lift, rough terrain, 4×4, gas
Simon	MP-60			G	$5,000	10/06	NCWI	Diesel, 60' lift
Skyjack	3220			G	$4,500	1/06	SCTN	Electric scissor lift, 20'
Skyjack	3220	2000		G	$2,750	1/06	WCCA	
Skyjack	SJ1113220	1998		F	$750	9/06	WCTX	Scissor lift, electric, 20' lift
Skyjack	SJKB-40-D	1999	527	G	$5,000	8/06	SEPA	Boom lift, diesel, 40' lift
Skytrak	3606T			G	$24,500	9/06	WCTX	Telescoping forklift
Skytrak	3606T	1998		G	$13,500	10/06	WCFL	Forklift, ROPS, 3-stage mast
Skytrak	3606T	1999		G	$20,000	9/06	WCTX	Telescoping forklift, 4×4, diesel, 6,000-lb. capacity
Skytrak	3606T	1999		G	$22,000	10/06	WCFL	
Skytrak	6036			G	$18,500	9/06	WCTX	Telescoping forklift, 4×4, diesel, ROPS, 6,000-lb. capacity
Skytrak	8042			G	$27,000	9/06	SECA	Telescoping forklift
Skytrak	8042			G	$27,500	9/06	SECA	Telescoping forklift
Skytrak	8042	1995		G	$35,000	3/06	WCWA	Variable-reach forklift, 4×4×4, Cummins 3.9L diesel, 42' 3-section boom
Skytrak	9038			G	$22,000	11/06	SCCA	Forklift 38' reach
Snorkel	SL-20	1999		G	$1,600	8/06	WCTX	Electric powered, 20' lift
Snorkel	SL-20	2000		G	$1,850	8/06	WCTX	Scissor lift, 20' lift
Snorkel	SL25			G	$2,000	10/06	SCPA	
Snorkelift	33G			G	$2,800	9/06	SECA	
Super Pac	400P			G	$4,500	3/06	WCWA	40' smooth drum roller, diesel, OROPS
Sweepster	NA			F	$700	10/06	NCWI	Sweeper, industrial, gas, hyd. angle, tow behind
Swinger	200	1977		F	$4,250	11/06	ECND	Articulating loader, 4-cyl. gas engine, ROPS, dirt bucket, pallet fork extension, new paint & tires, recent engine and pump work
Takuchi	TB007			G	$6,500	8/06	SECA	Excavator
Takuchi	TB015			G	$4,750	9/06	WCTX	Hyd. excavator, diesel
Takuchi	TB016	2000		G	$8,250	10/06	WCFL	Hyd. excavator, diesel, enclosed cab, digging bucket
Takuchi	TB025			G	$6,500	9/06	SECA	Mini excavator
Takuchi	TB035			G	$3,950	8/06	WCTX	Hyd. excavator, diesel
Takuchi	TB035	1998		G	$10,000	8/06	WCTX	Hyd. excavator, diesel, canopy, blade
Takuchi	TB035	1998		G	$10,000	8/06	WCTX	Hyd. excavator, diesel, canopy, blade, third valve
Takuchi	TB035	1999		G	$10,500	10/06	WCFL	Hyd. excavator, diesel, canopy, rubber tracks, aux. hyd.

Construction Equipment

Make	Model	Year	Hrs.	Cond.	Price	Sale	Location	Comments
Takuchi	TB035	1999		G	$11,500	10/06	WCFL	Excavator, diesel, enclosed cab, digging bucket
Takuchi	TB035	1999		G	$12,500	10/06	WCFL	Excavator, diesel, enclosed cab, digging bucket
Takuchi	TB070	1999		G	$18,500	10/06	WCFL	Hyd. excavator, diesel
Takuchi	TB135		3,700	G	$10,600	12/06	NWIL	Backhoe, track type, diesel
Takuchi	TB135	2001		G	$12,500	11/06	SWCA	Canopy
Takuchi	TB135	2002		G	$15,500	10/06	WCFL	Hyd. excavator, diesel, enclosed cab
Takuchi	TB135	2003		G	$16,500	10/06	WCFL	Hyd. excavator, diesel, enclosed cab, digging bucket
Takuchi	TB25			G	$10,000	1/06	WCCA	Rubber track excavator
Terex	760	2000		G	$19,000	1/06	WCCA	4WD, loader-backhoe
Terex	760	2000		G	$26,500	1/06	WCCA	Extendahoe, 4WD
Terex	TX760			G	$16,500	9/06	WCTX	TLB, 4×4, diesel
Terex	TX760			G	$22,500	7/06	ECNY	TLB, 4WD, diesel, EROPS, digging bucket
Terrimite	T5C		1,400	G	$7,000	9/06	NEIN	Mini backhoe, gas, canopy
Terrimite	T5C		1,280	G	$7,000	9/06	NEIN	Mini backhoe, gas, canopy
Terrimite	T5C	2000		G	$6,000	9/06	WCTX	TLB, diesel, OROPS, 12' digging bucket
Terrimite	T5C	2005	134	G	$12,000	5/06	SWCA	TLB, gas, canopy
Toyota	FGC25			G	$7,200	1/06	ECIL	Forklift, hard tires, 185" lift, Boggie wheels, front hyd. boom & hyd. motor
Toyota	426F			G	$4,000	3/06	ECMI	Hard tires, LP gas
Toyota	GU25	2000	1,907	G	$15,500	3/06	SEND	Forklift, 3 stage, side shift, LP or gas, air pneumatic tires, 48" forks, 5,000-lb. lift
Traverse	TL6035	1999		G	$22,500	8/06	WCTX	Telescopic forklift, 4WD, diesel, 6,000 lb capacity, ROPS, 35' lift, sliding deck
Tree Farmer	C4D			G	$2,600	3/06	SCIN	Log skidder
Trojan	1900Z			G	$10,500	8/06	WCTX	Rubber-tired loader, diesel, EROPS, gp bucket
Trojan	2000			G	$11,000	2/06	WCME	Wheel loader
Trojan	3000		3,717	G	$4,250	12/06	NEMN	Rubber-tired loader
Upright	TM12	1999		G	$1,100	1/06	WCOH	Scissors lift, electric, 12' lift, narrow
Upright	X26N	2001		G	$1,600	8/06	SEPA	Scissors lift, electric , 26' lift
Vermeer	8550	1998	1,744	G	$8,000	10/06	WCFL	Trencher, 80-hp. diesel, 60-72" depth, ride on
Vermeer	M455A			G	$3,500	9/06	NEIN	Trencher, JD diesel, backhoe attach, leveling blade, canopy
Vermeer	V3550A			G	$4,700	9/06	SECA	Trencher
Vermeer	V3550A			G	$5,000	9/06	SECA	Trencher
Vermeer	V3550A	2002	1,890	G	$3,500	5/06	SWCA	Trencher, 4WD, Deutz diesel, backfill blade, 4' digging depth, hyd. slide
Vermeer	V450			G	$3,000	9/06	NEIN	Backhoe combo, trencher, diesel
Volvo	L120C	2000		G	$64,000	7/06	ECNY	Rubber-tired loader, diesel, EROPS, gp bucket
Volvo	L190	1997		G	$42,500	10/06	WCFL	Rubber-tired loader, diesel, EROPS
Volvo	L50C			G	$25,500	8/06	WCTX	Rubber-tired loader, diesel, EROPS
Volvo	L50C			G	$25,500	8/06	WCTX	Rubber-tired loader, diesel, EROPS, gp bucket
Volvo	L50C	1997		G	$34,000	11/06	SCCA	Wheel loader
Volvo	L70			G	$13,500	3/06	ECIL	L70B payloader
Volvo	L70	2000		G	$58,000	10/06	WCFL	Rubber-tired loader, 125 hp. diesel, EROPS, 2.5- to 3-cubic yard bucket
Volvo	L70C	1999	4,500	G	$44,000	3/06	ECIN	Rubber-tired loader, diesel
Volvo	L70C	1999	4,500	G	$50,000	3/06	ECIN	Rubber-tired loader, diesel, cab
Volvo	L90B			G	$27,500	9/06	WCTX	Rubber-tired loader
Volvo	L90C	1997		G	$42,500	10/06	WCFL	Rubber-tired loader, diesel, EROPS

WHAT'S IT WORTH?

Construction Equipment

Make	Model	Year	Hrs.	Cond.	Price	Sale	Location	Comments
Wabco	440		4,400	G	$2,600	9/06	ECMN	471 Detroit diesel, cutting edge, front tilt steering, aux. for wing
Wabco	DD97			G	$3,200	4/06	ECND	48" sheepsfoot
Western	NA			G	$3,000	2/06	NWKS	Western Austin road blade
Wiggins	NA	1997		G	$15,000	6/06	NEIN	Forklift, Deutz diesel, 2 spd.
Woods	1015			G	$2,600	11/06	NCKY	Backhoe
Woods	1050			G	$6,300	1/06	NWIL	3-point backhoe, 24" bucket
Woods	40			G	$950	12/06	SCNE	Woods dual, 3-point hydraulic forklift
Yale	GLC040	1999		G	$2,750	8/06	WCTX	Propane powered, auto, 48" forks
Yale	GLC040	1999		G	$2,750	8/06	WCTX	Propane powered, auto, 48" forks
Yale	GLC040	1999		G	$2,750	8/06	WCTX	Propane powered, auto, 48" forks
Yale	GLC050		5,587	G	$1,500	9/06	NEIN	Forklift, LP, 5,000 lb.
Yale	GLP050	1978		G	$3,300	10/06	WCMA	5,000-lb. pneumatic-tired forklift, LP, 2 stage
Yale	NA			F	$300	9/06	NEIN	Forklift, LP
Yale	NA			G	$1,400	9/06	NEND	6,000-lb. forklift, Perkins diesel, needs trans. repair
Yale	NA			G	$1,600	9/06	NEIN	Forklift, LP, 10,000 lb.
Yale	NA			G	$1,600	11/06	NCIN	Forklift, 4K lb., gas, hard rubber
Yale	NA			G	$2,150	3/06	ECNE	Model 05, 3-point forklift attachment, 3-stage mast, 168" lift height, 4' forks
Yale	NA			G	$2,900	3/06	SWNE	Forklift, 8,000-lb. capacity, 4-cyl. gas engine, roll cage, 8.25-15 front & 7:00-12 rear tires, hd. forks
Yale	NA			G	$4,000	2/06	NCIN	Forklift, foam-filled pneumatic tires, 6,600-lb. capacity
Yale	NA			G	$5,750	1/06	WCCA	4,000-lb. LP, forklift
Yale	NA			G	$6,000	2/06	WCME	5,000-lb. forklift, LP, rotator
Yanmar	B172			G	$6,750	8/06	SEPA	Hyd. excavator, diesel, canopy
Yanmar	B25			G	$8,500	7/06	WCPA	Hyd. excavator, diesel, canopy, blade
Yanmar	B37			G	$10,000	10/06	WCFL	Hyd. excavator, diesel, canopy, rubber track
Yanmar	B50			G	$11,000	7/06	WCPA	Hyd. excavator, diesel, canopy, blade
Yanmar	B50	2000		G	$10,000	10/06	WCMA	Mini hyd. excavator, Yanmar diesel, backfill blade
Yanmar	B-6			G	$7,500	10/06	WCFL	Hyd. excavator, diesel, cab, blade, rubber track, offset boom

Notes

Cultivators

Location, location, location. What a cultivator is worth can depend on where it is. Recently I spoke with a farmer in Illinois hoping to sell a Buffalo 4630 cultivator. He didn't think it was worth much. Until I told him about what Buffalo 4630s had been selling for in Nebraska. Location, location, location.

Cultivators

Make	Model	Year	Cond.	Price	Sale	Location	Comments
Alloway	2030		F	$600	6/06	NWMN	Danish tine row crop cultivator, 12R-22, beet tools
Alloway	2070	1993	F	$800	3/06	NWMN	8R-30, 3 shank, tunnel shields, flat fold
Alloway	2130		F	$500	4/06	NWMN	12R-22, S tine
Alloway	2130		G	$1,000	4/06	NWMN	12R-22, adjustable cranks, rolling shields, cutaways
Alloway	2130		G	$2,000	11/06	NWMN	12R-30, flat fold, hd shanks, tunnel shields, adjustable row cranks, gauge wheels
Alloway	2130		G	$2,250	11/06	NWMN	Flat fold, 12R-30, hd shanks, tunnel shields
Alloway	2130		G	$4,400	3/06	ECND	Flat fold, 12R-30, gauge wheels, adjustable cranks, tunnel shields, safety lights
Alloway	2130		G	$9,000	7/06	NWMN	Flat fold, 24R-22, flip-up tooling, tunnel shields, adjustable row cranks, lift assist, gauge wheels
Alloway	3030		G	$1,000	1/06	NCCO	6R-30
Alloway	3030		G	$3,100	2/06	NWMN	Row crop, 12R-22, single shank
Alloway	3030		G	$4,000	2/06	NWMN	Row crop, 12R-22
Alloway	3030		G	$4,700	4/06	NWMN	12R-22, single shank, cutaways, disk shields
Alloway	3030		F	$4,900	1/06	NCCO	12R
Alloway	3030	1998	E	$29,000	2/06	WCMN	24R-22, single shanks, flat folds
Alloway	3030	1998	E	$33,000	2/06	WCMN	24R-22, single shanks, flat fold
Alloway	3030	2000	G	$7,000	6/06	NWMN	12R-22, single shank, beet tools, single lift assist
Alloway	3030	2000	G	$7,750	6/06	NWMN	12R-22, single shank, beet tools, single-lift assist
B&H	9100		G	$7,500	3/06	NCCO	8R, cutaways, sweeps, shield
B&H	NA		G	$4,100	3/06	NCCO	8R bar, ditchers, 7-packer wheels, flat fold
B&H	NA		E	$2,500	12/06	SCNE	6R
Brillion	NA		G	$275	2/06	SEMI	4R, 3 pt., Danish tine, rolling shields
Brillion	NA		F	$350	4/06	NWMN	S tine, 12R-22, Youngkrantz rolling shields
Buffalo	4630		G	$675	9/06	ECNE	4R-36, 3 pt.
Buffalo	4630		G	$1,800	12/06	ECNE	8R-30, flat fold, open top shields, Buffalo-scout guidance system
Buffalo	4630		G	$2,600	12/06	SCNE	12R-30, open top shields, Hiller wings
Buffalo	4650		G	$11,250	2/06	NWKS	16R-30, flat fold, dual rear lift-assist wheels
Buffalo	6300		G	$2,600	12/06	SCNE	6R-30, open top shields, Hiller wings
Buffalo	6600		G	$3,300	1/06	SCNE	6R-36, cutaway disk, ridging wings, shields
Case IH	1820		E	$2,200	1/06	NWIA	Flatfold 12RN
Case IH	1820	1995	E	$1,900	8/06	ECIL	12R-30, Vibra Shank, levelers
Case IH	183		F	$150	11/06	SCSD	8RW, tent shields
Case IH	183		G	$300	3/06	NCIL	8R-38, hyd. fold, Vibra tines
Case IH	183		F	$300	1/06	NWIL	8Rw, Danish tine, flat fold
Case IH	183		F	$300	1/06	NWIL	8RW, Danish tine, flat fold
Case IH	183		G	$350	11/06	SENE	6R-36, one owner, shedded
Case IH	183		G	$410	2/06	WCIL	8R-30, hyd. flat fold
Case IH	183		G	$485	1/06	SWOH	6R-30
Case IH	183		G	$525	8/06	NCIA	12R-30 flat fold cultivator, rolling shields
Case IH	183		G	$550	3/06	NCIL	6R-30
Case IH	183		G	$875	2/06	NWIL	12R-30, 3 pt.
Case IH	183		G	$1,000	3/06	WCMN	8R-30, rolling shields
Case IH	183		G	$1,150	2/06	ECIL	12R-30, flat fold
Case IH	183		G	$2,000	3/06	ECMI	12R-30, hyd. fold, S tine
Case IH	183		G	$3,200	3/06	ECNE	16R-30, hyd. wing fold, 3-shank gangs
Case IH	183		E	$3,500	9/06	NEND	16R-30, folding

Cultivators

Make	Model	Year	Cond.	Price	Sale	Location	Comments
Case IH	183		G	$6,500	3/06	NEND	16R-30, flat fold, rolling shields, stabilizer disks
Case IH	1830		E	$1,850	2/06	SCMI	8R, Danish tines
Case IH	1830		G	$3,250	12/06	SCMN	16R-30
Case IH	1840		G	$2,000	2/06	NWIA	12R-30, open top shields, hillers, hyd. fold
Elmers	NA		G	$1,000	3/06	NCCO	8R, cutaways, knives, shields
Hiniker	1000		F	$800	2/06	WCMN	12R-30, folding
Hiniker	1000		G	$3,800	12/06	NCIA	12R-30, shields
Hiniker	2000		G	$6,000	12/06	SEIA	12R, no-till, 3 pt., with sweeps
Hiniker	5000		F	$500	3/06	SWNE	8R-30, 3 pt.
Hiniker	5000		F	$600	3/06	ECNE	6R-30, riding wings, tow hitch
Hiniker	5000		G	$1,200	1/06	SCNE	8R-30
Hiniker	5000		G	$1,300	2/06	WCMN	12R-30, hyd. fold, rolling shields, liquid nitrogen applicator
Hiniker	5000		G	$2,250	3/06	SEND	No-till, 12R-30
Hiniker	5000		G	$2,500	3/06	SEIA	12R-30, no-till, Sukup guidance, rolling shields
Hiniker	6000		G	$2,500	3/06	SWNE	8R-30, 3 pt.
Hiniker	6000		G	$5,000	3/06	SEND	No-till hyd. fold, 12R-30
Hiniker	6000		G	$5,100	2/06	NECO	8R30, hyd.
IHC	133		F	$10	3/06	ECNE	4R-38
IHC	133		F	$60	3/06	ECNE	4R, 3 pt.
IHC	133		F	$60	2/06	WCOH	6R, Danish tine
IHC	133		F	$60	2/06	WCOH	6R, Danish tine
IHC	133		F	$65	3/06	ECNE	4R, 3 pt.
IHC	133		F	$140	8/06	NWIL	8R, 3 pt.
IHC	133		F	$150	4/06	SEMI	4R
IHC	133		F	$185	5/06	SEND	4R, 3 pt., Vibra Shank
IHC	133		F	$200	8/06	WCMN	12R-30, gauge wheels, guide controls
IHC	133		G	$575	7/06	NCIA	12R-30 hyd. fold cultivator
IHC	133		G	$700	3/06	NEMI	12R, folding
IHC	153		G	$120	2/06	SEIA	8RN, Kelderman fold
IHC	153		G	$125	11/06	SENE	6R-36, 3 pt.
IHC	153		G	$150	8/06	WCIA	8R-30
IHC	153		G	$200	3/06	NCIA	12R-30, flat fold
IHC	183		G	$200	8/06	SCMI	8R
IHC	183		G	$210	8/06	ECNE	8R-30
IHC	183		F	$250	1/06	NWIL	12R-30, 3 pt.
IHC	183		F	$350	4/06	NENE	8R, hyd. fold, Vibra Tine Shanks, shields
IHC	183		G	$1,900	3/06	WCMN	12R-30, flat-fold cultivator, rolling shields
IHC	458		G	$35	8/06	ECNE	Front mounted, bought new, shedded
IHC	463		F	$185	11/06	NEKS	4R, 2 pt.
IHC	68		F	$130	8/06	NWIL	4R, front mount
John Deere	825		F	$150	3/06	SEIA	8R
John Deere	825		F	$375	12/06	SCMN	8R-30
John Deere	825		G	$475	8/06	NCIA	12R
John Deere	825		F	$500	3/06	NEND	3 pt., 8R-30 shank style, disk stabilizers, open top tunnel shields
John Deere	825		G	$525	8/06	NEIL	6R
John Deere	843		G	$8,800	2/06	NWKS	8RN CH, 30"
John Deere	845		G	$750	8/06	NCIA	12R-30 flat-fold cultivator, rolling and slab shields
John Deere	845		G	$2,700	2/06	ECMN	12R-30, flat fold

Cultivators

Make	Model	Year	Cond.	Price	Sale	Location	Comments
John Deere	845		E	$5,000	1/06	WCIL	16R-30, Danish, rolling shields
John Deere	845	1997	G	$1,900	2/06	NWIN	12R, Danish
John Deere	85		G	$250	3/06	NCIL	8R
John Deere	85		G	$575	12/06	NWIL	12R
John Deere	85		G	$1,200	3/06	NCIA	12R-30 flat-fold cultivator, rolling shields
John Deere	856		G	$2,250	3/06	NCUT	12R-22
John Deere	856		G	$4,250	12/06	SCMN	12R-30
John Deere	856		G	$4,500	12/06	SCMN	12R
John Deere	856		G	$4,750	3/06	NENE	16R-30, hyd. fold, hyd. drive, liquid fertilizer, piston pump, one owner, shedded
John Deere	856		G	$9,000	12/06	SCMN	24R-20
John Deere	856	1998	G	$1,400	8/06	NCIA	8R-30, slab, rolling shields
John Deere	875		F	$800	4/06	SEPA	3 pt., depth wheels
John Deere	875		E	$1,550	8/06	ECNE	8R-36
John Deere	875		G	$1,700	8/06	WCIA	12R-30, flat fold
John Deere	875		G	$4,500	3/06	SEMN	12R-30, hydro fold, gauge wheels
John Deere	875	1994	F	$1,700	11/06	NEKS	12RN, spring reset, spring down pressure, always shedded
John Deere	885		F	$600	3/06	SWNE	8R-30, open top shields, gauge wheels
John Deere	885		G	$2,500	3/06	WCKS	Close row
John Deere	885		G	$3,500	1/06	WCTX	Tool bar, hooded spray setup
John Deere	885		G	$5,500	3/06	ECNE	12R-36
John Deere	886		G	$3,300	3/06	ECNE	6R-36
Kinze	NA		G	$3,200	12/06	SWMI	12R, applicator, no pump
Krause	4600		G	$6,100	2/06	NCIL	16R, Hiniker rolling shields, Buffalo guidance system
Krause	4612		G	$2,100	3/06	NCIL	12R-30, flat fold
Krause	NA	1993	E	$1,200	2/06	SWOH	8R-36, flat fold, like new
Lorenz	NA	1992	G	$400	3/06	SEND	12R-30, Danish, 5-rank, 3 pt.
Lorenz	NA	1992	E	$700	3/06	SEND	12R-30, Danish, 5-rank, 3 pt., like new
McKee	NA		F	$400	3/06	SEND	Danish tine, 12R-30, hyd. fold
Orthman	8300		G	$2,100	1/06	SWNE	8R-30
Orthman	8350		F	$350	9/06	SCNE	8R-30, baring-off disks, shields, super sweep, ridgers
Orthman	9300		G	$14,000	11/06	SCNE	12R-30, shields, baring-off disks, hyd. fold
Orthman	9300		E	$19,000	11/06	SCNE	16R-30, shields, baring-off disks, hyd. fold
Orthman	9300		E	$19,000	11/06	SCNE	16R-30, shields, 3 pt., hyd. fold
Orthman	9300		E	$23,000	11/06	SCNE	16R-30, shields, baring-off disks, 3 pt., hyd. fold
Sukup	NA		G	$675	3/06	ECNE	8R-30, rigid bar, open top shields
Sukup	NA		G	$700	3/06	ECNE	8R-30, rigid bar, open top shields
Wilrich	7722	1999	G	$22,000	4/06	NWMN	PT7722, 24R-22, hitch, disk shield, single shank
Wilrich	NA		G	$1,900	2/06	SEKS	16R-30

Disk Chisels

Used tillage equipment values have been holding strong since the second half of 2004. You would think that values on disk chisels would depend somewhat on the time of year they sell. The truth? Auction sale prices tend to spike higher from mid-November through the end of February, and then dip a bit from spring through fall. Same trend applies to ALL categories of equipment.

Disk Chisels

Make	Model	Year	Cond.	Price	Sale	Location	Comments
AC	500		G	$800	12/06	NWIL	11', 9-shank, tine harrow
AC	500		F	$800	12/06	NWIL	11', 9-shank
Brillion	12'		F	$450	9/06	NWIL	5-shank
Brillion	13-shank		G	$6,200	3/06	NEOH	Soil saver
Brillion	13-shank	2000	G	$12,750	6/06	NWMN	Commander II, high-clearance parabolic shanks on 15" spacing, self-leveling hitch, hyd. depth control, hyd. adjustable cushion, disk gangs
Case IH	11-shank		G	$1,500	5/06	SEND	Conser-Til, hyd. adjustable, front disks, 5-bar spike tooth harrow
Case IH	6500		F	$1,150	8/06	NECO	15' Conser-Til
Case IH	6500		G	$2,400	8/06	WCIA	10.5'
Case IH	6500		G	$2,700	1/06	SWOH	11-shank
Case IH	6500		G	$3,000	3/06	NEKS	9-shank, Conser-Til
Case IH	6500		G	$3,000	3/06	NEKS	9-shank
Case IH	6500		G	$4,500	3/06	NCIL	Conser-Til disk chisel, 9-shank, FFC leveler
Case IH	6500		G	$4,600	3/06	SEMN	Conser-Til disk chisel plow, 9-shank, spring cushion front gangs
Case IH	6650		G	$6,300	1/06	NWIL	Conser-Til disk chisel, 9-shank, leveler
Case IH	6650		G	$6,700	4/06	WCWI	Conser-Til
Case IH	6814		F	$2,800	12/06	SEMN	
Case IH	9-shank		G	$1,500	3/06	NWIL	
Case IH	9300	2005	E	$32,000	12/06	WCMN	9-shank ripper, lead shanks, rear-disk levelers
Dakon	12-shank		G	$1,200	10/06	SEMN	
Deutz Allis	1500		F	$875	1/06	WCIL	Min-till
DMI	1300		G	$3,200	8/06	NWIL	7-shank
DMI	1300		G	$3,300	6/06	WCMN	Ecolo Champ, 6-shank, parabolic arm, lead shank, tandem front, disk, rear disk levelers
DMI	2500		G	$5,000	12/06	NCIA	5-shank, in-line ripper, coulters
DMI	2500		G	$6,700	3/06	NEIA	5-shank, 3 pt.
DMI	5-shank		G	$8,750	8/06	NWIL	Ecolo-Tiger
DMI	527		G	$6,000	2/06	ECIL	12'
DMI	527		E	$8,750	3/06	NWIL	5-shank ripper, leveler
DMI	527		G	$10,900	1/06	NWIL	12', 5-shank disk ripper
DMI	527B		G	$6,400	8/06	WCMN	Ecolo-Tiger, covering disks, lead shanks
DMI	527B		G	$8,750	1/06	SESD	Disk ripper
DMI	530		F	$4,800	2/06	WCIL	13', 5-shank
DMI	530		G	$9,200	2/06	NCIL	Ecolo-Tiger disk chisel, 5-shank, disk leveler
DMI	530B		G	$6,600	8/06	NWIL	5-shank
DMI	530B		E	$14,000	9/06	WCOH	Yield-Till disk chisel
DMI	530B		E	$14,300	3/06	NEIA	Ecolo-Tiger deep-till, leveler
DMI	530B	2000	G	$15,200	12/06	SEIA	Ecolo-Tiger, 5-shank, disk-leveling bar
DMI	7-shank		F	$4,250	7/06	NWMN	Coulter chisel, offset & straight disk attachment
DMI	730		G	$4,250	8/06	WCMN	7-shank, lead shank, rear leveler
DMI	730		G	$5,100	12/06	SCMN	Ecolo-Tiger
DMI	730		G	$6,250	12/06	WCMN	Ecolo-Tiger disk ripper
DMI	730		G	$6,750	12/06	SCMN	7 shank, rear leveler
DMI	730		G	$7,500	8/06	WCMN	7 shank, Ecolo-Tiger, covering disks, lead shanks
DMI	730		G	$9,500	12/06	WCMN	Ecolo-Tiger

Disk Chisels

Make	Model	Year	Cond.	Price	Sale	Location	Comments
DMI	730		G	$10,500	12/06	WCMN	17.5', Ecolo-Tiger
DMI	730		G	$11,000	3/06	ECND	Ecolo-Tiger, 7-shank
DMI	730	1995	G	$8,100	8/06	WCMN	Front disks, rear covering disks, lead shanks
DMI	730	1996	E	$8,000	3/06	SEND	15', Ecolo-Tiger, like new
DMI	730B		G	$7,700	12/06	NWMO	7-shank
DMI	730B		G	$10,600	6/06	SCMN	7-shank ripper, double disk front
DMI	730B		G	$12,500	9/06	NCIA	7-shank 30" disk ripper, Ecolo-Tiger
DMI	730B	1997	G	$9,500	11/06	SCND	Disk ripper, 15" spacing
DMI	730B	1997	G	$12,000	2/06	WCMN	Deep-till
DMI	730B	2000	G	$16,500	3/06	NWMN	Ecolo-Tiger, 7-shank, hyd. wings, rear disk levelers
DMI	730B	2000	G	$18,500	2/06	ECMN	17.5', 7-shank, red
DMI	730B	2000	G	$19,000	11/06	ECND	7-shank, hyd. disk levelers
DMI	730B	2004	G	$15,250	3/06	SWMN	Ecolo-Tiger, 7-shank, leveler
DMI	Champ		F	$500	10/06	SEMN	Coulter Champ, 11-shank
DMI	Champ		G	$900	8/06	NEIL	Coulter Champ II 9-shank Coulter chisel, adjustable 4-bar heavy harrow
DMI	Champ		F	$2,100	3/06	SEPA	Coulter Champ, 10-shank soil saver
DMI	Champ		F	$2,500	11/06	WCMN	Coulter Champ, 9-shank, new shovels
DMI	Econo Tiger		G	$4,200	3/06	NCOH	Econo II, 9-shank
DMI	NA		G	$2,300	12/06	SCMN	Tiger ripper, 3-shank, 5 front coulters
DMI	Tiger II		F	$3,100	1/06	WCIL	5-shank ripper
DMI	Tiger II		F	$3,500	12/06	SCMN	
DMI	Tiger II		G	$4,100	8/06	NWIL	5-shank, leveler
DMI	Tiger II		G	$4,300	3/06	NCIL	5-shank, leveler
DMI	Tiger II		G	$6,400	3/06	ECMI	5-shank ripper, trailer type, 6-leg leveler
DMI	Tiger II		G	$6,700	8/06	NWIL	7-shank, leveler
Flex King	XL		F	$1,250	3/06	SWNE	XL Series 25' hyd. fold duckfoot rolling coulter, rear trash whips
Glencoe	11-shank		F	$1,400	3/06	NEMI	Soil saver
Glencoe	11-shank		P	$1,450	4/06	NEIA	Soil saver, rough
Glencoe	11-shank		G	$2,400	3/06	NWIL	
Glencoe	11-shank		G	$3,450	12/06	SEMN	Soil saver
Glencoe	13'		G	$950	9/06	SWIA	Adjustable gang
Glencoe	13'		F	$1,450	7/06	NWMN	Soil saver
Glencoe	13-shank		G	$3,800	3/06	NWMN	Soil saver, mechanical adjustable front disk, spring shank
Glencoe	14-shank		G	$2,600	9/06	SCMN	Soil saver
Glencoe	16'		G	$1,650	3/06	ECND	Soil saver, harrow
Glencoe	22'		G	$3,500	3/06	SWMN	Soil saver
Glencoe	5-shank		G	$2,550	8/06	NCIA	In-line 3 pt. ripper, auto reset, leveler
Glencoe	7-shank		G	$2,500	8/06	NWIL	
Glencoe	7-shank		G	$2,500	11/06	ECIL	
Glencoe	7-shank		G	$2,800	12/06	WCMI	Soil saver
Glencoe	7-shank		G	$4,250	8/06	NCOH	Soil saver
Glencoe	7400		G	$3,850	10/06	SEMN	13' soil saver
Glencoe	7400		G	$6,250	3/06	WCMN	SS7400, 16' soil saver disk ripper, walking tandems
Glencoe	8600		G	$7,750	8/06	WCMN	7-shank, rear leveler
Glencoe	9-shank		G	$2,100	3/06	NCIL	Soil saver
Glencoe	9-shank		G	$2,150	3/06	NWIL	
Glencoe	9-shank		G	$2,300	1/06	NEIN	

Disk Chisels

Make	Model	Year	Cond.	Price	Sale	Location	Comments
Glencoe	9-shank		G	$2,400	12/06	SEIA	Soil saver
Glencoe	9-shank		G	$2,600	8/06	WCIL	Soil saver, spring shanks, leveler
Glencoe	9-shank		G	$2,700	12/06	SEMN	Soil saver
Glencoe	9-shank		F	$2,800	3/06	SEPA	Soil saver, transport
Glencoe	9-shank		G	$2,900	1/06	WCIL	Yield builder, tine leveler
Glencoe	9-shank		G	$3,300	8/06	NCIA	Soil saver
Glencoe	SS7400		G	$6,500	1/06	NWIL	Disk chisel, 9-shank, leveler
John Deere	1710		F	$1,100	7/06	WCMN	Disk chisel, 14'
John Deere	1710A		F	$1,750	12/06	SEMN	17'
John Deere	1710A		G	$2,000	1/06	NECO	13', pt
John Deere	2100	2005	G	$4,500	12/06	SEIA	5-shank, 3 pt., coulters
John Deere	2700		G	$12,250	10/06	SEMN	Disk ripper
John Deere	2700		G	$16,750	12/06	SEMN	7-shank, mulch ripper
John Deere	2700		G	$18,500	12/06	SCMN	7-shank, 30" mulch ripper
John Deere	2700		E	$18,500	2/06	SCMN	Late model, 7-shank, 24", updated bearings
John Deere	2700	2001	G	$13,750	3/06	SWKS	Mulch ripper, 18', 9-shank, 24" spacing, rear conditioner disk
John Deere	2700	2001	G	$15,000	11/06	NEKS	18' disk ripper, chisel points
John Deere	2700	2001	G	$16,000	12/06	WCMN	7-shank
John Deere	2700	2003	G	$22,500	8/06	NCIA	5-shank disk ripper, auto depth stop, hyd. leveler
John Deere	510		G	$4,500	11/06	WCMN	Disk ripper, 7-shank
John Deere	510		G	$5,100	8/06	WCMN	7-shank
John Deere	510		G	$5,400	8/06	WCMN	7-shank
John Deere	510		G	$6,250	12/06	SCMN	17.5'
John Deere	510		G	$7,000	3/06	NESD	7-shank disk ripper
John Deere	510		G	$7,300	3/06	NCIA	5-shank disk ripper
John Deere	510		G	$8,000	2/06	NWIA	5-shank, 15'
John Deere	510		G	$8,800	3/06	WCIL	5-shank, nice
John Deere	510		G	$9,000	8/06	NCIA	5-shank disk ripper, new points, 1-year-old leveler
John Deere	510		G	$9,500	8/06	NCIA	Harrow, Summers drag
John Deere	510		G	$10,500	12/06	ECNE	7-shank, jumbo buster bar harrow, rock flex, light package
John Deere	510		G	$10,500	2/06	WCIA	7-shank
John Deere	510		G	$10,750	8/06	WCIA	7-shank, disk ripper
John Deere	510		G	$11,200	11/06	SCMN	5-shank
John Deere	510	1996	G	$10,000	11/06	ECND	Disk ripper, 7-shank
John Deere	510	1997	G	$6,750	12/06	WCMN	Disk ripper, 7-shank
John Deere	512		G	$13,000	9/06	NCIA	7-shank
John Deere	512		G	$21,500	12/06	ECIL	17.5' soil management system disk chisel, 800 acres total use
John Deere	512		G	$26,000	2/06	WCIA	9-shank
John Deere	512	2002	G	$13,000	3/06	SESD	Disk ripper, 5-shank, adjustable harrow
John Deere	512	2003	E	$18,750	2/06	ECMN	Disk ripper, 9-shank, 24" blades, rock cushion gangs, 22'6" width, one owner
John Deere	512	2005	G	$14,500	12/06	WCMN	Disk ripper, 7-shank, knock-out scrapers, new demo unit
Kent	24'		G	$2,200	5/06	SEND	Discovator, walking tandems on main frame, mechanical adjustment, rock flex front gang, 9" sweeps, 5-bar spike tooth harrow
Kent	36'		G	$1,400	3/06	SEIA	Discovator
Kent	NA		G	$7,000	2/06	SEKS	35.5' Discovator, walking tandems on main frame & wings

Disk Chisels

Make	Model	Year	Cond.	Price	Sale	Location	Comments
Kent	Series V		G	$4,000	12/06	SEMN	Discovator
Kent	Series V		G	$7,750	3/06	NEND	42.5' Discovator, double hyd. fold, spring-loaded front disks, 4 rank, 4-bar Flexi-Coil harrow, chemical booms
Kewanee	580		F	$565	3/06	NWIL	12', 9-shank
Krause	3100		E	$5,000	1/06	NECO	28', rolling harrow
Krause	3122		E	$4,500	1/06	NECO	22', harrow
Krause	3609	1990	G	$4,000	12/06	WCIL	12.5', 22" blades, 9" spacing, walking tandems, rear-leveling bar
Krause	4811		G	$6,250	12/06	SWMI	11-shank, 13' LandSaver, rear Danish tine
Landoll	2320		E	$8,100	2/06	NWIL	Weatherproofer II, 5-shank, lights, sharp
Landoll	2320		G	$9,000	8/06	NCIA	7-shank Weatherproofer II Disk Ripper, auto reset, disk front and back
Landoll	2320		E	$12,500	2/06	SEMI	5-shank
Landoll	2320		G	$13,000	12/06	NCIA	Weatherproofer II Disk Ripper, 5-shank, used 2 seasons
Landoll	876		G	$13,500	12/06	ECIL	30' Tilloll
Landoll	NA		G	$1,100	3/06	NWMN	19' coulter chisel
Landoll	NA		G	$2,250	3/06	NEKS	Weatherproofer
Landoll	NA		G	$4,200	1/06	NEIN	Soil saver
Landoll	NA		G	$4,800	10/06	SEMN	Weatherproofer, 5-shank
Landoll	NA	1990	G	$6,500	8/06	ECIL	Weatherproofer, 6-shank, leveler
Landoll	Tilloll		F	$1,700	7/06	ECIL	15'
Landoll	Tilloll		F	$2,450	12/06	ECMO	
M&W	1165		G	$3,300	2/06	ECIL	Earthmaster 5-shank, spring reset, leveler
M&W	1165		G	$3,400	2/06	ECIL	Earthmaster, 5-shank
M&W	1165		G	$3,550	1/06	ECIL	Earthmaster, 5-shank, disk chisel, levelers
M&W	1165		G	$4,250	7/06	NCIA	Earthmaster disk ripper, 5-shank
M&W	1165		G	$5,200	3/06	NCIA	Earthmaster disk ripper, 5-shank, new disk blades
M&W	1165		G	$6,400	12/06	NCIL	Earthmaster, new blades, leveler buster bar, used 1 season on 360 acres
M&W	1165		G	$7,500	12/06	NCIA	Earthmaster, 5-shank
M&W	1165	2002	G	$10,250	12/06	NWIL	Earthmaster, McFarlane harrow
M&W	1465		G	$2,550	3/06	ECIL	7-shank Earthmaster, leveling bar
M&W	1465		F	$2,750	12/06	SEMN	Earthmaster
M&W	1465		G	$4,100	8/06	NWIL	Earthmaster, 5-shank
M&W	1465		G	$4,600	9/06	NCIA	7-shank disk ripper
M&W	15'		G	$4,000	11/06	NCIN	Earthmaster, 7-shank
M&W	1875		G	$14,000	9/06	WCIA	Earthmaster, 24" blades
MF	7-shank		G	$2,300	1/06	SWOH	
Steiger	15'		G	$2,300	3/06	NEND	Coulter disk chisel
Sunflower	4010		G	$3,400	9/06	NEIA	4-coulter ripper, demo
Sunflower	42'	1996	G	$12,200	11/06	NWKS	42' Fallow King with pickers
Sunflower	4211	1986	G	$8,500	2/06	WCIL	Trash mulcher, 13-shank, 16' disk chisel, walking tandems, ridge leveler
Sunflower	4212		G	$7,500	8/06	SCMI	11-shank
Sunflower	4311		F	$2,800	8/06	NECO	9-shank
Sunflower	4311		G	$3,500	8/06	WCMN	9-shank
Sunflower	4311		G	$6,400	8/06	NWIL	18', 7-shank
Sunflower	4411	2000	E	$9,000	5/06	SCMI	17', 7-shank
Sunflower	4510		G	$4,800	8/06	NECO	19'

Disk Chisels

Make	Model	Year	Cond.	Price	Sale	Location	Comments
Sunflower	7-shank		G	$8,250	3/06	NWIL	
Sunflower	NA	2003	G	$15,000	4/06	NWMN	7-shank, tandem disk front and back, hd. harrow
Taylorway	10-shank		G	$1,400	9/06	NWOH	Disk chisel
Tye	Paratill		G	$2,250	3/06	NWIL	4-shank
Unverferth	NA		G	$3,600	4/06	SEMI	Zone builder, 3 pt., 4-shank subsoiler
White	435		F	$2,000	1/06	NEIN	12-shank
White	435		G	$2,600	4/06	SWOH	11-shank, pt
White	435		F	$2,750	11/06	WCMN	16-shank, walking tandems
White	435		G	$3,250	12/06	SEMN	
White	435		G	$3,700	2/06	NCOH	10-shank, walking tandems, frame for 12-shanks, hyd. lift disks
White	435		G	$4,000	8/06	WCMN	14-shank
White	435		G	$4,600	2/06	WCOH	12' disk chisel on 12" centers w/ disk centers
White	445		E	$3,250	9/06	NWIL	8'
Wilrich	6600		G	$4,000	1/06	WCIL	5-shank disk chisel, 6-shank rear bar
Wilrich	6600		G	$5,500	8/06	WCMN	5-shank, levelers

Notes

Disks

Sale prices can run higher at very nice retirement auctions, sales where all the folks with bidding numbers know how very well the retiring farmer cared for his equipment. Case in point: the 28-foot IHC 490 disk I saw sell on a retirement auction in east-central Illinois in January 2007. It sold for $8,500 – off the charts high for an older model disk like an IHC 490. Just goes to show, it pays to take care of your stuff.

Disks

Make	Model	Year	Cond.	Price	Sale	Location	Comments
AC	21'		G	$4,500	5/06	SCCA	Offset wheel
AC	2300		F	$500	4/06	SCMI	18', wing fold
AC	2300		F	$500	4/06	SCMI	18', wing fold
AC	2300		F	$600	7/06	NWMN	19' tandem
AC	2600		F	$750	8/06	NCOH	18.5', hyd. fold
AC	2600		F	$2,000	3/06	NEKS	28'
AC	2600		G	$4,000	4/06	WCMT	19', 23" blades
AC	2600		G	$4,000	4/06	WCMT	19', 23" blades
AC	8'		F	$375	1/06	NECO	Tandem, pt
Amco	14'		G	$5,500	7/06	WCCA	Offset
Amco	28'		F	$700	3/06	NWMN	Tandem, hd
Amco	F-15		G	$4,100	8/06	WCMN	35' tandem
Athens	NA		G	$7,500	8/06	SCFL	14' offset
Big G	28'		G	$4,250	4/06	NWMN	Tandem, hd, depth control, 10" spacing
Big G	32'		G	$6,000	2/06	NWKS	Model 3131-288, 32', hyd. fold offset, extra parts
Big G	NA		G	$2,500	9/06	NEND	Green Line 25' heavy tandem, new front blades
Burch	NA		G	$500	3/06	SWIN	12' wheel, 17" blades
Bush Hog	12'		G	$3,000	1/06	NEIN	Offset disk
Bush Hog	1440		G	$1,900	7/06	NCIA	20' rock flex
Bush Hog	1445		G	$1,400	9/06	NECO	22', tandem
Bush Hog	15'		F	$625	1/06	NCCO	
Bush Hog	15'		G	$5,000	5/06	SCCA	Offset wheel
Bush Hog	6'		G	$625	1/06	WCNE	Tandem end, 3 pt.
Case IH	3900		G	$6,300	3/06	NENE	21', tandem, harrow attachment
Case IH	3900		G	$6,500	7/06	ECIL	25', 6.5" spacing
Case IH	3900		E	$6,750	2/06	SENE	22'
Case IH	3900		G	$7,100	3/06	NWIL	
Case IH	3900		F	$7,350	1/06	NWIL	19.5', 7.5" spacings, harrow
Case IH	3900		G	$8,500	1/06	NEIN	20', rock flex
Case IH	3900		G	$9,300	12/06	NWIL	25', 3-bar harrow
Case IH	3900		G	$10,350	1/06	NEIN	21', rock flex
Case IH	3900		G	$15,000	12/06	ECIL	31', 3-bar flex harrow
Case IH	3900	1995	G	$9,500	11/06	SCSD	33.5', cushion gang, 9" spacing, mulcher
Case IH	3950		F	$6,750	2/06	WCIL	21.5', 9" spacing and 19" blade
Case IH	3950		G	$9,000	8/06	NEKS	27' hyd. fold tandem, 20" blades, hyd. self-leveling, one owner
Case IH	3950		G	$9,900	2/06	NEMO	19', 7" spacing, tandem, 3-bar spring tine harrow
Case IH	3950	1998	E	$17,600	1/06	NEIA	24' wingfold, 22" blades on 9" spacing, 3-bar harrow
Case IH	3950	2000	G	$13,500	11/06	WCIA	22.5'
Case IH	3950	2000	G	$22,750	12/06	WCIA	29'3", 9" spacing, 3-bar harrow
Case IH	3950	2004	E	$17,500	3/06	NWOH	30' rock flex
Case IH	485		F	$2,750	1/06	NCCO	25' wing
Case IH	496		P	$1,900	8/06	NWIL	22' wing
Case IH	496		F	$2,000	8/06	NEKS	24'
Case IH	496		G	$3,250	9/06	SEIL	25'
Case IH	496		G	$3,800	11/06	SCIL	25', 7.5" spacing
Case IH	496		G	$4,000	1/06	SCNE	25', new 20" front blades, 19" rear blades, 7.5" spacing
Case IH	496		G	$4,100	12/06	SWIL	18', 7" spacing, harrow
Case IH	496		G	$4,500	3/06	ECNE	24', hyd. fold, 9" spacing, front blades, 1 season old

Disks

Make	Model	Year	Cond.	Price	Sale	Location	Comments
Case IH	496		G	$4,600	12/06	SEMN	19'5"
Case IH	496		G	$4,975	8/06	WCIA	24'
Case IH	496		G	$5,000	3/06	NEKS	24', new blades
Case IH	496		G	$5,400	3/06	NCIL	22', 7.5" spacing
Case IH	496		G	$5,900	2/06	WCIA	24'
Case IH	496		G	$6,000	5/06	SEND	24' tandem, rock flex, 9" space, dual carrier wheels
Case IH	496		G	$6,150	3/06	NWOH	20', fold-up
Case IH	496		G	$6,300	3/06	NWIL	
Case IH	496		G	$6,500	8/06	ECNE	24', 22" blades, 9" spacing, adjustable, harrow
Case IH	496		G	$6,700	4/06	WCSD	32', hyd. fold
Case IH	496		G	$6,900	3/06	SCIA	25'
Case IH	496		G	$7,075	2/06	ECIL	22.5', 3-bar tine harrow, 7.5" spacing
Case IH	496		G	$7,500	1/06	SWOH	25', 3-bar harrow
Case IH	496		G	$7,700	11/06	SENE	27'10", hyd. fold, tandem wheels on wings, 20 ⅞" rear blades, 19.5" front blades, one owner, shedded
Case IH	496		G	$9,250	2/06	WCIL	32', shedded
Case IH	496		E	$9,500	8/06	ECNE	19', hyd. fold, 21.5" blades, 3-bar harrow, always shedded, one owner
Case IH	496		G	$9,500	2/06	ECNE	24', front blades
Case IH	496		E	$10,000	2/06	NENE	20', harrow, 21¾" blades
Case IH	496		G	$10,500	11/06	SCMN	
Case IH	496	1984	G	$7,100	2/06	SWOH	22', dual tandem wheels on wings, new 20" blades & bearings
Case IH	496	1989	E	$6,500	8/06	ECIL	24'
Case IH	770		G	$1,750	1/06	WCCA	14' offset wheel
Case IH	770		G	$3,500	1/06	WCCA	14' offset wheel
Case IH	770		G	$7,000	1/06	WCCA	15' offset wheel
Case IH	RMX340		G	$18,000	1/06	NWIL	24', 9" spacing, 1½ years old
Case IH	RMX340		E	$21,500	1/06	NWIA	34' tandem, hyd. depth control, Earthmaster 22" blades
Case IH	RMX340	2005	E	$25,500	2/06	NWIA	30' tandem, used approximately 1,200 acres
Crustbuster	16'		G	$1,500	2/06	SWNE	Offset, hd, 9.5l-15 tires
Crustbuster	18'		G	$800	12/06	ECMO	Center fold
Crustbuster	20'		P	$50	3/06	SWNE	Center fold, tandem, needs new blades
Crustbuster	28'		G	$3,900	1/06	NECO	Offset, folding
Crustbuster	40'		P	$825	2/06	NECO	For parts
Crustbuster	40'		G	$7,500	2/06	NECO	Folding tandem
EZ On	4600	2004	E	$33,500	12/06	WCMN	Cushion gang, 36' knotch blades
EZ On	NA		F	$1,300	11/06	NEND	30', tandem, half fold, 9" spacing, 19" blades
Ford	1441		G	$5,600	11/06	NWKS	38'
Ford	242		F	$900	3/06	NEKS	23'
Ford	243		G	$650	8/06	WCMN	16'
Hesston	2410		G	$2,100	4/06	WCSD	51'
Hesston	2440		G	$4,000	1/06	NEIN	19', rock flex
Hutchmaster	21'		G	$2,300	10/06	NCND	Offset
Hutchmaster	25'		G	$5,000	6/06	ECND	9" space, dual carrier wheels, hd
IHC	330		F	$300	3/06	NENE	14', notch front blades
IHC	330		G	$425	9/06	NECO	14', pt, tandem
IHC	330		G	$500	9/06	NECO	16', pt, tandem
IHC	370		F	$320	5/06	SEND	13' tandem

Disks

Make	Model	Year	Cond.	Price	Sale	Location	Comments
IHC	370		G	$800	2/06	SEMI	15' wheel
IHC	370		G	$3,600	3/06	SWOH	32' transport, double wing, drag
IHC	460		G	$1,900	1/06	NWKY	16', manual fold
IHC	470		G	$375	3/06	SEND	Tandem, 14'
IHC	470		F	$425	6/06	SWMN	13.5'
IHC	470		F	$450	3/06	NWOH	16'
IHC	470		G	$500	12/06	NEMO	18', wing fold, rear harrow
IHC	470		G	$525	4/06	NWMN	14' tandem
IHC	470		F	$600	9/06	ECNE	18' manual fold
IHC	470		E	$750	11/06	NEKS	16'
IHC	470		F	$925	9/06	NWIL	16'
IHC	470		G	$1,200	1/06	ECNE	17', manual fold, narrow spacing
IHC	470		F	$1,600	3/06	NWPA	Spike tooth harrow
IHC	475		G	$900	6/06	SCMN	18' tandem wing
IHC	475		F	$1,200	3/06	NWOH	20', fold up
IHC	475		G	$1,700	8/06	ECNE	21', hyd. fold, 9" spacing, 19" blades, Noble 3-bar harrow
IHC	475		F	$1,800	7/06	WCMN	Hyd., 21'
IHC	475		G	$2,125	2/06	ECNE	19.5', hyd. wings
IHC	475		G	$2,500	2/06	WCIL	18.5'
IHC	475		G	$5,100	4/06	WCMN	16' tandem
IHC	480		F	$300	3/06	NWIL	18', new tires
IHC	480		F	$400	8/06	WCIA	22'
IHC	480		F	$420	8/06	NCIA	21'
IHC	480		F	$450	8/06	NCOH	18' rock flex, Remlinger, 2-bar harrow
IHC	480		G	$475	9/06	NWOH	16' wing wheel
IHC	480		F	$500	3/06	WCMN	15' tandem
IHC	480		F	$700	3/06	ECNE	19.5', harrow
IHC	480		G	$900	3/06	ECNE	21', 9" spacing, manual-fold wings
IHC	480		G	$1,200	12/06	ECMO	
IHC	485		G	$1,950	1/06	ECNE	20', hyd. fold, 23" blades
IHC	490		F	$450	3/06	SEIA	22', fold-up
IHC	490		F	$1,000	12/06	SEMN	25'
IHC	490		F	$1,100	4/06	WCSD	32' tandem
IHC	490		F	$1,200	7/06	NWMN	Tandem, 30', dual carrier across, 9" space
IHC	490		G	$1,500	3/06	SWOH	32', double wing disk, drag
IHC	490		G	$1,550	9/06	SCMN	24' wing
IHC	490		G	$1,600	6/06	NWIL	21', 9" spacings
IHC	490		G	$1,900	8/06	ECNE	7.5" spacing, Noble 3-bar harrow
IHC	490		G	$2,000	8/06	SEMN	21'
IHC	490		F	$2,100	2/06	ECNE	21.5', harrow
IHC	490		G	$2,200	12/06	ECMO	
IHC	490		G	$2,200	1/06	WCIL	21', 7.5" spacing
IHC	490		G	$2,250	3/06	NCIA	21' hyd. fold, tandem
IHC	490		F	$2,500	3/06	NWIL	24' hyd. fold
IHC	490		G	$3,100	12/06	SEIA	24', 7.5" spacings
IHC	490		G	$3,500	1/06	WCIL	20' hyd. fold
IHC	490		G	$4,600	12/06	NWOH	24' wheel
IHC	490		G	$4,600	3/06	NCIL	22', 9" spacing
IHC	490		F	$5,000	1/06	NWIL	26', 7 .5" spacing, hyd. fold

Disks

Make	Model	Year	Cond.	Price	Sale	Location	Comments
IHC	490		G	$5,900	2/06	NCIL	28", 9" spacing
IHC	490	1986	G	$2,000	3/06	SEND	32' tandem
IHC	760		G	$3,500	2/06	WCMN	14' offset
IHC	770		G	$3,000	11/06	WCSD	13', one owner, hd
IHC	770		G	$3,100	11/06	NWMN	Offset, 15', dual carrier wheels, notched front, cone-back blades, 11" space
John Deere	210		P	$550	2/06	SCNY	14'
John Deere	210		G	$925	1/06	NEIN	14'
John Deere	210		G	$1,100	8/06	SEMN	15'
John Deere	210		G	$1,500	5/06	SWWI	Wheel
John Deere	210		E	$1,600	9/06	NWIL	15'
John Deere	210		G	$2,400	2/06	WCIL	14'
John Deere	215		F	$900	1/06	NEIN	
John Deere	215		F	$1,500	2/06	NCCO	15'
John Deere	215		G	$1,700	9/06	ECNE	14' tandem, one owner
John Deere	215		F	$2,000	3/06	NCCO	16'
John Deere	220		F	$250	4/06	NCOK	22' tandem, some welds
John Deere	220		F	$450	2/06	WCIA	20'
John Deere	220		G	$600	2/06	NECO	24' tandem
John Deere	220		G	$700	8/06	NCIA	19' hyd. fold
John Deere	220		F	$700	2/06	NCIN	20' center fold
John Deere	220		F	$750	3/06	NENE	29', harrow
John Deere	220		F	$1,500	1/06	NWIL	Hyd. fold
John Deere	220		G	$1,800	3/06	WCMN	22', deep cone, folding
John Deere	220		G	$1,800	9/06	NWMN	20' double-offset tandem field
John Deere	230		F	$800	11/06	SCNE	20' tandem, 9" spacing
John Deere	230		F	$900	7/06	WCMN	24'
John Deere	230		F	$925	2/06	NECO	26' tandem
John Deere	230		F	$1,025	3/06	SWOH	16'
John Deere	230		P	$1,250	2/06	NCCO	24'
John Deere	230		G	$1,250	8/06	NCIA	20' cone blade
John Deere	230		F	$1,300	3/06	SWOH	25', double wing
John Deere	230		F	$1,300	12/06	SEMN	24'
John Deere	230		G	$1,650	8/06	WCMN	20' tandem, 19" cone blades
John Deere	230		G	$1,800	3/06	NCIL	Wing fold, 9" spacing, 21'
John Deere	230		G	$1,800	3/06	WCMN	21.5' tandem, new shafts, bearings, blades, scrapers
John Deere	230		G	$2,000	4/06	SWSD	20' tandem, hyd. fold-up wings
John Deere	230		G	$2,200	4/06	NENE	21' hyd. fold tandem, mulcher
John Deere	230		G	$2,200	8/06	SCMN	21'
John Deere	230		G	$2,300	10/06	NECO	26' tandem
John Deere	230		G	$2,600	10/06	NCND	21' tandem
John Deere	230		G	$2,900	2/06	NWOH	26', fold up
John Deere	230		G	$3,000	12/06	WCMN	Wing fold
John Deere	230		G	$3,400	9/06	NECO	24', tandem, harrows
John Deere	230		G	$3,750	12/06	SEMN	25'
John Deere	230		G	$4,250	2/06	WCIL	25', 22" straight blades for no-till
John Deere	235		F	$1,750	2/06	NWOH	22', fold up
John Deere	235		G	$1,950	9/06	NCIA	19', 10" black gang
John Deere	235		G	$2,200	2/06	WCMN	21'

Disks

Make	Model	Year	Cond.	Price	Sale	Location	Comments
John Deere	235		G	$2,300	12/06	ECMO	21'
John Deere	235		G	$2,550	9/06	NENE	20', hyd. fold, 9" spacing, 20" blades, 3-bar harrow
John Deere	235		G	$2,800	3/06	NESD	27.5' tandem, 3-bar harrow
John Deere	235		G	$2,800	11/06	SWIA	22'
John Deere	235		G	$2,900	11/06	ECNE	21', tandem, mulcher, hyd. fold
John Deere	235		G	$3,000	12/06	NCIA	21', cone blades
John Deere	235		G	$3,100	8/06	NCIA	21' tandem, hyd. fold
John Deere	235		G	$3,500	2/06	WCMN	23', cushion gang
John Deere	235		G	$3,750	8/06	NCIA	22.5', wheel on outside, hyd. depth stop
John Deere	235		G	$5,400	2/06	WCIL	23', like-new Remlinger tine harrow
John Deere	2420		G	$2,300	10/06	NECO	10' offset, pt
John Deere	310		F	$1,700	2/06	NCCO	16'
John Deere	315		G	$1,700	12/06	WCMN	Tandem
John Deere	315		F	$1,800	2/06	NCCO	15'
John Deere	315		G	$1,900	3/06	NCCO	16' tandem
John Deere	330		G	$3,750	2/06	ECKS	25'
John Deere	330		G	$5,600	12/06	NCIA	27'
John Deere	331		G	$2,600	12/06	SEND	31'
John Deere	331		G	$3,250	2/06	NWMN	Tandem, 33', cone
John Deere	331		F	$4,000	2/06	WCIL	32', 22" blades, straight blades
John Deere	331		G	$4,900	6/06	NWIL	24' cone blade, 9" spacings
John Deere	331		G	$10,000	11/06	SECA	Wheel, hyd. folding wings
John Deere	335		G	$750	5/06	SCCA	21' double-offset wheel
John Deere	335		F	$1,100	8/06	NECO	33', harrow
John Deere	335		G	$2,100	1/06	NECO	28' tandem, folding
John Deere	335		G	$2,500	2/06	SEKS	
John Deere	335		G	$3,400	4/06	NWMN	Tandem, 33', 9" space
John Deere	335		G	$4,500	2/06	SCKS	Tandem, 22" blades, 9" spacing, 11L-15 tires
John Deere	335		G	$5,750	11/06	NWMN	Tandem, 30', 11" space, cone blades, walking tandems center, dual carrier wings
John Deere	335	1989	G	$4,100	6/06	NWMN	Double offset tandem field, 30', 22" blades, 9" spacing
John Deere	360		G	$4,250	3/06	NEND	Tandem, 28', cone blades
John Deere	375		G	$5,500	2/06	NWSD	40', all new, trail behind transport, hd
John Deere	630		G	$3,800	11/06	SEIA	14', 22" blades
John Deere	630		G	$4,000	11/06	SCNE	14', harrow
John Deere	630		G	$5,100	2/06	WCIA	22.5'
John Deere	630		G	$5,200	5/06	WCMN	24'
John Deere	630		P	$6,000	4/06	SCKS	32', blades badly worn, frame good
John Deere	630		G	$6,000	2/06	ECKS	26.5', new 22" blades in front
John Deere	630		G	$6,400	8/06	NWIL	21', coil tine
John Deere	630		G	$6,500	4/06	NESD	26.5' tandem, hyd. fore/aft, hyd. down pressure on front, tandem wheels on frame and wings, 3-bar mulchers, 1995 model
John Deere	630		G	$7,000	12/06	WCMN	23'7", wing fold
John Deere	630		G	$8,250	3/06	NEKS	24'
John Deere	630		G	$8,800	3/06	ECNE	27' tandem, hyd. level, 3-bar harrow
John Deere	630		G	$8,800	3/06	ECNE	25' tandem
John Deere	630		G	$10,900	1/06	WCIL	25', 7½" spacing
John Deere	630		G	$19,000	11/06	SCNE	32', 9" spacing, mulcher, hyd. fold

Disks

Make	Model	Year	Cond.	Price	Sale	Location	Comments
John Deere	630	1992	G	$13,000	1/06	SCKS	32', 9" spacing, single point depth control, bought new, shedded
John Deere	630	1993	G	$7,300	5/06	WCKS	32'
John Deere	630	1996	G	$11,400	3/06	SEIA	25'1", 7¼" spacing, hyd. fore/aft, hyd. wing control
John Deere	630	1997	G	$16,500	1/06	SCKS	32', 9 spacing, single-pt. depth control, bought new, shedded, SN 14131
John Deere	630	1998	G	$8,000	12/06	SWMI	20.5', dual wheeled, folding, hd, excellent 22" blades
John Deere	630	1999	G	$8,900	2/06	ECIL	24', 7.5', JD tine harrow
John Deere	635		G	$10,100	2/06	NEIN	Rock flex, 26', tandem wheels, 20" blade
John Deere	637		G	$14,450	3/06	ECNE	Tandem disk, 26'5" width, hyd. lift and wing fold, 22" blades, 3-bar rear harrow
John Deere	637		G	$20,000	11/06	SCNE	Wheatland, 32', 9" spacing, mulcher, hyd. fold
John Deere	637		G	$25,500	11/06	NCOH	Rock flex disk, 3-bar spike harrow, rolling basket, 26'5"
John Deere	637	2001	G	$17,500	2/06	WCIL	32'1", 9" spacing, 22" blades, single point depth control
John Deere	637	2001	G	$20,000	11/06	ECND	Rock flex disk, 35', JD 3-bar harrow, new bearings on front
John Deere	637	2002	E	$16,500	1/06	NWKY	25'
John Deere	637	2004	G	$26,000	3/06	SESD	Rock flex tandem, 32'1", adjustable harrow
John Deere	637	2005	E	$30,750	12/06	SWIA	32' tandem, rock flex, soil management system, walking tandems all around, center and outside filler, 9" space, single point depth control, low acres
John Deere	640		G	$4,500	1/06	NCCO	15.5'
John Deere	650		G	$10,000	3/06	NEKS	32' hyd. fold, 11" spacing
John Deere	650		G	$11,000	1/06	NECO	28' tandem
John Deere	650	1997	G	$8,000	6/06	NWMN	Field, hd, 33', 22" blades on 9" spacing, depth control
John Deere	670		G	$17,000	7/06	WCCA	33', folding, tandem
Kewanee	1000		G	$1,900	3/06	NWIL	18'
Kewanee	1000		G	$2,900	3/06	SEIA	20'
Kewanee	1010		G	$800	11/06	ECIL	Flat fold
Kewanee	1010		F	$1,050	8/06	NWIL	
Kewanee	1010		G	$1,100	8/06	SEMN	18'
Kewanee	1010		G	$2,500	1/06	NEMO	21' flat fold
Kewanee	1020		G	$425	6/06	NCIL	20', 7.5" spacing, flat fold
Kewanee	1020		F	$475	6/06	WCMN	22', hyd. fold, tandem wheels, wheels on wings
Kewanee	1020		G	$900	2/06	NWIL	Hyd. fold
Kewanee	1020		G	$975	7/06	NCIL	20'
Kewanee	1020		G	$1,200	2/06	WCMN	Hyd. fold, 22', like-new blades
Kewanee	1020		F	$1,500	2/06	NCIL	20' flat fold
Kewanee	1020		G	$1,600	12/06	SCMN	
Kewanee	1020		G	$2,750	10/06	SEMN	22.5', hydro wings
Kewanee	1175		G	$3,000	12/06	SCNE	22', folding, 9" spacing
Kewanee	1175		G	$4,400	3/06	NEOH	Transport, 25', single-bar harrow
Kewanee	1175		G	$4,500	2/06	SEIL	21'
Kewanee	2000		G	$4,250	7/06	NWIL	30", notched blades
Kewanee	730		F	$475	3/06	NCIN	14' manual fold wheel
Kewanee	810		G	$1,050	7/06	WCMN	12', hd
Krause	1401		G	$2,800	3/06	SENE	18'
Krause	1415		G	$3,350	2/06	WCNE	23' folding tandem
Krause	1418		G	$2,000	12/06	ECNE	25', hyd. fold, gauge wheels on wings
Krause	1480		G	$3,500	5/06	SCCA	19'6" offset wheel

Disks

Make	Model	Year	Cond.	Price	Sale	Location	Comments
Krause	1480		G	$6,000	5/06	SCCA	19'6" offset wheel
Krause	1482		F	$500	11/06	NCKS	16', hd offset
Krause	1497		G	$1,600	3/06	NWKS	1497A 13' offset
Krause	1588		G	$4,500	4/06	SEMI	18' rock flex, single fold
Krause	1592		F	$800	11/06	NEKS	16' center fold
Krause	1900		G	$1,650	1/06	NECO	24' tandem, folding
Krause	1900		G	$3,500	3/06	NCOK	20' offset, Degelman harrows
Krause	1900		G	$4,200	2/06	NCIN	22' hyd. fold-on duals
Krause	1904		G	$3,500	9/06	SWIA	21'
Krause	1950		G	$3,300	8/06	NECO	27'
Krause	1950		G	$3,500	3/06	ECND	Tandem, 34', rock flex, dual carrier wheels
Krause	1950		G	$4,700	2/06	SCMI	32', rock flex, fold-up
Krause	1950	1983	G	$5,000	12/06	WCIL	32' hyd. fold, 22" blades, 9" spacing
Krause	2100		F	$1,000	3/06	SWKS	45', tandem, folding, shopbuilt packer
Krause	2100		G	$4,500	4/06	WCSD	41', hyd. fold up
Krause	2162		G	$8,700	4/06	WCSD	44', rock flex, red, new cylinders, wing pins, good blades (22" blades now measure 21.5")
Krause	2400		G	$1,500	12/06	WCMN	Tandem
Krause	3950		E	$18,000	2/06	SCMI	27', rock flex, fold-up, 4-years use, one owner
Krause	4900		G	$7,000	4/06	SEND	25' rock flex, tandem H611
Krause	4950		G	$7,500	2/06	NECO	40', tandem, folding
Krause	4950		G	$11,000	2/06	WCIL	33', 8" spacing, 19.5' blades
Krause	4991		G	$13,250	8/06	WCKS	32'
MF	620		F	$950	11/06	SCND	Tandem, 23.5' spring cushion
MF	820		F	$550	9/06	NECO	22', tandem, folding
MF	820		G	$1,000	8/06	NECO	25'
MF	820		G	$2,400	2/06	WCIA	21'
MF	820		G	$2,600	8/06	NENE	25' tandem
MF	820		G	$3,900	3/06	ECIA	25', folding, buster bar
Miller	12'		E	$500	11/06	NEKS	Offset
Miller	12'		G	$2,000	3/06	NEOH	Offset
Miller	12'		F	$2,650	12/06	WCMI	Offset
Miller	14'		G	$1,900	3/06	SEMN	Offset, 24" blades
Miller	14'		G	$2,100	3/06	NEMI	Offset
Miller	16'		F	$90	10/06	NCKS	Rigid offset
Miller	16'		G	$1,900	1/06	NECO	Offset, harrow
Miller	20'		G	$1,500	2/06	NECO	Offset, pt
Miller	20'		G	$1,500	2/06	NWKS	Offset
Miller	22'		F	$650	3/06	NWKS	Offset
Rhino	F90B		G	$1,000	4/06	NEND	20' hd tandem, spring cushion gangs
Rome	12'		G	$12,000	4/06	WCMB	Canadian sale, breaking disk, hyd. lift
Schaefer	14'		G	$3,300	3/06	WCSD	Yellow, hd, offset
Schaefer	16'		G	$950	1/06	NECO	Tandem, pt
Schaefer	18'		G	$675	1/06	NECO	Tandem, pt
Schaefer	14'		G	$2,000	3/06	NCOK	Offset
Schaefer	14'		G	$3,600	4/06	WCSD	Yellow, hd, offset
Schaefer	16'		G	$450	2/06	WCNE	Tandem, pt
Schaefer	NA		F	$1,000	3/06	ECND	26' tandem, 24" blades

Disks

Make	Model	Year	Cond.	Price	Sale	Location	Comments
Summers	28'	2003	E	$20,500	7/06	NEND	Summers Diamond Series 10, 28', rock flex, less than 200 acres
Summers	34'		G	$17,250	11/06	NEND	Diamond, wing weight package, 10" space, 3-bar harrow, 24" blades
Summers	36'		E	$11,800	3/06	NESD	Rock flex
Summers	40'		G	$20,000	2/06	SEKS	40' Super Coulter, very nice
Sunflower	1231		G	$3,050	3/06	WCKS	21', folding
Sunflower	1232		G	$4,600	3/06	WCKS	24', tandem, some welds on tongue
Sunflower	1232		G	$6,250	3/06	NCKS	24', trifold
Sunflower	1232		G	$6,300	12/06	SCNE	27' tandem
Sunflower	1301		G	$4,700	2/06	NCKS	29' tandem, fronts 20.5", rears 19"
Sunflower	1433		G	$15,750	3/06	ECNE	25', hyd. fold, C-flex, bearing standards tandem, hyd. leveling, tandem wheels on wings, one owner
Sunflower	1434		G	$23,000	3/06	ECNE	29', C-flex, hyd. leveling, tandem, wheels on wings, one owner
Sunflower	1434	2002	G	$23,000	6/06	NWKS	C-flex, 9"×24" blades, Degelman harrow
Sunflower	1441-29		F	$2,600	8/06	NECO	29'
Sunflower	1541		G	$13,000	2/06	NWKS	38', hyd. fold, extra parts, harrow
Taylorway	12'		G	$900	1/06	NEIN	Offset
Taylorway	15'		F	$850	1/06	SCMI	Rock flex
Taylorway	15'		F	$1,300	7/06	NWMN	Tandem
Taylorway	21'		G	$2,500	10/06	NCND	Tandem, rock flex, folding wings
Towner	20'		G	$2,200	2/06	WCMN	Offset tandem, hd, 27" blades
Versatile	40'		G	$2,800	2/06	NECO	40' pt, folding tandem
White	20'		G	$4,000	2/06	NCOH	Hyd. fold, 9" spacing, transport disk, 1-bar harrow, tandem wheels
White	252		G	$575	9/06	NEIN	16', wing fold
White	253		G	$1,500	3/06	ECMI	18.5' wheel, wings
White	255		G	$400	8/06	NCOH	16', 2' manual wings
White	255		F	$525	1/06	SCMI	16'
White	256		G	$1,250	1/06	NEIN	20'
White	271		F	$950	3/06	NEKS	
White	271		G	$2,300	12/06	SEMN	
White	271		G	$2,450	8/06	NEIL	20', 20" blades
White	271		G	$3,250	12/06	SEMN	28' rock flex
White	271		G	$3,800	1/06	NEIN	23'
White	273		G	$4,000	4/06	SWOH	25'
White	273		G	$5,400	1/06	NEIN	21'
White	273	1984	G	$4,400	4/06	WCMB	Canadian sale, 20', tandem, 22" blades
Wilbeck	10'		G	$2,150	12/06	NEMO	22" notched blades, hd, offset
Wilbeck	15'		G	$1,800	8/06	NCMI	Offset wheel, 80% blades
Wilrich	20'		G	$700	1/06	ECNE	3-bar harrow
Wishek	742		F	$5,000	9/06	WCND	Tandem, center fold, 24', 11" space
Wishek	842	2000	E	$20,500	1/06	SESD	26'
Wishek	842T		G	$13,500	4/06	NWMN	26', 11" space, rock flex, hd tandem

Drills

About five years ago I fielded a request from a guy in Ohio who published a no-till newsletter. He asked me to write a guest column discussing trends on used no-till drills. I recall talking about the $1,000-per-foot theory, how nice-condition used no-till drills sold according to that premise. Today? Probably slightly less than $1,000 per foot, although spikes in the price of gas can and do drive up the demand for and the value of these drills.

Drills

Make	Model	Year	Cond.	Price	Sale	Location	Comments
Bourgualt	4350	1998	G	$20,000	4/06	NWMN	Air system, triple tank, 40' field cultivator, 3-bar harrow, all hyd., tank monitor, 7" space
Bourgualt	5710	1997	G	$43,250	4/06	WCMB	Canadian sale, 40' air drill, 4" openers, 4" rubber packers, Haukass markers
Bourgualt	5710	1997	G	$46,250	4/06	SWMN	Canadian sale, 40' air drill, mid-row banders, Flexi-Coil stealth 40 openers, 4" rubber packers, Haukass markers, complete with Bourgault 3225 air cart, (tow behind, 225-bu. 60/40 split tank), all shedded
Bourgualt	5710	2003	E	$73,000	3/06	NCND	Series II air seeder, 48', 5 fold, double shoot, mid-row banders, full floating hitch, 3" steel packers, tower run monitor, 2003 Bourgault 5350 commodity cart
Brillion	10'		G	$4,000	1/06	NEIN	Seeder
Brillion	1201		G	$4,400	6/06	SCMN	SureStand, 12' seeder, sharp
Brillion	1201		G	$4,500	3/06	ECIL	SST-1201 10' Turfmaker grass seeder
Brillion	1201		G	$4,600	12/06	SWWI	SST-1201 seeder, hyd. lift
Brillion	144		G	$6,000	5/06	SCMI	SST-144 12' seeder
Brillion	6'		F	$475	1/06	NCCO	3-pt. grass seeder
Brillion	6'		G	$1,500	3/06	NCCO	Grass drop seeder
Brillion	8'		G	$800	8/06	NCMI	8.5' 3- pt. seeder
Brillion	SS10		E	$6,650	5/06	SEWY	10' grass seeder, 3 pt.
Brillion	SS10		G	$6,975	3/06	NWIL	10' seeder
Brillion	SS12		G	$6,100	3/06	NEMI	12' seeder
Case IH	5100		G	$1,500	12/06	SEMN	12'
Case IH	5100		G	$2,500	3/06	NCIL	12', soybean special
Case IH	5100		G	$2,600	3/06	NWOH	21 run
Case IH	5100		G	$2,700	9/06	NECO	7"×14', seeder, pt
Case IH	5100		G	$3,100	4/06	WCWI	21×7", grass seed
Case IH	5100		G	$3,700	3/06	ECMI	21-hoe drill, double disk openers
Case IH	5100		G	$4,500	1/06	WCIL	Soybean special grain drill, grass seed, track scratcher
Case IH	5100	1992	G	$2,300	12/06	WCIL	Soybean special grain drill, marker tires, press wheels
Case IH	5200		F	$1,000	1/06	NEIN	20'
Case IH	5200		G	$1,450	1/06	NEIN	20'
Case IH	5200		G	$3,400	10/06	NECO	7"×16', pt, seeder
Case IH	5200		G	$3,500	9/06	NECO	16'×8", 3 pt., seeder
Case IH	5300		E	$2,700	8/06	SCMI	21-run grain drill
Case IH	5300		G	$4,800	3/06	NWOH	21-run drill, seeder
Case IH	5300	1997	E	$5,550	9/06	NWIL	18×7, soybean special, grass
Case IH	5400		G	$5,000	1/06	NEMO	Mulch-till, 15', grain drill
Case IH	5400		G	$5,300	12/06	WCMN	20' no-till soybean drill, Yetter coulter cart, brush fill auger
Case IH	5400		G	$5,600	3/06	NCNE	Mulch-till, 3 pt., 8" spacing, markers, acre monitor, less than 2,000 acres, one owner
Case IH	5400		G	$6,200	1/06	WCIL	Mulch-till, 20' no-till drill, Yetter no-till caddy, press wheels, Fuerst rear-style harrow
Case IH	5400		F	$8,000	1/06	NWIL	Soybean special grain drill, 15', 15" spacings, monitor, no-till system
Case IH	5400		G	$8,200	3/06	NWIL	15' no-till, coulter cart, grass seed, harrow, Yetter markers
Case IH	5400	1992	E	$8,100	12/06	SWIA	Mounted minimum-till drill, 15', 3 pt., gauge wheels, markers, grass seeder, harrow, 7" space, rear support
Case IH	5400	1993	G	$2,000	8/06	NEKS	15'

WHAT'S IT WORTH?

Drills

Make	Model	Year	Cond.	Price	Sale	Location	Comments
Case IH	5400	2000	F	$9,500	4/06	NWOH	20' no-till, needed blades
Case IH	6200		F	$1,400	9/06	NEND	(3) 12' press drill, dry fertilizer, transport
Case IH	6200		G	$2,500	3/06	NWMN	Press drills, (2) 12s, 6" spacing, rubber press, dry fertilizer, factory transport, front-folding Poma markers
Case IH	6200	1988	G	$3,600	5/06	SEND	Press drill, two 12s, 6" space, dry fertilizer, rubber press, factory transport, front-fold markers, grass seeder
Case IH	7100		G	$2,500	11/06	SCSD	Hoe drills, 2-12', 10" spacing, liquid fertilizer
Case IH	8500		G	$16,000	3/06	ECND	Air hoe drill, 45', Eagle beaks, rubber press, single bar harrow, liquid drop, full-run monitor, Haukaas sidearm markers, hyd. fill auger
Case IH	8600		F	$3,500	8/06	WCMN	30' air drill, individual row monitor, hyd. markers
Case IH	8600		G	$8,000	7/06	ECND	Air disk drill, 30' fill auger, all-run monitor, markers, track eliminators
Case IH	8600	1994	G	$4,100	3/06	SEND	30' air drill, PTO
Concord	2410	1995	G	$7,000	3/06	ECND	Air seeder, 24', 10" space disk levelers, twin 55 bushels, frame-mounted tanks, NH_3, rear hitch, markers, low acres, single owner
Concord	3310		G	$15,000	3/06	NWMN	Air seeder, 2,000 tow behind, 2-compartment tank, harrow
Concord	4010		G	$28,000	4/06	NCSD	4010-4R 5-plex air seeder, Case IH 2300 tank
Concord	4010	1995	G	$26,000	4/06	SEND	Air seeder, 40', 2,300 cart, hyd. fan, population, blockage monitors
Crustbuster	3200		F	$1,400	8/06	NECO	32.5', 10" spacing
Crustbuster	4025		G	$7,000	3/06	NWIL	30'×10"
Fargo	NA	2004	E	$42,500	3/06	ECND	Fargo Aire 34' air seeder on quad V tool, edge on shanks, Eagle beaks
Flexi-Coil	1610		G	$2,850	9/06	WCND	Commodity cart, 160 bu., twin compartment, hyd. fill auger
Flexi-Coil	1720		F	$7,500	3/06	WCMN	Air seeder, 30' bar, Yetter fertilizer disks, 30' bar, MaxEmerge units, markers, hyd. fold
Flexi-Coil	1720		G	$20,000	4/06	WCSD	Air seeder, double chute, 9" spacing, field ready
Flexi-Coil	5000		G	$24,000	4/06	NWMN	39' air drill, 4-position adjustable shank assemblies, 7.2" spacing, 2320 2-compartment tow behind tank, 6-run, double shoot, adjustable wheel tracking, hyd. fan
Flexi-Coil	5000		G	$32,500	4/06	WCSD	Air drill, 2320 pull-between cart, 230 bu.
Flexi-Coil	5000	1993	G	$34,000	4/06	WCMB	Canadian sale, 33', 9", single shoot
Flexi-Coil	5000	1996	G	$34,000	3/06	ECND	Seeding tool, 39', rubber press, 4", 2-bar harrow, full floating hitch, 350-lb. trip shanks
Flexi-Coil	5000	1997	G	$11,750	11/06	SCND	57', air seeder
Flexi-Coil	6000	1999	G	$30,000	9/06	WCND	Seeding tool, 40' double shoot, Barton openers, weight package, manifold, monitor, tandems across, Flexi-Coil 2320, commodity cart
Great Plains	10'		G	$3,750	8/06	NCOH	No-till, 15×7.5" press wheels, grass seeder
Great Plains	10'		G	$4,750	8/06	NCMI	Great Plains/Land Pride 10' pt. seeder
Great Plains	10'		G	$7,100	3/06	SEPA	No-till
Great Plains	10'		E	$10,750	3/06	NWOH	No-till, 15 run, #1005
Great Plains	1200		G	$10,000	2/06	NCOH	12' no-till grain, center pivot, tine harrow, seed firmers
Great Plains	1205		G	$7,000	1/06	SCMI	12' no-till
Great Plains	14'		G	$4,250	9/06	NECO	Solid stand, 14', 8", seeder
Great Plains	15'		G	$2,550	3/06	NWIL	
Great Plains	15'		G	$3,800	3/06	NCIL	No-till, 7.5" spacing, center pivot hitch, coulter cart

Drills

Make	Model	Year	Cond.	Price	Sale	Location	Comments
Great Plains	15'		G	$4,500	3/06	NWOH	Solid stand 15, 24 run, no-till, center pivot hitch
Great Plains	15'		G	$5,700	3/06	NWOH	Solid stand 15, 22 run, no-till, seeder, coulter caddy
Great Plains	15'		G	$9,000	3/06	NCOH	1,500 no-till hitch, Yetter markers
Great Plains	15'		G	$11,000	12/06	NWOH	No-till, center pivot, parallel linkage, no markers or fill
Great Plains	1500		E	$14,400	12/06	SCNE	15', no-till, coulters, markers, 7.5" spacing, drilled 600 acres
Great Plains	1500	2003	G	$14,750	1/06	WCIL	No-till, only 526 acres use, population monitor
Great Plains	1510		E	$12,500	3/06	NEKS	30', folding
Great Plains	20		F	$1,550	2/06	NECO	10"×20', 3 pt
Great Plains	20		G	$6,500	9/06	SCNE	Solid stand 20, 20' grain drill, 7.5" spacings, Orthman hyd. markers
Great Plains	20'		F	$675	1/06	SCNE	Grain, 10" spacing, markers, fertilizer, 3 pt., double disk openers
Great Plains	20'		F	$1,350	3/06	NWIL	Cart
Great Plains	20'		G	$1,450	12/06	WCMN	Press drill, 6" spacing, Great Plains pull package
Great Plains	20'		F	$2,800	3/06	NWIL	No-till
Great Plains	20'	1991	G	$6,300	1/06	NECO	3-pt. mount, 7.5" spacing
Great Plains	2000		E	$6,000	4/06	NEIA	20', solid stand
Great Plains	2020		G	$2,100	11/06	WCMN	20' press drill, 10" spacing, rear harrow, soybean special, very low acres
Great Plains	24'		F	$550	3/06	SEIA	
Great Plains	24'		F	$3,750	3/06	NCKS	Solid stand 24'
Great Plains	24'		F	$3,750	3/06	NCKS	Solid stand 24', grass seeder
Great Plains	24'		G	$4,700	2/06	ECIL	Hyd. fold drill, 8" spacing
Great Plains	24'		G	$12,500	8/06	NEKS	Solid stand hyd. folding grain drill, used on 5,086 acres
Great Plains	24'		G	$17,500	3/06	NWIL	
Great Plains	2410		G	$19,750	3/06	NEKS	Solid stand no-till, 24', hyd. fold, seed shaft monitor, controller, Tru-V openers, one owner
Great Plains	30'		F	$1,500	3/06	WCKS	Folding drill, 10", double disks
Great Plains	30'		F	$1,750	3/06	NCUT	
Great Plains	30'		G	$6,500	3/06	NEKS	Solid stand-30, hyd. fold, 9.5L-15 tires, Tru-V openers, one owner
Great Plains	30'		G	$7,000	3/06	NEKS	Solid state
Great Plains	30'		G	$7,500	2/06	NECO	7"×30', pt
Great Plains	30'		G	$15,000	4/06	WCSD	Double no-till, solid stand
Great Plains	30'	1991	G	$6,200	4/06	NCOK	Solid stand drills, 45×8" double disk, shaft monitor
Great Plains	30'	2001	G	$9,250	3/06	ECMI	Grain drill, press wheels, 7.5" w/ hyd. marker arms
Great Plains	40'		G	$6,250	2/06	NWKS	Multi-flex 40' hyd. fold hoe drill, extra parts
Haybuster	30'		G	$4,500	3/06	WCKS	No-till, 10" spacings, disks, markers
Herd	NA		G	$550	12/06	SEMN	Seeder
IHC	5100		G	$700	3/06	NWOH	21-run drill
IHC	5100		G	$1,100	1/06	WCIL	Grain drill, press wheels
IHC	5100		G	$1,200	3/06	WCMI	21-hoe double grain drill
IHC	5100		G	$1,300	10/06	SEMN	16×6", grass seed
IHC	5100		G	$1,400	1/06	WCIL	Grain drill, press wheels
IHC	5100		E	$3,200	3/06	NEOH	Soybean special, 21×7 grain drill, grass seeder
IHC	5100		F	$4,000	3/06	NWIL	12' soybean special, 7" spacing
IHC	5100		F	$4,000	3/06	NWPA	Soybean special, small grain attachment
IHC	5100		G	$4,500	2/06	WCME	
IHC	5100		G	$5,100	10/06	NCWI	Soybean special

WHAT'S IT WORTH?

Drills

Make	Model	Year	Cond.	Price	Sale	Location	Comments
IHC	6200		F	$750	7/06	NWMN	Grain drills, 2-14', IHC transport, markers
IHC	6200		G	$1,600	3/06	WCMN	14' press drill, 6" spacing, grass seeder
IHC	7100		F	$650	2/06	NCKS	Hoe drill, Acra-Plants
IHC	7100		F	$1,500	3/06	NCUT	Press wheel drills, four
IHC	7100		G	$6,500	4/06	WCSD	(2) 14' deep furrow press drills, hitch and road transport, 12" spacing
John Deere	1520		G	$11,500	3/06	NECO	3 pt., 7.5"×32' double disk grain drill, folding markers
John Deere	1530	1998	G	$14,500	3/06	SEMN	Soybean drill, 15'×15" spacings, no-till drill, air pressure units, fluted coulters
John Deere	1530	2000	E	$9,900	9/06	NEIA	15' no-till drill, like new, with new Blu Jet caddy for drill
John Deere	1560		E	$22,500	4/06	SEMI	No-till, 24 run, dolly, markers, Loup monitor
John Deere	1560		E	$23,000	2/06	SEMI	No-till, 24-run auger, fill markers
John Deere	1560	1999	G	$11,750	8/06	WCIL	Yetter markers, dolly, harrow, 12.5/15 tires
John Deere	1590		G	$41,750	12/06	ECMO	(2) 15' no-till, Houck hitch
John Deere	1590	2006	G	$18,300	12/06	ECMO	15', no-till, dolly wheel hitch
John Deere	1820	2001	G	$66,500	6/06	NWMN	Air seeder, 40', 7.5" spacing, floating hitch, dual caster gauge wheels
John Deere	1850		G	$19,000	12/06	SCMN	No-till
John Deere	1850		G	$24,000	2/06	SEKS	36' no-till air seeder, 7.5" spacing
John Deere	1850		G	$25,500	9/06	WCND	Seeding tool, 42', 7.5" space, JD 787 twin compartment, 230-bu. commodity cart, tow behind, hyd. fan, fill auger
John Deere	1890	2003	G	$80,000	11/06	ECND	Single disk air drill, 42.5', 7.5" space, single drop, spare hyd. markers
John Deere	1890	2004	G	$77,000	11/06	ECND	Between commodity cart, VariRate monitor, wear boots, Haukaas markers, harrow
John Deere	1890	2006	G	$103,000	11/06	ECND	Single disk air drill, 42.5', 7.5" single drop, extended wear boots
John Deere	1900		G	$42,000	12/06	ECMO	Wagon
John Deere	450		G	$4,800	9/06	SEIA	21×7.5, press wheels good, no grass seed or folding tongue
John Deere	450		G	$6,100	1/06	NCCO	Double disk grain drill, 21×7", seeder, agitator, press wheels
John Deere	450	1997	E	$11,100	9/06	NEIA	21×7.5, press wheels, markers, grass seed
John Deere	455		F	$4,900	12/06	WCMN	25', 10" spacing, markers
John Deere	455		G	$6,100	12/06	SCMN	
John Deere	455		G	$6,100	12/06	SCMN	
John Deere	455		G	$7,000	12/06	WCMN	25', 10" spacing markers
John Deere	455		E	$9,000	3/06	WCKS	35' folding drill, 10", Yetter markers
John Deere	455		G	$9,000	8/06	SCNE	30' folding drill, 7.5" spacing, double disk
John Deere	455		G	$9,000	3/06	ECNE	30', hyd. markers, loop monitor
John Deere	455		G	$9,500	3/06	NENE	10" spacing, 25' hyd. fold markers
John Deere	455		G	$11,400	8/06	NENE	30' folding drill, 7.5" spacing, electric over hyd., individual section controls, seed monitor
John Deere	455		G	$15,500	6/06	SCMN	30', front fold, 6" spacings, harrow, press wheels
John Deere	455		G	$19,000	4/06	NWMN	35', front fold JD marker, 6" space, wide packer wheels, dry fertilizer
John Deere	455		G	$19,000	2/06	SCKS	25' 2-section
John Deere	455		G	$21,500	4/06	WCSD	Minimum-till, 35' folding drill grass seeder, 7.5" spacing, Yetter markers, grass seeder
John Deere	455	1992	G	$8,250	4/06	SEND	25' hyd. fold drill, fertilizer attachment
John Deere	455	1999	G	$10,250	2/06	ECKS	Grain drill

Drills

Make	Model	Year	Cond.	Price	Sale	Location	Comments
John Deere	455	1999	G	$17,000	2/06	SCMI	Grain drill/seeder, markers, JD 250 monitor
John Deere	455	2001	E	$18,000	1/06	SCNE	Minimum-till 30' drill, 10" spacing
John Deere	455	2002	E	$35,500	1/06	SCKS	35', trifolding, hyd. markers, 7.5" spacing, fertilizer, fed-shaft monitor, drill box covers, SN 690404, bought new, shedded
John Deere	515		G	$1,700	1/06	WCIL	Unverferth Culti Planter II
John Deere	515		G	$5,900	11/06	NCIN	(2) grain drills on 530 carrier, front fold, 7.5" spacing
John Deere	520		F	$1,200	6/06	WCMN	Bean drill, bean meters, markers, press wheels
John Deere	520		G	$2,250	9/06	NECO	20'×8", 3 pt., double disk
John Deere	520		F	$2,950	2/06	WCIA	No-till cart
John Deere	520		G	$5,100	2/06	NECO	3 pt, 10"×25'
John Deere	750		F	$4,000	1/06	SCMN	15', 10" space no-till
John Deere	750		F	$6,950	12/06	NWIL	No-till, 3 pt., no markers, grass seeder
John Deere	750		F	$8,000	3/06	SWOH	15' no-till, Yetter markers
John Deere	750		F	$8,000	2/06	WCIL	15' no-till, grass seed, markers
John Deere	750		G	$9,000	2/06	WCIL	15' no-till, dolly wheels, Yetter markers, tine harrow
John Deere	750		G	$9,200	12/06	SEMN	15' no-till drill
John Deere	750		G	$9,250	3/06	NWOH	15' no-till drill, 24 run, quick-fill cross auger, dolly
John Deere	750		G	$9,250	12/06	WCIL	15' no-till grain drill, completely reconditioned two years ago
John Deere	750		F	$9,800	3/06	SEPA	15', dolly wheels
John Deere	750		G	$9,800	1/06	SCNE	No-till, Yetter markers, 7.5" spacing, grass seeder
John Deere	750		G	$9,900	12/06	NWWI	15' no-till drill
John Deere	750		G	$10,000	12/06	NWIL	15', no-till, dolly wheel, Yetter markers, monitor, 2-bar harrow, Remlinger hyd. driven fill auger
John Deere	750		G	$10,250	1/06	ECNE	15' drill, no-till, markers, grass seeder, 2-bar harrow, set to 15", have parts to convert to 7.5"
John Deere	750		G	$10,900	11/06	SCNE	No-till drill, 7.5" spacing, 24 run, with alfalfa seeder, cover tarp
John Deere	750		G	$12,000	2/06	NCIL	Grain drill, 15', no-till, dolly wheels
John Deere	750		G	$13,000	3/06	NWIL	15' no-till drill, dolly wheels, Yetter markers, grass seeder
John Deere	750		G	$13,300	3/06	SEPA	15', no-till, rebuilt bottom, grass box
John Deere	750		F	$13,500	4/06	SEPA	15' no-till drill, alfalfa seeder, foam system
John Deere	750		G	$14,500	2/06	WCMN	15' no-till drill, grass, markers, liquid fertilizer, 2-pt. hitch, tramline system, SDX closing wheels
John Deere	750		G	$14,750	3/06	NWOH	15' no-till drill, seeder, JD markers
John Deere	750		G	$16,500	11/06	NCOH	No-till grain, 24 unit
John Deere	750	1993	G	$8,200	2/06	SEIN	15', no-till, Kasco fill auger, population monitor, radar
John Deere	750	1993	G	$8,700	2/06	NWIN	15' no-till, caddy wheels
John Deere	750	1994	G	$12,500	2/06	NCIN	15' no-till grain, Kasco auger, fill attachment
John Deere	750	1994	G	$13,500	12/06	WCMI	No-till, 24 run, loading auger
John Deere	750	1995	G	$11,500	12/06	NEMO	Grain, front dolly wheels, Yetter markers
John Deere	750	1996	G	$9,400	2/06	NWOH	15' no-till, 24 run
John Deere	750	1997	G	$11,500	3/06	NWOH	15' no-till, dolly front, seeder, 24 run
John Deere	750	1997	G	$15,750	2/06	SWOH	15', no-till, only 350 acres on new disks & bearings, DMI cushion clutch
John Deere	750	1998	G	$16,000	2/06	WCOH	15' no-till, all new blades, Yetter markers, cover
John Deere	777		F	$2,000	7/06	NEND	Air drill, 32', 170 bu., twin compartment tank, hyd. fill auger, JD 1060 seeding tool, JD markers
John Deere	777		G	$5,500	4/06	NEND	Air, 32', 1060 seeding tool, hyd. markers, fill auger, 7" space

Drills

Make	Model	Year	Cond.	Price	Sale	Location	Comments
John Deere	777		G	$6,500	6/06	ECND	Air, 160-bu. commodity cart, 1060 seeding tool, 32', hyd. fold markers, hyd. fill auger, wing stabilizer
John Deere	777	1992	G	$12,000	3/06	NEND	Air, 42', 170-bu. commodity cart, 1060 seeding tool, wing stabilizer, complete reconditioning
John Deere	787		G	$12,500	3/06	NEND	Air, stainless steel shaft, bean cupped poly-load auger, JD 1060 41' seeding tool, markers, 4-rank, single harrow, 7" spacing
John Deere	787		G	$13,500	4/06	NEND	Air, 230-bu. tank
John Deere	8200		F	$300	3/06	WCKS	Grain, 16-10 w/ hitch, double disk
John Deere	8200		F	$300	3/06	WCKS	Grain, 16-10 w/ hitch, double disk
John Deere	8200		G	$550	11/06	SEIA	12' grain, grass seed attachment
John Deere	8200		F	$700	5/06	WCKS	Disk, 13'×10" spacing
John Deere	8200		G	$1,200	9/06	SCNE	16', 10" spacings
John Deere	8200		G	$1,650	12/06	NEMO	12' grain
John Deere	8200		G	$2,000	8/06	NECO	
John Deere	8200		G	$2,500	8/06	WCIL	21×7, grass seeder, press wheels, Fuerst harrow
John Deere	8200		G	$2,800	2/06	NECO	7×14, pt, seeder
John Deere	8200		G	$3,250	3/06	NEIA	Grain
John Deere	8200		G	$3,500	2/06	WCIL	Grain
John Deere	8300		F	$65	3/06	SWOH	18-hole grain
John Deere	8300		G	$500	3/06	NWOH	23-run
John Deere	8300		F	$650	1/06	WCNE	15', pt
John Deere	8300		G	$800	3/06	NWOH	18-run
John Deere	8300		G	$900	9/06	NEIN	Grain
John Deere	8300		G	$950	9/06	NWOH	23×7 grain, press wheels, depth bands
John Deere	8300		G	$1,000	10/06	WCWI	16' grain, double disks, grass attach
John Deere	8300		G	$1,200	3/06	SWNE	16 hole, 10" spacing, 7:50-20 tires
John Deere	8300		G	$1,250	7/06	WCCA	14' grain, double disk openers
John Deere	8300		F	$1,250	8/06	NECO	(3) 16×10
John Deere	8300		G	$1,250	2/06	SWNE	Grain, 16 hole, 10" spacing, press wheels, hyd. lift, one owner, always shedded
John Deere	8300		G	$1,400	12/06	SWIL	Grain, 23 run
John Deere	8300		G	$1,400	12/06	WCMI	13' grain, 23 run
John Deere	8300		G	$1,700	9/06	SCNE	16', 10" spacings
John Deere	8300		G	$1,700	1/06	SCMI	18-run, grain
John Deere	8300		G	$1,800	2/06	NECO	6"×14', pt
John Deere	8300		G	$1,875	1/06	SWOH	Grain, grass seeder, 23-7
John Deere	8300		F	$1,900	2/06	NCCO	Single disk grain drill, 21×7, hay seeder
John Deere	8300		G	$1,900	10/06	NECO	7"×14', pt, seeder
John Deere	8300		G	$2,000	8/06	NWIL	13', grass seeder
John Deere	8300		G	$2,200	1/06	NECO	12', pt, seeder
John Deere	8300		P	$2,300	11/06	NEIA	Rough, single disk, grass seed, not shedded
John Deere	8300		G	$2,500	2/06	NECO	6"×16', pt
John Deere	8300		G	$2,500	8/06	NCIA	10', grass seed, 7" spacings
John Deere	8300		G	$2,500	9/06	NECO	8"×14', pt, double disk
John Deere	8300		F	$2,700	2/06	NECO	3×8, ground drive
John Deere	8300		G	$2,800	1/06	NECO	12', pt, seeder disk
John Deere	8300		G	$2,900	9/06	NECO	8"×14', pt, double disk
John Deere	8300		G	$3,000	4/06	SEMI	18 run, seeder

Drills

Make	Model	Year	Cond.	Price	Sale	Location	Comments
John Deere	8300		G	$3,250	3/06	SWNE	Grain, 20 hole, 7.5" spacing, 7:50-20 tires
John Deere	8300		G	$3,300	3/06	NCCO	Double disk grain, 7"×20'
John Deere	8350		E	$900	11/06	NEKS	16-hole grain, press wheels, fertilizer
John Deere	8350		G	$2,500	4/06	SCMN	13' grain, 6" spacing, fertilizer, grass seeder
John Deere	9300		G	$600	2/06	WCNE	10'×6", pt, double disk
John Deere	9300		G	$1,250	3/06	SEND	(2) 10'
John Deere	9300		G	$1,500	12/06	NENE	3 sec, 12", steel press, fertilizer, 30', transports
John Deere	9300		F	$2,000	3/06	SWKS	30' hoe
John Deere	9300		G	$2,400	3/06	SWKS	20' hoe
John Deere	9300		G	$3,000	3/06	WCKS	Hoe, 10'×12", markers
John Deere	9300		G	$3,500	8/06	WCKS	2 hoe, 10×12" rubber press wheels
John Deere	9300		G	$3,700	3/06	SWKS	40' hoe
John Deere	9300		G	$6,600	2/06	WCKS	(4) hoe, 10×12, cover
John Deere	9300		G	$7,250	11/06	NWKS	40' hoe
John Deere	9300		G	$8,500	2/06	SWNE	32' grain hoe
John Deere	9350		F	$950	3/06	SEND	Press, three 10s, 6" space, dry fertilizer, rubber press, track eliminator
John Deere	9350		G	$1,000	3/06	ECND	Three 8's, dry fertilizer
John Deere	9350		F	$2,900	11/06	NWMN	Press, four 10s, black press, 6" space, dry fertilizer, JD markers, folding hitch
John Deere	9350		G	$3,000	4/06	ECND	Press drills, three 10s, dry fertilizer, rubber press, 6" space, factory markers
John Deere	9350		G	$5,500	3/06	NEND	Press, three 10s, factory transport, 6" space
John Deere	9350		G	$6,800	4/06	NESD	2×10' press, rock guards, rubber press, 6" spacing, double hitch, always shedded, 1995 models
John Deere	9350		G	$9,500	2/06	NWMN	Grain, four 10s, factory transport, markers
John Deere	9350		G	$15,000	2/06	NWSD	40', disk, 6" space, hyd. markers, stored inside, dry fertilizer, fitted tarps over each drill, transport, shiny clean
John Deere	9350	1987	G	$7,500	12/06	WCMN	40', 6", JD transport, markers, grass boxes, good disks
John Deere	9350	1992	G	$13,000	4/06	ECND	Press drills, four 10s, 40', black press, dry fertilizer, 6" space, rubber press, JD factory transport, markers
John Deere	9400		G	$5,400	11/06	ECND	40', black press wheels, transport
John Deere	9400		G	$12,500	9/06	SCNE	30' shoe
John Deere	9400		G	$19,000	3/06	NCUT	Three press
Krause	5200	2002	G	$8,500	8/06	WCKS	3 pt., markers, 7.5" spacing
Land Pride	1548		G	$1,250	12/06	NWIL	Grass seeder, PS1548
Lilliston	9680		G	$1,300	3/06	NWOH	18-run no-till
Marliss	20'		F	$1,950	9/06	SEIL	No-till, Sukup lift assist, hyd. markers
Melroe	201		F	$500	3/06	WCMN	(2) 12', hitch
Melroe	202		F	$400	6/06	SWMN	Press
Melroe	204		F	$1,150	3/06	NCUT	3
Melroe	240		F	$800	4/06	SCMN	Grain, grass
Melroe	244		F	$375	8/06	WCMN	12' end wheel, 6" spacing
Morris	30'	1986	G	$7,750	4/06	WCMB	Canadian sale, hoe, markers, factory transport
Morris	310		F	$425	10/06	NCND	30' hoe
Morris	34'	1995	G	$36,500	4/06	SEMB	Canadian sale, double shoot, Eagle beak openers, Morris 7180, tow-between tank, 1,800 bu., split tank

Drills

Make	Model	Year	Cond.	Price	Sale	Location	Comments
Morris	NA	1995	G	$35,000	11/06	NEND	Maxim, 4 rank, 7.5" space, solid steel press wheels, 49', double fold, Eagle beaks, edge on shanks, Morris 6300 double compartment tank, 300 bu., pintle hitch, rear rice tires, hyd. drive, fill auger
Sunflower	30'	2003	G	$27,000	11/06	NWKS	Disk, 10" spacing, 2003 model
Sunflower	9411		E	$8,250	3/06	NEOH	15', 23-hole drill, dual wheel cart, 1,847 acres
Sunflower	9421		G	$30,250	3/06	SWNE	30' grain, 7.5" spacing, hyd. front fold, double disk openers, stalk shield, hyd. markers, 3,110 acres, one owner
Sunflower	9421		G	$30,500	12/06	SCNE	20' no-till, 1,303 acres usage, 7.5" spacing, always shedded
Sunflower	9430		F	$15,000	1/06	SWNE	30' no-till, 6,786 acres, needed a complete set of new disk openers
Truax	NA		E	$3,300	12/06	WCMN	8' no-till grass
Truax	NA		E	$7,600	12/06	WCMN	10' no-till grass
Tye	10		G	$5,000	5/06	SCCA	20', 3 pt., grain, gauge wheels, markers
Tye	114-4330		F	$1,000	8/06	NECO	
Tye	14'		G	$1,500	1/06	NECO	3 pt., seeder
Tye	14'		G	$2,100	2/06	NECO	6×14, 3 pt.
Tye	15'		F	$900	3/06	NWIL	Seeder
Tye	20'		G	$1,250	1/06	WCNE	3 pt.
Tye	20'		G	$2,100	1/06	WCIL	V grain, 3 pt.
Tye	2015	1999	G	$6,500	8/06	NCOH	15' no-till, coulter caddy, hyd. markers
Tye	2020		G	$7,000	9/06	NECO	20', 10", 3 pt., seeder
Tye	40'		F	$3,500	1/06	WCTX	40' wheat, 3 pt., markers, missing ⅓ of the drops
Uft	5000		G	$3,250	9/06	WCOH	No-till
Wilrich	5100		F	$2,000	7/06	NWMN	Air seeder, 160-bu. tank, 30', gauge wheels, markers, packer wheels, 4-bar harrow
Wilrich	5100		F	$2,300	7/06	NWMN	Air seeder, 160-bu. tank, 30', gauge wheels, markers, packer wheels, 4-bar harrow

Notes

Field Cultivators

For a tractor or combine, sure. But for a field cultivator? Used to be folks wouldn't travel far at all to attend auctions outside their local areas, especially not to bid on something like a field cultivator. But today things are different. There aren't as many auctions around, and needs are so specific. Interested buyers these days will cross state lines and rack up big miles for the chance to acquire the field cultivator they're after.

Field Cultivators

Make	Model	Year	Cond.	Price	Sale	Location	Comments
AC	1300		F	$350	7/06	WCMN	30', 6" spacing, 3-bar Lindsay mounted spring tooth harrow
AC	1400		G	$1,700	2/06	WCMN	30', walking tandems, 3-bar harrow
Bervac	32'		G	$750	11/06	NCIN	
Bervac	520		G	$3,500	3/06	NWOH	20', Danish tine, rolling baskets
Brady	18'		G	$600	1/06	WCIL	Hyd. fold
Brady	19'		G	$250	8/06	ECNE	19', hyd. fold
Brillion	12'		G	$1,500	3/06	SEPA	3-pt. leveler
Case IH	4300		G	$5,100	11/06	NEKS	22.5', hyd. fold, walking tandems, 3-tine harrow
Case IH	4300		G	$5,400	12/06	SCMN	54.5'
Case IH	4300		E	$6,500	12/06	SWWI	24', like new
Case IH	4300		E	$7,500	3/06	NCIL	26'
Case IH	4300		G	$8,500	1/06	WCIL	28.5'
Case IH	4300		G	$8,900	1/06	WCIL	27', C-shank, 5-bar harrow
Case IH	4300		E	$10,200	1/06	NWIA	32'9", 3-bar mulcher
Case IH	4300		E	$11,000	11/06	SENE	32'9", hyd. fold, tandem wheels on wings, hard surface shovels, 3-bar harrow, shedded
Case IH	4300	1996	G	$9,350	12/06	NWIL	26'
Case IH	4300	1997	G	$6,800	3/06	NCIA	27.5', leveler
Case IH	4300	1998	G	$4,500	4/06	NWMN	36', 3-bar harrow
Case IH	4300	1999	G	$7,000	3/06	ECNE	32', hyd. fold, 3-bar harrow
Case IH	4300	1999	G	$7,900	3/06	NWMN	44'
Case IH	4300	2000	G	$6,800	3/06	NCIL	30', 3-bar coil tine harrow
Case IH	4600		G	$3,000	9/06	NCIA	27.5', 3-bar harrow
Case IH	4600		F	$3,900	2/06	ECNE	26', harrow, needed shovels
Case IH	4600		G	$4,600	2/06	ECNE	22'9", good shovels
Case IH	4600	1990	G	$5,700	12/06	WCIL	27.5', walking tandems, Remlinger 5-bar harrow
Case IH	4700		G	$5,250	3/06	NCND	43' tandems across, 3-bar harrow, Morris sections
Case IH	4700		G	$5,500	4/06	NWMN	41', walking tandems around, 3-bar mounted harrow
Case IH	4700	1988	G	$4,400	3/06	SEND	52', Vibra Shank, 3-bar harrow
Case IH	4800		G	$3,100	3/06	NEMI	28' Vibra Shank, walking tandem
Case IH	4800		E	$3,450	3/06	NEIA	24'
Case IH	4800		G	$4,100	2/06	WCIL	24', tine harrow
Case IH	4800		G	$4,500	2/06	NEMO	23', Kent 5-bar harrow, walking beam axle
Case IH	4800		G	$5,000	3/06	NWIL	
Case IH	4800		G	$5,200	3/06	SCIA	24'
Case IH	4800		G	$5,750	1/06	WCIL	30', walking tandems, also on the wings and 3-bar harrow
Case IH	4800		E	$5,800	2/06	NENE	25' Vibra Shank, harrow
Case IH	4800		G	$6,000	12/06	NCIL	24', 300-gal. poly chem tank mounted, 3-bar tine harrow
Case IH	4800		G	$6,000	1/06	NEMO	26.5'
Case IH	4800		G	$7,100	2/06	ECIL	27.5', Vibra Shank
Case IH	4800		G	$7,500	11/06	SCMN	
Case IH	4800	1992	G	$7,500	1/06	NEIA	24', Vibra Shank, 3-bar harrow
Case IH	4900		G	$2,600	3/06	NWIL	45'
Case IH	4900		G	$2,750	4/06	NCSD	43', vibra tiller
Case IH	4900		F	$2,750	12/06	SEMN	53'
Case IH	4900		F	$2,900	12/06	SCMN	40.5', 3-bar harrow
Case IH	4900		G	$4,000	2/06	WCMN	47', 6" spacing, 3-bar harrow
Case IH	4900		G	$7,000	3/06	ECND	44', 3-fold, tandems across, wing stabilizer wheels, 3-bar harrow, rear hitch, hyd.

Field Cultivators

Make	Model	Year	Cond.	Price	Sale	Location	Comments
Case IH	4900		G	$9,250	4/06	NEND	42', walking tandems around, gauge wheels, depth control, mounted harrows
Case IH	4900	1989	F	$2,750	8/06	WCMN	53', double fold, 4-bar harrow, 6 sets of oscillating tandems
Case IH	4900	1992	G	$5,500	12/06	WCMN	45', 3-bar harrow, walking tandems, almost new sweeps
Case IH	4900	1993	G	$6,000	9/06	WCIA	52', hyd. fold
Deutz Allis	1400		G	$950	8/06	WCMN	24', Noble 4-bar harrow, hyd. fold
DMI	Tigermate		G	$4,750	8/06	NWIL	28.5'
DMI	Tigermate		G	$5,000	3/06	NEIA	20.5'
DMI	Tigermate		G	$5,700	12/06	ECIL	42', 3-bar flex harrow
DMI	Tigermate		G	$8,400	12/06	SWMI	30', final finish tool, walking tandem, rear spring drag
DMI	Tigermate II		F	$7,500	2/06	WCIL	36', walking tandems on the main frame and wings, 3-bar rear harrow
DMI	Tigermate II		F	$16,000	2/06	WCIL	45', 3-bar harrow
DMI	Tigermate II	1997	G	$23,000	2/06	WCMN	50'
DMI	Tigermate II	2002	G	$19,000	2/06	ECMN	44.5', wing field cultivator, walking tandems, 4-bar finisher, NH_3 attachment
DMI	Tigermate II	2004	E	$12,300	7/06	NWIL	32'
DMI	Tigermate II	2004	E	$12,500	5/06	SCMI	28', harrow, new shovels
DMI	Tigermate II	2004	G	$16,750	2/06	NWIA	34', 4-bar drag
DMI	Tigermate II	2004	E	$26,400	6/06	SCMN	Red, 50.5' double fold, 4-bar harrow
Hesston	2240		F	$700	2/06	SEIL	25'
Hesston	640		F	$200	1/06	WCCA	High crop, mid-mount
Hesston	666		G	$900	1/06	WCCA	Mid-mount
Hiniker	1530		F	$500	3/06	SEIA	30', flat fold
Hiniker	1530		G	$850	12/06	NEMO	24.5, rear harrow
Hiniker	1530		G	$1,300	12/06	NWIL	28.5', flat fold, JD harrow
Hiniker	1540		F	$500	7/06	NWMN	40'
Hiniker	4500	2000	G	$6,100	2/06	NWIN	26', double walker
IHC	365		G	$2,400	1/06	WCNE	24', Danish tine, harrow
IHC	4500		F	$700	8/06	NWIL	30', harrow
IHC	4500		G	$800	8/06	SEPA	Vibra Shank, transport
IHC	4500		G	$1,000	3/06	NWMN	28.5', 3-bar harrow
IHC	4600		G	$1,300	8/06	NCMI	18', tine leveler
IHC	4600		G	$2,100	9/06	SEIA	26', 3-bar leveler
IHC	4600		G	$4,350	3/06	NWIL	24.5'
IHC	4600		G	$5,100	3/06	SEMN	27.5', new 7.5" sweeps, new 3-bar harrow, walking tandems
IHC	4700		G	$2,100	7/06	NEND	49', tandems across, 3-bar harrow
IHC	4700		G	$5,600	3/06	NWMN	Vibratiller, 37.5', walking tandems across, 3-bar harrow
John Deere	1000		F	$300	2/06	WCIA	30'
John Deere	1000		G	$400	11/06	ECIL	26', tine harrow
John Deere	1000		F	$400	3/06	NEMI	22', rear hitch
John Deere	1000		G	$600	8/06	WCMN	30', walking tandems, 3-bar harrow
John Deere	1000		G	$1,100	3/06	ECND	36', 3-bar harrow, knock-ons, spikes, shovels
John Deere	1000		G	$1,100	2/06	NCIL	31', drag
John Deere	1000		G	$1,500	11/06	SCNE	36', pt
John Deere	1000		G	$2,750	1/06	WCTX	
John Deere	1010		F	$200	8/06	SCMN	24'
John Deere	1010		F	$400	10/06	NCND	42', hyd. fold, 3-bar Herman harrow

Field Cultivators

Make	Model	Year	Cond.	Price	Sale	Location	Comments
John Deere	1010		F	$550	8/06	NCIA	30', 300-gal. water tank sprayer kit
John Deere	1010		G	$550	11/06	SCNE	19', harrow
John Deere	1010		G	$600	8/06	NEIL	22', flat fold
John Deere	1010		G	$650	8/06	NWIL	22', flat fold
John Deere	1010		F	$900	4/06	ECND	42.5', walking tandems, wing stabilizer, 3-bar Herman harrow
John Deere	1010		F	$950	3/06	NWIL	Harrow
John Deere	1010		G	$1,400	3/06	NCNE	25', flat fold, 3-bar harrow
John Deere	1010		G	$1,500	3/06	NWIL	
John Deere	1010		F	$1,600	2/06	NEIN	28', walking tandem, Remlinger harrow
John Deere	1010		G	$1,700	9/06	NWMN	21', flat fold, mounted harrow
John Deere	1010		G	$1,700	2/06	WCIL	24'
John Deere	1010		G	$1,850	3/06	NEMI	24', flat fold, walking tandem
John Deere	1010		F	$2,250	3/06	WCMN	60', converted to S-tine, 3-bar harrow
John Deere	1010		E	$3,000	2/06	SEMI	20', hyd. fold, walk tandem, rake
John Deere	1010		G	$4,500	2/06	NEIA	21'
John Deere	1050		F	$600	3/06	NEND	48', tandems across, wing stabilizer wheels
John Deere	1050		F	$1,100	3/06	WCMN	35', flat fold, 3-bar harrow
John Deere	1050		G	$2,500	11/06	NWMN	54', tandems across, 3-bar JD harrow
John Deere	1060		F	$2,750	7/06	WCMN	45', 7" spacing, rear hitch, mounted harrow
John Deere	1060		F	$3,500	12/06	WCMN	
John Deere	1100		F	$100	8/06	SCMN	21'
John Deere	1100		F	$2,800	2/06	NCCO	24', 3 pt., harrow
John Deere	1100	1974	G	$950	4/06	WCMN	One owner
John Deere	2200	2002	G	$38,000	11/06	ECND	56', AccuDepth, 6" space, double fold, 3-bar ⅜" harrow, rear hitch w/ hyd. to rear & knock-ons
John Deere	2200	2002	G	$38,000	11/06	ECND	56', AccuDepth, 6" space, double fold, 3-bar ⅜" harrow, rear hitch w/ hyd. to rear & knock-ons
John Deere	2210	2005	E	$23,000	3/06	SEMN	Leveler field cultivator, 30.5', 7.5" Perma-lock sweeps, 3-bar spike drag, basket crumbler, looks new
John Deere	2210	2006	E	$49,000	12/06	WCMN	50', AccuDepth, factory rear hitch, knock off shovels, 4-bar harrow
John Deere	940		F	$1,600	12/06	WCMN	38.5', S-tine shanks, summer 4-bar harrow
John Deere	940		F	$2,700	3/06	NCCO	20', S-tine, with baskets
John Deere	940	1990	G	$3,000	3/06	ECND	S-tine, 28', walking tandems, wing stabilizer wheels, 3-bar harrow, rear hitch, one owner
John Deere	960		F	$600	3/06	NCIN	22', S-tine
John Deere	960		F	$1,000	11/06	SCIL	24.5', Danish tine, baskets
John Deere	960		F	$1,250	12/06	WCMN	42.5', 3-bar Summers harrow
John Deere	960		F	$1,600	3/06	NWKS	26'
John Deere	960		F	$1,800	8/06	NCIA	30', hyd. wings
John Deere	960		G	$2,000	5/06	SCCA	3-pt, 24', hyd. folding wings, rear harrows
John Deere	960		F	$2,100	11/06	WCMN	41.5', mounted harrow
John Deere	960		F	$2,100	12/06	SEMN	
John Deere	960		G	$2,500	2/06	WCMN	24', mounted
John Deere	960		F	$2,600	12/06	SEMN	36'
John Deere	960		G	$2,700	9/06	NCIA	26', pt
John Deere	960		G	$3,000	11/06	NEKS	30', hyd. fold, spring shank, walking tandems, 3-bar harrow
John Deere	960		G	$3,000	2/06	WCOH	21', wing field cultivator, newly rebuilt cylinders

Field Cultivators

Make	Model	Year	Cond.	Price	Sale	Location	Comments
John Deere	960		G	$3,150	12/06	SCMN	44.5', 3-bar harrow
John Deere	960		G	$3,200	12/06	NWMO	30'
John Deere	960		G	$3,300	12/06	SCMN	44.5'
John Deere	960		G	$3,400	8/06	NEKS	32', hyd. fold, 5-bar spike tooth harrow, walking tandems
John Deere	960		G	$3,500	11/06	SCND	44', 9" spacing, double fold, harrows
John Deere	960		G	$4,000	2/06	NWOH	25', Remlinger spike tooth harrow, fold-up
John Deere	960		G	$4,100	8/06	SCMN	28.5', tandem walking axle
John Deere	960		G	$4,150	3/06	NWIL	
John Deere	960		G	$4,400	3/06	WCIL	24', 5-bar harrow
John Deere	960		G	$4,500	3/06	NESD	32', walking tandems all around, 3-bar harrow
John Deere	960		G	$4,700	3/06	NCKS	36', spring shank, spike leveler
John Deere	960		G	$4,750	6/06	ECND	36', tandems across, 3-bar harrow, single pt, F&S granular applicator
John Deere	960		G	$5,000	3/06	NCIA	32.5', walking tandems all around
John Deere	960		G	$5,500	3/06	NEND	44.5', tandem across, single pt. depth
John Deere	960		G	$5,500	2/06	SCKS	40', hyd. fold, 3-bar harrow, 9.5l-15 tires
John Deere	960		G	$7,500	4/06	ECND	44.5', tandems across, single pt.depth, rear hitch, hyd., spray boom, 3-bar harrow
John Deere	960		G	$7,800	3/06	ECIL	44', trifold, C-shank, 3-bar spring harrow
John Deere	980		G	$5,000	12/06	SCMN	44.5'
John Deere	980		G	$5,600	9/06	SEIL	27.5', Danish tine, 5-bar flex harrow
John Deere	980		G	$5,900	2/06	NEIA	15.5', rolling basket
John Deere	980		G	$7,300	1/06	WCIL	30.5', tine harrow
John Deere	980		E	$7,600	3/06	NWOH	30', Danish tine, tine harrow
John Deere	980		G	$7,800	3/06	NCIL	27.5'
John Deere	980		G	$8,000	3/06	SEIA	30', walking tandem, main and wings, 5-bar spike tooth harrow attachment
John Deere	980		G	$8,750	3/06	ECNE	Pull type, 32'9" width, hyd. lift and wing fold, tandem floating axles and floating wing tandems, 3-bar rear harrow
John Deere	980		G	$8,900	9/06	NCIA	44', single point depth control, low transport
John Deere	980		E	$9,000	2/06	ECMN	36.5', 3-bar mulcher, 6" spacing, one owner
John Deere	980		E	$9,000	2/06	SEMI	20', hyd. fold walking tandem, rake
John Deere	980		G	$9,000	2/06	WCMN	42.5'
John Deere	980		G	$9,500	8/06	NCIA	27.5'
John Deere	980		G	$9,500	2/06	NWMN	35.5', 3-bar JD harrow, walking tandems
John Deere	980		G	$9,600	3/06	SCIA	30'
John Deere	980		G	$10,000	8/06	NWIA	24.5'
John Deere	980		G	$10,000	12/06	SCNE	33', 3-bar harrow
John Deere	980		G	$10,000	2/06	SCMI	36', rear hitch, 5-bar spike, single point depth control, Perma-lock sweeps
John Deere	980		G	$10,750	12/06	WCMI	24.5', JD lock-on knock-off shovels
John Deere	980		G	$11,250	2/06	ECKS	36.5'
John Deere	980		G	$12,000	4/06	NESD	35.5', walking tandems on frame and wings, 3-bar mulchers, 1999 model
John Deere	980		G	$13,000	8/06	WCIL	38.5'
John Deere	980		G	$14,000	11/06	WCMN	36', tandems across, single pt. depth control, JD 3-bar harrow
John Deere	980		G	$15,000	6/06	NWMN	44.5', gauge wheels, tandems across, single point depth control, knock-ons, JD mounted harrow

Field Cultivators

Make	Model	Year	Cond.	Price	Sale	Location	Comments
John Deere	980		G	$17,500	2/06	NWMN	44.5', 3-bar JD harrow, walking tandems, gauge wheels
John Deere	980		G	$19,000	12/06	ECNE	44.5', trifold, hyd. depth control, JD 3-bar harrow, light package
John Deere	980		G	$20,000	12/06	SEMN	42'
John Deere	980	1994	G	$8,750	3/06	SWKS	Field finisher, hyd. fold, hyd. down pressure, gauge wheels, 3-tine harrow
John Deere	980	1997	G	$9,000	3/06	SCIN	44.5', 6" space, 5-bar harrow
John Deere	980	2001	G	$10,300	8/06	NCIA	25.5', 3-bar tine leveler
John Deere	980	2004	G	$14,000	8/06	NCIA	30.5', hyd. lock-ups
John Deere	985		G	$16,500	11/06	SCNE	52', pt, mulcher
John Deere	985		G	$18,000	12/06	SCMN	49.5', 3-bar harrow
John Deere	985		E	$19,500	3/06	SEMN	49.5', 3-bar mulcher, walking tandems on all wings, gauge wheels, low acres
John Deere	985		E	$24,500	3/06	NESD	61'
John Deere	985	1998	G	$17,000	12/06	WCMN	50.5', harrow
John Deere	985	1998	E	$26,000	1/06	SCKS	55.5', hyd. fold, 3-bar harrow, single pt., hyd. depth control, bought new, shedded, SN 812
John Deere	985	1998	E	$28,000	1/06	SCKS	55.5', hyd. fold, 3-bar harrow, single pt., hyd. depth control, bought new, shedded, SN 878
John Deere	985	2002	E	$33,000	4/06	ECND	55', tandems across, single pt., depth, wing stabilizers, new JD 7" knock-on shovels
Kent	36'		G	$125	3/06	WCKS	Field conditioner
Kent	Series V		G	$1,900	3/06	ECNE	22', hyd. fold, hyd. leveling, spray kit
Kewanee	370		G	$1,800	11/06	SCNE	29', walking axles, 2-bar harrow
King	24'		F	$1,500	2/06	NCCO	24', 3 pt., baskets
Kongskilde	18'		F	$950	1/06	NCCO	S-tine, baskets
Krause	3131		G	$6,500	2/06	WCIL	30' Landsman
Krause	4120		F	$1,600	12/06	NWMO	28.5', (3)9'6" sections, (narrow transport width), S-tine, tine harrow
Krause	4223		F	$400	2/06	SWNE	Field conditioner, 3-bar harrow
Krause	4231	1996	G	$10,750	2/06	WCIL	32.5', 9" spacing, 10" shovels, walking tandems on main frame and wings, 4-bar coil tine harrow
Krause	4231	1998	G	$10,750	6/06	NWKS	Tine harrow
Krause	5650	1998	G	$20,000	2/06	WCIL	47.5', 6" spacing, 7" shovels, walking tandems on main frame and wings, 4-bar coil tine harrow
MF	259		F	$300	8/06	NENE	42.5'
MF	259		F	$350	3/06	ECIA	30', folding, harrow, spray attachment
Miller	36'		P	$100	4/06	NWKS	Field conditioner
Morris	37'		G	$1,100	4/06	SEMN	Knock out shovels, Degelman 3-row tine harrows, Canadian sale
Remlinger	RTC 600		G	$1,500	3/06	SWOH	16', Danish tine, cultipacker
Sunflower	5033		G	$5,250	8/06	SCMI	23', NH_3 tank
Sunflower	5033		G	$8,000	1/06	NEIN	33', 3-bar coil tine harrow
Sunflower	5034		E	$9,250	3/06	NWIL	29', walking tandems, 5-bar spike tooth harrow
Sunflower	5034		G	$10,750	1/06	NEIN	35', 3-bar coil tine harrow
Sunflower	52'		G	$7,500	4/06	SCKS	52'
Sunflower	5531		E	$4,200	3/06	WCKS	37', 11" sweeps, harrow
Triple K	23'		G	$4,300	12/06	NWOH	Danish tine, older model
Triple K	28'		F	$1,000	7/06	NWMN	Walking tandems, twin baskets

Field Cultivators

Make	Model	Year	Cond.	Price	Sale	Location	Comments
Triple K	34'		F	$550	7/06	NWMN	Walking tandems, twin baskets
Triple K	40'		G	$750	3/06	NWMN	Danish tine, rolling baskets
Triple K	40'		G	$1,000	8/06	WCMN	5 bar, 3-bar harrow, baskets
White	285		G	$600	3/06	SENE	18'
Wilrich	2500		G	$1,000	11/06	WCIA	
Wilrich	2500		G	$1,650	1/06	NEIN	22'
Wilrich	2500		G	$1,700	3/06	ECND	48', 3-fold tandems across, 3-bar harrow
Wilrich	2500		G	$2,000	3/06	NEKS	42', trifold, 3-bar harrow
Wilrich	2500		G	$2,000	11/06	SCSD	48', triple fold
Wilrich	2500		G	$2,600	12/06	ECNE	27', hyd. fold, Wilrich hitch, 3-bar harrow
Wilrich	2500		G	$3,000	3/06	WCMN	34', walking tandems, 3-bar harrow
Wilrich	2500		G	$3,200	3/06	NWMN	45', walking tandems around, mounted harrow
Wilrich	2500		G	$3,900	8/06	WCIA	26', 4-bar harrow
Wilrich	2500		G	$4,550	2/06	NEIA	20', nice
Wilrich	2800		G	$3,500	3/06	WCMN	26', 4-bar harrow, 400-gal. spray unit, hyd. pump
Wilrich	3400		F	$1,750	11/06	WCMN	42', tandems across, 5-bar harrow
Wilrich	3400		G	$3,200	2/06	NCOH	20', 3-bar Remlinger harrow, rear extension tongue, spring shanks, walking tandems
Wilrich	3400		G	$3,450	2/06	NWIL	26'
Wilrich	3400		G	$3,800	4/06	WCWI	19', 3-bar harow
Wilrich	3400		E	$7,900	1/06	NEIN	24' soil finisher, 3 years old, like new
Wilrich	3400	1993	G	$5,750	4/06	NWMN	48', 4-bar harrow
Wilrich	3411		G	$7,300	2/06	WCIA	26'
Wilrich	3420	1997	G	$8,000	12/06	WCIA	31', 4-bar harrow
Wilrich	Quad 5		G	$5,800	3/06	SWMN	48', triple fold, new 4-bar harrow
Wilrich	Quad 5		G	$7,000	12/06	NCIA	33', 4-bar harrow
Wilrich	Quad 5		G	$7,750	8/06	NCIA	39', 4-bar leveler
Wilrich	Quad 5	1998	G	$7,750	12/06	NWIL	32', 5-bar harrow
Wilrich	Quad 5	2001	G	$22,000	4/06	NWMN	50' full floating hitch, double spring shank, Wilrich 4-bar harrow
Wilrich	Quad X	2003	E	$25,000	4/06	NWMN	50', full floating hitch, single spring shank, double in wheel track, knock-on shovel, flotation tires, Wilrich 4-bar harrow

Notes

Forage Equipment

Included here you'll find forage blowers, forage boxes, and forage choppers, both pull type and self-propelled. The single highest price item I ever personally stood and watch sell on a farm auction was a 1999 Claas Jaguar 860 forage chopper (292 engine hours) sold in April 2001 on a sale in southwest Wisconsin. It sold with hay head and corn head for $220,000. In March 2007 I saw a Claas Jaguar 860 chopper (no heads, 1,738 engine hours) sell for $98,000 in west-central Michigan.

Forage Blowers

Make	Model	Year	Cond.	Price	Sale	Location	Comments
Case IH	600	1991	G	$1,250	5/06	SCMI	
Gehl	1580		F	$500	3/06	WCMN	
Gehl	1580	2001	E	$1,950	5/06	SCMI	
Hustler	56		G	$200	3/06	SEMN	
IHC	56		F	$180	5/06	SWWI	
New Holland	28		G	$450	12/06	SEMN	
New Holland	28		G	$575	9/06	NEIN	Whirl-a-Feed blower
New Holland	28		G	$900	8/06	NCIA	Forage blower
New Holland	40		G	$1,400	10/06	NCWI	Short hopper
New Holland	60		G	$2,800	8/06	NCIA	Forage blower

Forage Boxes

Make	Model	Year	Cond.	Price	Sale	Location	Comments
Badger	BN 1050		G	$5,250	3/06	NEOH	Forage wagon, 16' box, tandem gear
Badger	BN 1055		G	$5,500	4/06	WCWI	Chopper box on Knowles tandem axle gear
Badger	BN 2060		G	$2,000	4/06	WCWI	
Badger	BN 950		F	$850	8/06	SEPA	Tandem, roof
Badger	BN 950		G	$2,250	4/06	WCWI	Chopper box on Badger tandem gear
Balzer	NA		G	$1,000	8/06	ECNE	Chuck wagon, front & rear discharge, 540 PTO, Balzer 6-bolt running gear
Dump Chief	7000		F	$950	8/06	ECNE	Side dump, hd gear, 10:00-16 tires
Gehl	920		G	$1,275	5/06	WCMN	Silage wagon, 16', tandem
Gehl	970		G	$3,100	8/06	NWIL	Silage wagon, tandem gear
Gehl	970		G	$3,250	12/06	SEMN	
Gehl	970		E	$5,650	11/06	NEIA	
Gehl	980		G	$600	3/06	NEIA	Tandem gear, nice
Gehl	980		G	$4,000	12/06	ECMO	Tandem axle
Gehl	980	2005	E	$3,800	8/06	SWWI	
H&S	7+4		G	$4,350	5/06	SWWI	16' twin auger chopper box, H&S 12-ton gear, brakes
H&S	7+4		G	$4,350	5/06	SWWI	16' twin auger chopper box, H&S 12-ton gear
H&S	7+4		E	$6,900	11/06	NCKY	Like new
H&S	7+4	2001	E	$9,100	3/06	NEMI	Self-unloading, H&S 614 tandem gear, used only two years, sharp
John Deere	112		F	$200	7/06	NCIL	Chuck wagon, JD 1064 gear
John Deere	112		G	$400	7/06	NCIL	Chuck wagon, JD 1064 gear
John Deere	112		G	$400	7/06	NCIL	Chuck wagon, JD 1064 gear, two sold-each for $400
John Deere	115		F	$540	7/06	NWIL	
John Deere	125		G	$950	12/06	NWIL	Chuck wagon, new paint
John Deere	125		G	$1,125	12/06	NWIL	Chuck wagon, new paint
John Deere	125		G	$1,150	12/06	NWIL	Chuck wagon, new paint
John Deere	125		G	$1,800	4/06	SWSD	Chuck wagon, hd gear
John Deere	216		G	$3,200	4/06	SWSD	Chuck wagon, hd gear
John Deere	714		G	$2,500	10/06	NCWI	Self-unloading, tandem axle gear
John Deere	714A		G	$3,800	8/06	NWIL	Forage wagon
John Deere	716		G	$8,000	8/06	NCIA	JD 1275 gear, tandem axles, 12.LI-15 tires
John Deere	716		G	$8,000	8/06	NCIA	Forage box on JD 1275 gear, tandem axles
John Deere	716A		G	$825	9/06	NEIN	Tandem gear

Forage Boxes

Make	Model	Year	Cond.	Price	Sale	Location	Comments
John Deere	716A		G	$1,000	9/06	NEIN	Tandem gear
John Deere	716A		G	$2,250	4/06	WCWI	Chopper box on JD 1275 gear
Meyers	16'		F	$700	2/06	NWOH	Tandem axle, 10-ton gear
Meyers	16'		G	$1,000	9/06	NEIN	
Meyers	4516		G	$7,000	12/06	SEMN	
Meyers	500		G	$3,900	3/06	NCWI	16' steel chopper on EZ Trail 8-ton wagon, float tires, adjustable tongue
Miller Pro	5200		G	$6,500	9/06	WCWI	Self-unloading box
Miller Pro	5200		G	$7,000	9/06	WCWI	Self-unloading box
New Holland	716		G	$600	1/06	NECO	16' front unload, 6-wheel, PTO
New Holland	716	1988	G	$1,500	5/06	SCMI	16', 10-ton gear
New Holland	716	1988	G	$1,500	5/06	SCMI	16', 10-ton gear
New Holland	716	1991	G	$6,400	4/06	SWOH	NH 610 10-ton gear, two sold on this sale, both for $6,400
New Holland	716	1991	G	$6,400	4/06	SWOH	NH 610 10-ton gear, two sold on this sale, both for $6,400
New Holland	816		G	$1,450	1/06	SCMI	16'
New Holland	816		G	$1,450	1/06	SCMI	16'
New Holland	816		G	$1,450	1/06	SCMI	16'
New Holland	816	1992	G	$1,900	5/06	SCMI	816-818, 16' forage wagon, NH 610 gear
New Holland	816	1993	G	$2,100	5/06	SCMI	816-818, 16' forage wagon, 10-ton gear
Richardton	1200		G	$1,500	8/06	WCMN	Dump box, top, always shedded
Richardton	1200		G	$2,500	1/06	SCNE	Multi purpose dump wagon
Richardton	700		P	$1,750	2/06	SCNY	Dump wagon
Richardton	700		G	$8,000	3/06	WCMN	Dump box, roof

Notes

Forage Choppers

Make	Model	Year	Hrs.	Cond.	Price	Sale	Location	Comments
Claas	15'			F	$1,400	8/06	NECO	6R forage head, off John Deere 5830 chopper
Fox	Super D			F	$2,750	3/06	SWOH	Self-propelled, diesel, direct cut, 3R CH, hayhead
Gehl	1060			F	$750	9/06	SCMN	
Gehl	1065			G	$4,500	4/06	WCWI	Auto-Max chopper
Gehl	1065			G	$8,500	3/06	WCMN	Auto-Max chopper, oscillating tandems, auto sharpener, 3R CH, 7' hayhead
Gehl	1200			F	$475	2/06	NECO	540 PTO, 3R-30 CH
Gehl	1200			G	$3,250	4/06	SWOH	2R CH
Gehl	1250			F	$2,925	3/06	SWOH	Hayhead, 2R-30 CH
Gehl	1285	2002		E	$35,000	2/06	SCNY	3R CH, 9' hayhead, metal stop, kernel processor
Hesston	7165			G	$1,750	8/06	NEIA	Pull type, 2RW CH (30"), hayhead
Hesston	7600		2,900	F	$4,400	1/06	NCCO	Field Queen, 3R CH, Cat 3208
IHC	720			G	$900	4/06	SCMN	2R CH & hayhead
IHC	830			G	$500	9/06	NEIN	2 heads
IHC	830			G	$1,600	9/06	NEIN	CH
John Deere	343			F	$700	9/06	NECO	3R-30 CH for John Deere 3960 chopper
John Deere	3800			G	$425	9/06	NEIN	2R chopper
John Deere	3800			F	$685	5/06	SWWI	Chopper w/ hayhead and 2R CH
John Deere	3800			G	$1,500	3/06	NENE	Silage cutter, 2R head, long tongue, always shedded
John Deere	3800			G	$2,200	8/06	WCMN	Forage chopper, hyd. controls w/ 2R-30 CH, always shedded
John Deere	3940			F	$800	9/06	NEIA	Hyd. swing
John Deere	3940			G	$1,400	3/06	NENE	Pull-type chopper
John Deere	3940			F	$1,750	3/06	ECNE	Electric hyd. controls, 2RW silage head
John Deere	3940			G	$1,900	2/06	WCNE	2RW CH, 1,000 PTO, electric/hyd. control, hyd. spout
John Deere	3950			F	$2,300	3/06	NEKS	No heads
John Deere	3950			G	$7,000	7/06	WCMN	Forage harvester
John Deere	3960			G	$1,300	9/06	NECO	PTO, spout controls, pt
John Deere	3960			F	$1,400	8/06	NEIA	No heads, electric controls
John Deere	3960			F	$1,500	8/06	NECO	
John Deere	3960			F	$1,600	8/06	SEMN	Chopper, long pole
John Deere	3960			F	$1,700	9/06	NEIA	
John Deere	3960			G	$4,400	9/06	NENE	Hydraulic & orbit drive spout, pt, 1,000 PTO, no heads
John Deere	3970			F	$2,200	3/06	NCUT	No heads
John Deere	3970			F	$3,000	7/06	WCMN	Forage harvester, 5.5' hay head
John Deere	3970			G	$4,600	9/06	NEIA	Iron guard, long tongue
John Deere	3970			G	$5,000	9/06	WCWI	Chopper, electric controls w/ 7' hayhead
John Deere	3970			G	$6,600	9/06	NEIA	Iron guard, new knives
John Deere	3970			G	$6,900	9/06	NEIA	Iron guard, long tongue, hyd. tongue
John Deere	3970	1994		G	$8,000	1/06	NCCO	Chopper, 3R CH
John Deere	5460	1977	7,511	G	$8,500	6/06	NECO	Cab, 2WD, diesel
John Deere	5460	1978	7,511	G	$9,000	9/06	NECO	Cab, SP, with John Deere 12' auger swather head, diesel
John Deere	5830		4,012	F	$16,000	3/06	NCUT	Forage harvester
John Deere	630			G	$3,300	3/06	NCUT	Hayhead
John Deere	676			G	$9,250	3/06	NCUT	Forage header
John Deere	688	2000		G	$14,000	8/06	SCNE	Header, for chopper
Kemper	NA			G	$18,000	8/06	SCNE	Champion 6008 8R CH for forage chopper
New Holland	1880			F	$5,100	2/06	NCCO	SP, 3R CH
New Holland	717			F	$110	1/06	SCMI	2RN CH

WHAT'S IT WORTH?

Forage Choppers

Make	Model	Year	Hrs.	Cond.	Price	Sale	Location	Comments
New Holland	717			F	$300	3/06	ECNE	Hayhead, 2RW CH
New Holland	717			F	$900	6/06	SWMN	2 CHs
New Holland	717			G	$1,020	2/06	NECO	1R CH
New Holland	717			G	$1,050	9/06	NECO	2R-30 CH, spout controls
New Holland	718			G	$800	2/06	NECO	1,000 PTO, 2R-30 CH
New Holland	770			F	$300	9/06	NECO	2R-30 CH
New Holland	770			F	$500	8/06	NEIA	1R CH, hayhead
New Holland	770			F	$600	8/06	NEIA	2R CH, hayhead
New Holland	782			F	$600	8/06	SEMN	Hayhead
New Holland	782			F	$650	8/06	SEPA	2R CH & hayhead
New Holland	782			G	$1,100	3/06	NCWI	Hayhead
New Holland	782			G	$1,900	3/06	NCWI	Hayhead, electric controls
New Holland	782			E	$3,800	9/06	NEIN	2 heads
New Holland	790			E	$4,050	11/06	NEIA	No heads
New Holland	790			G	$4,100	10/06	NCWI	2R CH, needs new knives
New Holland	818			G	$1,500	1/06	NECO	348 Chevy engine, 2R-30 CH
New Holland	824			G	$2,300	3/06	NCWI	2RN CH off NH 792 chopper
New Holland	890			G	$2,100	8/06	NCIA	Chopper w/ 2R-30 CH and hay head, electric spout control
New Holland	892			F	$300	9/06	NEIN	Hayhead
New Holland	900			G	$2,750	8/06	SEMN	
New Holland	900	1993		G	$7,000	5/06	SCMI	NH 990W 7' hayhead & NH 824 2R CH
New Holland	FP230			E	$0	12/06	SWWI	No sale at $12,500, with 2R CH & hayhead

Notes

Garden Tractors

Looking to buy and looking for the best deal on a garden tractor? Keep an eye on the classified section of the daily newspaper in the metro area nearest you. Big lawn and garden dealers selling lots of stuff to suburbanites. These dealers are also taking lots of used models in on trade. They need to move them to hold inventory down, hence the emergence of big auctions with lots of garden tractors for sale.

Garden Tractors

Make	Model	Year	Hrs.	Cond.	Price	Sale	Location	Comments
AC	B12			F	$175	8/06	NCIA	
AGCO	1718H			G	$1,200	3/06	SEMN	18 hp., hydro drive
Bush Hog	2345			G	$4,000	9/06	NWTN	54" cut
Cadet	3235			G	$900	9/06	NWTN	23 hp., 60" cut
Craftsman	LT2000	2004		E	$875	2/06	WCNE	17 hp., 42" deck, gas
Craftsman	NA			G	$275	12/06	WCIL	Gold, 42" cut, 6 spd., gas
Cub Cadet	102			F	$160	7/06	WCOH	
Cub Cadet	105			F	$150	7/06	WCOH	Hydrostatic
Cub Cadet	1210			G	$450	6/06	NEIN	
Cub Cadet	1405			G	$700	6/06	NEIN	
Cub Cadet	1450			F	$150	9/06	NCIA	Hydro riding lawn mower, 42" deck
Cub Cadet	1572	1988		G	$750	12/06	NWMO	17 hp., 60" deck
Cub Cadet	1650			E	$975	3/06	NCOK	Hydro 1650, with cultivator
Cub Cadet	1882			F	$400	9/06	NCOH	No deck, ran
Cub Cadet	2186			G	$1,400	3/06	SEND	Bagger
Cub Cadet	3206	2003	328	G	$2,100	8/06	SEMN	54" deck
Cub Cadet	3235	2005	171	G	$4,150	8/06	SEMN	60" deck
Cub Cadet	5252		67	E	$4,500	3/06	NWOH	Hydro, gas, 60" deck, 3 pt., PTO, 25 hp.
Cub Cadet	682			F	$400	1/06	WCIL	Riding lawn mower
Cub Cadet	7235		519	E	$7,100	8/06	NWOH	3 pt., PTO, diesel
Cub Cadet	7275		1,104	E	$10,400	8/06	NWOH	4×4, 3 pt., PTO, 417 loader, 4078 backhoe
Cub Cadet	782		1,170	F	$800	7/06	SEND	Kohler 17 hp., 44" deck, 3 pt., 100 hours on OH
Cub Cadet	782			G	$1,150	3/06	ECND	Mowing machine, 18 hp., hydro, 54" deck, 36' snowblower
Deweze	172			G	$2,250	8/06	NECO	All terrain
Dixon	6601			G	$475	9/06	NCIA	Front deck mower
Dyna-Mow	NA			G	$700	4/06	ECND	All-terrain mower, 11 hp.
Exmark	NA			G	$2,100	9/06	NEIN	Walk-behind mower, 60", hydro, gas
Ford	145			G	$800	2/06	NWKS	LGT 145 riding mower
Grasshopper	225			G	$1,900	9/06	NWTN	
Grasshopper	712	2000	482	G	$5,000	2/06	SENE	SL61 mower deck, Kubota 3-cyl. gas engine
Grasshopper	718			F	$1,900	4/06	NWMN	Zero-turn front deck mower, 52", engine needs work
Grasshopper	725		1,334	G	$2,700	9/06	NWTN	Commercial mower, 60" cut
Grasshopper	725K		620	G	$2,900	6/06	SCMN	Out front 61" rotary
Grasshopper	NA			G	$1,600	2/06	SEKS	ZTR mower, 54" front deck, SN 476520
Hustler	340			G	$1,500	9/06	NWTN	60" cut
Ingersoll	226			G	$1,150	12/06	NWIL	Gas
John Deere	110			G	$850	5/06	SCIL	Deck
John Deere	110			G	$1,200	7/06	NWIL	Running, restored, detailed restoration with much of prep & painting done by professional, all parts used in restoration were John Deere parts except the battery
John Deere	110			G	$1,800	7/06	NWIL	Running, restored, restorations were done by the John Deere collector center
John Deere	112			G	$3,600	7/06	NWIL	Running, unrestored, original
John Deere	118		107	E	$1,720	4/06	ECNE	Like new, bagger
John Deere	1420			G	$9,700	8/06	NECO	60" front deck, gas
John Deere	1435			G	$7,000	3/06	NWOH	Diesel, 72", front-mount deck
John Deere	1435	2005	396	G	$11,000	7/06	SEND	Front deck mower, 72" commercial deck
John Deere	175			G	$425	12/06	WCIL	Hydro, 38" deck, gas
John Deere	185			F	$550	7/06	SEND	Hydro, 38", Power Flow bagger, 17 hp. Kawasaki

Garden Tractors

Make	Model	Year	Hrs.	Cond.	Price	Sale	Location	Comments
John Deere	185	1989		F	$150	12/06	NWMO	5-spd., 38" deck
John Deere	210			G	$575	11/06	NCOH	10 hp., 47" mower deck
John Deere	212			F	$375	3/06	SWOH	
John Deere	212			F	$600	7/06	SEND	Deck, recent OH, deck bearings
John Deere	214			F	$125	8/06	NCNE	Riding mower
John Deere	240			G	$400	6/06	NEIN	
John Deere	240	1993		G	$575	12/06	NWMO	14-hp., 48" deck
John Deere	260			G	$800	8/06	SCNE	Mower, 46" deck
John Deere	260			G	$2,000	4/06	NWMN	18-hp., 48" deck, 36" snowblower
John Deere	265			G	$600	9/06	NEIN	Gas
John Deere	265			G	$875	7/06	NCIL	Lawn mower, hydro, 48" deck
John Deere	265			G	$1,800	8/06	SEMN	48" deck
John Deere	285			G	$1,400	11/06	WCMN	50" deck, bagger, snowblower
John Deere	300			G	$1,500	3/06	NWMN	Lawn tractor, tiller
John Deere	305			F	$100	8/06	WCNC	
John Deere	316			G	$500	10/06	NCWI	Hydro, older model
John Deere	316		370	G	$1,600	8/06	ECNE	46" deck
John Deere	318			G	$800	3/06	WCKS	Riding tractor mower, hydro, 48" deck, 18-hp. motor
John Deere	318		500	G	$2,600	3/06	SEPA	
John Deere	322		481	G	$3,300	3/06	SEMN	22 hp., 50" mower deck, hydro drive
John Deere	325		490	G	$1,800	6/06	ECND	17 hp., hydro, 54" mulching deck
John Deere	345			G	$1,900	9/06	NEIN	Riding mower, 54" deck, hydro
John Deere	345			G	$2,000	6/06	NEIN	
John Deere	345			G	$2,100	6/06	NEIN	
John Deere	345			G	$2,100	12/06	SCMN	
John Deere	345			G	$2,700	3/06	NWOH	Gas, 54" deck
John Deere	345	1995		F	$1,200	8/06	WCIL	18 hp., 48" deck, PS, liquid cooled, hyd. lift, foot hydro
John Deere	345	1995		G	$1,500	8/06	WCIL	18 hp., 48" deck, PS, liquid cooled, hyd. lift, foot hydro
John Deere	345	1995		G	$1,600	8/06	WCIL	18 hp., 48" deck, PS, liquid cooled, hyd. lift, foot hydro
John Deere	355			G	$1,250	9/06	NWTN	54" cut
John Deere	400			G	$2,000	12/06	WCIL	60" deck, hydro, 150 hours on OH, gas
John Deere	420			G	$2,600	12/06	NWIL	Gas
John Deere	420	1991		G	$3,600	12/06	NWMO	60" deck
John Deere	420	1992		G	$1,900	12/06	NWMO	60" deck
John Deere	425			G	$2,100	7/06	SEND	Lawn and garden, deck
John Deere	425			G	$2,150	12/06	SCMN	All-wheel steer, 60" deck
John Deere	425		1,087	G	$2,600	12/06	ECMO	20 hp., 54" cut
John Deere	425			G	$2,850	12/06	SCMN	
John Deere	425			G	$3,400	11/06	WCMN	Lawn tractor, 48" deck, snowblower
John Deere	425			G	$3,750	3/06	WCMN	All-wheel steer, 54" deck, gas
John Deere	425	1992	724	G	$2,850	12/06	NWMO	
John Deere	425	1993	1,119	G	$1,750	8/06	WCIL	20 hp., 60" deck, PS, liquid cooler, hyd. lift, foot hydro
John Deere	425	1994		G	$1,700	12/06	NWMO	20 hp., 60" deck
John Deere	425	1994	1,378	G	$1,700	12/06	NWMO	
John Deere	425	1995	1,052	G	$2,100	12/06	NWMO	
John Deere	430			G	$2,700	12/06	NWIL	Diesel
John Deere	445		628	G	$2,900	12/06	ECMO	22 hp., 60", fuel injected, 3 pt., rear PTO
John Deere	445			G	$3,800	11/06	WCMN	Lawn tractor, 54" deck, all-wheel steer
John Deere	445	1993	1,700	G	$1,800	2/06	SEIN	60" deck, hydrostat, PS

WHAT'S IT WORTH?

Garden Tractors

Make	Model	Year	Hrs.	Cond.	Price	Sale	Location	Comments
John Deere	445	1995		G	$2,100	12/06	NWMO	22 hp., 60" deck
John Deere	445	1995	786	G	$4,400	11/06	ECND	Deck, Cozy Cab
John Deere	445	1997	596	G	$4,500	11/06	ECND	Deck
John Deere	445	1998	731	G	$2,250	9/06	NCIA	Hydro, 60" deck
John Deere	455			G	$3,600	3/06	WCMN	60" mower deck, diesel
John Deere	455			G	$4,600	12/06	SCMN	All-wheel steer, 60" deck
John Deere	455			G	$5,000	8/06	SEIA	
John Deere	455	1998	690	G	$4,800	11/06	SEIA	All-wheel steer, 60" deck
John Deere	455	2000	225	E	$6,600	2/06	NWOH	Diesel, 22 hp., 60" hyd. deck, all-wheel steer, like new
John Deere	525			G	$1,400	7/06	SEND	Front mount, lawn and garden
John Deere	710			G	$2,150	3/06	SEND	Air-cooled Kawasaki engine, front-mount deck
John Deere	725			G	$3,000	3/06	WCMN	Front deck, new motor, 60" deck, gas
John Deere	910			G	$2,250	3/06	WCMN	Front deck, 60" deck, gas
John Deere	932			F	$2,500	8/06	NECO	
John Deere	F125	1992		G	$2,700	6/06	ECMN	Front mount, 54" deck, gas
John Deere	F525			F	$700	2/06	NWOH	Gas, 48" front-mount deck, hydro
John Deere	F525		510	F	$1,050	11/06	WCMN	48" front-mount deck, gas
John Deere	F620			G	$1,250	8/06	WCNC	
John Deere	F620			G	$1,450	8/06	WCNC	
John Deere	F680			G	$4,400	1/06	NCCO	Zero turning mower
John Deere	F680	2002	223	E	$6,250	8/06	NWIA	Like new, 54" deck, 20 hp.
John Deere	F687	2004	638	G	$3,300	8/06	WCIL	Commercial zero turn 23 hp., 60" deck
John Deere	F710	1994		F	$900	8/06	WCIL	Front-mounted mower, 48" deck, PS, hyd. lift
John Deere	F725			F	$1,000	3/06	NCUT	
John Deere	F725			G	$3,000	3/06	NWOH	Gas, 54" front-mount deck
John Deere	F725	2005	200	G	$4,900	7/06	SEND	Front deck mower, 20 hp., 54" mulch mower
John Deere	F735	2002	226	G	$6,750	12/06	SWIA	Front deck mower, liquid cooled, 20 hp., 2WD, 60" front deck
John Deere	F910			F	$900	8/06	SCNE	Front-mount mower, 72" deck
John Deere	F910			F	$1,000	8/06	SCNE	Front mount mower, 72" deck
John Deere	F912		1,125	G	$5,300	8/06	ECNE	Front deck, 60" deck
John Deere	F925	1996	855	G	$6,500	3/06	NWMN	60" front deck
John Deere	F932		2,184	F	$2,600	8/06	NECO	Front 72" deck, soft cab
John Deere	F935		3,005	G	$1,600	12/06	ECMO	Front mount, diesel, 72"
John Deere	F935			G	$2,000	6/06	NEIN	
John Deere	GT235			F	$2,000	3/06	SEPA	Good rubber, 150 hours on tach
John Deere	GT242			G	$900	12/06	SCMN	
John Deere	GT245		1,630	G	$1,600	9/06	NWTN	54" cut
John Deere	GT325		83	G	$1,900	9/06	NWTN	48" cut
John Deere	GX335		70	G	$3,500	10/06	SEMN	48" deck
John Deere	GX345			G	$2,850	9/06	NCIA	
John Deere	GX345		148	G	$3,250	12/06	ECMO	20 hp., PS, 54" cut
John Deere	GX345		80	G	$3,900	10/06	SEMN	48" deck
John Deere	GX345		25	E	$4,700	11/06	SCND	Like new, 54" deck, front-mount snowblower
John Deere	L120			G	$1,800	2/06	NWIN	Auto lawn tractor, one year old
John Deere	L130			G	$1,750	12/06	SCMN	
John Deere	LT155			G	$1,350	11/06	WCMN	Lawn tractor, 38" deck, 2-bag system
John Deere	LT160			G	$1,800	11/06	WCMN	Lawn tractor, 42" deck, 2-bag system
John Deere	LT180		204	G	$1,700	9/06	NCIA	Hydro, 48" deck

Garden Tractors

Make	Model	Year	Hrs.	Cond.	Price	Sale	Location	Comments
John Deere	LX176			F	$550	8/06	SEMN	38" deck
John Deere	LX188			G	$525	9/06	NWTN	48" cut
John Deere	LX188			F	$800	8/06	SEMN	48" deck
John Deere	LX188			G	$1,600	8/06	SEMN	48" deck
John Deere	LX255			F	$1,300	3/06	SWOH	
John Deere	LX277			G	$1,250	6/06	NEIN	
John Deere	LX279			G	$1,400	1/06	NEIN	Hydro, 48" deck
John Deere	LX288			G	$2,000	8/06	SEMN	48" deck
John Deere	LX288	1999		G	$1,800	12/06	NWMO	18 hp., 54" deck
John Deere	LX288	2002		G	$1,350	9/06	NCIA	Hydro, 48" deck
John Deere	RX95			G	$1,050	2/06	SWNE	Bagger, 12.5-hp. gas engine
John Deere	Sabre			G	$800	8/06	WCKS	
John Deere	SST16			G	$1,700	8/06	SCNE	Spin steer mower
John Deere	STX			G	$300	6/06	NEIN	38" cut
John Deere	X475	2002	471	G	$4,000	8/06	WCIL	23 hp., 54" deck, PS, liquid cooled, hyd. lift, foot hydro
John Deere	X475	2004	250	G	$5,400	7/06	SEND	Hydro, 23-hp., 62" convertible deck
John Deere	X475	2004	187	G	$5,600	1/06	NWIL	Hydro, 62" deck
John Deere	X495	2004	170	E	$7,800	3/06	NWOH	Diesel, 60" deck
John Deere	X495	2004		E	$8,000	8/06	SCNE	54" front blade, 62" midmount mower
John Deere	X585			G	$8,500	3/06	SEPA	4×4, 3 pt., good turf rubber
Kubota	BX2200			G	$6,100	12/06	NWIL	60" deck, 3 pt., PTO, 4×4
Kubota	G1800			G	$2,100	9/06	NWTN	Four-wheel steer
Kubota	G1900		615	G	$1,700	9/06	NWTN	Diesel, 60" cut
Kubota	G4200		570	G	$900	9/06	NWTN	Diesel, 44" cut
Kubota	G6200		1,148	G	$1,000	9/06	NWTN	48" cut
Kubota	G6200		1,081	G	$1,250	9/06	NWTN	44" cut
Kubota	T1460			G	$525	9/06	NWTN	12.5 hp., 40" cut
Kubota	T1460			G	$600	9/06	NWTN	12.5 hp., 40" cut
Kubota	T1670			G	$775	9/06	NWTN	15 hp., 40" cut
Kubota	T1670			G	$900	9/06	NWTN	15 hp., 40" cut
MTD	NA			F	$400	8/06	NCNE	Riding mower
Murray	NA	2001		E	$300	3/06	WCKS	Wide body, 16.5-hp., 42" cut, auto drive
Quinstar	Spirit			F	$375	1/06	ECNE	Zero turn riding lawn mower, zero turn radius, 14-hp. Briggs & Stratton, twin blades
Sabre	1742			G	$1,100	8/06	SEMN	42" deck
Schweiss	625Z			G	$2,250	9/06	NCIA	
Sears	Craftsman			G	$500	4/06	ECNE	20 hp., 46" deck
Sears	NA			F	$100	7/06	WCOH	ST16, no deck
Silver Eagle	LT2000-50D	2004	38	E	$4,900	5/06	NCKY	Dixie Chopper, zero turning radius, 20-hp., 50" cut
Simplicity	7116			F	$1,000	3/06	NWOH	Gas, 48" deck, snowblower
Simplicity	Landlord	2000	428	G	$3,200	1/06	NWIL	Riding mower, 20-hp., hydro, 54" deck, bagger
Snapper	NA			G	$325	3/06	NCOK	30" cut, 8.5-hp. Honda motor
Snapper	Z-Rider			G	$2,000	9/06	NCIA	
Toro	322D			F	$5,500	7/06	SEND	Riding lawn mower, 72" deck, Crownmaster
Toro	616			G	$475	9/06	NEIN	616-2, zero turn, gas
Toro	NA			G	$375	6/06	NEIN	38" cut
Troybilt	NA			G	$300	4/06	SWIN	6-hp. string trimmer mower
Walker Comm.	NA			G	$2,600	8/06	NECO	Commercial mower, 54" deck
Wheelhorse	C105			F	$150	2/06	NWKS	

Garden Tractors

Make	Model	Year	Hrs.	Cond.	Price	Sale	Location	Comments
Wheelhorse	NA			G	$500	5/06	SCIL	Deck
White	1650			F	$225	12/06	ECMO	42", 16.5 hp.
Woods	1850			G	$1,200	6/06	SCMN	50", out front zero turn mower, 18-hp. engine
Woods	3150		1,563	F	$290	2/06	ECIL	60" mower
Woods	5180			G	$2,100	3/06	ECND	18 hp., V-twin, 54" deck
Yazoo	NA			G	$2,950	9/06	NWTN	

Notes

Grain Handling Equipment

Grain boxes and carts, cleaners, dryers, trailers, and vacs are included in this section. Surges in the price of steel over the last couple years have helped push used grain cart and grain trailer values higher. As I was walking out of the National Farm Show in Louisville, Kentucky, this year, a showgoer hollered out, "Machinery Pete, what's a nice Demco 400-bu. wagon worth?" Answer: 20% to 25% more than it was worth 12 months ago.

WHAT'S IT WORTH?

Grain Bins

Make	Model	Year	Cond.	Price	Sale	Location	Comments
Behlen	1,600 bu.		G	$1,900	4/06	WCMN	Canadian sale, hopper bins, freestanding
Behlen	1,600 bu.		G	$1,900	4/06	WCMN	Canadian sale, hopper bins, freestanding
Behlen	1,700 bu.		G	$1,200	11/06	ECND	Steep cone bin
Behlen	6,000 bu.		G	$1,100	11/06	SENE	Drying bin w/ bottom, 6" vertical sweep auger, spreaders, unloading auger
Behlen	NA		G	$4,000	11/06	ECND	16' diameter bin, Micada bottom, high profile
Behlen	NA		G	$4,100	11/06	ECND	16' diameter bin, Micada bottom, remote lid
Behlen	NA		G	$7,000	11/06	SENE	25,000 bu., sweep auger, spreaders, unloading auger
Brock	1,000 bu.		G	$5,400	11/06	SEIA	Bulk bin
Brock	8,000 bu.	2002	G	$8,250	3/06	NEMI	Stirator, LP gas floor dryer, distributor
Brock	NA		G	$950	11/06	SEIA	2-ton bulk bin, 2 sold – each for $950
Brock	NA		G	$950	11/06	SEIA	2-ton bulk bin, 2 sold – each for $950
BSB	NA		F	$150	11/06	SENE	3,300-bu. grain bin, unloading auger
Butler	1,000 bu.		F	$50	3/06	WCMN	2 bins, $50 each
Butler	1,000 bu.		F	$50	3/06	WCMN	2 bins, $50 each
Butler	1,000 bu.		F	$135	2/06	SCMI	
Butler	10,000 bu.		G	$5,000	8/06	ECIL	27', 10,000-bu. drying bin, fan, heater, twin auger stirator, sweep, unload augers
Butler	20,000 bu.		G	$7,000	4/06	NEND	36' diameter, to be removed
Butler	4,000 bu.		G	$1,950	3/06	ECMI	Air fan, unloading auger, 18' diameter
Butler	NA		G	$1,500	6/06	WCMN	21', 4-ring, full floor, air, 6" unload
Butler	NA		G	$3,500	6/06	WCMN	24', 7½-ring, full floor, air, 8" unload, 5-hp., single phase, electric motor
Cenex	3,000 bu.		F	$300	4/06	NCSD	Grain bin, air stream
Cenex	2,200 bu.		P	$100	6/06	WCMN	16', 6-ring, no air, 2,200 bu.
Chicago	10,000 bu.		G	$4,050	8/06	NCOH	3-auger stirator, drying floor, bin sweep, 20-hp.
Chief	10,000 bu.		F	$300	11/06	SENE	Spreaders, unloading auger
Circle	1,600 bu.		G	$1,600	4/06	ECND	1,500-bu. hopper bin, 2 sold – each for $1,600
Circle	1,600 bu.		G	$1,600	4/06	ECND	1,500-bu. hopper bin, 2 sold – each for $1,600
Dry-Mor	10,000 bu.		F	$500	11/06	SENE	10,000 bu., spreaders, unloading auger
Friesen	3,000 bu.		G	$7,250	3/06	ECND	Hopper bin, sight glass, aeration, full-skid bottom
Friesen	3,000 bu.		G	$7,500	3/06	ECND	Hopper bin, sight glass, aeration, full-skid bottom
GSI	7,000 bu.		G	$4,500	8/06	SCMN	36', bottom 3 rings, approximately 7,000 bu.
Lode King	1,600 bu.		G	$2,100	11/06	NEND	1,600 bu., bin on skids, smooth sided
Lorrich	2,300 bu.		G	$2,500	4/06	NEND	Hopper bin
Lorrich	2,400 bu.		F	$2,400	9/06	NWMN	2,400-bu. hopper bin
Lorrich	2,400 bu.		F	$2,400	9/06	NWMN	2,400-bu. hopper bin, 2 sold – each for $2,400
Lorrich	2,800 bu.		G	$3,000	9/06	NWMN	2,800-bu. hopper bin
Lorrich	2,700 bu.		G	$3,400	3/06	NWMN	Hopper bin, 2,700 bu.
Lowry	1,400 bu.		G	$1,200	4/06	NEND	Portable hopper bin
Lowry	1,400 bu.		G	$1,600	3/06	SEND	Portable hopper bin
Lowry	1,500 bu.		G	$1,100	7/06	NWMN	Portable hopper
Lowry	1,500 bu.		G	$1,850	8/06	SCMN	Wet corn holding bin on transport
MFS	2,800 bu.		F	$300	3/06	WCMN	2,800-bu. bin
Micada	2,800 bu.		G	$3,400	4/06	NWMN	Conversion 2,800-bu. hopper bottom bin, 3-hp. aeration fan, 2 sold each for $3,400
Micada	2,800 bu.		G	$3,400	4/06	NWMN	Conversion 2,800-bu. hopper bottom bin, 3-hp. aeration fan, 2 sold each for $3,400
NA	2,000 bu.		G	$1,050	3/06	ECND	Hopper bin with air

Grain Bins

Make	Model	Year	Cond.	Price	Sale	Location	Comments
Sioux	1,300 bu.		F	$800	4/06	NCSD	Steel
Sioux	4,000 bu.		G	$1,650	4/06	NCSD	Steel grain, Caldwell blower
Sioux	NA	1997	E	$16,000	2/06	ECMN	36'× 3', Sukup 8"×19' vertical unload auger, PTO drive
Sioux	NA	1998	E	$16,000	2/06	ECMN	36'×33' grain bin
Stor-King	1,750 bu.		G	$4,100	3/06	ECND	Hopper bin, skid American Farm Fans
Stormor	10,000 bu.		F	$1,700	2/06	NWIL	24' diameter, burner, fans
Stormor	5,000 bu.		G	$3,500	3/06	NEMI	Aeration floor, fan
Stormor	5,500 bu.		G	$1,100	11/06	SENE	Unloading auger
Westeel	12,000 bu.		G	$4,100	11/06	ECND	12,000 bu., 7.5-hp., 3-phase fan, takeout
Westeel	4,300 bu.		G	$5,500	4/06	WCMN	Canadian sale, 4,300 bu. on skid base, Bridgeview hopper cones
Westeel	4,300 bu.		G	$5,500	4/06	WCMN	Canadian sale, 4,300 bu. on skid base, Bridgeview hopper cones
Westeel	NA		G	$5,750	11/06	ECND	19.2' diameter bin, Micada bottom & outside ladder, dual skids, remote lid
Westeel	NA		G	$5,800	4/06	WCMN	Canadian sale, 4,300 bu. on skid base, Bridgeview hopper cones
Westeel	NA		G	$5,800	4/06	WCMN	Canadian sale, 4,300 bu. on skid base, Bridgeview hopper cones
Westeel	NA		G	$5,900	11/06	ECND	19.2' diameter, Micada bottom, outside ladder, dual skids, remote lid
Westeel	NA		G	$6,000	11/06	ECND	19.2' diameter bin w/ Micada bottom & outside ladder, dual skids, remote lid
Westeel	NA		G	$6,100	11/06	ECND	19.2' diameter, Micada bottom, outside ladder, dual skids, remote lid
Westeel	NA		G	$7,200	11/06	ECND	19.2' diameter Roscoe, Micada bottom, 7.5 hp., 1-phase fan, outside ladder, dual skids, remote lid
Westeel	NA		G	$7,200	11/06	ECND	19.2' diameter Roscoe, Micada bottom, 7.5 hp., 1-phase

Grain Boxes & Carts

Make	Model	Year	Cond.	Price	Sale	Location	Comments
A&L	425		F	$1,100	3/06	NEKS	Grain cart, manual-fold auger, 1,000 PTO
A&L	425		F	$2,000	11/06	SENE	Grain cart, manual-fold auger, 1,000 PTO, aircraft tires
A&L	425		G	$2,500	12/06	NENE	Grain cart, 400 bu., hyd. fold auger w/ extension
A&L	450 bu.		G	$3,650	12/06	ECMO	Grain cart
A&L	47		G	$4,750	2/06	NEMO	Grain cart, 470 bu., 18.4×34 tires
A&L	47		G	$5,500	8/06	ECNE	Grain cart, 18.4-26 tires, roll tarp, 1,000 rpm, lights
A&L	650		P	$450	3/06	NWKS	Grain cart
A&L	650		G	$2,750	11/06	ECND	Grain cart
A&L	650		G	$5,200	3/06	ECNE	Grain cart, hyd. auger, flow control, 1,000 PTO, Shur-Lok roll tarp, lights, 24.5-32 tires
A&L	650 bu.		F	$1,100	11/06	SCSD	Grain cart
A&L	650T		F	$800	8/06	NWIL	Auger wagon
A&L	650T		F	$1,000	9/06	NECO	Grain cart, PTO, pt, tandem axle
A&L	650T		F	$1,200	8/06	NECO	Grain cart
A&L	700 bu.		G	$11,500	3/06	NCND	Grain cart, corner auger, hyd. or PTO drive, new roll tarp and gear box, 30.5-32 rubber (90%)

Grain Boxes & Carts

Make	Model	Year	Cond.	Price	Sale	Location	Comments
A&L	F500		G	$3,700	11/06	SCND	Grain cart, near 650 bu., extensions
A&L	F700		G	$11,000	2/06	NWMN	Grain cart, corner auger, roll tarp
A&L	F700	1989	G	$6,900	12/06	ECKS	Grain cart, 700 bu., corner unloading auger, Shur-Lok roll tarp, 1,000 PTO, 24.5-32 turf tires, rebuilt flighting
A&L	F705		G	$8,100	3/06	ECNE	Grain cart, corner unloading auger, roll tarp, 20.8R42 tires
A&L	F837		G	$9,300	2/06	NWKS	Grain cart
Atlas	200 bu.		G	$750	8/06	ECNE	12'×16' wooden wagon on hd 6-bolt gear, hoist, always shedded
Big 12	350 bu.		F	$1,000	8/06	ECNE	Grain cart, 20:00-20-26 ply aircraft tires, 1,000 PTO
Big 12	400 bu.		F	$650	4/06	NCOK	Grain cart, PTO driven
Big 12	400 bu.		F	$800	4/06	WCSD	Grain cart
Big 12	600		F	$1,750	8/06	ECNE	Grain cart, DK600, 1,000 PTO, 24.5-32 tires
Big 12	750 bu.		G	$3,200	3/06	ECNE	Grain cart
Big Ox	400 bu.		P	$350	4/06	NCKS	Rough
Bradford	200 bu.		G	$550	12/06	NEMO	Gravity wagon
Bradford	240-316		G	$400	1/06	SCMI	No gear
Bradford	240-316		G	$2,000	1/06	SCKS	Gravity wagon, Bradford 10T gear, 11l-15 tires, bought new, shedded
Bradford	240-316		G	$2,100	1/06	SCKS	Gravity wagon, Bradford 10T gear, 11l-15 tires, bought new, shedded
Brent	1084	2000	G	$18,500	11/06	SCND	Grain cart, 18.4-42 duals, roll tarp
Brent	1084	2000	G	$23,250	12/06	WCMN	Grain cart, duals, scale
Brent	1084	2006	E	$32,000	11/06	SCNE	Avalanche grain cart, 20" auger, floating axles, 480/80R42 offset duals, roll tarp, new fall of 2006
Brent	360		G	$2,125	8/06	NCIA	Westendorf gear
Brent	360		G	$2,125	8/06	NCIA	Westendorf gear
Brent	420		F	$2,100	3/06	ECNE	Grain cart
Brent	420		G	$3,600	3/06	SESD	Grain cart
Brent	420		F	$4,000	2/06	NCIL	Grain cart, scales
Brent	420		G	$4,800	3/06	NWIL	Grain cart
Brent	420		G	$5,750	12/06	WCMN	Grain cart, roll tarp
Brent	420		G	$6,000	1/06	NEMO	Grain cart
Brent	440		G	$5,100	1/06	WCIL	Gravity flow wagon
Brent	440		G	$5,500	1/06	WCIL	Gravity flow wagon
Brent	440		G	$6,500	12/06	NWIL	Gravity box, gear and brakes
Brent	440	1994	G	$3,500	5/06	SCMI	Gravity wagon, rear brakes
Brent	440	1995	G	$4,000	5/06	SCMI	Gravity wagon, rear brakes
Brent	440	1995	G	$4,000	5/06	SCMI	Gravity wagon, rear brakes
Brent	444	2000	G	$6,750	1/06	WCIL	Gravity wagon, brakes, lights w/ tip tops
Brent	444	2001	G	$6,750	1/06	WCIL	Gravity wagon, brakes, lights w/ tip tops
Brent	470		G	$7,900	11/06	NCOH	Grain auger buggy, tarp, lights, 1,000 rpm
Brent	470	1995	G	$5,500	3/06	NESD	Grain cart, roll tarp, like new
Brent	470	1996	G	$7,250	2/06	SWOH	Grain cart, scales, Shur-Lok roll tarp, 520-bu. capacity, front-corner unload
Brent	472		G	$4,800	3/06	SCIA	Auger cart
Brent	472		G	$8,000	3/06	NCIA	Grain cart, extension, corner auger
Brent	472	1992	G	$8,600	12/06	WCIA	Grain cart
Brent	540		E	$7,000	3/06	NEIA	Gravity wagon, gear, like new, pair – each sold for $7,000
Brent	540		E	$7,000	3/06	NEIA	Gravity wagon, gear, like new, pair – each sold for $7,000

Grain Boxes & Carts

Make	Model	Year	Cond.	Price	Sale	Location	Comments
Brent	544		G	$5,200	10/06	NEIA	600 bu., fenders, nice
Brent	544		G	$8,300	3/06	NCIA	Gravity, Shur-Lok roll tarp, truck tires, brakes
Brent	544		G	$8,450	12/06	SEIA	Gravity wagon, green, 425/65R-22.5 tires
Brent	544	2000	G	$7,700	2/06	ECMN	Gravity box, heavy gear, surge brakes, lights, 22.5 rubber, red, sharp
Brent	544	2000	G	$7,700	2/06	ECMN	Gravity box, heavy gear, surge brakes, lights, 22.5 rubber, red, sharp
Brent	570		G	$5,750	8/06	NEIA	Auger cart
Brent	570	1990	G	$8,100	2/06	NWIN	Auger cart
Brent	600 bu.		G	$7,100	7/06	NCIA	Gravity wagon, gear, truck tires, brakes, 2 wagons/each sold for $7,100
Brent	600 bu.		G	$7,100	7/06	NCIA	Gravity wagon, gear, truck tires, brakes, 2 wagons/each sold for $7,100
Brent	610		G	$4,750	3/06	SEMN	Grain train grain cart, 32 tires, corner auger
Brent	610		G	$5,200	8/06	NCIA	Grain cart, side auger
Brent	620		G	$4,900	11/06	ECND	Grain cart
Brent	620		G	$5,000	11/06	NWKS	Grain cart, rollover tarp
Brent	620		G	$5,250	12/06	WCMN	Grain cart, side auger
Brent	640		G	$6,800	4/06	NEIA	Green
Brent	640		E	$7,400	8/06	ECNE	Gravity wagon, shedded, 445/65R22.5 rubber, 10-bolt hubs, 4 brakes, unloading & warning lights
Brent	640		G	$7,500	8/06	NCIA	Gravity wagon, tires worn
Brent	640		G	$7,750	12/06	NCIA	Gravity wagon, red
Brent	640		G	$7,750	12/06	NCIA	Gravity wagon, red
Brent	640		G	$7,800	8/06	WCIA	Gravity wagon, surge brakes
Brent	640		E	$8,100	1/06	WCIL	Gravity wagon
Brent	640		E	$8,100	1/06	WCIL	Side dump wagon, bows, one w/ roll tarp
Brent	640		G	$8,500	3/06	NCIA	Gravity box, gear, truck tires, lights, brakes
Brent	640		G	$9,100	12/06	NCIA	Red gravity wagon
Brent	640		G	$9,250	12/06	NCIA	Red gravity wagon
Brent	640		G	$9,250	12/06	NCIA	Gravity wagon, red
Brent	640		G	$9,500	8/06	NCIA	Gravity wagon
Brent	640		G	$9,800	12/06	NWIL	Gravity box, gear and brakes
Brent	644	2001	G	$8,000	3/06	SEIA	Gravity wagon, lights, brakes
Brent	644	2006	G	$10,000	12/06	SWIA	Grain wagon, 650 bu., hd running gear
Brent	644	2006	G	$10,000	12/06	SWIA	Grain wagon, 650 bu.
Brent	670		G	$5,800	2/06	NCIN	Grain cart, tarp, one year on new auger flights
Brent	672		G	$7,800	3/06	NCIL	Grain cart, 24.5-32 tires
Brent	672		G	$10,200	3/06	NEKS	Grain cart, corner auger, Shur-Lok roll tarp, 1,000 PTO, light package
Brent	672	1995	G	$9,100	12/06	WCMN	Grain cart, diamond, nice paint, good auger
Brent	674		G	$8,600	11/06	ECND	Grain cart, corner auger, 2 seasons on flighting and bearings
Brent	674		G	$12,000	3/06	SEMN	Grain cart, corner auger, light kit, ladder kit, tarp
Brent	674	1998	G	$14,600	1/06	SCKS	Grain cart, 18" corner auger, PTO or hyd. drive, 30.5R-32 tires, extendable axles, bought new, shedded, SN B1682168
Brent	750 bu.	1994	G	$9,200	3/06	ECNE	New flighting on augers

Grain Boxes & Carts

Make	Model	Year	Cond.	Price	Sale	Location	Comments
Brent	770		G	$12,250	8/06	ECNE	Grain cart, corner auger, 24.5-32 tires, roll tarp, scales, 1,000 rpm, lights
Brent	770	1990	G	$7,500	2/06	SWNE	Grain cart, hyd. fold corner auger, 1,000 PTO, hyd. flow control, 24.5-32 diamond tread tires, one owner, recently refurbished
Brent	770	1991	G	$7,000	1/06	NECO	Grain cart
Brent	772		G	$10,100	8/06	NEIL	Grain cart, high & low tip tops
Brent	772		G	$10,250	3/06	NEND	Grain cart, corner auger, 750 bu., roll tarp, light kit, 30.5-32 singles
Brent	774		E	$10,750	4/06	NWKS	Grain cart, tip tops
Brent	874		G	$12,200	2/06	NCIL	Grain cart, corner auger
Brent	876		G	$17,000	3/06	ECND	Grain cart, 850 bu., corner auger, roll tarp, 30.5-32
Brent	880	2005	E	$20,000	3/06	ECMI	Grain cart, 900/60/32" Tellborg tires, large auger
Brent	880	2005	E	$20,500	12/06	SWIA	Grain cart, 850 bu., 20" corner auger
Brent	880	2006	E	$22,000	12/06	SWIA	850-bu. grain cart, 20" corner auger, diamond tires, hyd. spout deflector
Brent	974		G	$14,000	2/06	WCMN	950-bu. grain cart, digital scale, roll tarp
Brent	974	1998	E	$15,500	1/06	WCIL	Auger cart, roll tarp
Brent	976		E	$27,500	2/06	ECMN	Grain cart, straddle duals, roll tarp, one owner
Brent	976	2003	G	$15,750	3/06	SEIA	1,000-bu. grain cart, roll tarp, like new
Bush Hog	7×12		G	$775	8/06	NCIA	Steel barge, gear, hoist
Bush Hog	Barge		G	$600	1/06	NEIN	Barge wagon
Bushnell	250 bu.		G	$450	8/06	NCIA	JD 1065 gear
Bushnell	250 bu.		G	$650	8/06	NCIA	JD 1065 gear
Crysteel	600 bu.		G	$4,000	3/06	NENE	Belly dump truck wagon, 16.5-22.5 tires
Crysteel	NA		G	$3,000	9/06	NCIA	Truck wagon
Dakon	200 bu.		G	$575	3/06	NENE	Gravity wagon
Dakon	250		G	$750	3/06	SESD	Gravity wagon, 12-ton gear
Dakon	250		G	$775	8/06	NCIA	Gravity on JD 1065 gear
Dakon	250 bu.		G	$750	3/06	NENE	Gravity wagon, dry fertilizer auger attachment
Dakon	250 bu.		F	$1,200	6/06	SWMN	Gravity wagon
Dakon	275		G	$600	3/06	ECNE	Gravity box, gear
Dakon	280		G	$1,150	8/06	NCIA	Gravity wagon, extension, Dakon 1212 gear, 11×22.5 truck tires
Dakon	280		G	$1,950	3/06	SEMN	350-bu. gravity flow box, 14-ton gear
Dakon	350 bu.		G	$950	3/06	SESD	Gravity wagon, 12-ton gear
Dakon	400 bu.		G	$2,200	11/06	ECND	Gravity wagon on heavy gear, roll tarp
Demco	300 bu.		G	$1,750	2/06	ECMN	Gravity box, JD 1075 gear
Demco	325 bu.		G	$2,300	1/06	ECNE	Gravity wagon, hyd. bean fill auger
Demco	325 bu.		E	$3,600	3/06	NWIL	
Demco	365		G	$2,000	3/06	ECNE	Gravity wagon, Demco hd gear, lights, 385/65R225 tires, bought new
Demco	365		G	$3,750	2/06	ECMN	Gravity box, Demco heavy gear, lights, 22.5 rubber, green
Demco	365		G	$4,000	1/06	SCMN	Gravity box, purchased 1998
Demco	365		G	$4,000	2/06	ECMN	Gravity box, Demco heavy gear, lights, 22.5 rubber, green
Demco	365	2006	E	$5,900	12/06	WCMN	Gravity box, 12-ton gear, roll tarp
Demco	400 bu.		G	$2,450	3/06	ECNE	Gravity wagon

Grain Boxes & Carts

Make	Model	Year	Cond.	Price	Sale	Location	Comments
Demco	450 bu.		G	$4,800	3/06	NWIL	Brakes
Demco	550 bu.		G	$3,600	11/06	ECNE	Gravity wagon, brakes, 425-65×22.5 spare tire on wheel for Demco wagon, one good spare tire, two boxes sold – $3,600 each = $7,200 total
Demco	550 bu.		G	$7,500	8/06	WCMN	Gravity box, large tires, roll tarp, rear axle brakes, like new
Demco	550 bu.		E	$12,100	8/06	NCIA	Grain cart, corner auger, brand-new
Demco	650		G	$8,700	1/06	SWMN	
Demco	650		G	$8,700	1/06	SWMN	
Demco	750	2002	G	$9,800	2/06	NWIL	Grain cart, corner auger, Shur-Lok roll tarp
Demco	750	2003	E	$11,200	1/06	SCNE	Posi-Flow grain cart
DMI	280 bu.		F	$850	1/06	NWIL	Gravity box, tongue, extension
DMI	280 bu.		G	$1,400	1/06	NWIL	Gravity box, tongue, extension
DMI	280 bu.		G	$1,650	1/06	NWIL	Gravity box, tongue, extension
DMI	280 bu.		G	$2,000	1/06	NWIL	Gravity box, extension tongue
DMI	300		G	$1,400	9/06	SEIA	Gravity flow wagon, tarp
DMI	300	1982	G	$2,000	2/06	NWIN	Wagon, brush auger
DMI	300 bu.		G	$1,100	8/06	WCIL	Gravity wagon
DMI	300 bu.		E	$1,600	1/06	WCIL	Big Little wagon
DMI	300 bu.		G	$1,900	2/06	WCIL	Gravity wagon
DMI	312		G	$1,200	3/06	NCIL	D312, center dump wagon
DMI	350		G	$900	10/06	SEMN	Gravity wagon, center dump
DMI	350		G	$1,250	10/06	SEMN	Gravity box, center dump
DMI	350 bu.		G	$2,000	2/06	ECIL	Gravity wagon
DMI	400 bu.		G	$1,000	8/06	SCMI	Gravity wagon, center dump, 12-ton gear, with auger
DMI	400 bu.		G	$2,550	3/06	SEIA	Gravity wagon, center dump
DMI	440		E	$3,000	11/06	WCIA	Wagon, lights, brakes, 2 sold – each for $3,000
DMI	440		E	$3,000	11/06	WCIA	Wagon, lights, brakes, 2 sold – each for $3,000
DMI	450 bu.		G	$3,100	2/06	WCIL	Gravity wagon, brakes, lights, two doors
DMI	D400		G	$1,650	12/06	SEIA	Gravity wagon
DMI	D400A		F	$1,000	8/06	WCIL	Gravity wagon
DMI	D400A		G	$3,700	4/06	SEMI	Gravity wagon, 30" metal extension, tarp
DMI	D470		G	$4,800	12/06	SEIA	Gravity wagon, brakes, 425/65R-22.5 tires
DMI	D470		G	$4,800	12/06	SEIA	Gravity wagon, brakes, 425/65R-22.5 tires
DMI	D470		G	$4,850	12/06	SEIA	Gravity wagon, brakes, 425/65R-22.5 tires
EZ Flow	200 bu.		G	$485	3/06	NCIL	Gravity wagon
EZ Flow	220		G	$500	8/06	SEMN	Gravity box on gear
EZ Flow	250 bu.		F	$900	8/06	NEKS	Gravity wagon
EZ Flow	250 bu.		F	$1,050	8/06	NEKS	Gravity wagon
EZ Flow	275 bu.		G	$1,150	8/06	WCMN	Gravity box, gear
EZ Flow	280 bu.		F	$700	6/06	NWIL	Gravity wagon, 10-ton EZ Trail 1074 gear
EZ Flow	300		P	$25	8/06	NCIA	Gravity, lights, 12.5L-16 tires
EZ Flow	300		F	$300	8/06	NCIA	Gravity wagon
EZ Flow	300		F	$300	8/06	NCIA	Gravity wagon
EZ Flow	300 bu.		G	$700	9/06	SEIA	Gravity flow and running gear
EZ Flow	300 bu.		G	$1,600	3/06	NCIL	Gravity wagon, 1074 gear
EZ Flow	300 bu.		G	$2,100	3/06	NCIL	Gravity wagon
EZ Flow	300 bu.		G	$2,100	3/06	NCIL	Gravity wagon
EZ Flow	320 bu.		G	$1,850	11/06	WCMN	Gravity wagon, 10-ton gear
EZ Flow	320 bu.		G	$1,900	11/06	WCMN	Gravity wagon, 10-ton gear

WHAT'S IT WORTH?

Grain Boxes & Carts

Make	Model	Year	Cond.	Price	Sale	Location	Comments
EZ Flow	475 bu.		G	$6,500	4/06	ECND	Grain cart, center auger
EZ Trail	250 bu.		G	$1,000	3/06	NENE	Gravity box wagon
EZ Trail	300 bu.		G	$600	2/06	ECIL	Wagon
EZ Trail	3400		G	$3,500	4/06	SEPA	Bin wagon, roll tarp
EZ Trail	3400		E	$5,800	3/06	SEMN	Gravity box, 10-ton gear, roll tarp, EZ Trail hyd. seed/brush auger, looks new
EZ Trail	350		G	$600	11/06	ECIL	Gravity flow on 1072 gear
EZ Trail	500		E	$4,000	2/06	NWIL	Grain cart, 1,584 gear, brakes, lights, 16.5×16.1 (10-ply) tires
EZ Trail	500		E	$4,000	2/06	NWIL	Grain cart, 1,584 gear, brakes, lights, 16.5×16.1 (10-ply) tires
EZ Trail	500		E	$4,000	2/06	NWIL	Grain cart, 1,584 gear, brakes, lights, 16.5×16.1 (10-ply) tires
EZ Trail	500		G	$4,400	12/06	ECIL	Grain cart, PTO, 12.1-26 diamond tires
EZ Trail	500		G	$4,600	8/06	WCIL	Grain cart
EZ Trail	500	2000	G	$4,750	2/06	ECKS	Grain cart
EZ Trail	500 bu.		G	$4,750	8/06	WCMN	Grain cart
EZ Trail	510		G	$5,500	12/06	ECIL	Grain cart
EZ Trail	700 bu.		G	$6,750	3/06	SEMN	Grain cart, light kit
EZ Trail	850	1997	G	$7,600	2/06	WCIL	Grain cart
EZ Trail	NA		G	$575	4/06	WCWI	Kicker box on gear
Farm King	250 bu.		G	$650	9/06	SEIA	Gravity flow and running gear
Ficklin	185		G	$500	2/06	NCIL	Gravity wagon, gear
Ficklin	185		G	$500	2/06	ECIL	Gravity wagon, JD gear
Ficklin	185		G	$550	2/06	WCIL	Gravity flow on JD 1065, electric gear
Ficklin	185		G	$560	2/06	ECIL	Seed wagon, hyd. fold auger
Ficklin	250 bu.		G	$585	8/06	ECIL	Wagon
Ficklin	325 bu.		G	$1,400	8/06	NEKS	Gravity wagon
Ficklin	435		G	$975	1/06	SCMI	Gravity wagon
Ficklin	435		G	$1,250	12/06	WCIL	300-bu. gravity wagon on hd gear
Ficklin	435		F	$1,800	3/06	NCNE	500-bu. gravity wagon, 9:00-20 tires, hyd. drive brush auger, Harvest-Tek inoculator
Ficklin	4500		G	$1,700	11/06	WCMN	Gravity wagon, 12-ton gear, lights, like new
Ficklin	4500		G	$1,700	11/06	WCMN	Gravity wagon, 12-ton gear, lights, like new
Ficklin	4500		F	$2,800	2/06	ECIL	450-bu. wagon, brakes and lights
Ficklin	4500		G	$4,600	1/06	NWIL	Gravity box, 3 compartment, soybean auger, Kory 12-ton gear
Ficklin	CA14000		G	$8,200	3/06	NWMN	Grain cart, 650 bu., hyd. corner auger
Ficklin	CA9600		G	$6,600	2/06	ECIL	600-bu. grain cart
Ficklin	CA9600	1999	G	$7,000	8/06	NCIA	500-bu. grain cart, corner auger
Grainovator	150 bu.		G	$1,100	3/06	NEND	Weigh wagon, Weigh-Tronix scale, Wisconsin 12-hp. electric start motor
Grainovator	NA		F	$600	3/06	NENE	Tandem-axle auger wagon, hyd. swing auger
Grainovator	NA		G	$1,950	3/06	NWIL	Auger cart, 2 compartment, tandem axle, hyd. swing-away auger
Grainovator	NA		F	$2,100	9/06	WCOH	Self-unloading wagon
H&S	450 bu.		G	$2,400	8/06	SCMN	Extension pole, flotation tires
Huskee	200 bu.		G	$475	2/06	WCNE	Gravity box, no gear
Huskee	225 bu.		G	$825	3/06	SENE	Gravity wagon

Grain Boxes & Carts

Make	Model	Year	Cond.	Price	Sale	Location	Comments
Huskee	225 bu.		G	$900	4/06	NCKS	Gravity wagon
Huskee	250 bu.		G	$1,200	3/06	ECND	Gravity wagon on 4-wheel gear
J&M	1050		G	$26,500	3/06	ECND	Grain cart, scale, roll tarp
J&M	200 bu.		F	$350	12/06	WCIL	Gravity wagon on hd running gear
J&M	200 bu.		G	$475	3/06	WCMN	Gravity, Minnesota 10-ton gear
J&M	200 bu.		G	$675	12/06	NWOH	Gravity wagon
J&M	250		F	$375	12/06	WCIL	Gravity wagon
J&M	250		G	$600	12/06	WCIL	Gravity wagon
J&M	250		G	$675	12/06	WCIL	Gravity wagon
J&M	250		G	$1,100	12/06	SCMN	Gravity wagon, JD 1065 gear
J&M	250		G	$1,100	1/06	SCMI	Gravity wagon, Farmers Pride gear, metal side extensions
J&M	250		G	$1,250	12/06	NWOH	Gravity wagon
J&M	250 bu.		G	$750	11/06	NCIN	Gravity wagons, 2 sold – each for $750
J&M	250 bu.		G	$750	11/06	NCIN	Gravity wagons, 2 sold – each for $750
J&M	250 bu.		G	$850	8/06	SCMN	On AC running gear, flotation tires
J&M	250 bu.		G	$1,650	8/06	NCOH	Gravity wagon
J&M	250 bu.		G	$1,650	8/06	NCOH	Gravity wagon
J&M	300 bu.		G	$1,100	8/06	WCMN	Gravity box, 12-ton
J&M	325		G	$4,100	12/06	NWOH	Gravity wagon on 13-ton gear
J&M	350		G	$1,600	3/06	NCIL	Gravity wagon, 12-ton gear
J&M	350		G	$1,600	3/06	NCIL	Gravity wagon, 12-ton gear
J&M	350		E	$2,000	9/06	NEIN	Gravity wagon
J&M	350		G	$2,100	3/06	NCIL	Gravity wagon, 12-ton gear
J&M	350		G	$2,100	8/06	NCIA	Gravity box, gear, 16.5-16.1 tires
J&M	350		G	$2,100	1/06	NWIA	Gravity wagon
J&M	350		G	$2,200	3/06	NCOH	Gravity wagon
J&M	350		G	$2,500	8/06	NCIA	Gravity box, gear, 16.5-16.1 tires
J&M	350		G	$2,750	8/06	NCIA	Gravity box, gear, 16.5-16.1 tires
J&M	350		G	$2,900	3/06	NCOH	Gravity wagon
J&M	350		G	$3,500	2/06	SCMI	350 side-dump gravity wagon, 13-ton J&M gear, metal extension
J&M	350		G	$3,500	2/06	SCMI	350 side-dump gravity wagon, 13-ton J&M gear, metal extension
J&M	350 bu.		G	$1,150	8/06	SCMN	On P&H 10-ton gear
J&M	350 bu.		G	$1,350	8/06	NCOH	Gravity wagon, 15-ton gear
J&M	350 bu.		G	$1,600	8/06	SCMN	On J&M running gear, flotation tires
J&M	380 bu.		G	$3,700	3/06	WCMN	Gravity box, hd 20-ton gear
J&M	380 bu.		G	$3,750	3/06	WCMN	Gravity box, hd 20-ton gear
J&M	385		G	$2,950	11/06	WCMN	Gravity wagon, 12-ton gear
J&M	385		G	$2,950	11/06	WCMN	Gravity wagon, 12-ton gear
J&M	385		G	$3,700	3/06	NCOH	Gravity wagon
J&M	500 bu.		F	$2,600	3/06	NWPA	Old gravity wagon, sold at 500 bu., but looked like 300 bu.
J&M	500 bu.		G	$5,500	1/06	ECNE	Grain cart, unloading auger, 18.4-42 tires
J&M	525		G	$5,500	3/06	ECNE	Grain cart, 14" hyd. fold corner auger, lights, 23.5-25 16-ply tires on hd rims, one owner
J&M	525		G	$6,750	3/06	NENE	525-14, 525-bu. grain cart, hyd. corner auger, hyd. flow control, 1,000 PTO, 23.1-26 tires, one owner, shedded

Grain Boxes & Carts

Make	Model	Year	Cond.	Price	Sale	Location	Comments
J&M	525		G	$10,000	3/06	ECNE	Grain cart, 14" hyd. fold corner auger, lights, 23.5-25 16-ply tires on hd rims, one owner
J&M	525-14		G	$8,000	9/06	SCNE	Grain cart, 525 bu., 14" auger, 18.4-42 tires, green
J&M	550 bu.		E	$3,700	9/06	NEIN	Gravity wagon
J&M	550 bu.	2003	G	$7,100	2/06	SWNE	Gravity wagon, lights, electric brakes, 385/65R22.5 tires
J&M	600 bu.		E	$4,800	9/06	NEIN	Gravity wagon
J&M	620		G	$8,000	1/06	WCIL	Grain cart, corner dump
J&M	675	1998	G	$8,750	4/06	NWMN	Grain cart, 750 bu., corner auger, roll tarp, 540 PTO, adjustable rear axle
J&M	750		G	$9,000	11/06	NWMN	Grain cart, 1,000 PTO, 30.5-32 diamond tires, adjustable axles
J&M	750		G	$9,400	3/06	NCNE	Grain cart, 16" corner unloading auger, 30.5L-32 tires, lights, one owner
J&M	750		G	$10,000	12/06	ECNE	Grain cart, corner unloading auger, hyd. flow control, big 1,000 PTO, adjustable axles, light package, 20.8R42 10-ply tires
J&M	750		G	$11,000	4/06	NESD	Grain cart, roll tarp, 1999 model
J&M	750		E	$12,000	7/06	ECIL	Grain cart
J&M	750		G	$15,000	12/06	SCNE	Corner auger wagon, SN 2357, 18" corner auger
J&M	750		E	$17,000	11/06	SENE	Grain cart, unused, roll tarp, corner unloading auger, 24.5R-32 tires
J&M	750	2001	G	$13,750	2/06	SWNE	Grain cart, hyd. fold corner auger, 1,000 PTO, hyd. flow control, hyd. end flipper, light kit, 24.5-32 diamond-tread tires, one owner
J&M	825 bu.	1999	G	$10,500	2/06	WCMN	Grain cart, 420-80-46 duals
J&M	875		G	$13,000	4/06	SWOH	Grain cart, front auger
J&M	875	2003	G	$18,500	12/06	SEND	Grain cart
J&M	NA	1994	G	$6,000	4/06	NCSD	Gravity wagon, 490 bu., with cover
J&M	NA	2005	E	$16,750	3/06	NEND	18" corner auger, PTO, roll tarp, hyd. adjustable spout, inspection window, light package, new 24.5-32 rubber
John Deere	1210		F	$600	3/06	SWNE	400-bu. grain cart
John Deere	1210		G	$800	12/06	NWIL	Grain cart
John Deere	1210		F	$900	12/06	NWIL	Auger cart
John Deere	1210		G	$1,500	8/06	NEIA	Grain cart
John Deere	1210		G	$1,700	1/06	WCIL	Grain cart, front horizontal auger
John Deere	1210		G	$3,000	8/06	WCIL	Grain cart
John Deere	1210A		F	$875	1/06	NCCO	Grain cart
John Deere	1210A		F	$1,400	3/06	NWIL	
John Deere	1210A		G	$1,600	3/06	SEIA	400-bu. auger wagon
John Deere	1210A		G	$2,500	1/06	WCNE	Single axle, PTO
John Deere	210		G	$1,550	4/06	WCSD	Grain cart, tandem axle, auger
John Deere	400		G	$2,100	2/06	NWOH	Grain cart
John Deere	425 bu.		F	$850	3/06	SWNE	Grain cart, hyd. fold auger, 1,000 PTO
John Deere	500		G	$3,400	12/06	SCMN	Grain cart
John Deere	500		G	$3,500	3/06	ECIL	Grain cart, PTO, 18.4-26 diamond-tread tires
John Deere	500		G	$3,750	3/06	NCIL	Grain cart
John Deere	500		G	$4,200	4/06	SCKS	Grain cart
John Deere	650		G	$1,400	2/06	NECO	Single axle, PTO

Grain Boxes & Carts

Make	Model	Year	Cond.	Price	Sale	Location	Comments
Kilbros	1200		G	$5,700	3/06	NCIL	550-bu. grain cart, roll tarp
Kilbros	1200		G	$5,750	11/06	ECND	Grain cart, 800 bu., roll tarp, new floor auger and gear box, diamond tires, 1,000 PTO
Kilbros	1200		G	$7,800	11/06	SWIA	Grain cart, new flighting, tarp, lights
Kilbros	125 bu.		F	$275	1/06	SCMI	
Kilbros	1400		G	$8,750	2/06	SEKS	Grain cart
Kilbros	1400		G	$10,000	2/06	WCIL	Grain cart, front auger, hyd. rear door, 1,000 PTO, tarp
Kilbros	1400	2000	G	$10,250	3/06	SEND	Grain cart, 750 bu., roll tarp, 1000 PTO, 23.1-26 diamonds
Kilbros	1600	1995	G	$9,000	2/06	WCIL	800-bu. grain cart, 30.5-32 tires, two sets of PTO drive shafts (large & small 1,000)
Kilbros	1800		G	$7,250	8/06	WCMN	Front unload
Kilbros	1800		G	$13,500	2/06	ECNE	Grain cart, 1,000 bu.
Kilbros	1800		G	$14,500	12/06	ECMO	Grain cart
Kilbros	1800	1998	G	$7,000	12/06	WCKS	Grain cart, 30.5L-32 12-ply tires
Kilbros	1820	2005		$18,000	3/06	SWKS	975-bu. grain cart, warranty, new/unused
Kilbros	1820	2005	E	$18,000	3/06	SWKS	975-bu. grain cart, warranty, unit has been demonstrated
Kilbros	1820	2005	E	$18,500	3/06	SWKS	975-bu. grain cart, warranty, unit has been demonstrated
Kilbros	225		G	$500	12/06	NEMO	Gravity wagon
Kilbros	250		G	$550	7/06	NCIL	Gravity wagon, 250 bu., 10-ton gear, 4 sold @$550 each
Kilbros	250		G	$550	7/06	NCIL	Gravity wagon, 250 bu., 10-ton gear, 4 sold @$550 each
Kilbros	250		G	$550	7/06	NCIL	Gravity wagon, 250 bu., 10-ton gear, 4 sold @$550 each
Kilbros	250		G	$550	7/06	NCIL	Gravity wagon, 250 bu., 10-ton gear, 4 sold @$550 each
Kilbros	250		G	$1,000	7/06	NCIL	Gravity wagon, 10-ton gear
Kilbros	300		G	$700	11/06	SEIA	Gravity wagon, gear
Kilbros	300		G	$750	11/06	SEIA	Gravity wagon, gear
Kilbros	300		G	$775	11/06	ECIL	Gravity wagon, 10-ton gear
Kilbros	300		G	$800	8/06	NWIL	Gravity wagon, JD gear
Kilbros	300		G	$800	8/06	NWIL	Gravity wagon, JD gear
Kilbros	300		G	$800	2/06	NCIN	Gravity wagon, steel extensions
Kilbros	300		G	$900	8/06	NWIL	Gravity wagon, JD gear
Kilbros	300		G	$900	8/06	NWIL	Gravity wagon, JD gear
Kilbros	350		E	$0	12/06	SWWI	No sale at $2,700, new, gear
Kilbros	350		F	$500	9/06	WCWI	Gravity box, gear
Kilbros	350		F	$550	2/06	WCOH	Gravity bed
Kilbros	350		F	$550	2/06	WCOH	Gravity bed
Kilbros	350		F	$550	2/06	WCOH	Gravity bed
Kilbros	350		G	$700	8/06	NCIA	Gravity wagon, gear, hyd. auger
Kilbros	350		G	$700	9/06	SWIA	Gravity wagon, Westendorf gear
Kilbros	350		G	$725	3/06	SWOH	Gravity wagon, 10-ton gear
Kilbros	350		G	$750	2/06	NEIN	Gravity wagon, on Farmers Pride 10-ton gear
Kilbros	350		G	$800	3/06	NCIL	Gravity wagon, JD 1065 gear
Kilbros	350		G	$800	12/06	WCMN	Gravity wagon, hd gear
Kilbros	350		G	$825	8/06	NCIA	Gravity wagon, auger
Kilbros	350		G	$900	8/06	NCOH	Gravity wagon, Kilbros 10-ton gear, roll tarp
Kilbros	350		G	$900	9/06	WCWI	Gravity box, gear
Kilbros	350		G	$900	12/06	WCMN	Gravity wagon, hd gear
Kilbros	350		G	$900	1/06	SCMI	JD 1065 gear
Kilbros	350		G	$950	12/06	WCIL	Gravity box
Kilbros	350		G	$950	12/06	WCIL	Gravity box

WHAT'S IT WORTH?

Grain Boxes & Carts

Make	Model	Year	Cond.	Price	Sale	Location	Comments
Kilbros	350		G	$950	2/06	WCOH	Gravity bed
Kilbros	350		G	$950	1/06	SCMI	Gravity wagon, Farmers Pride gear, wood side extensions
Kilbros	350		G	$975	12/06	WCIL	Gravity flow wagon
Kilbros	350		G	$1,000	2/06	SCMI	Gravity wagon, JD 1065A gear, metal extension
Kilbros	350		G	$1,050	2/06	NCIN	Gravity wagon
Kilbros	350		G	$1,100	1/06	NEMO	Gravity wagon
Kilbros	350		G	$1,100	1/06	SCMI	Gravity wagon, Farmers Pride gear, metal side extensions
Kilbros	350		F	$1,250	4/06	SEMI	Gravity wagon, JD 1065A gear, Kilbros seed auger, Shur-Lok tarp
Kilbros	350		G	$1,400	2/06	WCOH	Gravity bed
Kilbros	350		G	$1,400	2/06	WCOH	Gravity bed
Kilbros	350		G	$1,600	2/06	SCMI	Gravity wagon, JD 1065A gear, metal extension
Kilbros	350		G	$1,700	8/06	NEIL	Gravity wagon, EZ Trail 1074 gear
Kilbros	350		G	$1,750	2/06	SEIN	Gravity wagon, JD 1075 gear
Kilbros	350		E	$1,850	3/06	NWOH	Gravity wagon on Farmers Pride 10-ton gear
Kilbros	350		E	$1,900	3/06	NWOH	Gravity wagon, metal extension, Kory 6072 10-ton gear
Kilbros	350		G	$1,900	2/06	SEIN	Gravity wagon, JD 720 gear
Kilbros	350		G	$2,000	4/06	SEMI	Gravity wagon, JD 1065A gear, tarp
Kilbros	350		G	$2,050	1/06	SWOH	Gravity wagon, Kilbros gear
Kilbros	350		G	$2,300	12/06	NWOH	Gravity wagon, 10-ton gear, 20" truck tires
Kilbros	350	1998	G	$2,500	12/06	SWMI	Gravity wagon, 2001 Kory 8-ton long-reach model, 6072 flotation tires, gear like new, Shur-Lok installed 2001, roll top, nice 6" hyd. unloading auger, used for seed bean storage
Kilbros	375		F	$325	3/06	NCNE	Gravity wagon, AC gear
Kilbros	375		G	$1,000	3/06	NCIL	Gravity wagon, DMI gear
Kilbros	375		G	$1,200	11/06	WCIL	Gravity wagon, Kilbros 12-ton gear, 16.5×16.1 tires
Kilbros	375		G	$1,250	8/06	NCIA	Gravity wagon
Kilbros	375		G	$1,650	8/06	NEIL	Gravity wagon, EZ Trail 1074 gear
Kilbros	375		E	$3,200	2/06	SEMI	Gravity, 12-ton gear
Kilbros	385		G	$2,050	8/06	ECNE	Gravity flow seed tender, Sudenga electric shutoff auger, telescoping spout, roll tarp, JD 1065A gear, 11L-15 tires
Kilbros	385		G	$2,250	2/06	SEMI	Gravity, hyd. auger, JD gear, roll tarp
Kilbros	385		G	$2,700	8/06	NEIL	Gravity wagon, 1285 gear
Kilbros	385		G	$2,750	3/06	ECNE	Gravity wagon, 12-ton gear, one owner
Kilbros	385		E	$3,900	2/06	SEMI	Gravity, 12-ton gear
Kilbros	385		E	$3,900	2/06	SEMI	Gravity, 12-ton gear
Kilbros	390		E	$5,950	2/06	SEMI	Gravity, extension, 12-ton gear, roll tarp, 16.5×16 tires
Kilbros	400		G	$1,500	9/06	NWOH	Center dump wagon on Kory 10-ton gear
Kilbros	475		G	$1,600	11/06	ECNE	Auger wagon, set for 30" rows
Kilbros	475		G	$3,200	1/06	SCNE	Grain cart, center unload, hyd. auger, lights
Kilbros	475		G	$5,050	3/06	NENE	Grain cart
Kilbros	475	1994	G	$5,000	3/06	SEND	Grain cart, center auger, roll tarp, 1,000 PTO, 23.1-26 diamonds
Kilbros	475 bu.		E	$4,250	2/06	SENE	Grain cart, tarp
Kilbros	490		G	$4,050	4/06	WCSD	Grain cart, feed wagon, extensions
Kilbros	490		G	$5,100	2/06	WCIL	Grain cart, roll tarp, 1,000 PTO, corner auger, 30.5-32 tires
Kilbros	490		G	$6,000	2/06	ECIL	PTO grain cart, hyd. folding auger
Kilbros	490	2001	G	$7,100	2/06	SCMI	Grain cart, lights, tarp

Grain Boxes & Carts

Make	Model	Year	Cond.	Price	Sale	Location	Comments
Kilbros	500 bu.		G	$1,900	8/06	WCIA	Gravity wagon, 2 doors
Kilbros	550		G	$4,800	2/06	NEIN	Gravity wagon, Kilbros 1890 gear
Kilbros	690	2002	G	$7,750	4/06	NWMN	Grain cart, roll tarp, PTO
Kinze	1040		F	$9,500	3/06	NWKS	Grain cart
Kinze	1040		G	$15,500	8/06	WCMN	Grain cart, 24" tracks
Kinze	1040		G	$20,000	3/06	NENE	Row crop grain cart, EZ250 digital scale, Firestone 15.4-38 dual tires
Kinze	1040	1998	F	$15,500	12/06	NEKS	Grain cart, 18.4-38 tires, duals, rollover tarp, PTO drive
Kinze	1040	1999	G	$13,000	3/06	NWKS	Grain cart, roll tarp
Kinze	1050	2003	G	$27,500	12/06	WCKS	Grain cart, Harvest commander, 1,000 PTO drive, hydraulic gate, 20-inch discharge, rollover tarp, 18.4-42 tires, duals, front window, rear hitch
Kinze	1050	2004	E	$47,000	12/06	WCMN	Sof-Trak, 36" tracks, roll tarp
Kinze	640		G	$9,100	12/06	NCIA	Grain cart
Kinze	640	1994	G	$7,900	3/06	ECNE	Grain cart, hyd. shutoff, extension axles, 24.5-32 tires, light kit
Kinze	800		G	$7,500	11/06	ECND	Grain cart, roll tarp, PTO, corner auger
Kinze	840		G	$10,000	8/06	SCNE	Grain cart, 1,000 PTO, roll tarp
Kinze	840	1999	G	$14,250	3/06	NWIL	Electric scale
Kinze	840	2001	G	$17,500	3/06	ECNE	Grain cart, 850-bu. capacity, side extensions, 16" hyd. fold unload auger, PTO drive, roll tarp
Kory	165		F	$250	12/06	SEMN	Gravity wagon, gear
Kory	185		G	$1,050	9/06	NWIL	Gravity wagon, 10-ton gear
Kory	220		F	$300	3/06	ECNE	Gravity wagon, Bush Hog hd gear
Kory	225 bu.		G	$1,400	3/06	ECNE	Steel gravity wagon, 10-ton, 4-wheel gear, hyd. drive side mount loading auger, side extensions
Kory	300 bu.		F	$350	6/06	NWIL	Center dump wagon
Kory	340		G	$1,550	9/06	ECNE	Gravity box wagon
Kuker	200 bu.		G	$550	3/06	NENE	Gravity box wagon
Lundell	1290		G	$600	9/06	ECNE	Gravity box wagon
Lundell	200 bu.		G	$850	1/06	WCNE	Gravity, 4-wheel, running gear
Lundell	300 bu.		G	$725	8/06	NCIA	Gravity, 8-bolt Westendorf gear
Lundell	300 bu.		G	$725	8/06	NCIA	Gravity, 8-bolt Westendorf gear
Lundell	300 bu.		G	$800	3/06	NENE	Gravity wagon
M&W	250		G	$800	3/06	NCIL	Gravity wagon, gear
M&W	275 bu.		G	$625	3/06	ECNE	Gravity wagon
M&W	300		F	$1,900	1/06	NWIL	Gravity wagon
M&W	300 bu.		G	$850	3/06	NEIA	Gravity wagon, red top, gear
M&W	300 bu.		G	$1,100	2/06	NCIL	Little red wagon
M&W	300 bu.		G	$1,450	8/06	WCIL	Gravity wagon, 2 sold - for $1,450 each
M&W	300 bu.		G	$1,450	8/06	WCIL	Gravity wagon, 2 sold - for $1,450 each
M&W	300 bu.		G	$1,750	3/06	NWIL	Side dump wagon
M&W	300 bu.		G	$1,750	3/06	NWIL	Gravity wagon, side dump
M&W	350 bu.		G	$850	3/06	NEIA	Gravity wagon, white top, gear
M&W	350 bu.		G	$2,600	12/06	WCIL	Gravity flow wagon on hd running gear
M&W	375 bu.		G	$1,575	12/06	NWIL	Little Red Wagon
M&W	375bu.		G	$1,575	12/06	NWIL	Little Red Wagon
M&W	400		G	$1,225	1/06	NWIL	Little Red Wagon
M&W	400 bu.		G	$1,000	11/06	WCIL	Gravity wagon, side dump

Grain Boxes & Carts

Make	Model	Year	Cond.	Price	Sale	Location	Comments
M&W	400 bu.		G	$1,050	12/06	NWIL	Gravity wagon, airplane tires
M&W	400 bu.		G	$2,100	8/06	NWIL	Gravity wagon, hd gear
M&W	400 bu.		G	$2,150	3/06	NWIL	Side dump wagon
M&W	400 bu.		G	$2,300	12/06	SEIA	Little Red Wagon, gravity flow wagon, center dump, brakes and truck tires
M&W	400 bu.		G	$2,450	12/06	SEIA	Little Red Wagon gravity flow wagon, center dump, brakes, truck tires
M&W	400 bu.		G	$3,250	6/06	SCMN	Two compartments
M&W	400 bu.		G	$3,750	12/06	NWIL	Side unload wagon
M&W	4250		G	$4,000	1/06	NWIL	Gravity wagon, brakes
M&W	4300A		G	$2,600	3/06	NWIL	Gravity wagon, 400 bu., side dump
M&W	4300A		G	$2,600	3/06	NWIL	Gravity wagon, 400 bu., side dump
M&W	4300A		G	$2,900	3/06	NWIL	Gravity wagon, 400 bu., side dump
M&W	4300A		G	$2,900	3/06	NWIL	Gravity wagon, 400 bu., side dump
M&W	450		E	$5,000	7/06	NWIL	Little Red Wagon, side dump
M&W	4800		G	$3,500	8/06	WCIL	Grain cart
McCurdy	150 bu.		G	$675	8/06	NCOH	Gravity wagon
McCurdy	200 bu.		F	$325	2/06	SCMI	Gravity wagon, JD gear
McCurdy	250 bu.		G	$600	3/06	NENE	Gravity wagon
McCurdy	250 bu.		G	$1,800	1/06	SWOH	Gravity wagon, gears
McCurdy	275 bu.		G	$775	3/06	ECNE	Gravity wagon, auger
Minnesota	250		F	$475	11/06	WCMN	Gravity box on Kasten gear
Minnesota	250		G	$575	9/06	SCMN	Gravity box, extensions on gear
Minnesota	250		F	$900	3/06	SEMN	Gravity box, 10-ton gear
Minnesota	250		G	$1,000	3/06	SEMN	Gravity flow box, 10-ton gear
Minnesota	250		G	$1,600	9/06	NWMN	Gravity box, box extension on Minnesota 10-ton gear
Minnesota	250		G	$1,850	3/06	SEMN	Gravity box, 10-ton gear
Minnesota	260		G	$950	8/06	NEIA	Gravity box, 10-ton gear
Minnesota	260		G	$1,150	12/06	SWWI	Gravity wagon
Minnesota	400		E	$3,150	3/06	NEIA	Gravity wagon, gear
Nubilt	250 bu.		G	$775	3/06	WCMN	Gravity box on 971 Lindsay gear
Nubilt	250 bu.		G	$900	4/06	NWMN	Gravity box, tarp
Nubilt	250 bu.		G	$1,150	3/06	WCMN	Gravity box on hd NuBilt gear
Nubilt	275 bu.		F	$650	5/06	SEND	Gravity wagon
Nubilt	300 bu.		G	$1,300	3/06	WCSD	Gravity wagon, hyd. unloading auger, hd JD gear
Orthman	996	2004	G	$17,000	6/06	NWKS	Grain cart
Parker	125 bu.		G	$500	3/06	SEND	Gravity wagon on JD 4-wheel gear
Parker	131		F	$175	3/06	SCIN	Hopper, gears
Parker	150 bu.		G	$550	12/06	NEMO	Gravity wagon
Parker	155 bu.		G	$475	9/06	NEIN	Gravity wagon, 6-ton gear, new paint
Parker	165		F	$375	11/06	ECIL	On Case gear
Parker	180 bu.		G	$1,600	3/06	ECMI	Gravity box, extensions on 8-ton gear, flotation tires
Parker	200		G	$750	2/06	NWIN	Gravity box, gear
Parker	200		G	$1,200	3/06	NCIA	Gravity, Sudenga brush auger
Parker	200 bu.		G	$3,100	3/06	ECNE	Wagon, bean fill auger
Parker	250		G	$2,200	8/06	NEKS	Gravity wagon, hyd. seed auger
Parker	2500		G	$1,125	12/06	SWWI	Gravity wagon
Parker	2500		G	$1,550	12/06	SWWI	Gravity wagon

Grain Boxes & Carts

Make	Model	Year	Cond.	Price	Sale	Location	Comments
Parker	2500		G	$1,700	8/06	NCIA	Gravity wagon, 24" extension, JD gear, 8-bolt wheels, 16.5-16.1 tires
Parker	2500		G	$1,750	3/06	SEMN	Gravity box, 400 bushel, 16-ton gear, brakes
Parker	2500		G	$2,000	9/06	NCIA	Single door, JD 1075 gears, 12-ply tires
Parker	2500		G	$2,000	9/06	NCIA	Single door, JD 1075 gear, 2 sold – each for $2,000
Parker	2530		G	$2,000	9/06	NCIA	Single door, JD 1075 gear, 2 sold – each for $2,000
Parker	2530		G	$2,000	9/06	NCIA	Single door, JD 1075 gear
Parker	2600		G	$1,550	9/06	NCIA	JD 1075 gear, 12 poly tires
Parker	2600		G	$1,700	9/06	ECNE	Gravity box wagon
Parker	2600		G	$1,750	6/06	NCIA	359-bu. gravity box, gear
Parker	2600		G	$3,200	8/06	WCIL	Gravity wagon, 1180 gear
Parker	2600		G	$3,600	8/06	WCIL	Gravity wagon, 1180 gear
Parker	275 bu.		G	$1,150	3/06	WCMN	Gravity box
Parker	300 bu.		G	$625	9/06	SEIA	Gravity flow on Parker running gear
Parker	300 bu.		G	$900	7/06	NCIL	Gravity wagon
Parker	300 bu.		G	$900	7/06	NCIL	Gravity wagon
Parker	300 bu.		G	$1,175	4/06	SCMN	Gravity box, gear
Parker	325 bu.		G	$1,150	12/06	NWIL	Wagon
Parker	325 bu.		G	$1,150	12/06	NWIL	Wagon
Parker	350 bu.		G	$1,000	7/06	NWIL	Gravity wagon
Parker	350 bu.		G	$2,100	3/06	NWIL	Gravity wagon, hd gear
Parker	350 bu.		G	$2,550	7/06	NWIL	Gravity wagon, Kewanee gear
Parker	400 bu.		F	$1,700	12/06	SWWI	Gravity wagon, Parker gear
Parker	400 bu.		G	$2,000	8/06	ECNE	Grain cart, tandem axle, hyd. & manual slide gate
Parker	400 bu.		F	$2,250	12/06	NWIL	Gravity wagon, Parker 1276 gear
Parker	4000		G	$1,800	8/06	NCIA	Gravity wagon, lights
Parker	4000		G	$1,900	8/06	NCIA	Gravity wagon, lights
Parker	4000		G	$2,050	8/06	NCIA	Gravity, 2-door, gear
Parker	4000		G	$2,200	8/06	ECNE	Gravity wagon, 400 bu., lights, brakes
Parker	4000		G	$2,300	8/06	NCIA	Gravity wagon, lights
Parker	4000		G	$2,650	8/06	NCIA	Gravity wagon, lights
Parker	4000		G	$2,700	4/06	NEIA	Gravity wagon, heavy gear
Parker	4500		G	$3,250	1/06	SCNE	Grain cart, center unload, set up for 30" rows, lights
Parker	4500		G	$4,200	11/06	WCIL	Auger wagon, 450 bu., side dump, 1,000 PTO
Parker	4800		G	$3,900	8/06	NCIA	Gravity, 19L-16.1 tires, lights
Parker	4800		G	$4,200	2/06	SEIN	500-bu. wagon, brakes
Parker	4800		G	$4,550	8/06	ECIA	Gravity box, factory gear, 425/65R × 22.5 truck tires
Parker	4800		G	$4,700	2/06	SEIN	500-bu. wagon, brakes
Parker	4800		G	$4,900	8/06	NCIA	Gravity, truck tires, lights, brakes
Parker	4800		G	$5,000	8/06	ECIA	Gravity box, factory gear, 16.5L-16.1 flotation tires
Parker	4800		G	$5,200	8/06	NCIA	Gravity, truck tires, lights, brakes
Parker	4800		G	$5,700	8/06	NCIA	Gravity, truck tires, lights, brakes
Parker	500		G	$7,500	3/06	NCIA	Grain cart, corner auger, tarp, 18.4-26 tires
Parker	510		G	$5,800	1/06	NCCO	Grain cart
Parker	5500		G	$4,600	8/06	NCIA	Gravity wagon, brakes, lights, 18" wide truck tires
Parker	5500		G	$5,700	8/06	NCIA	Gravity wagon, brakes, lights, 18" wide truck tires
Parker	575 bu.		G	$5,500	11/06	ECND	Grain cart, 1,000 PTO
Parker	605	2001	G	$8,300	8/06	NCIA	Gravity, truck tires, lights, brakes
Parker	614		E	$9,200	1/06	NWIA	Grain cart, 700 bu.

Grain Boxes & Carts

Make	Model	Year	Cond.	Price	Sale	Location	Comments
Parker	6250		E	$7,600	1/06	NWIA	Grain wagon
Parker	6500		G	$3,900	3/06	SWMN	650-bu. grain cart, side discharge, flotation tires
Parker	6500		G	$5,500	11/06	NCIN	Grain cart
Parker	675		F	$7,250	6/06	SCMN	Grain cart, roll tarp, 1,000 PTO
Parker	7250		G	$7,750	3/06	ECNE	Grain Chariot gravity wagon, one owner, 445/65R22.5 tires
Parker	7250		E	$9,500	8/06	WCIL	Gravity wagon, 445/65R22.5 tires, 2985 gear, brakes, lights, like new
Parker	737	2003	G	$13,500	12/06	SWMI	Grain cart, 750 bu., 16' angled hyd. auger, 30.5-32 tires
Uft	400 bu.		G	$3,100	12/06	NWIL	Auger cart, new augers
Uft	400 bu.		G	$3,200	1/06	NWIL	Grain auger cart
Uft	444		F	$2,000	9/06	NCIA	Grain cart
Uft	500		G	$4,750	3/06	NWIL	Grain cart, tarp
Uft	500 bu.		F	$2,000	11/06	WCMN	Grain cart, hyd. fold auger
Uft	575 bu.		G	$8,300	6/06	ECND	Roll tarp, diamond tires, hyd. drive
Uft	700 bu.		G	$4,500	3/06	WCKS	Grain cart
Uft	750		G	$3,900	4/06	SWOH	Grain cart, tarp
Unverferth	230		G	$1,800	1/06	SWOH	Gravity wagon, gears
Unverferth	275		G	$1,050	2/06	NEIN	Gravity wagon on 8-ton gear
Unverferth	325		G	$2,600	3/06	WCMN	Gravity box, on 12-ton gear, 10:00×20 tires
Unverferth	335		E	$1,600	2/06	SCMI	Gravity wagon, no gear
Unverferth	335		E	$1,600	2/06	SCMI	Gravity wagon, no gear
Unverferth	335	2004	E	$2,750	12/06	WCMN	Split box, roll tarp, no running gear, flatbed mount
Unverferth	335	2004	E	$5,200	12/06	WCMN	Split box, roll tarp, 12-ton gear
Unverferth	3500		G	$2,550	12/06	ECMO	GC3500 grain cart, 350 bu., new augers
Unverferth	4500		G	$5,100	6/06	WCMN	Grain cart
Unverferth	4500		G	$6,800	3/06	SEPA	Long auger, average rubber
Unverferth	5000		G	$6,000	8/06	WCMN	Grain cart, scale auger, new 2 years ago
Unverferth	530		G	$8,000	8/06	NWIL	Gravity wagon, brakes
Unverferth	630		G	$8,700	2/06	NWIA	Gravity wagon, brakes, lights, red
Unverferth	630		G	$8,700	2/06	NWIA	Gravity wagon, brakes, lights, red
Unverferth	630	1999	G	$8,100	2/06	WCIL	
Unverferth	630	1999	G	$8,100	2/06	WCIL	
Unverferth	7200	2002	E	$14,000	9/06	WCIA	Grain cart, 17" unload, like new
Unverferth	8250	2005	E	$17,000	3/06	NWOH	825-bu. grain cart
Westendorf	400 bu.		G	$3,500	3/06	ECNE	Gravity wagon, 2212 gear, 11R22.5 tires, lights, one owner, shedded
Wetmore	400 bu.		G	$1,450	2/06	SCKS	Grain cart
Year-A-Round	500 bu.		F	$3,300	6/06	SWMN	Gravity wagon, surge brakes
Year-A-Round	550 bu.		G	$3,000	8/06	WCMN	Gravity box, hd gear
Year-A-Round	550 bu.		G	$3,300	8/06	WCMN	Gravity box, hd gear
Year-A-Round	550 bu.		G	$5,700	3/06	WCMN	Harvest box on hd gear

Grain Dryers

Make	Model	Year	Hrs.	Cond.	Price	Sale	Location	Comments
Airstream	260C		2,441	G	$6,850	8/06	SCMN	Continuous flow or batch portable, LP gas, gas hose, electrical cable
American	2412			G	$4,200	3/06	ECND	Auto batch dryer, 3-phase electrical
Behlen	700			G	$3,900	12/06	NWIL	4-column continuous-flow Energy Saver, 3-phase dryer
Behlen	750 bu.			F	$350	9/06	NECO	HLX, 1,000 PTO
Behlen	HL			F	$225	10/06	NECO	HLX, 750 bu., PTO
Behlen	NA			G	$2,750	11/06	ECND	Continuous flow, 3 phase, preheater
Behlen	NA			G	$3,750	11/06	ECND	Continuous flow, 3 phase, preheater
Chief	450			F	$625	3/06	ECND	PTO
Dry Mor	400 bu.			F	$750	8/06	SCMI	Batch grain dryer
Farm Fans	270			G	$16,000	1/06	SCMN	1-phase grain dryer, 1,198 hours, one owner
Farm Fans	270			E	$16,500	1/06	NWIA	Portable continuous-flow corn grain dryer
Farm Fans	AB 350A			F	$3,000	2/06	NEIN	Auto batch dryer
Farm Fans	AB8B			F	$1,300	1/06	SCMI	Single phase
Farm Fans	CF/AB 270		882	G	$15,000	9/06	WCND	Portable grain dryer, Calc-U-Dry Moisturematic, single phase
Grain Chief	450			F	$350	4/06	NEND	PTO batch dryer
Grain Chief	450			G	$2,000	4/06	WCMN	Canadian sale
GT	570			F	$500	9/06	NWMN	PTO batch grain dryer, snorkel attachment
GT	580			F	$1,300	7/06	NEND	Portable batch dryer
GT	NA			G	$1,300	4/06	NEND	1,400-bu. hopper, transport
Kansun	10-25/2-15	1981		G	$7,400	6/06	NWIL	LP system, single phase
Kansun	NA			G	$2,400	6/06	SCMN	#21016, steel
Kansun	NA			G	$7,700	6/06	SCMN	#21518, stainless steel
Moridge	275			F	$110	12/06	WCIL	LP grain dryer
Moridge	8440			G	$400	3/06	SEND	Batch dryer, PTO
Moridge	8770			G	$1,300	4/06	NEND	PTO portable batch dryer, transport
Super B	AS 20			G	$2,100	2/06	SCMI	350-bu. capacity
Super B	AS600			G	$9,300	1/06	NEIA	233-bu. auto electric/LP batch dryer, stored inside
Super B	NA		1,049	G	$3,500	3/06	NWMN	Continuous-flow portable batch dryer
Super B	SD 250	2002	806	G	$24,000	12/06	SEIA	SD 250 VQ Energy Miser, continuous-flow grain dryer, 806 hours, Quantum dryer controller
Tox-O-Wik	1440			G	$3,100	4/06	NEND	Continuous-flow dryer, single phase, 10-hp. electrical motor
Tox-O-Wik	500 bu.			F	$110	7/06	NCIA	Batch dryer
Tox-O-Wik	5700			F	$900	4/06	NWMN	Continuous-flow portable dryer, 540 PTO
Vertec	VT6500			G	$18,500	4/06	ECND	Continuous-flow grain dryer, 1 phase, electronic moisture control

WHAT'S IT WORTH?

Grain Trailers

Make	Model	Year	Cond.	Price	Sale	Location	Comments
American	38'		F	$600	2/06	WCIL	Roll tarp
American	38'	1972	F	$1,800	4/06	ECND	Hopper bottom, 38', needs repair
Chamberlain	38'	1973	G	$3,700	3/06	NECO	Double hopper, rollover tarp
Chamberlain	38'	1978	F	$4,000	7/06	NWMN	Aluminum hopper bottom, 66" sides, spring suspension, roll tarp, 11×24.5 rubber
Chamberlain	42'	1984	G	$11,500	11/06	SCNE	Aluminum hopper bottom, roll tarp
Cornhusker	40'		G	$5,100	4/06	WCSD	Grain trailer
Cornhusker	40'	1974	G	$10,000	12/06	ECNE	Tandem axle, Cornhusker strap-down tarp, cable traps, air ride suspension, 11R22.5 tires, aluminum rims on outside tires
Cornhusker	40'	1980	G	$10,000	12/06	ECNE	Tandem axle, aluminum, Shur-Lok roll tarp, spring ride suspension, 11R22.5 tires on Dayton wheels
Cornhusker	42'	1998	G	$14,000	12/06	WCKS	Aluminum sides, 78" sides, tandem axle, spring ride suspension, 2-spd. traps, rollover tarp, front/rear ladders
Cornhusker	46'	1976	G	$11,000	12/06	ECNE	46.5', triple-axle steel grain trailer, air-lift tag axle, new Shur-Lok roll tarp, spring ride suspension, new brakes & suspension last season, aluminum rims on outside tires
Cornhusker	46'	1990	G	$13,750	3/06	NENE	Triple axle, 2-spd. traps, Shur-Lok roll tarp, 11R25 tires on aluminum rims, new rear end bushings
Dakota	26'	1998	G	$10,900	1/06	SCKS	Tandem axle, hopper bottom, side discharge, 295/75R22.5 tires, Shur-Lok roll tarp, bought new, VIN: 1H9SH262WY193827
Dakota	26'	1998	G	$10,900	1/06	SCKS	Tandem axle, hopper bottom & side discharge, 295/75R22.5 tires, Shur-Lok roll tarp, bought new, VIN: 1H9SH2622WY193826
Dorsey	NA	1979	F	$8,700	4/06	NCSD	40', roll tarp (2004)
Fruehauf	NA	1974	G	$4,250	4/06	WCSD	21' hopper pup trailer, 2 axle, pintle hitch
Hawk	NA		G	$10,000	6/06	SCMN	34', steel
Hawk Master	24'	1998	G	$11,500	12/06	WCKS	Steel sides, 66" sides, single axle, spring ride suspension, air brakes, single hopper, rollover tarp, 11R24.5 tires, steel rims, front/rear ladders
Hawkeye	42'	1979	F	$3,700	2/06	NWSD	Hopper trailer
Hawkeye	42'	1991	G	$6,600	3/06	ECNE	Spring ride
Hillsboro	16'	1996	G	$8,100	2/06	NEIN	Grain dump trailer, tandem axle, Shur-Lok tarp
Hobbs	38'	1975	F	$3,600	7/06	NWOH	Steel grain hopper trailer
Jet	22'		G	$7,000	8/06	NCIA	Late hopper trailer, duals
Jet	22'	1986	G	$7,500	8/06	WCIL	Hopper bottom
Jet	22'	1996	E	$9,500	2/06	NWOH	Single axle, single-bottom dump, Shur-Lok tarp
Jet	42'	1987	G	$6,000	11/06	SCSD	Grain trailer, good tires, roll tarp, good tires
Jet	42'	1998	G	$10,000	12/06	NEKS	Hopper trailer, double hopper, tandem axle, rollover tarp, spring ride, steel sides, 11R24.5 tires, steel rims
Jet	42'	2000	G	$9,800	12/06	NEKS	Hopper trailer, double hopper, tandem axle, rollover tarp, spring ride, steel sides, 11R24.5 tires, steel rims
Jet	NA	1999	G	$15,500	2/06	SCMI	800 bu., new tires, never seen salt, Shur-Lok tarp
Maurer	38'	2001	G	$15,000	3/06	NWMN	Spring ride, Shur-Lok roll tarp, side chute, sight gauges
Maurer	28'	2001	G	$11,900	4/06	NCKS	Tandem single hopper trailer
Maurer	38'	2002	G	$18,000	3/06	NWMN	Hopper trailer, spring ride, Shur-Lok roll tarp, side chute, sight gauge

Grain Trailers

Make	Model	Year	Cond.	Price	Sale	Location	Comments
Maurer	38'	2003	G	$13,750	2/06	NCIL	Center dump, Shur-Lok roll tarp
Maurer	NA	1999	G	$13,200	3/06	NCKS	33'2", hopper trailer
Merritt	42'	1979	F	$5,250	3/06	WCMN	Hopper bottom
Merritt	42'	1980	F	$6,000	1/06	NCCO	Double hopper
Merritt	42'	1981	G	$8,000	3/06	WCMN	Hopper bottom, low hopper
Merritt	42'	1981	G	$9,000	3/06	WCMN	Hopper bottom
Merritt	42'	1983	G	$9,500	3/06	SWNE	Roll tarp, 11R24.5 tires
Merritt	42'	1988	F	$7,000	11/06	NWMN	42'×96"×78", hopper bottom, roll tarp, 11×24.5 rubber on steel, spring suspension
Merritt	43'	1996	G	$16,000	6/06	NWKS	43'×102"×80" double-hopper grain trailer, rollover tarp, 285/75R24-5 tires, aluminum wheels, air ride
Neville	26'	2005	E	$13,500	1/06	SCKS	Tandem axle, dual hoppers bottoms, Shur-Lok roll tarp, 285/75R24.5 tires, bought new, always shedded
Neville	NA	2006	E	$14,000	12/06	WCKS	28', tandem axle, spring ride, dual hoppers, 68K-lb. GVW, 11R22.5 tires, steel rims, front & rear ladders, rollover tarp, rear pintle hitch
Timpte	2862	2003	E	$16,250	3/06	NESD	28'×102 tandem axle, Super Hopper
Timpte	2862	2006	E	$18,700	3/06	NESD	28'×102" tandem axle, Super Hopper
Timpte	2862	2006	E	$19,000	3/06	NESD	28'×102" tandem axle, Super Hopper
Timpte	32'	1997	G	$15,700	3/06	ECNE	All-aluminum hopper bottom grain trailer, Ag Hoppers, 66" sides, Shur-Lok roll tarp
Timpte	38'	1974	G	$7,000	2/06	SEKS	Hopper bottom, Shur-Lok roll tarp
Timpte	40'	1982	G	$6,500	4/06	NWMN	Hopper bottom, 40'×96"×66" sides, roll tarp, spring ride, 10:00×20 on Dayton wheels
Timpte	40'	1983	G	$11,500	11/06	SCNE	Supper Hopper aluminum, roll tarp
Timpte	40'	1985	G	$9,000	4/06	NWMN	Hopper bottom, 40'×96"×66" sides, roll tarp, spring ride, 11×24 on steel
Timpte	40'	1986	G	$11,600	1/06	NECO	Grain trailer
Timpte	40'	1993	G	$13,000	12/06	ECIL	Super Hopper grain trailer, 24.5 rubber, rollover tarp
Timpte	42'	1979	G	$8,600	11/06	NWKS	Grain hopper
Timpte	42'	1982	G	$4,700	2/06	WCMN	Aluminum Super Hopper grain trailer, roll tarp, needs work
Timpte	42'	1986	G	$6,000	7/06	NWMN	Hopper bottom, 72" sides, spring suspension, roll tarp, 11×24.5 rubber
Timpte	42'	1988	G	$13,500	2/06	WCIL	Hopper bottom grain trailer, 66" sides, roll tarp, 2 spd. doors, 11R-24.5 tires
Timpte	42'	1992	G	$14,500	11/06	SCND	Super Hopper aluminum grain trailer, 96"×78", spring ride, Shur-Lok roll tarp
Timpte	42'	1994	G	$15,250	3/06	NCND	Hopper bottom, 42'×96"×84" sides, air ride, 11-24 on steel, roll tarp
Timpte	42'	1994	G	$15,250	4/06	ECND	42'×72"×96", air ride, roll tarp, 11×24.5 on steel
Timpte	42'	1995	G	$12,000	6/06	NCIA	Hopper, air ride, roll tap
Timpte	42'	1995	G	$14,500	11/06	SCND	Super Hopper aluminum grain trailer, 96"×78", air ride, Shur-Lok roll tarp
Timpte	42'	1995	G	$15,500	12/06	WCKS	Aluminum sides, 78" sides, tandem axle, air ride suspension, 11R24.5 tires, steel rims, rollover tarp, front/rear ladders, 2-spd. traps, 2 rows of lights, stainless steel rear
Timpte	42'	1995	G	$15,500	2/06	SEKS	Super Hopper

Grain Trailers

Make	Model	Year	Cond.	Price	Sale	Location	Comments
Timpte	42'	1995	G	$16,500	12/06	WCKS	Aluminum sides, 78" sides, tandem axle, air ride suspension, 11R24.5 tires, outside aluminum rims, rollover tarp, front/rear ladders, 2-spd. traps, 2 rows of lights, ss rear
Timpte	42'	1995	G	$17,000	3/06	NESD	42'×66" double hopper grain trailer
Timpte	42'	1996	G	$18,500	2/06	SEKS	Super Hopper, Shur-Lok roll tarp
Timpte	42'	1996	G	$21,000	6/06	SCMN	42'×66"×96" hopper grain trailer, air ride, new tarp, new brakes
Timpte	42'	1996	G	$21,500	3/06	SEMN	Super Hopper grain trailer, 42'×96"×66", roll tarp, Scale-o-Matic, air ride, ss cargo doors and corners
Timpte	42'	1998	E	$20,500	2/06	ECMN	Super Hopper, 42'×66"×96" grain trailer, roll tarp, Spring Ride, 27" hopper, less than 25,000 miles on trailer, one owner
Timpte	42'	1999	G	$17,000	11/06	SCNE	Super Hopper aluminum, roll tarp
Timpte	42'	1999	G	$17,000	11/06	NEND	42'×86"×102", air ride, air scale, 24.5 rubber on polished aluminums
Timpte	42'	1999	E	$22,000	2/06	ECNE	Grain trailer, ag hoppers, stainless steel back
Timpte	42'	2000	E	$20,000	12/06	WCMN	Ag hopper, aluminum, spring ride, roll tarp
Timpte	42'	2000	G	$22,000	8/06	WCIA	66" sides, ag hoppers, roll tarp, brakes, air ride, outside aluminum wheels, 11×24.5 tires (70%)
Timpte	42'	2001	G	$17,500	12/06	WCKS	Aluminum sides, 66" sides, tandem axle, spring ride suspension, rollover tarp, 2-spd. traps, 24.5" Low Pro tires, steel rims, front/rear ladders, pintle hitch on rear
Timpte	42'	2001	G	$18,000	12/06	WCKS	Aluminum sides, 66" sides, tandem axle, spring ride suspension, rollover tarp, 2-spd. traps, 11R24.5 tires, steel rims, front/rear ladders
Timpte	42'	2001	E	$24,000	9/06	WCIA	Ag hopper bottom, air ride, crank cover, stainless rear end, used on farm only, like new
Timpte	42'	2002	G	$18,600	6/06	NCIA	Super Hopper, spring ride, roll tarp
Timpte	42'	2002	E	$25,500	12/06	WCMN	Ag hoppers, alum, air ride, roll tarp
Timpte	42'	2003	G	$19,000	12/06	WCKS	Aluminum sides, 72" sides, tandem axle, spring ride suspension, Ag Hoppers, 2-spd. traps, rollover tarp, 11R24.5 tires, outside aluminum rims, 2 rows of lights
Timpte	42'	2004	E	$26,500	12/06	WCMN	Hopper bottom, aluminum, ag hoppers, air ride, roll tarp
Timpte	42'	2005	G	$21,000	12/06	WCKS	Aluminum sides, 72" sides, tandem axle, spring ride suspension, Ag Hoppers, 2-spd. traps, rollover tarp, 11R24.5 tires, outside aluminum rims, 2 rows of lights
Timpte	42'	2005	E	$23,500	11/06	SCNE	Super Hopper, aluminum, ag hopper, roll tarp
Timpte	42'	2005	G	$23,750	12/06	WCKS	Aluminum sides, 66-inch sides, tandem axle, spring ride suspension, Ag Hoppers, 2-spd. traps, rollover tarp, 11R22.5 tires, steel rims, 2 rows of lights
Timpte	42'	2006	G	$22,500	12/06	WCKS	Aluminum sides, 66-inch sides, tandem axle, spring ride suspension, Ag Hoppers, 2-spd. traps, rollover tarp, 11R22.5 tires, steel rims, 2 rows of lights
Timpte	42'	2006	G	$23,000	12/06	WCKS	Aluminum sides, 66-inch sides, tandem axle, spring ride suspension, Ag Hoppers, 2-spd. traps, rollover tarp, 11R22.5 tires, steel rims, 2 rows of lights

Grain Trailers

Make	Model	Year	Cond.	Price	Sale	Location	Comments
Timpte	45'	1973	F	$3,200	2/06	NCCO	
Timpte	48'	1997	G	$12,500	3/06	NWKS	Triple-axle grain trailer
Timpte	48'	1997	G	$14,250	3/06	NWKS	Super Hopper, triple axle, 66" sides, spring ride, air ride, tag axle, roll tarps
Timpte	NA	1995	G	$12,000	3/06	ECKS	Super Hopper grain trailer
Wheeler	38'	1994	G	$10,350	2/06	NCIN	Hopper bottom grain trailer, newer tires, roll tarp
Wheeler	40'	1993	G	$7,000	2/06	NWIN	Hopper bottom semitrailer
Wilson	30'	1984	G	$11,250	2/06	NWKS	Aluminum hopper grain trailer
Wilson	40'	1981	G	$12,700	3/06	SWMN	Hopper bottom trailer, roll tarp
Wilson	40'	1995	G	$19,500	11/06	NCIN	Aluminum hopper bottom, aluminum wheels
Wilson	42'	1978	G	$9,750	3/06	SWMN	Hopper bottom trailer, roll tarp
Wilson	42'	1978	G	$10,500	12/06	WCMN	Aluminum hopper bottom, new roll tarp, DOT'd
Wilson	42'	1979	G	$9,500	3/06	NEND	Hopper bottom, 42'×66"×96", Courtney Collapsible 18" risers, new roll tarp, 11×24.5 on steel, spring ride, complete reconditioning
Wilson	42'	1980	G	$11,250	3/06	SEMN	42'×96"×66" Ag Hopper trailer, roll tarp, spring ride
Wilson	42'	1981	G	$13,250	3/06	SWMN	Hopper bottom trailer, roll tarp
Wilson	42'	1986	G	$14,000	11/06	NEND	Pacesetter, 42'×78"×96", spring suspension, roll tarp
Wilson	42'	1999	G	$17,000	12/06	WCKS	Aluminum sides, 66" sides, tandem axle, air ride suspension, rollover tarp, 2-spd. traps, 11R24.5 tires, steel rims, front/rear ladders
Wilson	42'	1999	G	$20,000	12/06	WCMN	Pacesetter, aluminum hopper bottom, roll tarp
Wilson	43'	1991	G	$14,000	6/06	NWKS	43' ×96" ×66" double hopper grain trailer, rollover tarp, 11R24.5 tires, aluminum wheels
Wilson	43'	1999	G	$19,000	3/06	NCNE	Pacesetter grain hopper trailer, Shur-Lok roll tarp, 66" sides, new brakes, 11R24.5 tires, one owner
Wilson	43'	2001	G	$19,900	8/06	ECNE	66" sides, air ride, all-aluminum wheels, new brakes
Wilson	48'	1994	G	$22,000	3/06	ECNE	Triple-axle grain trailer
Wilson	Commander	1995	G	$14,500	3/06	NESD	4000 Commander, 43', tandem-axle hopper bottom, 72" sides, ag doors, roll tarp, 24.5 tires
Wilson	Commander	1997	G	$18,000	3/06	NESD	4000 Commander, 43', tandem-axle hopper bottom, 72" sides, ag doors, roll tarp, 24.5 tires
Wilson	Commander	2002	F	$14,000	3/06	NESD	4000 Commander, 21', single-axle hopper bottom, ag doors, roll tarp, 24.5 tires
Wilson	Commander	2003	E	$25,250	2/06	NWOH	41', Shur-Lok tarp, tandem axle, 2-bottom dump
Wilson	DWH400	1995	G	$24,000	9/06	WCND	Tri-axle, rear-axle lift, 46'×96"×84", Sunriser 20" topper, electric lift, spring ride, roll tarp, 11×24.5 on polished aluminums

Grain Vaccums

Make	Model	Year	Cond.	Price	Sale	Location	Comments
Brandt	4500	1996	G	$8,200	3/06	ECND	Cleanup package
Brandt	4500	2001	E	$8,000	3/06	NCND	1,000 PTO, cleanup package, tubing
Brandt	5000	2004	E	$9,750	7/06	SEND	Used very little, only 9 loads, like new
Brandt	5000EX	2005	E	$10,750	12/06	NENE	1,000 PTO, one owner, shedded, used very little
Brandt	5000EX	2005	E	$12,500	4/06	NEND	All accessories including, cleanup kit, less than 2,000 bu. of use, like new
Conveyair	2975	1989	G	$2,300	3/06	NWMN	Tubing for center unload of 27' bins
Conveyair	3000		G	$4,000	4/06	WCMB	Canadian sale
Conveyair	6006		F	$900	7/06	SEND	
Conveyair	955		F	$1,550	11/06	NWMN	Extra pipe, cleanup package
Conveyair	NA	2005	G	$9,000	12/06	WCMN	6" vacuum, 4,000 bu./hr., self-contained hydraulics, silencer, hydraulic boom, air-lock spd. control, anti-plug screen, vacuum gauges
Conveyair	NA	2005	E	$16,000	12/06	SWIA	Ultima 6, cleanup kit, less than 5,000 bu.
DK	466	2004	71 G	$8,500	11/06	ECND	3.0 air lock
Handlair	1400	1985	G	$2,900	3/06	ECND	Flex hose, pipes, 540 PTO, one owner
Handlair	3000		G	$5,000	4/06	SWSD	Pneumatic conveying system, 50' flex & straight pipe, attachments
Handlair	560		G	$4,250	3/06	WCMN	1,000 PTO
Kongskilde	300		F	$700	7/06	SEND	PTO, cleanup package, 540 PTO
Kongskilde	NA		F	$1,500	7/06	NWMN	Cleanup kit, 1,000 PTO, extra pipe
Kongskilde	NA		G	$3,900	2/06	WCIL	Tubing
Neuro	675		G	$2,250	4/06	ECND	540 PTO
REM	1026		F	$2,400	7/06	NWMN	
REM	1026		G	$4,200	12/06	NWIL	1,000 PTO
REM	1026B		G	$4,300	9/06	NCIA	
REM	1026B	2001	G	$6,500	3/06	NEND	Hyd. fold auger, flex, straight and rubber pipe cleanup package
REM	2100		G	$10,500	4/06	SEMN	Canadian sale
REM	2100	2003	G	$5,500	4/06	NWMN	8" tubes
REM	4205		G	$2,200	10/06	SEMN	
REM	552		G	$2,700	9/06	NECO	PTO, extra pipe
REM	552		G	$2,800	10/06	NECO	PTO, new hose
REM	552		G	$3,700	4/06	WCMB	Canadian sale
REM	NA		G	$4,000	4/06	WCSD	
Walinga	510		F	$600	3/06	ECND	Cleanup package
Walinga	510		F	$900	10/06	NCND	
Walinga	510		G	$5,250	3/06	SESD	Standard, precleaner, section of rubber hose flex hose
Walinga	614	1989	G	$5,000	4/06	ECND	Deluxe
Walinga	6614		E	$9,550	9/06	SEIA	
Walinga	714		G	$10,500	1/06	NWIA	Deluxe Agri vacuum, 8" intake, 1,000 PTO, tubes
Walinga	7614	2002	E	$14,000	4/06	NEND	Extra pipe, cleanup package, very little use
Walinga	NA	1999	G	$5,200	6/06	NWMN	5", chrome blower, 2 rubber flex, 2 metal flex pipe sections

Grinder Mixers

Gehl quit making grinder mixers recently. The value of used grinder mixers shot up instantly. When very nice ones show up at auction now, it's Katie, bar the door. Here's proof: The two highest selling New Holland 355 mixers I've seen in the last 10 years. In December 2006 one went for $9,500 in south-central Illinois, the other for $10,000 in March 2007 in northeast Indiana.

WHAT'S IT WORTH?

Grinder Mixers

Make	Model	Year	Cond.	Price	Sale	Location	Comments
Artsway	425A		F	$500	9/06	NEIN	Scales
Artsway	450		G	$2,600	5/06	WCMN	Roller mill, 6-cut, very clean
Bearcat	950		F	$300	1/06	NECO	Hyd. augers, hammer mill
Bearcat	950		F	$800	2/06	NWSD	Grinder-mixer
Bearcat	950		G	$1,400	12/06	SEMN	
Bearcat	950		G	$2,100	2/06	NECO	Hammer mill, hyd. auger
Bearcat	950A		F	$350	2/06	NECO	Hammer mill, hyd. auger
Case IH	1350		F	$2,300	8/06	NWIL	Grinder-mixer mill, scale and auger extension
Farmhand	810		F	$385	9/06	ECNE	
Farmhand	815H		G	$800	12/06	WCIA	No scale
Farmhand	817		G	$1,600	3/06	NCCO	
Farmhand	822		G	$1,000	5/06	SEND	Grinder-mixer mill
Farmhand	822		E	$5,700	1/06	NEIN	Scales
Farmhand	825		G	$950	3/06	WCSD	No scales, always shedded
Farmhand	900B		G	$2,800	1/06	NECO	PTO, single axle
Farmhand	900B		G	$3,000	2/06	NECO	1,000 PTO, hyd. elevator
Farmhand	Feedmaster		F	$500	4/06	SWSD	
Gehl	100		G	$1,200	1/06	NECO	Hyd. augers, hammer mill
Gehl	100		G	$1,300	8/06	NWIL	Auger feeder
Gehl	100		G	$2,800	3/06	ECNE	Hyd. drive, Gehl electronic 3-bar scale
Gehl	100		G	$3,000	3/06	NENE	Grinder-mixer, scale, always shedded
Gehl	100		G	$3,100	11/06	NWMN	Grinder-mixer
Gehl	125		E	$0	12/06	SWWI	No sale at $8,500; wanted $11,750
Gehl	125		G	$4,600	11/06	SWOH	Mix-All
Gehl	125		G	$6,000	12/06	ECNE	Mix-All, 540 PTO, 3-bar scale, Orbit drive augers, magnet auger extension, always shedded, 700E scale
Gehl	125		E	$6,250	2/06	NEIN	Scales, hyd.
Gehl	135		G	$3,000	12/06	WCIA	No scale
Gehl	135		G	$3,200	12/06	ECIL	Mix-All, incline w/ long out auger
Gehl	170		F	$1,600	12/06	ECMO	
Gehl	170		E	$7,900	4/06	NENE	Hyd. driven grinder-mixer, digital scale, auger extension
Gehl	170	2005	E	$16,000	12/06	WCMN	Grinder-mixer
Gehl	55		F	$350	3/06	ECNE	Mix-All, grinder-mixer
Gehl	55		E	$3,500	2/06	SENE	2-ton
Gehl	65		F	$120	9/06	NENE	1,000 PTO, 2 sold – each for $120
Gehl	65		F	$120	9/06	NENE	1,000 PTO
Gehl	95		F	$500	11/06	NWMN	Mix-All, grinder-mixer
Gehl	95		F	$600	2/06	SWIN	
Gehl	95		G	$900	3/06	SEND	
Gehl	95		G	$1,800	4/06	NEND	Mix-All, 21" hammer mill
Gehl	Mix-All		G	$1,200	10/06	SCMI	2 ton
Haybuster	C9		F	$900	4/06	NEND	Tub grinder
Haybuster	H1000		F	$2,600	4/06	SEPA	Bale grinder, PTO
Haybuster	H1000		G	$5,000	11/06	NCKY	Tub grinder
Haybuster	H1000		G	$7,000	1/06	NECO	PTO, tandem axle
Haybuster	H1100		G	$5,200	2/06	NECO	1,000 PTO, hyd. elevator
Haybuster	H1100		G	$6,200	9/06	NECO	Tub grinder, 1,000 PTO, pt, tandem axle
Haybuster	H1100	2002	G	$24,000	3/06	SWNE	Tilt tub grinder, 9.5L-15 tires on walking tandems, ¾" corn screen, one owner

Grinder Mixers

Make	Model	Year	Cond.	Price	Sale	Location	Comments
Haybuster	NA		G	$8,000	3/06	ECMI	Tub grinder, 300 hp., 3406 Cat diesel
Henke	B240		G	$5,250	3/06	NENE	Quick Mixer B240-247 single-axle mixer-feeder wagon, Eaton microprocessor digital scale
Hesston	BP20		F	$2,750	8/06	NWIL	Tub grinder
Hesston	BP25		E	$4,500	12/06	SWWI	Tub grinder
Hesston	BP25		G	$5,000	12/06	NWIL	Tub grinder
IHC	1150		F	$200	12/06	NEMO	
IHC	1150		P	$350	7/06	SEND	Magnet
IHC	1150		G	$450	3/06	NWIL	Scale
IHC	1150		F	$550	11/06	SEIA	
IHC	1250		P	$100	11/06	SCSD	Scale, 540 PTO, unload system needs work
IHC	1250		G	$2,000	3/06	NENE	Scale, shedded
John Deere	400		F	$750	1/06	SESD	Grinder
John Deere	750		G	$1,900	8/06	NCIA	Hyd. auger, Brady grinder-mixer
Knight	2375		G	$3,000	2/06	WCMN	TMR mixer, end scale
Knight	3130		E	$18,000	3/06	WCMN	Real Auggie, TMR mixer
Knight	3300		G	$7,600	1/06	SCMI	Real Auggie mixer, scales
Knight	3575		G	$13,000	9/06	WCWI	Portable TMR, Digistar scale
Lorenz	100		F	$350	2/06	SEIL	
Lorenz	100		G	$2,100	4/06	WCMN	Magnet
NDE	NA	2005	G	$23,750	11/06	SEIA	Tub grinder, #1552
New Holland	350		P	$150	1/06	SCMI	
New Holland	352		F	$300	9/06	NEIN	
New Holland	352		F	$500	11/06	WCSD	
New Holland	352		F	$800	1/06	NEMO	
New Holland	352		G	$1,200	9/06	NEIN	
New Holland	352		G	$1,350	10/06	SEMN	Mill mixer
New Holland	352		G	$1,600	1/06	NEIN	
New Holland	352		G	$2,050	12/06	SEMN	
New Holland	352		G	$2,300	3/06	NEKS	Always shedded
New Holland	354		G	$500	9/06	NEIN	Extended unloading auger
New Holland	354		G	$1,150	3/06	SENE	
New Holland	354		G	$3,500	2/06	WCMN	Scale
New Holland	355		G	$2,100	8/06	SEMN	Mill
New Holland	355		F	$4,250	12/06	SWWI	
New Holland	355		G	$4,300	12/06	SCNE	Shedded, scale, hyd. drive augers
New Holland	355		E	$8,500	3/06	SEND	Feed grinder, electronic scale, like new
New Holland	355		G	$9,500	12/06	SWIL	Grinder-mixer
New Holland	357		P	$75	1/06	SCMI	Feed grinder
New Holland	358		G	$0	12/06	SWWI	No sale at $8,500; wanted $12,000
New Holland	358	1995	G	$10,000	4/06	WCMB	Canadian sale, power bale feeder, hyd. unload, 20' unload auger, bunk feed spout
OMC	420		G	$800	2/06	WCNE	Hammer mill, PTO
OMC	432		G	$900	2/06	NECO	Hyd. auger
OMC	95		F	$70	3/06	ECNE	
OMC	95		G	$500	8/06	ECNE	One owner, shedded
OMC	95		G	$1,250	2/06	NWSD	Grinder-mixer
Oswalt	230		G	$300	9/06	NEIN	TMR mixer, scales
Roto Grind	760		G	$3,500	3/06	NCUT	
Roto Grind	NA	2002	G	$7,250	3/06	ECMI	Burr mill, hd, 10" auger, 3 pt.

Hay Balers

Auction sale prices on round balers seemed to be slightly cheaper in 2006 in states hit by drought conditions, such as South Dakota, western Nebraska, Kansas, Colorado, Wyoming, and Montana. Look at our sale price data on JD 535 round balers to see what I'm talking about. Will used round balers remain depressed in these regions in 2007? Depends on how cooperative Mother Nature is, I guess. We'll see.

Hay Balers

Make	Model	Year	Cond.	Price	Sale	Location	Comments
Case IH	3450	1986	F	$950	3/06	NEKS	Round, midsize, single tie, dual gauge wheels, 540 PTO
Case IH	3650		F	$850	9/06	SCNE	Round
Case IH	3650		F	$950	3/06	NWIL	
Case IH	3650		G	$2,850	4/06	NENE	Soft core big round, shedded
Case IH	8430	1990	E	$3,700	11/06	NEKS	Make 4'×4' bales, weigh 900 lb.
Case IH	8455		F	$2,500	8/06	SEPA	Round, monitor
Case IH	8460		F	$2,500	1/06	SESD	Round, 1991 model
Case IH	8465		F	$3,500	3/06	NEKS	Round, monitor, 31.5-15 tires
Case IH	8480		G	$2,000	5/06	WCMN	Fixed chamber round, 200 bales last summer
Case IH	8480		F	$2,400	8/06	WCMN	Round, 1,000 PTO, belts
Case IH	8480		F	$3,100	1/06	SESD	Round
Case IH	8480	2000	G	$7,000	7/06	SEND	Round
Case IH	8545	1990	G	$6,300	3/06	NCCO	
Case IH	8575		G	$32,000	3/06	SEMN	Silage special, big square, 3'×3'×8' bales, 23,000 bales, SN FH0163791
Case IH	8580		F	$6,000	3/06	NCUT	Big square
Case IH	8580		G	$17,000	3/06	NCUT	Big square
Case IH	8580	1993	F	$7,400	3/06	NWKS	Square, 48" bale length, hyd. bale tension, hyd. pickup lift, less than 50,000 bales, 28L-26 tires
Case IH	8580	1996	G	$23,000	3/06	WCKS	Big square, 34,000 bales
Case IH	8590	1998	G	$30,000	3/06	WCKS	Big square
Case IH	LBX332	2005	G	$45,000	7/06	SEND	Large square, 3×3, rotary cutter, knotter fan, bale eject, hyd. bale chute
Case IH	RBX562		E	$11,500	9/06	NEIA	Round, net wrap
Case IH	RBX562	2003	G	$11,000	4/06	NEND	Round, hyd. pickup, bale kicker
Case IH	RBX562	2004	F	$7,750	12/06	WCMN	Round
Case IH	RS561		F	$6,750	1/06	SESD	Round
Case IH	RS561		G	$9,500	12/06	SEMN	Round, net wrap
Case IH	RS561	2001	G	$7,800	11/06	SCND	Round, auto cycle
Gehl	1460		F	$1,800	3/06	SEPA	1460 TDC, round
Gehl	1475		G	$5,100	3/06	NCMN	Round
Gehl	1600		F	$1,000	12/06	WCMN	Round
Gehl	1870		G	$3,100	12/06	WCMN	Round
Gehl	1870		G	$3,600	10/06	SEMN	Round, new belts, net wrap
Gehl	1875		G	$4,800	12/06	ECMO	Round
Gehl	1875		G	$6,600	12/06	ECIL	1875 TDC, round, auto wrap
Gehl	2500		F	$1,400	11/06	SCND	Twin 18-hp. gas engine, bucket
Gehl	2880		G	$6,700	9/06	NWTN	Round
Hesston	4550		G	$1,600	12/06	NWIL	Little square
Hesston	4550		G	$5,800	12/06	SEMN	Square
Hesston	4590	2002	G	$12,750	2/06	NCCO	
Hesston	4590	2003	G	$11,300	2/06	NCCO	
Hesston	4590	2003	G	$11,700	2/06	NCCO	
Hesston	4600	1984	F	$3,600	1/06	NCCO	
Hesston	4690		G	$8,000	5/06	SCCA	In-line, Deutz 4-cyl. diesel
Hesston	4690		G	$10,500	5/06	SCCA	In-line, Deutz 4-cyl. diesel
Hesston	4755		F	$13,000	3/06	NCUT	
Hesston	4760	2002	G	$41,000	3/06	SEMN	Cutter big square, 3'×3'×8' bale, double auger system, 18,300 bales, SN HK73306

Hay Balers

Make	Model	Year	Cond.	Price	Sale	Location	Comments
Hesston	4790		G	$38,000	11/06	SECA	3×4, roller chutes
Hesston	4790	1999	G	$25,000	5/06	WCMN	3×4 big square, last bale eject, auto lube, 30,000 bales
Hesston	4790	1999	G	$35,000	8/06	WCMN	4×4 baler, auto luber, auto eject, roller chute, 9,730 bales
Hesston	4790	2002	G	$31,000	11/06	SECA	3×4 hay, roller chute
Hesston	4790	2002	G	$31,000	11/06	SECA	3×4 hay, roller chute
Hesston	4790	2003	G	$44,000	3/06	NCCO	3'×4' bales, done 24K bales, cutter attachment, auto lube, moister tester, monitor, 2003 Hesston 4925 accumulator
Hesston	4790	2003	G	$45,000	11/06	SECA	3×4
Hesston	4790	2003	G	$45,000	11/06	SECA	3×4, roller chute
Hesston	4790	2003	G	$45,000	11/06	SECA	3×4, roller chute
Hesston	4790	2004	G	$47,000	11/06	SECA	3×4, roller chute
Hesston	4900		G	$15,000	11/06	SECA	Big
Hesston	4910		G	$33,000	3/06	NCUT	
Hesston	5500		F	$250	4/06	NWSD	
Hesston	5500		G	$2,250	11/06	WCWI	Round, new belts
Hesston	555T		G	$6,250	9/06	NWTN	Round
Hesston	5580		P	$500	1/06	SESD	Round
Hesston	5585		F	$2,500	3/06	ECNE	
Hesston	5585		E	$4,100	2/06	SENE	Round
Hesston	5585	1987	G	$3,000	11/06	NEKS	Round, 540 shear pin, PTO
Hesston	560		G	$1,600	1/06	WCNE	Kicker, monitor
Hesston	560	1989	G	$3,900	11/06	NEKS	Round, self-contained hyd. unit
Hesston	856A		G	$5,200	8/06	NWIL	Wide net wrap
Hesston	856A	2002	G	$9,750	11/06	NEKS	Round, double twine tie, hyd. pickup, bale push bar, bale ramps, gauge wheels, bale counter
Hesston	956A	2004	G	$14,000	12/06	NWIL	
John Deere	100		E	$18,000	3/06	NEKS	3'×3' bales
John Deere	100		F	$18,500	3/06	SEPA	Big square, applicator, monitor, 11,400 bales
John Deere	326		F	$2,750	2/06	NEIA	
John Deere	327		E	$4,000	2/06	NEIA	Very nice
John Deere	328		G	$7,000	2/06	ECMN	40 ejector
John Deere	328	2005	G	$11,000	2/06	SCMI	Less than 2,000 bales
John Deere	337		G	$3,000	7/06	ECIL	Wire hay
John Deere	338		E	$9,000	3/06	NWIL	5,000 bales
John Deere	338		E	$15,000	4/06	SEMI	JD 40-lb. thrower
John Deere	346		G	$1,975	2/06	NECO	PTO, twine tie, pt
John Deere	346		F	$2,150	3/06	SWOH	PTO
John Deere	346		G	$2,400	3/06	NWOH	Twine
John Deere	346		G	$2,450	2/06	NECO	PTO, small square, twine tire
John Deere	346		F	$3,600	2/06	NCCO	
John Deere	346		E	$7,500	11/06	SENE	Like new, shedded, one owner, twin tie
John Deere	348		G	$6,800	12/06	ECIL	Wire
John Deere	348		E	$8,900	8/06	ECNE	Small square, hyd. tension, Farmhand accumulator
John Deere	348		G	$9,000	3/06	ECIL	Square wire tie, Harvest Tec Model 443
John Deere	348	2003	G	$9,000	2/06	NCCO	
John Deere	375		F	$5,750	5/06	WCMN	Round
John Deere	375	1991	G	$3,650	12/06	ECMO	Round
John Deere	385		G	$5,100	3/06	NENE	Big round
John Deere	430		G	$7,700	2/06	NEIA	Round, twine

Hay Balers

Make	Model	Year	Cond.	Price	Sale	Location	Comments
John Deere	446		E	$5,000	8/06	SCMI	Round, 4×4 bales, very little use
John Deere	457		G	$12,000	2/06	WCIA	MegaTooth pickup, surface wrap
John Deere	457	2004	E	$18,000	3/06	NWOH	Round, edge net wrap
John Deere	466		G	$6,300	8/06	SETN	Round
John Deere	466		F	$7,600	3/06	SEPA	Round, monitor
John Deere	466		G	$9,200	9/06	NEIA	Round, net wrap, MegaTooth, variable core, converging wheels, kick bar
John Deere	467	2002	G	$14,400	11/06	NEKS	Round, MegaTooth, wide pickup, bale push bar, bale ramps, gauge wheels, bale counter
John Deere	510		F	$500	9/06	NECO	Round, hyd. tie
John Deere	510		F	$600	8/06	SEMN	Round
John Deere	510		F	$650	1/06	SESD	Round
John Deere	510		F	$700	3/06	SEIA	Round
John Deere	510		F	$750	1/06	SESD	Round
John Deere	510		F	$900	11/06	NWMN	Round
John Deere	510		F	$950	7/06	WCMN	Round
John Deere	510		F	$1,100	1/06	SESD	Round
John Deere	530		G	$2,800	8/06	NEKS	Round, hay saver wheels, 31-13.5 tires, 540 PTO
John Deere	530		F	$2,950	12/06	NWIL	Round
John Deere	530		G	$3,000	11/06	SWIA	Round, new belts & monitor
John Deere	530		G	$3,500	9/06	NEIA	Round
John Deere	530		G	$4,000	12/06	WCIL	Large round, one owner, always shedded
John Deere	535		F	$4,400	11/06	SCNE	Round, kicker
John Deere	535		G	$4,600	3/06	WCKS	Round, monitor
John Deere	535		G	$4,600	9/06	NEIA	Round
John Deere	535		F	$4,700	1/06	SESD	Round
John Deere	535		F	$5,000	8/06	NECO	Round
John Deere	535		G	$5,250	8/06	SCNE	Round
John Deere	535		F	$5,250	1/06	SESD	Round
John Deere	535		F	$5,300	8/06	NECO	Round, gathering wheels
John Deere	535		F	$5,900	1/06	NCCO	Round
John Deere	535		G	$6,600	11/06	WCSD	Round monitor, Tucker wheels, new style belts
John Deere	535		G	$7,800	1/06	NEIN	Round
John Deere	535		G	$9,500	4/06	WCMB	Canadian sale, round, heavy silage belt lacing, Gandy applicator
John Deere	535		G	$10,000	8/06	NCIA	Round, mesh wrap, rebuilt
John Deere	535		G	$10,500	2/06	NWSD	Round, monitor, stored inside
John Deere	535		G	$10,600	11/06	SCNE	Round, kicker
John Deere	535	1989	F	$3,800	11/06	NEKS	Round, 540 slip clutch PTO, surface wrap, bale push bar
John Deere	535	1989	G	$5,250	12/06	NWMO	Round, converging wheels, kicker, net wrap
John Deere	535	1991	F	$2,000	3/06	NWKS	Round
John Deere	535	1992	F	$2,900	3/06	NWKS	Round
John Deere	535	1993	F	$5,200	8/06	WCMN	Round, push bar, hyd. lift pickup, 6,300 bales
John Deere	535	1994	G	$6,000	11/06	NEKS	Round, double twine tie, 540 slip clutch PTO
John Deere	535	1996	E	$10,200	3/06	SEND	Round, bale monitor, auto tie, bale kicker
John Deere	566		F	$7,350	8/06	NECO	Round
John Deere	566		G	$8,750	2/06	SWNE	Big round, 540 PTO, gauge wheels
John Deere	566		G	$10,250	9/06	NEIA	Round, net wrap, hyd. pickup, kick bar, oiler
John Deere	566		G	$12,200	9/06	NEIA	Round, net wrap, moisture kit, new belts

Hay Balers

Make	Model	Year	Cond.	Price	Sale	Location	Comments
John Deere	566	1997	G	$7,300	11/06	NEKS	Round, 540 PTO, gauge wheels
John Deere	566	1997	G	$10,200	12/06	NWMO	Round, 540, wrap, kicker, converging wheels, 8,200 bales
John Deere	566	1997	G	$11,000	5/06	WCMN	Round, monitor
John Deere	566	1998	G	$10,400	12/06	ECMO	Round, monitor, regular pickup, surface wrap, push bar
John Deere	566	1999	G	$9,900	12/06	NWMO	Round, 540, wrap, kicker, converging wheels
John Deere	566	1999	G	$10,000	3/06	SWKS	Big round, 1,000 PTO, MegaTooth pickup, converging wheels
John Deere	566	1999	G	$11,000	3/06	NEKS	Round, MegaTooth
John Deere	567		G	$12,000	9/06	NEIA	Round, net wrap, MegaTooth, hyd. pickup, variable core, 1,000 PTO
John Deere	567		G	$12,250	9/06	NEIA	Round, net wrap, MegaTooth, hyd. pickup, variable core, moisture kit, 540 PTO
John Deere	567		F	$15,000	3/06	NCUT	Round
John Deere	567		F	$15,500	1/06	SESD	Round, 2002 model
John Deere	567		G	$22,000	4/06	WCWI	Round, silage, MegaWide pickup, cover edge net wrap
John Deere	567		G	$25,600	1/06	SWNE	MegaWide round, 2,500 bales, net wrap, monitor
John Deere	567	2001	G	$12,000	11/06	NEKS	MegaTooth round, electric double twine tie, 1,000 slip clutch PTO, hyd. pickup
John Deere	567	2001	G	$12,900	11/06	NEKS	MegaTooth round, double twine tie, 540 slip clutch PTO, hyd. pickup
John Deere	567	2001	G	$14,000	8/06	SCNE	Round, 1,000 PTO, bale kicker
John Deere	567	2002	G	$12,600	11/06	NEKS	MegaWide round bale, 540 PTO, gauge wheels
John Deere	567	2002	G	$15,100	12/06	NWMO	Round, net wrap, MegaWide, hyd. pickup, 7,400 bales
John Deere	567	2002	G	$17,000	2/06	SENE	Round, 10,497 bales, cover edge net wrap, 1,000 PTO, 41-13.50-15 flotation tires, Heartland 669 stalk chopper
John Deere	567	2002	G	$19,100	1/06	SESD	Round, net wrap
John Deere	567	2003	G	$20,750	3/06	SWKS	MegaWide, 1,000 PTO, net wrap
John Deere	567	2004	G	$17,500	12/06	SWIA	MegaWide round, hyd. pickup,-JD monitor, no kicker, 2,420 bales
John Deere	567	2006	E	$24,000	8/06	NEIA	Round, net, only 310 bales
John Deere	567	2006	E	$28,250	12/06	WCMN	Round, cover edge, MegaWide, net wrap, Harvest Tec preservative applicator, 1,207 bales
Krone	KR260		G	$1,750	8/06	SEPA	Round, monitor
New Holland	270		F	$250	10/06	SEMN	
New Holland	270		F	$300	9/06	SCMN	
New Holland	273		F	$440	8/06	SWWI	Thrower
New Holland	273		G	$850	1/06	WCNE	PTO, tie
New Holland	273		F	$950	3/06	SEPA	Thrower
New Holland	273		G	$1,300	3/06	ECMI	Square
New Holland	273		F	$1,300	5/06	SEWI	Thrower
New Holland	273		F	$1,300	1/06	SWNE	Square
New Holland	273		F	$2,000	2/06	SWPA	
New Holland	273		G	$2,800	3/06	NWIL	
New Holland	276		F	$700	1/06	NEIN	
New Holland	276		F	$900	1/06	NEIN	
New Holland	276		G	$1,000	1/06	NECO	PTO, pt
New Holland	276		F	$1,550	7/06	ECND	Square
New Holland	276		G	$1,600	2/06	NECO	PTO, pt, twine
New Holland	276		G	$1,850	3/06	SEND	Square, hyd. tension

Hay Balers

Make	Model	Year	Cond.	Price	Sale	Location	Comments
New Holland	276	1974	G	$1,700	3/06	NCCO	
New Holland	278		F	$750	5/06	WCMN	Small square
New Holland	278		G	$3,000	2/06	SENE	Hayliner, twine tie, 31-13.50-15 flotation tires
New Holland	311		G	$3,000	4/06	SCMN	Chute, nice
New Holland	311		E	$3,250	12/06	SWWI	Chute
New Holland	311		G	$4,200	12/06	WCMI	
New Holland	311		F	$5,100	3/06	SEPA	Hayliner, kicker
New Holland	315		G	$1,600	2/06	NECO	
New Holland	315		G	$2,500	10/06	NCWI	Kicker
New Holland	315		G	$2,700	3/06	WCMN	Square
New Holland	315		G	$2,900	12/06	SWIL	Square
New Holland	315	1980	F	$3,500	2/06	SCNY	#70 thrower
New Holland	320		G	$1,000	1/06	WCNE	Twine
New Holland	320		G	$2,400	1/06	NCIL	Square
New Holland	320		F	$3,800	1/06	NCCO	
New Holland	326		F	$1,100	1/06	WCTX	
New Holland	425		G	$4,200	4/06	WCMT	425T small square, 16×18" bales, PTO drive, hyd. tension, bale turn chute
New Holland	565		G	$5,750	2/06	SWIN	
New Holland	565		G	$6,700	12/06	SEMN	Square
New Holland	570		E	$8,000	12/06	SWWI	Thrower, very nice
New Holland	575	1992	G	$6,500	3/06	NEMI	Square, auto applicator
New Holland	590		E	$33,500	2/06	NCIL	Big square, applicator, like new
New Holland	590	1997	G	$20,000	2/06	WCMN	3×3 square, Knotter fans, bale ejector, roller chute
New Holland	630		G	$5,000	12/06	SWWI	Round, twine only
New Holland	630		E	$5,100	6/06	NCPA	Round, paint still on pickup
New Holland	638	1999	G	$7,400	1/06	SCMI	Round
New Holland	644		G	$6,750	4/06	SWIN	Round, auto wrap, hay savers
New Holland	644		G	$9,800	8/06	NCMI	Round, 4'×5', silage special, net wrap, cab controls
New Holland	644	1998	G	$15,000	3/06	NEMI	Silage special round, 4'×5' bales, net wrap, Bale Command controls, chemical applicator
New Holland	648		F	$2,800	3/06	NCUT	Round, auto wrap
New Holland	648		G	$6,250	9/06	NWTN	Round
New Holland	650		G	$4,900	12/06	NWIL	Round
New Holland	654		G	$5,300	9/06	NWTN	Round
New Holland	654		G	$12,600	3/06	ECIL	Round, wrap and twine and Bale Command
New Holland	660		F	$2,100	3/06	NCUT	Round, surface wrap
New Holland	660		F	$2,900	12/06	ECMO	Round
New Holland	660		F	$3,200	3/06	NCUT	Round, auto wrap
New Holland	660		F	$4,300	3/06	ECKS	Round
New Holland	660		F	$4,500	8/06	NECO	Round
New Holland	660		G	$5,600	10/06	NCND	Round, auto wrap
New Holland	660		F	$8,000	1/06	SWNE	Auto wrap, round
New Holland	664		G	$8,700	4/06	NWSD	Round, endless belts, auto wrap, 540 PTO
New Holland	664	1996	F	$3,500	11/06	NEKS	Round, auto wrap, gauge wheels
New Holland	664	1997	G	$8,700	1/06	SESD	Round, net wrap, 2,500 bales
New Holland	664	1998	G	$11,000	4/06	WCMT	Round, dual pickup gauge wheels, hyd. pickup lift, gathering wheels, Bale Command monitor, net wrap, twine tie, makes 5'×6' bale, 6,315 total bales, very nice

Hay Balers

Make	Model	Year	Cond.	Price	Sale	Location	Comments
New Holland	688		P	$400	5/06	SEND	Auto wrap, for parts, fire damage
New Holland	688		G	$7,500	8/06	SCNE	Round
New Holland	688		G	$7,500	12/06	SWWI	Round, twine only
New Holland	688		F	$10,750	12/06	SEMN	Round, net wrap
New Holland	688		G	$13,500	12/06	SEMN	Round, net wrap
New Holland	688		G	$14,500	12/06	SEMN	Round, net wrap
New Holland	688		E	$15,250	2/06	ECNE	Round, moisture tester
New Holland	688		G	$18,000	3/06	WCMN	Large round, net wrap or twine, endless belts, gathering wheels, in-feed disk, rubber back wrap roles, expeller kit, 1,000 PTO
New Holland	688		E	$22,500	9/06	WCNE	Round, two or three years old, like new
New Holland	688	2000	G	$6,050	12/06	ECMO	Round
New Holland	688	2000	G	$9,000	2/06	WCNE	Round, auto wrap, 1,000 PTO
New Holland	688	2000	G	$12,750	11/06	WCMN	Round, net wrap
New Holland	688	2001	G	$14,500	4/06	WCMB	Canadian sale, Bale Command, 4,000 bales
New Holland	845		F	$2,500	2/06	SWPA	Round
New Holland	846		F	$1,300	3/06	SEPA	Round
New Holland	846		F	$1,600	8/06	NWIL	Round
New Holland	849		G	$1,250	9/06	NWTN	Round
New Holland	850		F	$400	1/06	WCNE	Round , electric twine
New Holland	850		F	$600	3/06	NWIL	
New Holland	850		F	$650	7/06	ECND	Round
New Holland	850		F	$1,050	3/06	SWOH	Round, PTO
New Holland	850		F	$1,050	6/06	SEND	PTO, round
New Holland	851		P	$100	3/06	NWKS	Round, hyd. twine, 540 PTO
New Holland	851		F	$400	3/06	ECNE	Round
New Holland	851		F	$400	4/06	WCSD	Round
New Holland	851		F	$500	12/06	ECMO	Round
New Holland	851		F	$600	11/06	NEKS	Round, 1,000 PTO, gauge wheels
New Holland	851		F	$700	7/06	SEND	Round
New Holland	851		G	$700	9/06	NEIN	Round
New Holland	851		F	$825	4/06	SWSD	Round
New Holland	851		F	$875	5/06	SEND	Round
New Holland	851		F	$975	3/06	NWIL	
New Holland	851		G	$1,050	9/06	NWTN	Round
New Holland	851		F	$1,300	8/06	NEIA	Round
New Holland	852		F	$700	9/06	NWIL	Round
New Holland	853		G	$3,000	3/06	NWIL	
New Holland	853		G	$3,850	9/06	NWTN	Round
New Holland	853	1986	G	$1,075	12/06	ECMO	Round
New Holland	855		F	$500	3/06	NWKS	Round, 1,000 PTO
New Holland	855		F	$850	1/06	SESD	Round
New Holland	855		G	$1,100	9/06	NECO	Round, auto tie, bale bumper
New Holland	855		G	$1,100	1/06	WCNE	Kicker, monitor
New Holland	855		F	$1,500	6/06	SWMN	Round
New Holland	855		G	$1,500	11/06	SCSD	Round
New Holland	855		G	$1,550	12/06	ECMO	Round, automatic oiler
New Holland	855		G	$2,000	2/06	NCKS	Round
New Holland	855		G	$2,900	12/06	SWIL	Round

Hay Balers

Make	Model	Year	Cond.	Price	Sale	Location	Comments
New Holland	855		G	$3,150	3/06	NEKS	Round, auto wrap
New Holland	855		G	$3,500	2/06	SWIN	Large round, kicker, monitor
New Holland	855		G	$3,500	3/06	SWIN	Round, kicker
New Holland	BB940	2001	G	$37,000	2/06	SENE	Square, Harvest Tec 4464 monitor, crop cutter, 6-knife crop cutting system, inoculators, auto lube, 14,426 bales, one owner
New Holland	BR740		G	$14,000	3/06	SEPA	400 bales, monitor, extra sweep
New Holland	BR780		E	$11,250	2/06	WCNE	Round, 4,419 bales, gathering wheels, net & twine wrap
New Holland	BR780	2003	G	$11,000	12/06	ECMO	Round, monitor, auto wrap, gauge wheels, bale ramp, regular pickup
New Holland	BR780	2003	G	$16,700	8/06	NEIA	Round, 6,000 bales
New Holland	BR780	2004	E	$16,500	6/06	NWSD	Round, monitor, auto wrap, only 3,000 bales through it, extra sweep
New Holland	BR940	2002	G	$38,000	2/06	WCMN	3×3 square, Knotter fans, bale eject
New Holland	D2000		G	$9,750	1/06	SESD	Large square, 14,000 bales
New Idea	456		P	$150	3/06	SEIA	Round
New Idea	456		F	$600	1/06	SESD	Round
New Idea	484		G	$2,600	8/06	SETN	Round, 5×4 bale size
New Idea	486		F	$750	1/06	SESD	Round
New Idea	4865		G	$3,500	3/06	NEKS	
New Idea	4865		G	$7,000	8/06	NWIL	Net wrap
New Idea	571		G	$1,775	12/06	NWIL	Square, kicker
New Idea	571		G	$2,500	3/06	NWIL	
OMC	595		F	$600	3/06	WCSD	Roll, bales weighed 1,200-1,300 lb.
OMC	NA		F	$450	10/06	NCND	Round, drum style, 1,100-lb. bale size
Vermeer	504I		G	$3,550	8/06	NCOH	Silage, round, monitor
Vermeer	505I		G	$2,500	3/06	NENE	Round, Tucker wheels, monitor, always shedded, one owner
Vermeer	5500	2004	G	$9,600	12/06	NWMO	Round, twine, gather, hyd. pickup, 81 bales
Vermeer	554XL		G	$9,500	12/06	SEMN	Round, Accu-Tie
Vermeer	605		F	$725	4/06	SCMN	Round
Vermeer	605C		P	$200	3/06	NEKS	Round, rough
Vermeer	605F		P	$175	9/06	SCNE	Round
Vermeer	605F		F	$550	11/06	SCND	Round
Vermeer	605F		F	$650	11/06	NEKS	Round
Vermeer	605F		G	$1,500	12/06	NEMO	Large round, gathering wheels, 540 PTO
Vermeer	605F		G	$1,500	12/06	NEMO	Large round
Vermeer	605F		G	$2,750	1/06	NEMO	Large round
Vermeer	605F	1991	F	$700	7/06	SEND	Round
Vermeer	605J		F	$1,750	8/06	SCNE	Round, kicker wheels
Vermeer	605J		F	$2,700	1/06	SESD	Round
Vermeer	605J		F	$3,600	8/06	NECO	Round
Vermeer	605K		G	$5,000	12/06	SEMN	Round
Vermeer	605L		F	$2,700	3/06	NWIL	
Vermeer	605M	2005	E	$26,000	8/06	ECIA	Big round, like new, had only done 175 bales
Vermeer	605 Super J		G	$2,300	10/06	SEMN	Round

Loaders

You've been to sales, you've seen it firsthand. What? The hunger buyers have for acquiring good-quality used loaders. There's an old rule in the auction biz: even when the farm economy is tough, good-quality used equipment selling for under $10,000 will still be in high demand. Used loaders are the perfect example.

Loaders

Make	Model	Year	Cond.	Price	Sale	Location	Comments
Allis-Chalmers	500		G	$1,850	12/06	SEIA	
Allied	580		G	$2,700	9/06	SEIA	Hyd., 10-20 Series mounts
Allied	595		G	$3,000	3/06	WCMN	Hyd., 7' bucket
Allied	595		G	$3,400	9/06	NCIA	84" quart bucket, like new
Allied	794		G	$2,550	1/06	NEIN	8' bucket, quick-tach
Allied	795		G	$5,000	8/06	WCIA	Case mounts
Case IH	710		G	$4,500	10/06	NCND	Grapple
Case IH	710	1993	G	$3,200	7/06	SEND	Front mounted
Case IH	890	1998	E	$6,700	12/06	WCIA	Like new, 96" bucket, Case IH 7230, mounts
Case IH	NA		G	$450	5/06	SCMI	8' tine bucket for 655 loader
Dual	215		G	$2,700	4/06	NEND	Woods dual 215, quick-tach, 84" bucket, 4-tine grapple, Case IH Maxxum mounts
Dual	300		G	$1,500	2/06	NCCO	Grapple
Dual	3100		G	$3,000	8/06	NECO	
Dual	320		F	$700	7/06	SEND	
Dual	320		F	$800	2/06	NECO	5' bucket, grapple, control
Dual	320		G	$900	8/06	ECNE	Front mount, 5' bucket, grapple fork, 540 PTO
Dual	320		G	$1,900	4/06	NEND	Hyd., 6' bucket, grapple
Dual	325		G	$1,325	3/06	ECNE	6' bucket
Dual	340		G	$1,000	9/06	NECO	JD 3010 mounts, pump controls
Dual	340		G	$1,100	3/06	ECNE	Hyd. front end, 7' bucket
Dual	350		F	$700	5/06	SEND	Bucket, grapple fork, PTO pump
Farmhand	258		G	$1,800	11/06	WCMN	Grapple
Farmhand	520		G	$1,600	11/06	SCND	F520
Farmhand	F10		F	$200	11/06	SCNE	
Farmhand	F10		G	$600	11/06	SCNE	
Farmhand	F11		F	$225	5/06	SEND	Bucket, grapple fork, PTO pump
Farmhand	F11		F	$650	2/06	NECO	Pump, controls
Farmhand	F11		F	$750	9/06	NECO	Pump, controls
Farmhand	F11		F	$750	9/06	NECO	3-spool controls, pump
Farmhand	F11		G	$1,175	2/06	WCNE	Pump, controls, 5' dirt bucket
Farmhand	F11		G	$4,000	3/06	ECND	
Farmhand	F235		F	$1,350	7/06	SEND	Grapple, cab controls, quick-tach bucket
Farmhand	XL1140		G	$5,700	1/06	SCNE	High-lift front end, 8' bucket, grapple fork, pallet fork, 2-prong bale spear, 3-way valve, quick-tach
Farmhand	XL7440		G	$3,500	3/06	NCWI	Fully hyd. quick-tach, quick-tach buckets
Great Bend	900		G	$1,000	3/06	ECND	HiMaster, 8' bucket
Great Bend	900		G	$1,250	6/06	NECO	HiMaster, 7' grapple bucket
Great Bend	900		G	$1,600	7/06	NWIL	6' bucket
IHC	2000		G	$1,000	8/06	NEIA	7' bucket
IHC	2350		G	$1,700	11/06	WCMN	
IHC	2350		F	$1,800	3/06	SEPA	
IHC	2350		G	$2,000	9/06	SCMN	Full hyd.
IHC	2350		G	$2,500	2/06	WCMN	
John Deere	148		F	$1,900	4/06	WCWI	Bucket
John Deere	148		G	$2,000	3/06	NCCO	
John Deere	148		G	$3,000	2/06	WCMN	
John Deere	148		G	$3,200	2/06	NCIL	
John Deere	148		G	$3,250	3/06	ECND	Mounts for JD 4020

Loaders

Make	Model	Year	Cond.	Price	Sale	Location	Comments
John Deere	148		G	$3,400	9/06	NCIA	
John Deere	148		E	$3,750	11/06	NEIA	Like new
John Deere	148		G	$3,900	9/06	NENE	6' bucket, no grapple
John Deere	148		G	$4,225	2/06	WCIL	6' bucket
John Deere	158		G	$2,400	2/06	NWIN	
John Deere	158		G	$2,800	4/06	NEND	8' bucket
John Deere	158		G	$3,250	3/06	NEND	7' bucket, grapple
John Deere	158		E	$4,300	6/06	ECND	4-tine grapple, 8' bucket, JD controls
John Deere	158		H	$4,500	8/06	SCMN	120" bucket, fits JD 20/40 Series
John Deere	158		G	$4,700	8/06	ECNE	7' bucket, used very little
John Deere	158		G	$5,000	12/06	NWIL	
John Deere	158	1991	G	$5,100	3/06	NWMN	Joystick control
John Deere	168		F	$2,200	3/06	NWKS	Bucket
John Deere	168		G	$5,500	11/06	SCNE	Front mount, 8' bucket
John Deere	245		G	$2,250	5/06	WCMN	
John Deere	260		G	$1,800	3/06	SEPA	Bucket, forks
John Deere	260		G	$4,000	8/06	SCNE	8' bucket, 30 Series mounts
John Deere	260		F	$4,100	1/06	NCCO	Quick-tach brackets
John Deere	265		G	$4,700	12/06	ECMO	Self-leveling, joystick, independent valve, frames to fit 30-55 Series JD row crop tractor
John Deere	265		G	$4,800	3/06	NCCO	Brackets
John Deere	280		E	$5,650	3/06	NEKS	
John Deere	48		F	$700	8/06	NWIL	
John Deere	48		G	$1,400	8/06	SWWI	All hyd.
John Deere	58		G	$1,200	12/06	SEND	Mounts, controls
John Deere	58		G	$1,700	3/06	NEKS	
John Deere	620		G	$2,900	2/06	WCMN	
John Deere	640		P	$3,750	8/06	SCNE	Self-leveling, 72" bucket, rough
John Deere	720		G	$4,300	3/06	SCIA	7,000 mountings
John Deere	720		G	$7,100	4/06	WCMN	Joystick, 8' bucket, grapple, to fit JD 4450 on same sale
John Deere	720	1993	G	$5,500	1/06	SCKS	7' bucket, one owner, quick-tach coupler
John Deere	725		G	$5,000	1/06	NECO	Bucket, grapple
John Deere	725		G	$5,000	2/06	WCIL	84" hd material bucket, off JD 4230, brackets will fit JD 3020-4455 tractors
John Deere	725		G	$5,400	3/06	ECMI	Hyd., bale forks, quick-tach material bucket
John Deere	725		G	$5,500	11/06	SCNE	Bucket, grapple fork
John Deere	740		P	$2,750	8/06	SCNE	Front end, rough
John Deere	740		G	$5,200	1/06	WCNE	JD mounts, grapple
John Deere	740		E	$7,000	3/06	SEIA	Joystick, 7' bucket
John Deere	740	1993	G	$5,500	7/06	SEND	Self-leveling, high lift, grapple, 8' bucket, joystick controls
John Deere	746		G	$6,000	4/06	SEPA	Material bucket
John Deere	840		G	$7,500	12/06	SCMN	Off JD 8000 Series tractor
John Deere	840		E	$9,000	3/06	SEMN	98" bucket, quick-tach, looks new
John Deere	840		E	$9,000	2/06	ECMN	Self-leveling, 9' bucket, one owner
Koyker	565		G	$2,500	8/06	ECNE	Quick-tach front-mount loader, 7' bucket, grapple fork, tractor hydraulics, pallet forks sold separate for $450
Koyker	K5		G	$600	4/06	NWMN	Mounts for JD
Koyker	K5		G	$800	4/06	ECND	Mounts for JD 4020, joystick control
Koyker	K5		G	$1,200	11/06	SCNE	JD 4020 mounts, bucket & bale lift attachment

Loaders

Make	Model	Year	Cond.	Price	Sale	Location	Comments
Koyker	K5		G	$1,800	3/06	ECNE	Front mount, 8' bucket, manure teeth, bale spear
Koyker	K5		G	$1,900	11/06	ECNE	Quick-tach, tractor mounts for JD 3010 to JD 50 & 55 Series tractors up to 160 hp.
Koyker	K5		G	$2,300	9/06	ECNE	Quick-tach, 7' bucket, grapple fork
Koyker	K7		F	$950	7/06	WCMN	Cat cutting edge, fits large-frame tractors, green
Koyker	Super K		G	$1,000	8/06	NEKS	
Leon	636		G	$1,000	8/06	WCMN	Came off IHC 1086 tractor
Leon	790		G	$2,450	12/06	SEMN	IHC mounts
New Holland	7314		G	$2,600	11/06	WCMN	9' bucket, demo unit, very nice
Schwartz	2070		G	$1,750	2/06	NECO	7' bucket, grapple
Westendorf	TA 26	2004	E	$3,300	8/06	ECIA	Same as new, 84" bucket, JD mountings
Westendorf	TA 28		E	$3,250	12/06	SWWI	
Westendorf	TA 28		G	$3,800	8/06	SEMN	
Westendorf	TA 45		E	$4,500	1/06	NWIA	7' bucket, IH mounts
Westendorf	TA 46		G	$4,250	3/06	NENE	Quick-tach, joystick, bucket, grapple fork (AC 8010 tractor mountings)
Westendorf	WL 21		G	$1,500	12/06	NWIL	
Westendorf	WL 22		F	$1,100	8/06	SEMN	
Westendorf	WL 42		G	$2,700	3/06	NENE	Quick-tach, 7' bucket
Westendorf	WL 42		E	$3,375	11/06	NEKS	7' bucket, 7' dozer blade
Westendorf	WL 42			$4,000	8/06	SWIA	7' bucket, quick-tach
Woods	315		E	$3,400	3/06	ECND	Quick-tach, 8' bucket, grapple, joystick control

Notes

Manure Equipment

My wife, who is not a farm girl, has always gotten a kick out of seeing "manure pump" on sale bills on my messy desk. Me? Hey, it doesn't matter what the thing is to me. If it sells on an auction and we can get a sale price on it, we are happy to bring you the facts in *What's it Worth?*

Manure Pumps

Make	Model	Year	Cond.	Price	Sale	Location	Comments
Balzer	NA		G	$3,400	3/06	SWMN	Hyd. tilt
Better Bilt	NA		G	$900	3/06	NENE	PTO drive turban
Dry Hill	NA		E	$9,600	2/06	SCNY	40'
Houle	NA		G	$4,000	4/06	WCWI	3 pt. pit pump
Huskee	NA		G	$600	10/06	SEMN	Pit pump
N-Tech	NA		G	$1,000	4/06	WCWI	Lagoon pump
Van Dale	NA		G	$2,500	10/06	SEMN	Pit pump

Manure Spreaders

Make	Model	Year	Cond.	Price	Sale	Location	Comments
Allis-Chalmers	NA		F	$500	6/06	SEND	Single axle, PTO, single beater
Badger	12500		F	$1,275	3/06	SWOH	Tandem wheel, 3,150 bu., liquid spreader
Badger	12500		F	$4,500	3/06	SEPA	12500L, tandem axle
Badger	BN102-10		F	$100	3/06	WCMN	Manure agitator, pump
Badger	NA		P	$575	4/06	WCWI	Manure tank, salvage
Balzer	NA		F	$600	3/06	NEKS	Honey wagon
Better-Bilt	1,000 gal.		G	$2,700	4/06	NENE	Slurry tank
Better-Bilt	1,500 gal.		F	$900	3/06	NEKS	Single axle, honey wagon, 540 PTO
Better-Bilt	1100		F	$1,350	5/06	SCMI	Liquid tank, single axle
Better-Bilt	2,500 gal.		F	$1,100	2/06	NECO	
Better-Bilt	2100		F	$600	3/06	NCIA	Liquid spreader, pump, 23.1-26 tires
Better-Bilt	3400	1997	G	$11,500	3/06	NENE	Tandem axle, honey wagon, liquid manure cart, 6" intake, hyd. drive vacuum pump, 4-shank rear injector, one owner
Calumet	4,500 gal.		G	$2,600	3/06	SWMN	Tandem manure tank spreader
Case IH	575		G	$4,800	5/06	SEND	Tandem-axle spreader, single beater
Clay	1,500 gal.		G	$1,150	8/06	WCIA	Honey wagon
Clay	3,200 gal.		F	$1,000	3/06	WCMN	Custom-built manure tank, oscillating tandem axles
Clay	3000		F	$1,550	3/06	WCMN	Slurry model, hyd. drive, oscillating tandems
Dual	600		G	$1,100	2/06	NECO	PTO, pt
Dual	600		G	$1,900	12/06	SCNE	Tandem axle
Dual	600		G	$2,400	2/06	WCNE	Tandem, PTO, new floor
Farmhand	440		G	$1,150	1/06	WCNE	PTO, truck frame, pt
Farmhand	450		G	$1,000	5/06	SEND	Power wagon tandem spreader
Farmhand	450		G	$2,500	7/06	SEND	Manure spreader
Farmhand	NA		F	$210	2/06	WCNE	Power box, 12'×6', pt, walking
Farmhand	NA		F	$1,150	3/06	NCCO	Power box spreader
Frontier	MS 1117		E	$3,700	8/06	NECO	New, demo
Fruehauf	8,000 gal.	1970	F	$4,500	3/06	ECMI	Aluminum tanker trailer, 3×9 spread manure, equipped, axle needs repair
Gehl	250		F	$700	5/06	SWWI	
Gehl	312		F	$700	1/06	NEMO	Scavenger manure spreader
Gehl	312		G	$1,200	6/06	NCPA	
Gehl	315		F	$250	9/06	SCMN	Scavenger
Gehl	325		G	$2,000	9/06	SCMN	Tandem, poly floor, gate
Gehl	425		G	$2,650	9/06	SCMN	Tandem, hyd. gate
H&S	125		G	$4,000	11/06	SECA	
H&S	1800		F	$300	9/06	SCMN	Tandem auger spreader
H&S	310		G	$2,200	2/06	WCMN	Manure spreader, tandem, new gear box, beaters

WHAT'S IT WORTH?

Manure Spreaders

Make	Model	Year	Cond.	Price	Sale	Location	Comments
H&S	310		G	$5,100	11/06	NCKY	Tandem spreader
H&S	3302		G	$5,400	3/06	NEMI	Tandem V-bottom, rear discharge
H&S	370		G	$3,000	9/06	WCOH	Dual axle
H&S	370		G	$8,200	12/06	SEMN	
H&S	NA		G	$1,400	6/06	SWMN	Slush gate
Hesston	5431		G	$8,200	4/06	WCWI	
Houle	6000	2001	E	$26,000	5/06	SCMI	Tandem liquid manure tank, 4-shank injector
Houle	7,500 gal.	2003	G	$39,000	3/06	ECMI	Steerable triaxle, super manure tanker, injectors
IHC	155		G	$975	9/06	NEIN	
IHC	530		G	$2,250	11/06	SWOH	PTO drive
IHC	540		F	$550	9/06	NECO	PTO, pt
IHC	560		G	$2,400	3/06	ECNE	Single axle, bought new
John Deere	450		G	$2,600	3/06	NWIL	
John Deere	455		F	$2,350	1/06	SEPA	Hyd. feed and end gate, steel bad
John Deere	54		F	$45	5/06	SWWI	Spreader, wood hauler
John Deere	54		G	$700	3/06	NCIL	PTO
John Deere	54		G	$2,500	2/06	ECMN	Single-axle spreader, Gratz chain
John Deere	660		G	$2,750	3/06	SEND	Tandem axle
John Deere	680		F	$1,200	7/06	WCMN	Spreader
John Deere	780		G	$2,200	11/06	WCMN	Tandem hydro push spreader, fiberglass floor and sides
John Deere	785		G	$9,550	8/06	NCIA	Hyd. push tandem spreader, hyd. slop gate, two beaters
John Deere	785		G	$12,000	3/06	SWNE	10:00-20 tires on walking tandems, hyd. push off, unload & slop gate, rear beaters, 1,000 PTO
John Deere	790		P	$60	1/06	NEMO	
Kelly Ryan	5×12		E	$1,950	8/06	ECNE	Single axle, one owner, shedded
Kelly Ryan	NA		G	$1,700	8/06	WCIA	6'×18' tandem-axle spreader
Knight	1030		G	$12,500	12/06	SWWI	Upper beater good
Knight	180		F	$1,300	12/06	SWIL	Hyd. gate
Knight	225 bu.		G	$1,025	10/06	WCWI	Spreader, end gate
Knight	252		G	$2,000	8/06	NWIL	Hyd. gate
Knight	350		G	$950	8/06	NWIL	Hyd. gate
Knight	350		F	$1,700	8/06	NEIA	
Knight	350		F	$1,800	7/06	SEND	Tandem-axle manure spreader
Knight	650		G	$2,600	2/06	NECO	Truck mounted box
Knight	716		G	$750	12/06	NWIL	
Knight	8018		F	$1,250	7/06	WCMN	Side slinger, tandem axle
Knight	8018	1998	P	$5,000	2/06	SCNY	Tandem
Knight	8024		G	$4,250	8/06	WCMN	Side discharge spreader
Knight	8024		G	$6,500	1/06	SCMI	Slinger spreader, tandem axle
Knight	8032		G	$7,200	3/06	NWIL	Slinger
Knight	8140		G	$26,000	12/06	SEMN	Pro Twin slinger spreader
Meyers	160 BU		G	$475	8/06	SWWI	End gate
Meyers	190		F	$800	7/06	SWWI	
Meyers	225		F	$750	5/06	SEWI	
Meyers	2550		G	$16,750	3/06	WCMN	Tandem-axle spreader, 1,000 PTO hyd. gate, poly floor, new in 2004
Meyers	3245		G	$5,000	2/06	WCMN	R Series tandem-axle manure spreader, 2,600 gal.
Miller Pro	2160		F	$1,050	8/06	SEPA	Hyd. rear gate
New Holland	145		F	$1,900	5/06	SEWI	End gate

Manure Spreaders

Make	Model	Year	Cond.	Price	Sale	Location	Comments
New Holland	145		E	$2,600	12/06	SWWI	
New Holland	165		G	$2,600	2/06	WCNE	Slop gate, one owner, 1,000 PTO
New Holland	165		G	$2,850	1/06	NEIN	
New Holland	185		G	$4,800	12/06	SWWI	Slurry side
New Holland	185		E	$6,000	12/06	SWWI	
New Holland	190		F	$5,100	3/06	SEPA	Tandem, rear gate, PTO
New Holland	195		G	$10,000	12/06	SEIA	Hyd. gate, 540 PTO
New Holland	213		G	$2,600	8/06	SEPA	Wood floor
New Holland	305		G	$1,150	8/06	WCIL	
New Holland	308		F	$1,000	8/06	SCMI	Side slinger, 2 sold on same sale – each for $1,000
New Holland	308		F	$1,000	8/06	SCMI	Side slinger, 2 sold on same sale – each for $1,000
New Holland	327		G	$1,550	2/06	SWIN	130 bu.
New Holland	328		G	$850	2/06	NECO	PTO, 4'×10'
New Holland	329		F	$375	3/06	WCMN	
New Holland	510		G	$1,050	9/06	NWIL	163 bu.
New Holland	516		F	$1,000	4/06	NESD	Single axle, single beater, 205 bu.
New Holland	518		G	$2,100	8/06	NCMI	Single axle
New Holland	519		G	$3,200	4/06	WCMT	Consigned from a neighbor, 217 bu., single beater, PTO drive, wood floor, good shape no rust
New Holland	679		G	$4,350	10/06	NECO	5'×14', pt, PTO
New Holland	680		F	$2,200	9/06	NWIL	Tandem axle, slop gate, new drag chain
New Holland	680		G	$3,500	2/06	ECIL	Hyd. tail gate
New Holland	680		G	$4,000	3/06	SEMN	Tandem axle, slop gate
New Holland	680		G	$10,000	4/06	WCSD	Tandem axle
New Holland	680	1985	G	$2,250	5/06	SCMI	Tandem axle, slush gate
New Holland	790		P	$400	1/06	SCMI	Tandem axle
New Holland	790		G	$2,900	11/06	NWMN	Tandem axle, chain bed, double beater
New Holland	791		G	$3,000	11/06	SCSD	410 bu., new side, new poly floor
New Holland	791		G	$3,100	3/06	NWIL	Tandem axle, PTO
New Holland	795		F	$1,800	4/06	NCKS	
New Idea	12A		G	$550	8/06	ECNE	Ground driven, shedded
New Idea	12A		G	$650	12/06	NWIL	Spreader
New Idea	17		G	$1,275	9/06	NEIN	Ground drive
New Idea	205		G	$900	12/06	WCIL	PTO, hyd. tailgate, always shedded
New Idea	206		F	$300	11/06	SENE	Shedded
New Idea	210		F	$350	3/06	ECNE	4'×12', PTO drive
New Idea	211		F	$900	8/06	WCIL	
New Idea	213		F	$550	9/06	SEIA	
New Idea	213		F	$1,300	1/06	WCIL	PTO, top beater
New Idea	217		F	$750	3/06	NENE	Single axle, PTO drive
New Idea	224		F	$2,050	2/06	NEIN	Tandem axle
New Idea	353		G	$2,800	3/06	NWOH	Tandem axle, double beaters
New Idea	3618		G	$2,600	1/06	SCMI	180 bu., slop gate
New Idea	3618		G	$3,050	4/06	SEMI	Single axle, 2 beaters, end gate
New Idea	3618		G	$3,700	3/06	NWIL	
New Idea	362		G	$800	8/06	SETN	PTO driven
New Idea	3622		G	$2,800	12/06	NWIL	
New Idea	3622		E	$5,100	3/06	NWIL	
New Idea	3626		F	$2,300	8/06	SEPA	Galvanized, 250 bu.

Manure Spreaders

Make	Model	Year	Cond.	Price	Sale	Location	Comments
New Idea	3626		G	$2,500	3/06	NCWI	235 bu., single, hyd. feed end gate, plastic floor
New Idea	3626		G	$2,675	8/06	NCOH	Single axle, slop gate, poly floor
New Idea	3632		G	$1,800	4/06	WCWI	Tandem-axle spreader, hyd. gate
New Idea	3632		G	$2,200	10/06	SEMN	
New Idea	3632		G	$4,800	3/06	NWIL	
New Idea	3632		G	$5,000	12/06	SEIA	Hyd. gate
New Idea	3639		G	$3,600	2/06	NCCO	PTO
New Idea	3743		G	$7,250	8/06	NWIL	Tandem axle, double beater, slop gate
New Idea	3743	2005	E	$9,800	12/06	WCMN	Tandem-axle spreader, poly, 1,000 PTO floor, hyd. gate

Notes

Mowers & Conditioners

I love this category. To me it encapsulates everything I hope our data can do for you: provide you with current values, even on things like sickle mowers, haybines, hay inverters, and batwing mowers (all included in this category). What's a Woods 3180 batwing mower worth? See the 13 we've got listed. Average auction price = $5,127.

WHAT'S IT WORTH?

Mowers & Conditioners

Make	Model	Year	Cond.	Price	Sale	Location	Comments
Alamo	NA		G	$2,650	8/06	NEKS	13' side-fold shredder, 540 PTO
Artsway	6'		G	$200	8/06	NCIA	Belly mower
Befco	15'		G	$6,250	12/06	NWMO	
Befco	NA		G	$1,600	11/06	NCKY	Cyclone, 7' finishing mower
Befco	NA		E	$1,800	9/06	SCMN	14' 3-pt. rotary bat mower, like new
Big Ox	7'		G	$900	11/06	ECNE	7' shredder, hd, 3 pt.
BMB	5'		F	$200	8/06	ECNE	Shredder, pt, 540 PTO
BMB	5'		G	$260	8/06	ECNE	Shredder
BMB	7'		F	$525	3/06	WCKS	3-pt. mower
Brillion	12'		P	$650	8/06	NEIA	Rotary cutter, rough, pt
Bush Hog	10'		F	$900	1/06	SEPA	10' rotary mower, heavy built
Bush Hog	12'		G	$2,100	2/06	SEMI	Chopper
Bush Hog	12615		G	$6,450	8/06	ECNE	Batwing shredder, 1,000 PTO
Bush Hog	14'		G	$2,300	3/06	SWKS	Shredder
Bush Hog	15'		G	$4,600	4/06	SWOH	Batwing rotary cutter
Bush Hog	15'	2004	E	$9,000	1/06	NECO	Folding, rotary, PTO
Bush Hog	16'		F	$2,025	9/06	NECO	Rotary mower, pt, PTO
Bush Hog	2009		F	$2,500	3/06	SEPA	HM2009, 3 pt.
Bush Hog	24'		G	$8,000	2/06	NECO	1,000 PTO
Bush Hog	256		G	$600	12/06	ECMO	6' rotary cutter, 3 pt.
Bush Hog	256		G	$725	11/06	SWOH	Rotary mower
Bush Hog	2610L		F	$6,600	3/06	SEPA	Batwing mower
Bush Hog	2615		P	$2,000	2/06	WCIL	15' hyd. fold shredder, rough
Bush Hog	2615		F	$3,000	1/06	NWIL	Batwing mower, hard tires
Bush Hog	2615		G	$5,750	2/06	SEKS	Legend, 15' batwing mower
Bush Hog	2615		G	$6,250	1/06	WCIL	15' batwing mower, mulching blades, SN 00013
Bush Hog	2615		G	$7,000	3/06	WCIL	15' batwing mower
Bush Hog	2615		G	$7,500	2/06	WCIL	Legend batwing mower, 1,000 PTO, 6 solid tires, chains
Bush Hog	2615		G	$8,500	1/06	NCCO	15' batwing rotary mower
Bush Hog	2615		G	$9,900	1/06	SWOH	Legend batwing, rotary cutter
Bush Hog	2615	2001	E	$7,700	1/06	WCIL	15' batwing shredder, 8 solid tires
Bush Hog	2620		F	$3,900	8/06	NECO	20' batwing mower
Bush Hog	268		G	$800	3/06	NEKS	Rotary cutter
Bush Hog	268		F	$1,300	1/06	SEPA	8' rotary mower, 3 pt.
Bush Hog	268		G	$2,300	5/06	SCMI	8' trailer rotary chopper
Bush Hog	287		G	$900	8/06	NCMI	3-pt. rotary mower
Bush Hog	315		F	$3,200	12/06	WCMI	15' batwing, rotary chopper
Bush Hog	3615		G	$4,300	12/06	NWIL	Batwing mower, solid tires
Bush Hog	5'		F	$50	11/06	SETN	
Bush Hog	5'		F	$275	6/06	NECO	Rotary mower, 3 pt., PTO
Bush Hog	5'		F	$300	9/06	SCNE	3-pt. rotary shredder
Bush Hog	5'		F	$350	6/06	NECO	Rotary mower, 3 pt., PTO
Bush Hog	6'		F	$200	10/06	NCKS	Rotary mower
Bush Hog	6'		F	$350	9/06	NEIN	3-pt. rotary mower
Bush Hog	6'		F	$375	3/06	ECNE	Shredder, pt
Bush Hog	6'		F	$400	6/06	NECO	Rotary mower, 3 pt., PTO
Bush Hog	6'		G	$450	3/06	SEMN	3-pt. rotary brush mower
Bush Hog	7'		F	$475	2/06	NWIN	3-pt. rotary mower
Bush Hog	7'		G	$700	9/06	NEIN	Rotary mower

Mowers & Conditioners

Make	Model	Year	Cond.	Price	Sale	Location	Comments
Bush Hog	7'		G	$1,300	12/06	ECMO	Disk mower
Bush Hog	7'		G	$1,350	6/06	ECND	3-pt. trailing mower
Bush Hog	7'		G	$2,400	2/06	ECNE	Shredder
Bush Hog	8'		G	$1,500	8/06	NCNE	Rotary mower
Bush Hog	9'		G	$800	3/06	WCIL	9' chopper mower
Bush Hog	900		G	$1,350	2/06	SENE	ATH900, 3-pt. finishing mower
Bush Hog	SM60		G	$3,500	2/06	SCMI	6' ditch bank mower
Bush Hog	SQ600		G	$700	5/06	SEWY	6' rotary mower, 3 pt.
Bush Hog	SQ72		G	$375	4/06	ECND	6' cutting width
Case IH	1100		G	$1,850	5/06	SEND	Trailing sickle mower, 9' bar
Case IH	1300		G	$1,050	11/06	ECIL	Sicklebar mower
Case IH	1300		G	$1,150	2/06	ECIL	9' sickle mower
Case IH	1300		G	$1,350	3/06	NWIL	9'
Case IH	3205		G	$800	3/06	NWMN	Rotary disk mower
Case IH	60		G	$400	6/06	SCMN	60", 3-pt. finishing mower
Case IH	8312		F	$3,700	3/06	NWKS	Rotary, pt mower, conditioner
Case IH	8350		G	$3,700	4/06	NEND	Mower, conditioner, 12', hyd. swing, auger head
Case IH	8360		G	$3,250	12/06	SEIA	Center pivot mower, conditioner
Case IH	8370		P	$1,000	10/06	NCKS	16', swing tongue, steel conditioners, rough
Case IH	8370		F	$2,000	3/06	NCUT	Haybine
Case IH	8370		G	$2,750	12/06	WCMN	14' mower, conditioner, swing tongue
Case IH	8370		G	$3,750	12/06	SEND	14' Haybine
Case IH	8370	1990	G	$3,250	7/06	WCMN	Mower, conditioner, 14'
Case IH	8380		F	$1,750	3/06	NEKS	
Case IH	DCX131		G	$12,750	12/06	SEMN	13' mower, conditioner
Case IH	DCX131	2004	E	$14,750	3/06	NWOH	13' disk mower, conditioner, center pivot
Case IH	DCX161		G	$12,400	12/06	SWWI	15'
Crustbuster	15'		F	$2,300	3/06	WCKS	Folding rotary batwing mower, tires poor
Deutz Fahr	NA		G	$1,000	9/06	NEIN	Hay tedder
Douglas	NA		G	$325	9/06	SCMN	4' rotary cutter
Farm King	5'		G	$300	8/06	NWIL	Rotary mower
Farm King	650		G	$550	11/06	SCND	Y650R, finishing mower, 3 pt.
Farm King	7'		G	$1,100	11/06	ECND	3-pt. finish mower
Farm King	7'		E	$1,350	6/06	NCIA	3-pt. finishing mower, used twice
Farmhand	1510	2003	G	$3,000	12/06	NWIL	Batwing mower, soft tires
FMC	5'		F	$250	2/06	WCNE	5' rotary mower, 3 pt.
Ford	5'		G	$300	12/06	NENE	3-pt. shredder
Ford	515		F	$150	8/06	WCMN	3-pt. sickle mower
Ford	515		G	$350	3/06	SWIN	7' belt drive, sicklebar mower
Ford	8'		F	$475	6/06	NECO	Flail mower, 3 pt., PTO
Ford	9'		G	$1,150	1/06	SCMI	
Ford	901		G	$350	3/06	NWIL	5' rotary mower
Ford	917		F	$400	8/06	SEPA	3 pt.
Galfre	9'	2002	G	$3,000	12/06	NEMO	9' rotary disk mower
Gehl	2275		F	$675	9/06	SCNE	Pt
Gehl	2360		G	$4,250	12/06	NWIL	Disk mower
Gehl	2360		G	$5,500	8/06	NWIL	Disk conditioner
Gehl	2365		G	$6,900	12/06	ECIL	10' conditioner
Gehl	2412		G	$6,500	3/06	NCMN	Disk mower

WHAT'S IT WORTH?

Mowers & Conditioners

Make	Model	Year	Cond.	Price	Sale	Location	Comments
Gehl	2412	1999	G	$7,500	2/06	SCNY	
Gehl	880		F	$225	9/06	SCMN	
Gehl	880		F	$250	9/06	SCMN	
H&S	8'	2000	G	$1,500	3/06	NEMI	Hay tedder, PTO
H&S	9'		G	$1,000	8/06	NEIA	Tedder
Hesston	1010		F	$225	12/06	NEMO	Mower, conditioner
Hesston	1014		F	$425	3/06	ECNE	Crimper
Hesston	1014+2		G	$1,600	1/06	WCNE	14'
Hesston	1085		G	$1,500	3/06	NCWI	9' mower, conditioner
Hesston	1120		F	$550	12/06	WCIL	9' mower, conditioner
Hesston	1120		G	$2,500	8/06	NWIL	9' mower, conditioner
Hesston	1160		F	$4,600	8/06	ECNE	14', 110" crimper, shedded
Hesston	1170		G	$2,000	3/06	NEKS	
Hesston	12'		F	$400	8/06	WCMN	
Hesston	1345		G	$17,000	4/06	WCWI	12', hyd, swivel tongue
Hesston	14'		F	$1,050	4/06	NEND	Hyd. swing, all hyd.
Hesston	PT10		G	$1,200	7/06	WCOH	
Howse	10'		F	$750	3/06	NEKS	3-pt. rotary cutter
Howse	10'		F	$750	1/06	SWNE	3-pt. rotary mower
Howse	10'		G	$2,000	6/06	NECO	3-pt. rotary mower, PTO
Howse	5'		F	$250	9/06	SCNE	3-pt. shredder
Howse	5'		G	$325	10/06	SCMN	3-pt. rotary brush mower
Howse	5'		E	$410	3/06	NWIL	
IHC	100		F	$200	1/06	NWIL	Sicklebar mower
IHC	100		G	$625	7/06	NCIA	7', 2-pt. mower, belt drive
IHC	100		G	$800	4/06	NCSD	8' mower
IHC	100		G	$1,025	3/06	NCIA	7' pull Pitmanless mower
IHC	1000		G	$600	6/06	ECND	7' sickle mower
IHC	1000		G	$875	2/06	NCIL	9' sickle mower, 3 pt.
IHC	1100		F	$400	7/06	SEND	Trailing sickle mower, 7' bar
IHC	1100		G	$900	4/06	NCSD	9' mower
IHC	1100		G	$1,350	11/06	SCSD	9' mower, pt
IHC	1100		G	$1,600	3/06	SEND	Trailing sickle mower, 9'
IHC	1190		F	$1,100	9/06	NECO	9', pt, PTO
IHC	1300		G	$300	2/06	WCIL	3-bar sickle mower
IHC	1300		F	$335	8/06	WCIL	9' sickle mower
IHC	1300		G	$375	11/06	SCIL	9' sickle mower
IHC	1300		G	$425	8/06	NCOH	3-pt. sicklebar mower, as is
IHC	1300		G	$550	12/06	ECMO	
IHC	1300		G	$1,000	12/06	NWOH	9', 3-pt. sickle mower
IHC	200		F	$150	8/06	NCOH	7' semi-mounted sickle mower
IHC	25		F	$65	8/06	ECNE	Sickle mower
IHC	27		F	$190	9/06	ECNE	7' bar sickle mower, belt drive
IHC	311		F	$300	7/06	NWMN	Rotary mower
IHC	990		G	$550	7/06	NCIL	
IHC	990		G	$600	8/06	SCMI	9'
IHC	Cub Lowboy		F	$800	2/06	SWPA	5' rotary mower
John Deere	1209		F	$310	5/06	SWWI	
John Deere	1209		G	$2,100	1/06	NEIN	

Mowers & Conditioners

Make	Model	Year	Cond.	Price	Sale	Location	Comments
John Deere	1214		F	$400	8/06	ECNE	Oil cooler
John Deere	1219		F	$950	12/06	NWIL	Mower, conditioner
John Deere	1219		F	$1,700	3/06	NEOH	
John Deere	1219		F	$3,150	1/06	WCIL	Mower, conditioner
John Deere	1219		G	$4,000	1/06	NEIN	
John Deere	1418		G	$3,200	11/06	SCNE	14' rotary shredder, 3 pt.
John Deere	1418		E	$3,500	3/06	NEKS	Cutter
John Deere	1424		F	$900	7/06	SEND	14'
John Deere	1508		F	$2,250	12/06	NWMO	15' hyd. fold
John Deere	1508		G	$3,000	12/06	NEMO	15' batwing mower
John Deere	1508		G	$3,500	3/06	ECIL	15' batwing mower
John Deere	1508		G	$4,100	2/06	NWIN	15' batwing
John Deere	1508		G	$5,000	3/06	SEIA	Batwing mower
John Deere	1508	1998	P	$1,700	7/06	SEND	
John Deere	1509		G	$2,375	3/06	NWIL	
John Deere	1517		G	$3,750	12/06	ECMO	15' rotary cutter, 540 PTO, dual center wheels, stump jumpers, laminated wheels
John Deere	1517		G	$5,200	3/06	NEOH	15' batwing mower
John Deere	1517		G	$6,350	1/06	NWIL	15' batwing mower
John Deere	1517		G	$6,500	11/06	SEIA	15' batwing mower
John Deere	1518		G	$3,400	2/06	SCKS	10' single-fold rotary mower
John Deere	1518		G	$4,100	12/06	ECMO	Rotary cutter
John Deere	1518		F	$5,500	3/06	NCCO	Flail mower
John Deere	1518		F	$5,500	2/06	SWNE	15' batwing rotary mower
John Deere	1518		G	$7,500	2/06	SWNE	15' batwing rotary mower
John Deere	1518	1994	G	$6,400	12/06	SWMI	15' double batwing rotary field chopper
John Deere	1518	1995	G	$4,300	12/06	NWMO	15' hyd. fold
John Deere	1518	1998	G	$4,000	2/06	WCIL	15' rotary cutter, 6 laminated tires, 1,000 rpm, PTO
John Deere	1518	2001	G	$6,200	12/06	NWMO	15' hyd. fold
John Deere	1600		F	$850	8/06	ECNE	Oil cooler, 14' head
John Deere	1600		G	$4,100	6/06	NCIA	12' center pivot mower, conditioner
John Deere	1600		G	$4,500	12/06	WCMN	Swing tongue
John Deere	1600	1993	F	$2,600	7/06	WCMN	Mower, conditioner, 14', conditioner rolls, drawbar swivel
John Deere	1600A		F	$2,100	11/06	SCSD	Mower conditioner, newer rollers and bearings
John Deere	1600A		G	$3,100	8/06	WCMN	14', 640, PTO
John Deere	2018		G	$7,300	8/06	SEPA	Batwing mower
John Deere	22		F	$625	6/06	SWMN	Hay conditioner
John Deere	260		G	$1,800	2/06	WCMN	3-pt. disk mower
John Deere	261		G	$475	12/06	ECMO	Grooming mower, 5', 3 pt.
John Deere	270		F	$1,125	12/06	NWMO	Disk mower
John Deere	275	2002	G	$4,200	12/06	NWMO	Disk mower
John Deere	275	2003	G	$3,800	12/06	NWMO	Disk mower
John Deere	275	2003	G	$4,100	12/06	NWMO	Disk mower
John Deere	275	2003	E	$5,000	3/06	NENE	9' disk mower, less than 500 acres use, used 2½ seasons
John Deere	275	2004	E	$3,500	3/06	NWIL	Disk mower, quick hitch, like new
John Deere	307		F	$100	3/06	NWKS	Mower, 3-pt. shredder
John Deere	350		F	$350	9/06	NWMN	Mounted sickle mower, 7' bar
John Deere	350		G	$450	3/06	SEIA	Sickle mower
John Deere	350		G	$450	3/06	ECND	9' sickle mower, 3 pt.

Mowers & Conditioners

Make	Model	Year	Cond.	Price	Sale	Location	Comments
John Deere	350		G	$480	1/06	WCIL	9' sickle mower
John Deere	350		G	$575	3/06	SEIA	Sickle mower, PTO
John Deere	350		G	$675	9/06	NCIA	7' 3-pt. mower
John Deere	350		F	$750	6/06	SEND	Sickle mower, 9', 3 pt.
John Deere	350		G	$750	9/06	SWIA	7' sicklebar mower
John Deere	350		G	$800	4/06	NESD	Mounted sickle mower, 7' bar
John Deere	350		G	$800	8/06	SEMN	Sicklebar mower
John Deere	350		E	$850	8/06	ECIL	9', 3-pt. sickle mower
John Deere	350		G	$975	2/06	NWIN	9', 3-pt. bar
John Deere	350		G	$1,075	11/06	SCNE	Sicklebar mower, 7', 3 pt.
John Deere	350		G	$1,100	3/06	WCIL	9' sickle mower
John Deere	350		G	$1,200	3/06	ECNE	7' sickle mower
John Deere	350		G	$1,300	3/06	NWIL	9'
John Deere	350		G	$1,300	2/06	WCIL	Sickle mower, 9' bar
John Deere	350		E	$1,350	2/06	WCIL	9' bar mower, used only on 54 acres
John Deere	350		G	$1,700	8/06	NCIA	9'
John Deere	37		F	$195	8/06	WCMN	9' bar, pt
John Deere	37		F	$375	4/06	NEND	Trailing sickle mower, 7' bar
John Deere	37		G	$400	8/06	NCIA	7' pull mower
John Deere	37		F	$475	11/06	NEND	7' trailing sickle mower
John Deere	37		G	$475	3/06	SESD	Mower, pt
John Deere	37		G	$700	3/06	SEIA	Sickle mower, pt
John Deere	38		F	$35	1/06	WCIL	9' sicklebar mower
John Deere	38		F	$280	11/06	ECNE	9' sickle mower
John Deere	403		G	$325	2/06	NECO	4', 3-pt rotary
John Deere	403		G	$500	10/06	SENY	
John Deere	407		G	$400	11/06	ECIL	7' mower
John Deere	413		G	$350	1/06	WCIL	4' rotary mower
John Deere	413		G	$400	9/06	NWTN	3-pt. hitch rotary cutter, 4' cut
John Deere	450		G	$400	9/06	ECNE	9' mower
John Deere	450		G	$800	4/06	WCSD	Trail mower, 540 PTO
John Deere	450		G	$1,050	4/06	NEND	Trailing sickle mower, 9' NH bar
John Deere	450		G	$1,300	3/06	ECND	9' trailing mower
John Deere	503		F	$200	12/06	NWMO	
John Deere	503		F	$300	7/06	NWOH	5' chopper, 3 pt.
John Deere	506		F	$375	7/06	SEND	3-pt. mower
John Deere	506		G	$500	8/06	SWWI	5' rotary mower
John Deere	509		G	$425	3/06	NCIA	5' rotary cutter
John Deere	513		G	$375	5/06	SEWY	5' rotary mower, 3 pt.
John Deere	530	2005	E	$10,300	12/06	NWIL	Disk mower
John Deere	54		G	$475	2/06	NWIL	4' rotary mower
John Deere	606		G	$450	1/06	WCCA	3-pt., 6' rotary
John Deere	606		G	$500	2/06	SCMI	6' rotary chopper
John Deere	606		F	$625	1/06	SEPA	Rotary mower, transport
John Deere	606		G	$700	2/06	SWNE	3-pt. rotary mower, 540 PTO
John Deere	609		G	$500	3/06	NEMI	3 pt., 6' PTO
John Deere	616		F	$775	5/06	SEWI	Rotary mower
John Deere	707		G	$475	2/06	NCIN	14' chopper
John Deere	709		F	$425	12/06	NWIL	7' rotary mower

Mowers & Conditioners

Make	Model	Year	Cond.	Price	Sale	Location	Comments
John Deere	709		G	$650	3/06	SWNE	7' 3-pt. rotary mower, 1,000 PTO
John Deere	709		G	$700	3/06	ECND	3-pt. rotary ditch mower
John Deere	709		G	$850	12/06	ECIL	3-pt. rotary mower
John Deere	709		G	$1,000	3/06	NWIL	3-pt. rotary mower
John Deere	709		G	$1,200	12/06	NCIA	Rotary cutter
John Deere	709		G	$1,700	2/06	NWIL	7', 3-pt. rotary mower
John Deere	717		G	$3,000	12/06	ECNE	3-pt. shredder, 540 PTO, single trail wheel
John Deere	720		F	$2,000	3/06	SEPA	
John Deere	735	2005	G	$12,000	12/06	NWMO	Impeller, rockshaft hitch, turnbuckle angle adjustment
John Deere	735	2005	E	$15,500	2/06	SCMI	120 center pivot, flail conditioner, only 140 acres
John Deere	752		G	$2,250	1/06	SEPA	Hay fluffer
John Deere	820		G	$2,900	12/06	ECMO	Stub guards, hyd. swing tongue, 5-bar reel
John Deere	820		G	$6,100	2/06	NEIN	9'
John Deere	920		G	$5,100	12/06	ECMO	Hyd. swing tongue, roll conditioner
John Deere	920		G	$6,300	9/06	NWTN	
John Deere	925		G	$6,200	12/06	SEMN	Impeller
John Deere	926		G	$9,000	12/06	SEMN	Impeller
John Deere	926		G	$9,300	12/06	SCMN	Impeller, 9'9" cut
John Deere	926		F	$11,000	3/06	SEPA	
John Deere	930		F	$3,800	8/06	SEPA	
John Deere	930	1997	F	$2,750	7/06	WCMN	12', impeller conditioner
John Deere	935		G	$10,000	12/06	NEMO	12'
John Deere	936	2001	E	$13,500	3/06	SEIA	Like new
John Deere	945		G	$9,800	11/06	NEKS	12' mower, conditioner
John Deere	946	2002	E	$11,250	12/06	WCMN	MoCo, 14', 1,000 PTO, 3 pt.
John Deere	946	2003	E	$10,750	1/06	SCMI	13'
John Deere	946	2006	G	$16,000	11/06	NEKS	Rotary mower conditioner
John Deere	946	2006	E	$19,500	12/06	WCMN	14', 1,000 PTO, 3 pt.
John Deere	956	2002	G	$18,500	3/06	ECMI	14.5' flails
John Deere	960		G	$3,500	8/06	NCIA	27.5'
John Deere	HX14		E	$4,400	3/06	SEND	14' rotary mower, like new
John Deere	HX15		E	$9,300	8/06	NECO	New, 15' batwing mower
John Deere	HX15		E	$10,100	12/06	WCMN	Batwing mower, 15' double fold, scalp kit, 540 PTO, one year of use
John Deere	HX15	2003	G	$6,000	12/06	WCMN	Rotary cutter, 15', 1,000 PTO
John Deere	LX6	1994	F	$600	8/06	NEIA	3-pt. rotary mower, had some dings
John Deere	MX10		G	$3,200	4/06	NESD	10' mounted rotary mower
John Deere	MX10		E	$4,750	12/06	WCMN	1,000 PTO, 3-pt. mount, two years old
John Deere	MX10	2004	G	$4,100	3/06	NCCO	10' rotary mower, 2 pt., hyd. shift
John Deere	MX7		G	$2,000	11/06	NCIN	3-pt. rotary mower
John Deere	MX7	2003	G	$1,600	2/06	SCNY	3-pt. rotary mower
John Deere	MX8		G	$2,850	12/06	ECMO	8' rotary cutter, semi-mount, hyd. offset, stump jumpers
John Deere	MX8	2002	G	$2,100	3/06	NENE	3-pt. shredder
King	6'		G	$750	11/06	NEOH	Buhler-King, 6' mower
King Kutter	5'		F	$175	3/06	ECMN	Rotary mower, 3 pt., +10% buyers premium
King Kutter	5'		G	$550	4/06	SCMN	Rotary mower, pt
King Kutter	6'		F	$200	3/06	NWKS	3-pt. shredder
King Kutter	6'		G	$600	3/06	SEPA	Rotary mower, 3 pt.
Kirchner	NA		G	$625	3/06	NCND	Hyd. swath fluffer

WHAT'S IT WORTH?

Mowers & Conditioners

Make	Model	Year	Cond.	Price	Sale	Location	Comments
Kuhn	5'		F	$700	9/06	NWMN	3-pt. disk mower
Kuhn	5'		G	$850	6/06	NWMN	3-pt. disk mower
Kuhn	7'		G	$3,050	1/06	NWIL	Disk mower
Kuhn	GF452		F	$1,600	2/06	SCNY	4-star tedder
Kuhn	GMD 600		G	$4,900	12/06	NCIA	3-pt. disk mower
Kuhn	GMD 700		G	$4,600	11/06	SWIA	9' disk mower, 3 years old
Land Pride	15'		G	$4,000	1/06	WCIL	Batwing mower
Land Pride	1572		G	$550	4/06	SWIN	6' rotary cutter
Land Pride	25-60		G	$350	2/06	NCIN	3-pt. finish mower, 5'
Land Pride	5015		G	$3,900	3/06	NWIL	15' batwing mower, solid tires
Land Pride	5015		G	$6,500	11/06	SEIA	15' batwing mower
Land Pride	5020		G	$8,700	9/06	NCIA	Commander, batwing mower
Land Pride	9'		G	$3,000	1/06	NEIN	3-pt. disk mower
Land Pride	NA		G	$700	8/06	NCIA	72", 3-pt. finish mower, 3 blades, 540, 4 wheels
Land Pride	NA		G	$850	12/06	NWIL	90" finish mower
Land Pride	RCR2584		G	$600	1/06	WCIL	7' mower
Lely	NA		F	$1,000	2/06	NCCO	Lely Roterra, 16'
Lely	NA		F	$2,300	2/06	NCCO	Lely Roterra, 14'
M&W	15'		G	$4,000	12/06	SWIL	Batwing mower, 540 PTO
M&W	15'		G	$4,100	12/06	SCNE	Batwing shredder
M&W	1520		G	$2,000	11/06	SCNE	16' shredder, 6R-30
M&W	1532		G	$3,900	3/06	NCIL	Batwing mower, 15'
M&W	PC415		F	$230	2/06	NCIN	4' rotary chopper
Macdon	5010		G	$7,000	6/06	NWSD	Mower, conditioners, pt
MC	9'		G	$800	11/06	SWIA	Rotary scythe, set up for cornstalks
MC	NA		G	$1,100	10/06	SEMN	Rotary scythe
MF	15'		G	$4,200	2/06	SEIL	Batwing mower
MF	6'		G	$700	3/06	ECMI	3-pt. sicklebar mower
MF	7'		F	$100	3/06	ECNE	Sickle mower, 7' bar
MF	9'		G	$1,400	4/06	WCMN	Canadian sale
Miller Pro	1150		F	$2,500	3/06	SEPA	Tedder, transport
Mott	NA		G	$275	8/06	SEPA	7.5' flail mower, 3 pt.
New Holland	1116		G	$3,250	10/06	NCND	14' hay conditioner
New Holland	116		F	$500	8/06	WCMN	16', 1,000 PTO
New Holland	116		F	$1,600	1/06	SWNE	14'
New Holland	116		G	$4,600	8/06	NCMI	14', 10' rolls
New Holland	116		G	$5,200	12/06	SEND	14'
New Holland	116		G	$5,500	3/06	WCMN	Hyd. swing
New Holland	1411		G	$6,100	12/06	NWMO	Discbine
New Holland	1411		P	$6,850	11/06	NEIA	Discbine, rough, never shedded
New Holland	1411		G	$8,500	12/06	SWIL	Discbine
New Holland	1411	2004	E	$12,250	9/06	NEIN	Discbine, mowed 500 acres, like new
New Holland	1431		F	$5,250	8/06	WCMN	Discbine, 13'7", 1,000 PTO, rubber crimp
New Holland	1431		E	$14,300	2/06	NCIL	Discbine, 13', like new
New Holland	1431	1998	G	$9,300	7/06	SEND	Rotary Discbine, 13', straight hitch
New Holland	1431	1998	G	$11,000	3/06	NEMI	13' Discbine
New Holland	1431	2000	G	$13,250	5/06	SCMI	12' Discbine
New Holland	1432		G	$9,500	9/06	WCWI	Discbine, hd quick hitch, used two seasons
New Holland	1465		E	$8,000	1/06	NEIN	Good rolls, like new

Mowers & Conditioners

Make	Model	Year	Cond.	Price	Sale	Location	Comments
New Holland	1475		G	$4,200	2/06	SWNE	14' hyd. swing mower, conditioner
New Holland	1475		G	$5,200	5/06	SEND	16', 540 rpm
New Holland	1475		G	$14,100	2/06	ECNE	Swinger windrower, 16' #2300 head
New Holland	1475		E	$17,500	9/06	WCNE	Two or three years old, like new
New Holland	1475	2000	G	$7,900	1/06	SWNE	16' hyd. swing
New Holland	162		G	$2,125	6/06	NCPA	Tedder
New Holland	163		G	$2,750	2/06	SWIN	4-wheel hay tedder
New Holland	163		G	$3,600	3/06	SWIN	4-rotor hay tedder
New Holland	166		G	$1,000	1/06	WCNE	Hyd. driven, pt
New Holland	166		G	$1,500	8/06	NCMI	Hay inverter, wheel drive
New Holland	166		G	$2,400	11/06	WCSD	Windrow inverter, can throw to either side, extension to put 3 windrows together
New Holland	166		G	$3,100	9/06	WCWI	Hay inverter
New Holland	166		G	$3,250	12/06	SWWI	Inverter, hyd. driven
New Holland	166		E	$4,000	3/06	WCMN	Hay inverter, like new
New Holland	166		G	$4,025	3/06	ECIL	Hay inverter
New Holland	166		E	$6,100	3/06	NWOH	Hay inverter, long belt table
New Holland	166	1993	G	$3,000	5/06	SCMI	Hay inverter, extension
New Holland	166	2005	E	$5,200	12/06	WCMN	Hay tedder
New Holland	254		G	$700	4/06	SWIN	Hay tedder
New Holland	408		G	$5,000	3/06	SWIN	8' Discbine, equal angle hitch
New Holland	411		F	$3,400	3/06	NWIL	
New Holland	435		F	$900	11/06	NWMN	Trailing sickle mower, 9' bar
New Holland	450		F	$300	1/06	NWIL	Mower
New Holland	451		G	$425	8/06	SEPA	3-pt. sickle mower
New Holland	451		G	$500	1/06	WCIL	9' sicklebar mower
New Holland	451		G	$1,000	2/06	ECNE	7', 3-pt. sickle mower
New Holland	455		G	$500	8/06	NCOH	7' sicklebar mower, pt
New Holland	456		G	$1,900	3/06	SEND	9' sickle mower
New Holland	456		G	$2,000	3/06	NCND	Trailing mower, 9' sickle
New Holland	456		E	$2,500	11/06	NEKS	Trailer mower
New Holland	467		F	$550	10/06	WCWI	7'
New Holland	469		F	$350	9/06	NEIN	
New Holland	469		G	$550	12/06	NEMO	9' mower conditioner
New Holland	469		F	$1,300	6/06	NCPA	9'
New Holland	472		F	$300	1/06	WCTX	Mower, conditioner
New Holland	472		G	$3,600	11/06	SWOH	
New Holland	477		F	$700	8/06	SEMN	
New Holland	477		G	$1,100	12/06	SWWI	Older 7'
New Holland	477		G	$1,500	11/06	NEOH	Older but clean
New Holland	477		F	$1,600	2/06	SWPA	7'
New Holland	477		G	$1,725	3/06	ECMN	7', new sickle & belt, +10% buyers premium
New Holland	479		P	$400	9/06	WCOH	
New Holland	488		F	$425	9/06	NWIL	9'
New Holland	488		F	$1,800	2/06	SWIN	9', short guards
New Holland	488		P	$2,800	2/06	NEIA	Very rough
New Holland	488		G	$3,100	2/06	SWIN	9', adjustable hitch
New Holland	488		E	$3,100	11/06	NEKS	9', cylinder
New Holland	488		G	$5,500	3/06	NWIL	

Mowers & Conditioners

Make	Model	Year	Cond.	Price	Sale	Location	Comments
New Holland	489		F	$425	9/06	NEIN	
New Holland	489		G	$2,500	8/06	NCMI	9'
New Holland	489		E	$2,800	2/06	SENE	9'
New Holland	489		G	$3,400	3/06	NEIA	
New Holland	492		F	$2,400	1/06	SEPA	
New Holland	492		F	$3,500	3/06	SEPA	
New Holland	492		G	$3,500	1/06	NCIL	
New Holland	492		G	$4,500	3/06	ECIL	9'
New Holland	492		G	$5,200	4/06	SEMI	9'
New Holland	495		F	$600	9/06	NECO	12', pt, red
New Holland	495		G	$1,300	9/06	SCNE	12', pt
New Holland	495		G	$1,600	8/06	NCIA	12', 9' rubber rolls
New Holland	499		G	$3,100	11/06	WCMN	12', swing tongue hitch
New Holland	499		G	$5,500	12/06	SEND	12'
New Holland	499	2003	E	$10,500	3/06	SEND	Used less than 600 acres, new sickles
New Holland	499	2004	E	$11,900	8/06	WCMN	12', used on approximately 55 acres, like new
New Holland	55		G	$500	12/06	NCIA	Sickle mower
New Holland	617		G	$2,300	12/06	WCIL	9' rotary disk mower
New Holland	617		G	$4,900	4/06	SWIN	9.5' disk mower
New Holland	617		G	$5,600	3/06	WCMN	Disk mower, 540 PTO
New Idea	272		E	$1,000	3/06	NEOH	Cutditioner
New Idea	272		G	$1,000	10/06	SEMN	Cutditioner
New Idea	272		G	$1,400	10/06	SEMN	Cutditioner
New Idea	279		G	$1,000	6/06	NCPA	Cutditioner
New Idea	5209		F	$3,400	9/06	NWIL	Mower, conditioner
New Idea	5209		G	$6,400	2/06	ECMN	9'
New Idea	5209		G	$8,100	8/06	SEMN	
New Idea	5209		E	$9,400	12/06	NWIL	Disk mower
New Idea	5212		E	$9,000	2/06	NWIL	12' disk mower conditioner, like new
New Idea	5409		G	$2,800	1/06	NEMO	9' rotary disk mower
New Idea	5410	2004	G	$4,100	3/06	NENE	10' disk mower
Pequea	910		G	$1,100	4/06	WCWI	Hay tedder
Pequea	910		E	$1,900	10/06	SCMI	Hay tedder
Pequea	910		G	$2,100	3/06	NWOH	9' hay tedder
Reese	2400		F	$500	8/06	NEIA	8' cutter
Rhino	20'		G	$2,700	11/06	SENE	Flex-20 20' batwing shredder, solid rubber tires
Rhino	20'		F	$3,700	8/06	SEPA	Batwing mower
Rhino	5'		G	$400	1/06	WCNE	3-pt. rotary mower, S5
Rhino	6'		F	$375	5/06	SEWY	3-pt. rotary mower
Rhino	8'		G	$1,100	8/06	SETN	Hydro cylinder, pt
Rhino	DB150		G	$1,700	5/06	SEWY	5', 3 pt., side arm, hyd. drive
Rhino	DB150		G	$3,300	8/06	SCFL	Ditch bank mower
Rhino	RC20	2003	G	$11,000	8/06	WCKS	Mower, conditioner
Rhino	SE15		G	$2,400	3/06	SEIA	Batwing mower
Rhino	SE15		F	$2,500	6/06	NWIL	Batwing mower, 15', hard rubber tires
Rhino	SE15		G	$3,700	12/06	NWMO	540 PTO
Rhino	SE15		G	$5,750	3/06	ECNE	Batwing shredder, pt
Rhino	SE15		G	$6,000	3/06	SWNE	15' batwing shredder, hyd. cold, 1,000 PTO
Rhino	SE5		G	$400	2/06	NCIN	5' rotary chopper

Mowers & Conditioners

Make	Model	Year	Cond.	Price	Sale	Location	Comments
Rhino	SE5		E	$1,200	3/06	NWIL	
Rhino	SE6		G	$800	11/06	NEIA	
Rhino	SE6		G	$1,050	8/06	NECO	3-pt. rotary mower
Rhino	SE6		G	$1,300	3/06	ECNE	6', 3-pt. rotary shredder, one owner
Rhino	SE7		G	$1,900	8/06	NECO	Rotary mower
Rhino	SR15		G	$3,950	12/06	NWMO	540 PTO
Rhino	SR20		E	$12,000	11/06	SENE	20' batwing shredder, unused, big, 1,000 PTO, aircraft tires
Rhino	TW96		G	$3,300	3/06	NCCO	Twin rotary mower
Rowse	9'		G	$3,200	11/06	ECND	Trailing sickle mower
Servis	1310		G	$250	7/06	WCCA	Rotary cutter
Servis	5'		G	$300	1/06	ECNE	Rotary mower, pt
Sidewinder	5'		F	$100	12/06	ECMO	5', 3-pt. rotary cutter
Taylorway	1510		G	$6,700	8/06	NCIA	15' batwing, hard rubber tires, chains all the away around
Tiger	5'		G	$1,300	8/06	WCMN	60" side-mounted rotary mower
Vermeer	1030		G	$13,500	12/06	SEMN	DiscPro
Vicon	CM216		G	$950	11/06	WCMN	Disk mower, 7', 3 pt.
Vicon	CM240		G	$1,200	12/06	NEMO	7' rotary disk mower
Woods	106		G	$1,000	3/06	ECND	Ditch bank mower, PTO, 3 pt.
Woods	120		G	$4,600	3/06	NWMN	Batwing mower
Woods	1260		G	$4,200	10/06	NEIA	10' rotary cutter
Woods	15'		G	$4,900	8/06	NCIA	Rotary batwing mower, hyd. fold
Woods	184		G	$410	3/06	NWIL	7', 3-pt. rotary mower
Woods	20'		G	$7,100	9/06	NCIA	Batwing mower, airplane tires
Woods	315		F	$1,600	7/06	SEND	Ditch bank mower, 10'
Woods	3180		F	$3,500	8/06	WCIL	15' batwing mower
Woods	3180		F	$3,950	8/06	WCIL	15' batwing mower
Woods	3180		G	$4,000	3/06	NWIL	
Woods	3180		G	$4,000	12/06	NWIL	Batwing mower, new paint, solid tires
Woods	3180		G	$4,000	12/06	NWIL	Batwing mower
Woods	3180		F	$4,100	8/06	NWIL	Batwing mower, soft tires
Woods	3180		G	$5,700	1/06	NCIL	Batwing, 1,000 PTO, 6 aired tires
Woods	3180		G	$6,500	2/06	NCIL	Batwing mower, 15'
Woods	3180		E	$8,600	3/06	NWOH	15' batwing mower
Woods	3180	1996	E	$5,500	8/06	ECIL	Batwing, 15' chopper
Woods	3180	1999	G	$5,800	12/06	NEMO	Batwing mower
Woods	3180	2000	G	$5,100	2/06	NWIL	15' batwing mower
Woods	3180	2003	G	$5,900	9/06	NWIL	15' batwing mower, solid tires
Woods	7144		E	$9,000	6/06	SCMN	7144RD, 12', pt, turf batwing rotary PTO mower, like new, very low hours
Woods	84		F	$750	1/06	NWIL	3 pt. rotary mower
Woods	84		G	$1,025	3/06	ECIA	Woods Cadet, 3-pt. mower
Woods	8400		G	$1,600	1/06	SEPA	Rotary mower, transport
Woods	BW180		G	$6,150	3/06	NCIL	15' batwing mower
Woods	BW180	2004	G	$5,600	7/06	NWIL	15' batwing mower, soft tires
Woods	Cadet 72		F	$425	11/06	WCIL	3-pt. mower
Woods	Cadet 72		F	$425	2/06	WCIL	
Woods	Cadet 84		G	$800	11/06	ECND	3-pt. mower
Woods	D80		G	$425	2/06	ECIL	3-pt. mower
Woods	H106		G	$1,350	7/06	SEND	3-pt. ditch bank mower

WHAT'S IT WORTH?

Mowers & Conditioners

Make	Model	Year	Cond.	Price	Sale	Location	Comments
Woods	HD 315		F	$2,000	8/06	NWIL	15' batwing mower, 1,000 PTO
Woods	HD 315		G	$4,200	3/06	SEND	Batwing mower, 15', hyd. fold
Woods	HD 315		G	$5,750	8/06	NCOH	15' batwing mower
Woods	HD210R-5		G	$3,000	2/06	NWMN	Single-wing rotary mower, weight box
Woods	L306		F	$200	3/06	SWMN	6' belly mower
Woods	MD 172		G	$800	1/06	NWIL	6', 3-pt. rotary mower, two years
Woods	MD 172		G	$1,000	3/06	NWIL	
Woods	MD 172	1996	G	$750	12/06	NWIL	6' 3-pt. road mower, 22' harrow Gator
Woods	MD184		E	$725	1/06	WCIL	
Woods	MD184		G	$1,600	6/06	NWIL	8', 3-pt. rotary mower
Woods	MD315		G	$4,000	8/06	NEIL	Batwing mower
Woods	MD315		G	$4,100	3/06	NCIL	15' batwing mower
Woods	RD6000		G	$525	12/06	SEMN	3-pt. mower
Woods	RD7200		G	$725	12/06	NWIL	6', 3-pt. finish mower
Woods	RD7200		G	$1,600	7/06	NWIL	6' finish mower
Woods	RM306		G	$250	10/06	SWOH	6' wide, 3-pt. mounted, PTO driven, two rear adjustable dolly wheels
Woods	RM306		G	$700	5/06	SEND	3-pt. grooming mower
Woods	RM360		G	$350	9/06	NWTN	Finishing mower
Woods	RM660		G	$625	9/06	SEIA	3-pt., 6' finish mower
Woods	RM660		G	$800	12/06	SCMN	3-pt., finishing mower
Woods	RM90		G	$600	8/06	NCIA	3-pt., 3-blade mower
Woods	RM90		G	$800	8/06	SEPA	3-pt., rotary finishing mower
Woods	S106		G	$1,300	4/06	ECND	Ditch bank mower

Notes

Mulchers

In the North we call it pop, in the South it's soda. Different terminology for the same thing. I find the same phenomenon with soil-finishing implements. In Kansas these tillage tools are called one thing, in Pennsylvania it's slightly different. Soil finishers, mulch trashers, field conditioners, the list goes on.

Mulchers

Make	Model	Year	Cond.	Price	Sale	Location	Comments
AerWay	NA		G	$4,300	2/06	NCIL	Soil aerator, 3-pt.
AerWay	NA		G	$6,400	3/06	NCCO	12' pasture aerator
Bearcat	12'		G	$700	1/06	NEIN	
Bervac	42'		F	$1,100	4/06	SEND	Seed bedding tool, 42', walking tandems
Bourgault	40'		G	$5,500	4/06	NWMN	Coil packer
Brillion	10'		F	$160	9/06	NWIL	Cultimulcher
Brillion	10'		F	$190	3/06	NEMI	Cultipacker
Brillion	10'		G	$1,250	12/06	WCMN	Packer, 3-pt. mount
Brillion	11'		G	$600	3/06	NEMI	4" axle, 11' cultipacker
Brillion	12'		P	$200	2/06	NCIL	Cultimulcher
Brillion	12'		G	$300	11/06	SWOH	Cultipacker
Brillion	12'		G	$425	3/06	NWOH	Cultipacker
Brillion	12'		G	$525	12/06	WCMI	Cultipacker
Brillion	12'		F	$650	4/06	SCMI	Cultimulcher, transport
Brillion	12'		F	$700	4/06	SCMI	Cultimulcher
Brillion	12'		G	$700	3/06	ECMI	4" axle × 12' center bearing cultipacker
Brillion	12'		G	$1,100	1/06	WCIL	Cultimulcher, inboard wheels
Brillion	12'		F	$1,300	3/06	NWPA	Cultipacker
Brillion	14'		G	$300	10/06	SWOH	Cultipacker, tow tongue
Brillion	14'		G	$650	8/06	NCOH	Double cultimulcher
Brillion	14'		G	$1,700	11/06	WCSD	Cultipacker, cultivates & packs at same time
Brillion	14'		G	$1,850	1/06	SCMI	Crowfoot, cultipacker on wheels
Brillion	15'		F	$625	3/06	NCCO	
Brillion	15'		F	$1,250	1/06	NEIN	
Brillion	15'		G	$2,500	1/06	NEIN	
Brillion	15'		E	$2,600	3/06	NCIL	Cultimulcher
Brillion	15.5'		F	$2,500	2/06	NCCO	
Brillion	16'		G	$475	9/06	NWOH	End transport packer
Brillion	16'		G	$600	1/06	SCMI	Cultipacker, wheels
Brillion	16'		G	$2,050	8/06	NEIL	Crowfoot front
Brillion	18'		F	$2,800	1/06	NWKY	18' U-fold roller
Brillion	20'		F	$200	9/06	NENE	Seed packer, pt
Brillion	20'		F	$225	2/06	SEMI	Crowfoot packer
Brillion	20'		G	$450	2/06	SEMI	Crowfoot packer
Brillion	20'		E	$6,900	2/06	SEMI	X-fold solid packer
Brillion	21'		G	$4,600	12/06	SEIA	Cultimulcher, hyd. fold
Brillion	21'		G	$5,400	2/06	NCIN	Soil groomer
Brillion	22'		G	$4,400	3/06	SEIA	Cultimulcher
Brillion	25'		F	$2,100	2/06	NWOH	Crowfoot cultipacker, vertical fold up, WP-1081
Brillion	28'		G	$5,100	1/06	NWKY	28' X-fold roller
Brillion	30'		E	$6,400	1/06	NWKY	30' X-fold roller
Brillion	5'		G	$400	3/06	ECMI	4" axle × 5' cultipacker pup, 2 sold at $400 each
Brillion	5'		G	$400	3/06	ECMI	4" axle × 5' cultipacker pup, 2 sold at $400 each
Brillion	9 shank	2002	E	$13,100	3/06	NCCO	Land Commander, Schmeizer hyd. roller, nice
Brillion	X108		G	$4,500	12/06	WCMI	25' X-fold cultipacker
Brillion	X108		G	$5,050	3/06	NWOH	22' cultipacker, vertical fold
Brillion	X108		E	$7,600	8/06	SCMI	23' cultipacker
Brillion	XL	2003	G	$10,500	12/06	SWMI	Optimizer 32' Series XL crowfoot X-fold cultipacker
Brillion	XL144		G	$6,700	2/06	NCIL	32' roller, flat fold

Mulchers

Make	Model	Year	Cond.	Price	Sale	Location	Comments
Brillion	XL144		E	$8,750	3/06	NWOH	32' X-fold cultipacker
Brillion	XL144	2005	E	$11,000	5/06	SCMI	32' X-fold cultipacker
Case IH	415		G	$3,300	3/06	NCUT	Cultipacker
Case IH	4200		E	$6,100	2/06	NEIA	12' soil finisher, Remlinger 5-bar harrow, like new
Case IH	4200		G	$11,750	2/06	WCIA	20' soil finisher
DMI	25'	1990	G	$2,400	11/06	WCMN	Crumbler packer
Dunham	15'		F	$1,600	1/06	NCCO	
Dunham	15'		F	$1,600	1/06	NCCO	
Dunham	15'		F	$1,700	1/06	NCCO	
Dunham	20'		F	$3,200	3/06	NCOH	Hyd. fold transport packer
Dunham	22'		G	$550	12/06	SEIA	Harrowgator
Dunham Lehr	14'		G	$1,700	1/06	NECO	Solid front & rears
Dunham Lehr	25'		F	$2,000	3/06	SWOH	Cultipacker, double wing
Eversman	PS240		G	$900	9/06	SCNE	By Artsway, 20' tiller, 8R-30, 3 pt., dual gauge wheels, JD 8R-30 planter mounts, 1 set of lift assist wheels & brackets
Flexi-Coil	33'		G	$2,250	9/06	WCND	Coil packer, hyd. fold
Flexi-Coil	45'		G	$7,000	10/06	NCND	Packer
Flexi-Coil	48'		G	$8,500	4/06	NWMN	Coil packer, down pressure springs, hyd. fold
Flexi-Coil	50'		G	$9,000	3/06	WCMN	S-tine coil harrow packer
Flexi-Coil	75	1993	G	$12,250	11/06	ECND	Spiral packer, 56'
Flexi-Coil	92		G	$5,000	3/06	NEND	System 92, harrow packer, 4-rank adjustable, 50'
Flexi-Coil	System 75		F	$4,250	9/06	WCND	Packer, 45', hyd. fold, tricycle wheel on hitch
Flexi-Coil	System 95		G	$8,000	2/06	NWMN	55' harrow packer
Flexi-Coil	System 95		G	$12,000	3/06	NEND	60' harrow packer, one owner
Flexi-Coil	System 95	2003	E	$13,000	12/06	WCMN	70' harrow packer
FMC	RC240		G	$350	2/06	WCNE	21', 3-pt. roto-tiller
Glencoe	15'		F	$400	9/06	SEIA	11-shank soil saver
Glencoe	18'		G	$2,750	9/06	NEIA	Soil finisher
Glencoe	21'		G	$2,000	8/06	WCIL	Soil finisher
Glencoe	22'	2001	E	$12,500	1/06	SWOH	Land finisher, 5-bar harrow, walking tandems, less than 300 acres
Glencoe	24'		F	$2,000	2/06	WCMN	Mulch finisher
Glencoe	32'		F	$1,600	3/06	SEIA	Soil finisher
Glencoe	4300		G	$3,000	9/06	SEIA	21.5' soil finisher, heavy drag harrow
Glencoe	4500		G	$5,300	2/06	NCIN	22' soil finisher, hyd. fold, SF4500, hd harrow, one season on new sweeps & blades
Howard	NA		G	$1,000	5/06	SEWY	5', 3-pt. roto-tiller
IHC	18'		G	$450	6/06	NWKS	Seed bed conditioner
IHC	315		G	$875	3/06	NWIL	14' cultimulcher
IHC	315		G	$2,000	3/06	ECMI	15' packer, mulcher
IHC	415		G	$1,300	1/06	WCNE	Solid start, harrow
John Deere	200		G	$7,200	2/06	SCMI	Seed bed finisher, used one season
John Deere	550		G	$3,000	3/06	NCNE	22.5' Mulch Master field finisher, rolling pickers, herbicide kit
John Deere	712		G	$3,750	2/06	NEIN	9-shank
John Deere	714		F	$4,500	3/06	NCIL	11-shank
John Deere	714		G	$7,000	3/06	NWOH	11-shank
John Deere	714		G	$7,500	8/06	WCMN	21', folding coulter chisel, cushion gangs, 5-bar spike tooth harrow

Mulchers

Make	Model	Year	Cond.	Price	Sale	Location	Comments
John Deere	714		G	$8,000	4/06	ECND	24', 17-shank, true depth, walking tandems, hyd. disk pressure, weight package
John Deere	714		G	$9,000	8/06	SCNE	21' mulch tiller w/ walking tandems
John Deere	714		G	$10,000	12/06	WCMI	11-shank
John Deere	714	1998	G	$3,250	2/06	NWIN	13' soil saver
John Deere	722		F	$1,000	3/06	ECIL	25' soil finisher
John Deere	722		G	$4,500	12/06	SEMN	24' mulch finisher
John Deere	722		G	$5,250	12/06	SEMN	Mulch finisher, 5-bar harrow
John Deere	724		F	$1,700	4/06	NWKS	
John Deere	724		F	$4,000	3/06	SEND	Soil finisher, 30', rock flex front disk, single point depth, tandems across, 9" sweeps, 5-bar harrow
John Deere	724		G	$4,600	8/06	SEMN	30' mulch finisher
John Deere	724		G	$6,250	8/06	WCIA	30' finisher, spike harrow
John Deere	726		G	$11,000	12/06	SEMN	17.5' mulch finisher
John Deere	726		G	$13,500	3/06	NENE	27', hyd. fold field finisher, dual walking tandems, JD 5-bar harrow, manual leveling
John Deere	726		G	$13,500	2/06	WCIA	21'9"
John Deere	726		G	$17,500	11/06	NCOH	Mulch finisher, JD spike, 5-bar flex harrow, 25'
John Deere	726		G	$19,500	2/06	WCIA	30'9"
John Deere	726		G	$19,750	2/06	WCIA	33'9"
John Deere	726		G	$22,000	2/06	WCIA	
John Deere	726		E	$23,000	3/06	NESD	36.5' mulch finisher, rolling basket, like new
John Deere	726		E	$27,500	2/06	NCIL	30'9" soil finisher, 5-bar spike tooth drag
John Deere	726	1997	E	$13,750	3/06	NWIL	18'9" mulch finisher, walking tandems, hyd. disk gang, flex fold, C-shanks, 5-bar coil tine harrow, new shovels
John Deere	726	2001	G	$21,750	12/06	SEIA	24'9" soil finisher, hyd. disk gang, spike harrow
John Deere	726	2003	G	$21,000	1/06	NWIL	24.5' soil finisher, 5-bar spike tooth harrow, walking tandems, new sweeps
John Deere	726	2003	G	$21,500	3/06	NESD	24.5' field finisher
John Deere	726	2003	G	$25,000	12/06	NCIA	27.5', 5-bar tine harrow
John Deere	726	2006	E	$37,000	12/06	WCMN	Soil finisher, 38.5', single-point depth control, 5-bar harrow, knock-off shovels, front. hyd. disk, rear hitch
John Deere	970		P	$1,600	3/06	NCCO	16'
John Deere	970		P	$1,600	2/06	NCCO	16'
John Deere	970		G	$5,000	3/06	NEOH	25' cultimulcher
Kent	18'		G	$2,750	11/06	WCMN	Soil finisher, 5-bar spike tooth harrow
Kent	22'		G	$4,000	3/06	SEIA	Soil saver, manual
Kewanee	12'		F	$700	8/06	NWIL	Cultimulcher
Kewanee	12'		G	$4,500	2/06	NEIA	Soil finisher, older
Kewanee	14'		F	$600	4/06	SEMI	Cultimulcher
Kewanee	14'		G	$1,775	8/06	NWIL	Drill hitch
Kewanee	15'		G	$950	3/06	NCIL	Cultimulcher
Kewanee	15'		G	$1,050	12/06	NEMO	Cultimulcher, dual inboard wheels
Kewanee	15'		G	$1,350	2/06	NCIL	Cultipacker
Kewanee	15'		G	$2,250	2/06	NECO	Double packer wheels & harrow
Kewanee	16'		F	$1,500	3/06	NCCO	
Kewanee	18'		G	$2,800	2/06	NCCO	
Kewanee	20'		F	$1,200	3/06	NCIL	Cultimulcher, flat fold
Kewanee	20'		G	$2,750	1/06	NWIL	Hyd. fold cultimulcher

Mulchers

Make	Model	Year	Cond.	Price	Sale	Location	Comments
Kewanee	25'		G	$3,400	1/06	WCNE	Solid front & rear
Kewanee	30'		G	$7,700	3/06	NCCO	Flat fold
Kewanee	88		F	$750	9/06	NECO	14' crowfoot roller harrow, solid rubber
Krause	15'		G	$1,700	9/06	NEIA	Field finisher
Krause	3112		G	$4,950	2/06	NEIA	12' soil finisher
Krause	4226		G	$5,250	3/06	SWNE	26' rolling packer
Krause	4400		G	$2,750	2/06	SWNE	20' V-packer, hyd. fold, 9.5L-15 tires, one owner
Krause	4418		G	$3,400	1/06	NECO	19' V-wheel packer
Krause	6164		G	$9,500	4/06	SWOH	25' Landsman, 3-bar spike harrow, rolling basket
Krause	Landsman		G	$4,250	2/06	NECO	15'
Kubota	4'		G	$400	4/06	SEIA	3-pt. 4' tiller
Landoll	22'		E	$8,800	2/06	SENE	Soil finisher
Landoll	850		G	$7,000	12/06	SCNE	19' Finisholl, 10" sweeps, hyd. fold, 3-bar harrow
Landoll	850		E	$13,000	2/06	NWIL	Finisholl, 18.5', 5-bar drag, like new
Landoll	875		E	$13,750	2/06	SEIL	875-21 Tilloll, like new
Morris	41'		F	$2,250	3/06	NCND	Coil packer
Riteway	RHP6058		G	$9,000	6/06	NWMN	Harrow packer, 58', hd 5-bar harrow sections, 1.75" coils
Summers	25'	2003	G	$2,000	8/06	NENE	Rotary packer
Summers	28'	1990	G	$3,200	3/06	ECND	Coil packer, hyd. fold
Summers	40'		G	$3,750	3/06	SWMN	Coil packer, hyd. fold
Sunflower	4212		G	$5,900	2/06	SCWI	11-shank
Sunflower	4212		G	$6,250	9/06	SCNE	19' rigid trash mulcher
Sunflower	4212	1999	G	$7,600	3/06	SWKS	4212-13, 16'3" trash mulcher, rear reel chopper, approximately 1,000 acres of use
Sunflower	4212	2000	G	$9,500	2/06	WCIL	Trash mulcher, 11-shank 14' disk chisel w/ walking tandems and ridge leveler
Sunflower	4232		G	$12,300	3/06	SWNE	26' flex 21-shank stalk slicer chisel, hyd. front disk, Red Ball, hyd. fold, stainless steel fertilizer tubes, rear finger whips, rear-hitch attachment, one owner
Sunflower	6220		G	$8,500	1/06	NCIL	Soil finisher, 15' center fold, 5-bar drag
Sunflower	6220		G	$10,000	3/06	NWIL	18'
Sunflower	6331		F	$5,700	2/06	WCIL	25' soil finisher, 5-bar harrow
Sunflower	6331		G	$13,000	1/06	NECO	Land finisher, disk, sweeps, treaders, pickers
Sunflower	6332		G	$15,500	3/06	NCNE	23' mulch finisher, 4-bar harrow
Sunflower	6332	1996	G	$17,000	2/06	ECIL	26' soil finisher, rolling baskets, tine harrow
Sunflower	6332	1997	E	$15,000	1/06	WCIL	23.5', 5-bar mounted harrow
Sunflower	6430		G	$9,200	3/06	NEKS	30' one-pass land finisher, 4-bar harrow
Sunflower	6432		G	$17,400	3/06	SWNE	36' land finisher, walking tandems, 3-bar harrow, rolling packer
Sunflower	6432		G	$23,500	8/06	SCNE	36' land finisher, 3-bar harrow
Sunflower	7212		G	$2,800	8/06	NECO	17.5' soil conditioner
Triple K	20'		G	$500	3/06	ECND	Seed bedder, rolling baskets
Triple K	30'		G	$525	4/06	NWMN	Seedbedder, rolling baskets
Triple K	30'		G	$2,100	3/06	NWMN	Soil conditioner, twin baskets, 4-rank
Triple K	31'		G	$2,250	3/06	ECND	Seed bedder, rolling baskets
Troy-Bilt	NA		G	$575	1/06	NWIL	Bronco 5-hp. roto tiller, 2 years old
Troy-Bilt	NA		G	$800	12/06	SWIA	Garden tiller, Kohler 8-hp., rear tine

Planters

We're looking at more acres of corn in 2007. What do you need to plant them? A planter. In late 2006 and early 2007, I saw strong demand for quality used planters at auction. Prices skyrocketed in December and January, then backed off around mid-March. How high did they go? How about $17,000 for a 6-row (yep, 6-row) JD 7200 planter sold in west-central Michigan in December.

Planters

Make	Model	Year	Cond.	Price	Sale	Location	Comments
Black Mach	NA		G	$8,200	12/06	ECIL	12R-30 corn or 15R-15 bean, JD units
Case IH	1200		G	$39,000	12/06	SCNE	AFS 12R-30, liquid coulters, pivot transport, full computer monitor control, only used on 475 acres of corn, SN CBJ022189
Case IH	1200	2001	G	$8,000	3/06	WCKS	8R, trash whippers, fertilizer attachment, monitor
Case IH	1200	2003	G	$26,000	3/06	ECNE	24R-20 on Friesen front-fold bar
Case IH	1200	2005	G	$55,000	3/06	ECNE	Pivot transport system, pt
Case IH	900		F	$750	9/06	SCMN	8R-30, dry fertilizer, rigid, transport
Case IH	900		F	$850	12/06	ECMO	4R cyclo airflow plano-tiller, no-till coulters
Case IH	900		F	$1,000	3/06	ECNE	Cyclo Air, Hiniker 3800 Econo-Till ridge tool bar, V-gauge wheels, new disk openers, firming points, seed shoes
Case IH	900		F	$1,200	9/06	SCMN	8R-30 folding planter
Case IH	900		F	$1,600	9/06	NCIA	8R-30, pt, Yetter row cleaner, population monitor
Case IH	900		F	$2,250	12/06	SEMN	12R-30, vertical fold
Case IH	900		F	$2,300	3/06	NCNE	12R-30, Cyclo Air, hyd. fold, insecticide, squeeze pump, double-disk fertilizer openers, dual lift assist, monitor
Case IH	900		G	$3,400	11/06	SCIL	12R-30, Kelderman fold, insecticide, trash wheels, coulters
Case IH	900		G	$3,700	3/06	NEKS	6R-30, liquid fertilizer, Cyclo Air
Case IH	900		G	$4,200	1/06	NWIL	8R-30, liquid starter
Case IH	900		G	$5,100	9/06	NCIA	12R, insecticide, Early Riser monitor
Case IH	900		G	$7,500	3/06	WCMN	3 pt., air, 12R-30, corn and bean lift assist, herbicide, insecticide, disk cut-aways
Case IH	900		G	$8,600	2/06	ECIL	12R-30, front fold planter, insect, Yetter trash whippers, firming wheels
Case IH	900		G	$8,750	3/06	NWIL	12R-30, Kelderman front fold
Case IH	900	1992	F	$1,700	11/06	NEKS	6R-30, Cyclo Air
Case IH	900	1993	G	$2,750	5/06	SCMI	6R-30, corn, dry fertilizer
Case IH	900	1993	G	$6,250	1/06	NEIA	8RW Kelderman front fold, Dawn trash whippers, monitor, insecticide
Case IH	900	1994	F	$1,000	3/06	NWKS	8R
Case IH	950		F	$1,900	8/06	NCOH	6R-30, Cyclo Air, liquid, no-till
Case IH	950		F	$2,000	2/06	WCKS	8R, Cyclo
Case IH	950		F	$4,000	1/06	NWIL	8RW, monitor, smart boxes, Yetter coulters
Case IH	950		G	$7,000	3/06	ECND	12R-30, vertical fold, 3 pt., lift assist, liquid drop fertilizer, (2) 100's edible bean, corn, soybean drums, population monitor, single owner
Case IH	950		G	$9,000	3/06	NCIA	12R-30 vertical fold, 3 pt. planter, population monitor, Yetter finger trash whippers, new disk openers, shoes, furrow fillers
Case IH	950		G	$18,500	1/06	SESD	16R-30, front fold
Case IH	950	1994	G	$15,000	3/06	SEMN	12R-30, front fold, dry fertilizer, Dawn row cleaners
Case IH	950	1995	E	$13,000	8/06	ECIL	Front fold, 12R-30, 955 upgrades, insecticide, min-till coulters, trash kickers, monitor
Case IH	950	1995	G	$19,000	5/06	SEND	Cyclo, 12R-30, hyd. wing fold, front fold, dry fertilizer, rear lift assist, full-performance monitor
Case IH	950	1997	G	$3,000	3/06	NCIL	8R-36, pt, vertical fold, trash whippers, insecticide, corn and bean drums, Early Riser monitor
Case IH	955		F	$1,600	9/06	SCMN	16R, 15" interplant

Planters

Make	Model	Year	Cond.	Price	Sale	Location	Comments
Case IH	955		G	$13,500	2/06	NEMO	6R/11R split row, Case IH 5000 cart, track remover
Case IH	955	1996	E	$7,750	3/06	NEKS	6R, corn & bean
Case IH	955	1996	G	$15,000	2/06	NWIA	12R-30, Cyclo Air, tool bar, Early Riser monitor, insecticide, herbicide, hyd. vertical fold
Case IH	955	1997	G	$7,000	11/06	NEKS	8RW, dry fertilizer, insecticide, herbicide, 3 drums, monitor
Deutz Allis	385		G	$1,300	3/06	ECIA	6R, monitor, dry fertilizer, no-till coulters
IHC	800		G	$350	8/06	NEIA	4RW, monitor, insecticide, dry fertilizer, one owner
IHC	800		F	$350	11/06	ECIL	8R-36, endwise transport, residue managers, insect, Cyclo II monitor
IHC	800		F	$400	8/06	NWIL	8R-36, end transport
IHC	800		F	$500	4/06	SEMI	6R-30 corn, liquid fertilizer
IHC	800		F	$600	5/06	SEND	8R-30 Cyclo, monitor
IHC	800		F	$625	12/06	NWWI	4R-30
IHC	800		F	$700	6/06	NCIA	8R-30, 900 updates, insecticide, monitor
IHC	800		F	$700	3/06	NWPA	6R Cyclo air, dry fertilizer
IHC	800		F	$800	3/06	NWIL	8R-36
IHC	800		F	$900	3/06	NWOH	6R-30, corn, 3-pt., 200-gal. liquid fertilizer tank, no-till openers
IHC	800		F	$900	12/06	SEND	8R-30
IHC	800		F	$950	1/06	SESD	6RN
IHC	800		G	$1,000	3/06	SEND	12R-30, Cyclo air, corn, sunflower, pinto & soybean drums, monitor
IHC	800		P	$1,050	2/06	SCNY	6R, corn
IHC	800		G	$1,250	3/06	NWOH	6R-30, liquid fertilizer, corn
IHC	800		F	$1,500	11/06	WCMN	16R-22, liquid fertilizer, no openers, 2-lift assist
IHC	800		G	$1,500	2/06	SEIA	8RN, hyd. fold
IHC	800		F	$1,500	3/06	NEKS	8R, liquid fertilizer
IHC	800		G	$2,400	7/06	ECND	8R-30, dry fertilizer, cross-fill auger
IHC	800		G	$2,500	2/06	NCKS	Cyclo Air 6R-30
IHC	800		F	$3,000	3/06	SEPA	6R, coulters
IHC	800		G	$4,100	2/06	NWSD	8R Cyclo Air, always shedded, dry fertilizer, herbicide boxes, markers, monitor, stored inside
IHC	800		G	$8,000	11/06	NEND	Cyclo, 12R-30, trailing, dry fertilizer, hyd. end transport
IHC	800		G	$9,500	3/06	NEKS	Cyclo 16R-30, rear horizontal fold planter, 1,000 PTO, insecticide boxes, new 900 Series covering disks, new hopper tops, Accu-Plant, notched openers
IHC	800		G	$10,300	12/06	ECIL	16R-30, 900 updates, furrow openers, insecticide, performance center monitor, very nice
IHC	800		G	$17,200	12/06	ECIL	32R-15, 900 updates, 2 performance center monitors, very nice soybean planter
IHC	800	1980	P	$200	12/06	WCIL	8RW, hyd. fold, 3-pt. planter, Dickey-john monitor, trash managers
John Deere	1700		G	$6,600	9/06	SCNE	8R-30 vacuum
John Deere	1700	2003	G	$13,250	8/06	WCKS	MaxEmerge, 8R, 250 monitor markers
John Deere	1710		G	$11,750	9/06	NCIA	12R-30, row cleaners, 250 monitor
John Deere	1710		G	$13,000	12/06	SCMN	12R-30, vacuum

Planters

Make	Model	Year	Cond.	Price	Sale	Location	Comments
John Deere	1710	2004	E	$45,000	12/06	WCMN	24R-22 MaxEmerge plus, mounted on K&M folding bar, Rawson hyd. drives, 3 vacuum units, liquid fertilizer, Red Ball monitors, rear hitch to pull Gandy, 120-bushel seed tote, flex tubes, sold as unit
John Deere	1710	2004	E	$45,000	12/06	WCMN	24R-22 MaxEmerge plus, mounted on K&M folding bar, Rawson hyd. drives, 3 vacuum units, liq. fertilizer, Red Ball monitors, rear hitch to pull Gandy, 120-bushel seed tote, flex tubes, sold as unit, 2 sold on same sale – $45K each
John Deere	1720		G	$21,000	2/06	WCMN	12R-30 MaxEmerge plus stack fold, Martin row cleaners, Red Ball liquid fertilizer, hd lift assist, Dawn 1,200 closing wheels
John Deere	1720		G	$32,000	12/06	SCMN	16R-30, stack fold
John Deere	1720	2006	E	$51,000	11/06	SCNE	XP vacuum, 16R-30, stacking bars, hd down-force springs, liquid fertilizer, box extensions, lift assist, used one season, shedded
John Deere	1720	2006	E	$51,000	11/06	SCNE	MaxEmerge XP vacuum, 16R-30, stacking bars, hd down force springs, liquid fertilizer, box extension, lift assist, bean, corn and small corn plates, Seedstar monitor, used one season
John Deere	1730		G	$10,500	12/06	NWWI	8R-22 toolbar, liquid fertilizer, vacuum, 2 Demco 250 saddle tanks
John Deere	1750		E	$8,100	2/06	SEMI	Conservation, 4R MaxEmerge vacuum, 36"
John Deere	1750		E	$8,500	9/06	NECO	8R-30, pt, VacuMeter, several plates
John Deere	1750		F	$9,750	12/06	NWWI	6R-30, conservation, dry fertilizer, vacuum
John Deere	1750		G	$10,500	8/06	SCNE	8R-30 MaxEmerge, conservation
John Deere	1750		G	$10,500	12/06	NWWI	6R-30, conservation, dry fertilizer, finger pickup
John Deere	1750		G	$11,750	12/06	NWWI	6R-30, conservation, dry fertilizer, vacuum, loaded
John Deere	1750		G	$12,500	12/06	NWWI	6R-30, conservation, dry fertilizer, vacuum, loaded
John Deere	1750		G	$16,750	12/06	NWWI	8R-30, conservation, dry fertilizer, vacuum
John Deere	1750	1999	G	$11,000	4/06	WCKS	8R, liquid fertilizer
John Deere	1750	2000	G	$13,500	2/06	SWNE	Conservation 8R-30 air, liquid fertilizer
John Deere	1750	2003	E	$14,000	3/06	NWOH	6R-30 no-till, liquid fertilizer, finger pickup, 250 monitor, planted approximately 900 acres
John Deere	1760		G	$17,000	8/06	NCIA	12R, insecticide units, fertilizer starter pump
John Deere	1760		G	$24,000	12/06	SEMN	12R-30, wing fold, MaxEmerge plus, 3-bu. boxes
John Deere	1760		E	$26,000	3/06	NEIA	12R-30 conservation MaxEmerge plus VacuMeter planter, monitor
John Deere	1760	1996	E	$23,000	11/06	WCIA	12R-30, Yetter row cleaners
John Deere	1760	1997	G	$15,500	1/06	NEIN	12R-30, 4,000 acres
John Deere	1760	1997	G	$21,500	12/06	NCIA	12R-30, hyd. wing fold, vacuum, 250 monitor
John Deere	1760	1997	E	$23,500	1/06	NWIA	Conservation 12RN, hyd. front fold, JD monitor
John Deere	1760	1997	G	$28,000	12/06	NWIL	Conservation MaxEmerge plus 12R-30 VacuMeter, insecticide, Yetter trash wheels, CompuTrak 250 monitor
John Deere	1760	1997	G	$31,250	2/06	ECMN	Conservation 12R-30 wing fold, liquid, 3-bu. hoppers, 250 monitor
John Deere	1760	1998	G	$27,000	2/06	NWIN	12R, liquid 250 monitor, row cleaners
John Deere	1760	2001	G	$18,500	2/06	SCMI	8R corn, 3-bu. hopper, liquid fertilizer, single disk opener, Keaton seed firmer, long tongue, front fold, SeedStar monitor

Planters

Make	Model	Year	Cond.	Price	Sale	Location	Comments
John Deere	1770		G	$18,000	8/06	SCNE	12R-30
John Deere	1770		G	$25,500	8/06	NECO	16R-30, liquid fertilizer
John Deere	1770		G	$26,500	9/06	NCIA	16R
John Deere	1770		G	$27,500	11/06	NCIN	12RN, front fold, conservation MaxEmerge plus, liquid fertilizer, no-till, smart boxes, monitor, vacuum
John Deere	1770		G	$30,250	3/06	NWIL	12R, vacuum
John Deere	1770		G	$32,000	4/06	NESD	12R-30, front-fold MaxEmerge, VacuMeter, dry fertilizer, single disk openers, Keeton firmers, Dawn row cleaners, 3-bu. boxes, 250 monitor
John Deere	1770		G	$34,500	12/06	SCMN	16R-30, liquid fertilizer
John Deere	1770		G	$50,500	12/06	ECNE	16R-30, conservation, insecticide, (8) 70-gal. liquid fertilizer tanks, herbicides, set up for band or broadcast, JD trash furrow openers, Red Ball monitor, ½ disconnect, light package
John Deere	1770		G	$64,000	3/06	NENE	16R-30, hyd. front fold, liquid fertilizer
John Deere	1770		G	$69,500	12/06	SEMN	NT, 16R-30, CCS, XP Pro shaft unit, pneumatic down-pressure, 1350 monitor, accu-sensors, corn & bean disk
John Deere	1770		G	$71,000	9/06	NCIA	24R-30, 350 monitor
John Deere	1770	1998	F	$28,000	6/06	SCMN	Conservation, MaxEmerge Plus, VacuMeter, 16R-30, (4) 80-gal. poly liquid fertilizer tanks
John Deere	1770	2001	E	$75,000	2/06	WCIL	Conservation 24R-30 planter, ½ width drive disconnect, SeedStar monitor, insecticide, hd down-pressure springs, plastic rotary scrapers, corn and soybean disks
John Deere	1770	2002	G	$47,000	3/06	SEMN	MaxEmerge, 12R-30, liquid fertilizer, two 250-gal. poly tanks, JD pumps, 3-bushel seed boxes, Yetter trash whippers, flute coulters in furrow, vacuum
John Deere	1770	2004	G	$53,000	12/06	ECMO	16RN, CCS, Pro Series units, trash cleaners, pneumatic down-pressure, mechanical drive, walking gauge wheels, liquid fertilizer
John Deere	1770	2005	E	$48,000	12/06	SWIA	12R-30, CCS tanks, no-till, Martin trash whippers w/ depth bands, Martin closing wheels, Keeton seed firmers, Martin drag chains
John Deere	1770	2005	G	$80,000	12/06	NWMO	NT, 24R, markers, vacuum seed meter, pneumatic down force, corn and bean disks
John Deere	1780		G	$10,600	3/06	ECIL	8R-30/15R-15, vacuum, no-till, 3-bu. boxes, 3 sets of disks, JD Computer-Trak 250 monitor w/ radar, travel lights, nice
John Deere	1780		E	$11,000	11/06	WCIA	8R-30/15-15 interplant
John Deere	1780		F	$17,000	2/06	WCIA	12R/23R, fluted coulters, 250 monitor
John Deere	1780		G	$24,250	12/06	WCMN	12/23 front fold, liquid fertilizer, monitor
John Deere	1780		G	$31,500	3/06	SEMN	24R-20, MaxEmerge plus VacuMeter conservation, pneumatic down-pressure, 3-bu. seed boxes, (2) 300-gal. poly fertilizer tanks
John Deere	1780	1999	G	$27,000	12/06	WCMN	12/23, mechanical drive, hyd. down-pressure, 250 monitor
John Deere	1780	2000	G	$37,750	3/06	SEIA	16/31, ½ width disconnect, 3-bu. hoppers, SeedStar monitor less display, adjustable hd down pressure, no-till
John Deere	1780	2001	G	$52,000	4/06	NWMN	MaxEmerge plus, 24R-22, front fold, hopper extension, population monitor, JD 250 w/ liquid fertilizer attachment
John Deere	1790		G	$82,500	2/06	SEKS	24R-20 CCS, SeedStar monitor, Tiger shank, Yetter trash whips

Planters

Make	Model	Year	Cond.	Price	Sale	Location	Comments
John Deere	1790	2003	G	$66,500	3/06	SEIA	CCS 16/31, no-till coulters, scales, air down-pressure, lights & hyd. on back
John Deere	1790	2004	E	$61,500	2/06	ECMN	CCS, 24R-20, front fold, Pro Series × row units, pneumatic down-force system, one owner
John Deere	7000		F	$400	9/06	NWIL	8R-38, front fold
John Deere	7000		F	$450	3/06	SEIA	4R
John Deere	7000		F	$525	3/06	SEIA	4R
John Deere	7000		F	$550	3/06	ECMN	4R corn, liquid fertilizer, monitor, +10% buyers premium
John Deere	7000		G	$550	9/06	NEIN	4R, liquid fertilizer
John Deere	7000		F	$675	6/06	NCIL	12R-30, insecticide, monitor, straight bar
John Deere	7000		G	$700	7/06	NWIL	8R, end transport
John Deere	7000		F	$700	12/06	SCMN	8R-36, liquid fertilizer
John Deere	7000		F	$775	2/06	SCMI	8R-30 corn, dry fertilizer
John Deere	7000		F	$800	11/06	NEKS	6R-30, furrow openers
John Deere	7000		G	$800	11/06	WCIL	8R-36, Kelderman fold
John Deere	7000		G	$850	7/06	NWIL	8R, set up for beans
John Deere	7000		F	$900	3/06	WCIL	8R-30, no-till coulters, monitor
John Deere	7000		F	$900	3/06	NEMI	12R, end pull
John Deere	7000		F	$1,000	6/06	SWMN	8RN, monitor, herbicide, fertilizer
John Deere	7000		F	$1,000	6/06	WCMN	12R-30, manual fold, JD 100 monitor, Kinze seed firmers
John Deere	7000		G	$1,000	8/06	NWIL	4R-36, no-till
John Deere	7000		F	$1,000	1/06	SCMI	8R-30 corn, liquid fertilizer, insecticide, monitor
John Deere	7000		G	$1,025	3/06	NWIL	6R, fertilizer tanks
John Deere	7000		G	$1,100	9/06	ECNE	4R-36, liquid fertilizer, quick-fill tanks, furrow openers, finger pickup and bean cups
John Deere	7000		G	$1,100	9/06	NWIL	4RW
John Deere	7000		F	$1,100	2/06	WCIA	8R-30
John Deere	7000		G	$1,100	1/06	WCIL	4RW no-till, monitor
John Deere	7000		F	$1,200	3/06	NWOH	8R-30, dry fertilizer, corn, cross auger
John Deere	7000		G	$1,200	6/06	NWIL	8R-36
John Deere	7000		G	$1,200	9/06	NCIA	8R-30, liquid fertilizer
John Deere	7000		F	$1,200	11/06	SCSD	8RW, liquid fertilizer, herbicide, insecticide
John Deere	7000		F	$1,250	8/06	NCIA	8R-30 pull, hd furrowers, monitor, Kinze bean units, herbicide, insecticide
John Deere	7000		F	$1,250	12/06	ECMO	6RN, no-till coulters, hd down-pressure springs, liquid fertilizer, monitor
John Deere	7000		F	$1,250	2/06	WCIA	8RW
John Deere	7000		G	$1,300	12/06	NENE	
John Deere	7000		F	$1,300	12/06	NWWI	6R-30, dry fertilizer, finger pickup
John Deere	7000		G	$1,300	2/06	WCIL	4R-36
John Deere	7000		F	$1,325	2/06	WCIA	12R-30 wing fold
John Deere	7000		F	$1,350	2/06	NECO	8R30
John Deere	7000		G	$1,350	12/06	SEMN	4R
John Deere	7000		F	$1,400	1/06	NECO	8R-30, pt
John Deere	7000		G	$1,400	3/06	NWIL	6R, fertilizer, tanks
John Deere	7000		F	$1,400	8/06	NECO	16R-30, liquid fertilizer
John Deere	7000		F	$1,400	9/06	NWIL	6R, insecticide
John Deere	7000		G	$1,500	5/06	SWWI	4R corn, monitor
John Deere	7000		F	$1,575	2/06	ECIL	8R-30, Yetter openers, smart boxes, Dickey-john monitor

WHAT'S IT WORTH?

Planters

Make	Model	Year	Cond.	Price	Sale	Location	Comments
John Deere	7000		F	$1,600	8/06	NWIL	8RW, front fold
John Deere	7000		F	$1,700	3/06	NCKS	6R-30
John Deere	7000		G	$1,700	6/06	NWIL	7R-25, 3-pt. bean
John Deere	7000		F	$1,700	8/06	NCIA	8R-30, Kinze bean units, no-till coulters, trash whippers
John Deere	7000		G	$1,750	7/06	WCMN	8R-30, liquid fertilizer
John Deere	7000		G	$1,800	3/06	SWOH	6R-30, dry boxes, monitor, late style seed rings
John Deere	7000		F	$1,800	3/06	NWIL	4R, no-till, Yetter trash whippers, bean cups
John Deere	7000		F	$1,800	8/06	ECNE	8R-30, rigid frame, fertilizer
John Deere	7000		G	$1,800	12/06	WCIL	8RW, Kelderman fold, Yetter no-till, trash managers, one owner
John Deere	7000		F	$1,800	1/06	SCNE	6R-36, pt, fertilizer tanks, pump, DJ monitor
John Deere	7000		F	$1,900	3/06	NWOH	6R-30, corn, Unverferth Cultiplanter II
John Deere	7000		F	$1,900	9/06	SEIL	12R-30, no-till, factory front fold, monitor
John Deere	7000		G	$1,950	3/06	NEKS	6R-30, liquid
John Deere	7000		G	$2,000	4/06	SEMI	4R-38, Rawson no-till openers, dry fertilizer, monitor, insecticide
John Deere	7000		G	$2,000	4/06	SCKS	6R plate
John Deere	7000		G	$2,000	12/06	SEMN	8R-30
John Deere	7000		F	$2,000	12/06	SEMN	12R-30
John Deere	7000		G	$2,100	8/06	ECNE	4RW, insecticide, furrow openers, monitor, shedded, one owner
John Deere	7000		G	$2,100	1/06	WCIL	6R-30, insecticide, trash wheels, Unverferth Cultiplanter II
John Deere	7000		G	$2,150	9/06	NWOH	6R-30, liquid fertilizer, no-till coulter, monitor
John Deere	7000		F	$2,250	3/06	NWIL	6R-30
John Deere	7000		G	$2,600	8/06	NCIA	8R-30 pull, finger trash whip, monitor, Keeton seed firmers, herbicide, insecticide, flex gauge wheel sold w/ 4 liquid fertilizer tanks and squeeze pump, new finger units and backup plates 105 acres ago
John Deere	7000		G	$2,600	12/06	SEMN	6R-30, liquid
John Deere	7000		G	$2,600	2/06	SCKS	6R-30, plateless, dry fertilizer, insecticide JD monitor
John Deere	7000		G	$2,800	12/06	NEMO	6RN no-till, insecticide boxes
John Deere	7000		G	$2,800	12/06	NWIL	8R-36, Kelderman front fold, Yetter no-till coulters & trash wheels, Lock 'N Load insecticide, corn units rebuilt in '06
John Deere	7000		G	$2,900	3/06	SCIN	Liquid fertilizer
John Deere	7000		G	$2,900	8/06	ECIA	6R-30, liquid fertilizer
John Deere	7000		G	$2,900	1/06	ECNE	8R-36, liquid fertilizer, spray kit, Yetter openers
John Deere	7000		F	$2,960	8/06	ECNE	8R-36, front fold
John Deere	7000		F	$3,000	2/06	WCMN	16R-22, front fold, monitor, built by Wayne's Welding
John Deere	7000		G	$3,000	2/06	NWIL	6R-30, coulters, MaxEmerge, trash wheels, insecticide, monitor, updates for no-till
John Deere	7000		G	$3,100	4/06	SCMN	6R-30, dry fertilizer, chemical boxes, monitor
John Deere	7000		G	$3,100	4/06	WCWI	6R-36
John Deere	7000		G	$3,100	12/06	NWWI	6R-30, dry fertilizer, finger pickup, cross auger
John Deere	7000		G	$3,200	4/06	NEND	8R-30, dry fertilizer, pt, markers, monitor
John Deere	7000		G	$3,300	9/06	NENE	4R-36 MaxEmerge vacuum planter, T-band insecticide, one owner
John Deere	7000		G	$3,600	4/06	SWOH	12R-30, liquid fertilizer, insecticide, belt meters
John Deere	7000		G	$3,700	12/06	SEMN	12R-30

Planters

Make	Model	Year	Cond.	Price	Sale	Location	Comments
John Deere	7000		G	$3,750	1/06	NEMO	6RN, no-till
John Deere	7000		G	$3,800	10/06	SEMN	6R
John Deere	7000		G	$4,000	4/06	ECND	12R-30, pt, box extension, insecticide, liquid drop fertilizer, corn, Sunflower fingers, bean cups
John Deere	7000		G	$4,000	2/06	WCOH	Conservation 6R
John Deere	7000		G	$4,250	9/06	WCWI	6RN corn, liquid fertilizer
John Deere	7000		G	$4,400	3/06	ECNE	12R-30
John Deere	7000		G	$4,500	7/06	NWOH	6R-30, no-till, liquid fertilizer, 200 monitor
John Deere	7000		G	$4,500	12/06	NWWI	6R-30, dry fertilizer, finger pickup, monitors
John Deere	7000		G	$5,200	4/06	NEIA	6R, fertilizer
John Deere	7000		F	$5,200	1/06	NWIL	12R-30, Kelderman front fold, insecticide, no-till coulters, row managers, Dickey-john Seed Manager monitor
John Deere	7000		G	$6,000	3/06	NESD	8R-30, monitor, dry fertilizer, herbicide, trash whippers
John Deere	7000		G	$7,700	2/06	NCIN	12R, front fold, liquid fertilizer, Kinze brush meter, monitor, insecticide, Yetter fertilizer
John Deere	7000		G	$8,000	3/06	ECIL	16R-30, front fold, furrow openers, insecticide, Dickey-john 3000 Scanamatic, JD smart box control
John Deere	7000		G	$9,100	2/06	SEIN	8RN, liquid fertilizer, no-till, front fold
John Deere	7000		G	$10,750	3/06	NEND	Front fold, 16R-30, insecticide, new Dickey-john monitor, radar, bean cups, sunflower and corn fingers all redone
John Deere	7000		G	$15,000	2/06	NWKS	16R-30, front-fold cultivator, liquid fertilizer
John Deere	7000	1976	G	$2,900	2/06	SWOH	8R-36, liquid fertilizer, Kinze soy units, insecticide finger seed units, end transport, no-till seed, fertilizer coulters
John Deere	7000	1978	G	$3,500	4/06	ECND	Trailing, 8R-30, dry fertilizer, insecticide
John Deere	7000	1979	G	$2,950	4/06	WCMN	6R-30, almost new ridge cleaners and brush soy meters
John Deere	7100		F	$550	3/06	WCKS	3-pt. 8R toolbar, JD 71 flex 8R planter
John Deere	7100		F	$700	8/06	ECNE	8R-30, hyd. drive, gauge wheels, Orthman markers, seed & insecticide boxes
John Deere	7100		P	$700	1/06	WCTX	Rough, 8R, missing box covers, stored with seed in boxes
John Deere	7100		F	$1,000	8/06	WCIL	8R-30, insecticide
John Deere	7100		G	$1,150	9/06	NCIA	8R-30 3-pt., monitor
John Deere	7100		G	$1,200	8/06	NCIA	12R, semi-mounted, Kinze units sold separate
John Deere	7100		F	$1,250	1/06	NECO	3-pt., 8R-30
John Deere	7100		G	$1,250	5/06	SCCA	8R-38
John Deere	7100		F	$1,250	2/06	WCNE	6R-36, 3-pt., monitor
John Deere	7100		F	$1,300	2/06	NCCO	6R-30, MaxEmerge
John Deere	7100		F	$1,300	2/06	NCCO	8R-30, MaxEmerge, bean cups, cover
John Deere	7100		F	$1,300	9/06	NCIA	15R-18 skip row, lift assist, Kinze bean meters
John Deere	7100		F	$1,350	6/06	NWIL	12R-30, no-till coulters, insecticide, JD Computrac 200 monitor w/ radar
John Deere	7100		G	$1,400	12/06	NENE	8×30
John Deere	7100		F	$1,500	8/06	NCIA	12R-30, Kinze bean units, lift-assist wheels
John Deere	7100		F	$1,600	8/06	ECNE	12R-30
John Deere	7100		F	$1,600	1/06	WCNE	6R MaxEmerge, fertilizer, insecticide, herbicide, monitor, corn and bean cups
John Deere	7100		G	$1,800	7/06	WCMN	8R-30, monitor, 3-pt.
John Deere	7100		F	$1,900	12/06	SCMN	12R-30
John Deere	7100		G	$2,000	2/06	NECO	8R-30, 3-pt.
John Deere	7100		G	$2,000	2/06	NECO	8R-30, 3-pt.

Planters

Make	Model	Year	Cond.	Price	Sale	Location	Comments
John Deere	7100		G	$2,000	2/06	NECO	8R-30, 3-pt.
John Deere	7100		F	$2,000	2/06	NCCO	6R-30
John Deere	7100		F	$2,000	2/06	NCCO	6R-30, MaxEmerge
John Deere	7100		G	$2,000	11/06	SCNE	6R-36, insecticide, furrow openers
John Deere	7100		F	$2,000	12/06	SEMN	12R-30
John Deere	7100		F	$2,000	1/06	NCCO	MaxEmerge 6R
John Deere	7100		F	$2,100	3/06	NWOH	11R bean, Kinze meters, 3-pt.
John Deere	7100		G	$2,100	3/06	SEND	8R-30 corn
John Deere	7100		G	$2,100	12/06	NENE	14R-18 bean, JD radical bean meters, monitor
John Deere	7100		G	$2,200	8/06	SCMN	8R-30, Kinze bean units
John Deere	7100		G	$2,200	12/06	WCMN	12R-24, 1.6-bu. extension, Kinze bean meters, finger pickup, lift assist, dual rate, Dickey-john monitor
John Deere	7100		G	$2,400	2/06	WCNE	6R-30, 3-pt.
John Deere	7100		F	$2,550	1/06	SESD	6RN, 3-pt.
John Deere	7100		G	$2,600	8/06	NCIA	12R-30, 3-pt., 2 lift assist, herbicides, insecticide, 200 monitor, seed firmers, 12 Kinze bean units
John Deere	7100		G	$3,300	3/06	NWMN	3 pt., 12R-30 finger, M2000 population monitor, insecticide, lift assist, plumbed for liquid fertilizer
John Deere	7100		G	$5,500	11/06	SCMN	12R-30
John Deere	7100		G	$8,000	11/06	NCOH	Bean, 15R-15
John Deere	7100		G	$9,000	3/06	ECNE	12R-36, Orthman bar, Orthman hyd. markers, liquid fertilizer pump, Keeton seed firmers
John Deere	7100	1985	G	$5,750	6/06	NWMN	Plate, 12R-22, liquid fertilizer, Mustang liquid insecticide, Lock 'N Load dry insecticide attachments
John Deere	7200		F	$3,000	9/06	NCIA	16R-30, hyd. fold, Dickey-john monitor
John Deere	7200		F	$3,400	3/06	ECKS	8R
John Deere	7200		F	$3,600	3/06	NWKS	8R MaxEmerge II, pt
John Deere	7200		F	$3,600	11/06	NEKS	6R-30 MaxEmerge II vacuum planter, furrow openers
John Deere	7200		P	$4,250	2/06	NCIL	MaxEmerge II, 6RN, tongue welded
John Deere	7200		G	$4,700	3/06	NWIL	8R-30
John Deere	7200		F	$4,900	11/06	NEKS	12R-30, flex fold vacuum
John Deere	7200		G	$5,050	1/06	SCMN	8R-30 vacuum, 3-bu. boxes
John Deere	7200		F	$5,400	3/06	SWOH	6R-30, no-till, conservation, liquid, monitor, MaxEmerge, 2 boxes
John Deere	7200		G	$5,500	2/06	NECO	8R-30
John Deere	7200		G	$5,750	8/06	SCNE	MaxEmerge II, 8R-30
John Deere	7200		E	$6,000	9/06	NEIN	6R, liquid fertilizer
John Deere	7200		G	$6,500	1/06	WCNE	8R-30, beet, corn, bean
John Deere	7200		G	$6,600	3/06	NEOH	6R-30 MaxEmerge II, Martin row cleaners
John Deere	7200		G	$6,600	12/06	SEMN	8R-30, liquid fertilizer
John Deere	7200		G	$6,750	12/06	SCMN	8R-30
John Deere	7200		G	$7,000	3/06	SCIA	6R-30, no-till
John Deere	7200		G	$7,100	8/06	NEIL	12R, front fold, MaxEmerge II
John Deere	7200		G	$8,000	3/06	SWNE	Conservation 8R-30, MaxEmerge II VacuMeter
John Deere	7200		F	$8,000	11/06	WCMN	12RN, front-fold planter, liquid fertilizer, insecticide, population monitor
John Deere	7200		F	$8,000	3/06	NCOH	MaxEmerge II, 12R-30, front fold, vacuum liquid, no-till coulters, aux. pump

Planters

Make	Model	Year	Cond.	Price	Sale	Location	Comments
John Deere	7200		G	$8,100	3/06	WCKS	8R-30, vacuum, MaxEmerge II, liquid starter, herbicide boxes, monitor
John Deere	7200		G	$8,200	12/06	NWWI	6R-30, conservation, dry fertilizer, finger pickup
John Deere	7200		G	$8,750	3/06	ECMI	12R-30 vacuum, dry fertilizer, double-disk openers
John Deere	7200		G	$10,500	2/06	ECIL	Vacuum, 12R-30, insecticide
John Deere	7200		G	$13,500	2/06	SEIL	12R-30 conservation, MaxEmerge II
John Deere	7200		G	$15,000	12/06	ECIL	12R-30, no-till, 3-bu. boxes, Computrac 250 monitor w/ radar
John Deere	7200		G	$15,000	1/06	WCIL	MaxEmerge II, 12RN, front-fold vacuum, monitor, shedded
John Deere	7200		G	$15,000	2/06	NEIN	12R-30, front-fold vacuum, MaxEmerge II, corn, single disk fertilizer openers, liquid fertilizer, row cleaners
John Deere	7200		G	$15,200	3/06	NCIA	12R-30, vacuum pull, hyd. wingfold, box extension, insecticide, Dawn finger trash whippers, Computrac 250 monitor
John Deere	7200		G	$16,000	3/06	NCNE	16R-30, MaxEmerge II, front fold, liquid fertilizer, insecticide, squeeze pump, Sunco fertilizer disk openers, finger pickup, plastic seed boxes, JD 250 monitor, hd springs
John Deere	7200		G	$16,500	9/06	NCIA	16R
John Deere	7200		G	$17,000	12/06	WCMI	MaxEmerge II, 6R-30, corn
John Deere	7200		G	$18,000	12/06	NENE	12R-30 vacuum, wing fold, Agri-Products liquid fertilizer in furrow openers, Yetter trash whips, JD 250 monitor
John Deere	7200		G	$25,500	8/06	NCIA	16R-30 vacuum planter, 3-bu. boxes, Sunco trash whippers, 250 Computrac monitor
John Deere	7200		G	$26,000	12/06	SCMN	16R-30, vacuum
John Deere	7200		G	$26,000	12/06	SCMN	24R-30
John Deere	7200	1988	F	$1,900	3/06	NWKS	8R-30
John Deere	7200	1990	G	$8,500	3/06	NWMN	8R, liquid or dry fertilizer, insecticide, herbicide, 250-gal. tanks, Redball, JD 100 monitor
John Deere	7200	1991	E	$26,750	12/06	NWOH	12R-30 no-till vacuum front fold, very nice
John Deere	7200	1994	G	$18,400	2/06	ECIL	12R-30 conservation, MaxEmerge II, wing fold
John Deere	7200	1994	E	$21,000	1/06	WCIL	16R-30 conservation, Lock 'N Load insect boxes, residue managers, SN 655219
John Deere	7200	1998	E	$37,000	12/06	NCIA	16R-30, trash whippers, 3-bu. boxes, 250 monitor, 2 seasons on rebuild
John Deere	7240		F	$5,300	8/06	WCIL	6R/11R, worn, 150 monitor
John Deere	7240		F	$7,700	4/06	SEPA	6R vacuum meter, interplants, deluxe seat boxes, no-till, liquid fertilizer, liquid insecticide
John Deere	7240	1994	G	$15,250	2/06	NWOH	6R/11R split row, MaxEmerge II, 150 monitor, liquid fertilizer
John Deere	7300		F	$1,600	3/06	NWKS	8R-30 MaxEmerge
John Deere	7300		F	$2,300	8/06	NECO	8R-30, insecticide, Lock 'N Load
John Deere	7300		G	$3,000	8/06	SCNE	8R-30
John Deere	7300		G	$3,250	11/06	WCMN	8R MaxEmerge II, VacuMeter, mounted trash whippers, Dickey-john monitor
John Deere	7300		F	$3,300	3/06	ECNE	8RW, seed box extension, insecticide boxes
John Deere	7300		G	$3,800	11/06	SWIA	6R-36, MaxEmerge, 3-bu. boxes, insecticide, always shedded
John Deere	7300		G	$4,400	2/06	NECO	8R-30, 3-pt.
John Deere	7300		G	$4,400	9/06	NCIA	12R-30, hyd. fold, 250 monitor

Planters

Make	Model	Year	Cond.	Price	Sale	Location	Comments
John Deere	7300		G	$4,450	11/06	SENE	6R-36, vacuum planter, insecticide boxes, JD furrow openers, set up for band or broadcast, large & small corn plates, bean plates, sorghum plates
John Deere	7300		G	$5,250	8/06	NECO	12R-30, wing fold
John Deere	7300		G	$5,300	2/06	NECO	8R-30
John Deere	7300		G	$5,400	1/06	NCCO	MaxEmerge II, 6R
John Deere	7300		G	$6,000	3/06	NCND	MaxEmerge vacuum, 12R-22, box extension, trash whippers, groovers, lift assist, JD monitor
John Deere	7300		G	$6,000	8/06	SCNE	12R-30 MaxEmerge II planter
John Deere	7300		G	$6,200	3/06	SESD	12RN, vertical fold, radar, 250 JD monitor, bean and corn plates, insect boxes
John Deere	7300		G	$6,600	8/06	SCMN	12R-30, wing fold, insecticide, 3-pt., JD 200 monitor
John Deere	7300		G	$6,700	3/06	SWNE	Min-till, 8R-30 MaxEmerge II VacuMeter, capture ready, John Blue squeeze pump
John Deere	7300		F	$6,750	2/06	WCMN	12R-22, vacuum
John Deere	7300		G	$7,000	11/06	NEKS	16RN, vacuum
John Deere	7300		G	$7,100	11/06	ECNE	8R-30, vacuum planter, 3-pt., insecticide, spray & liquid fertilizer equipment, JD monitor, JD openers
John Deere	7300		G	$7,100	1/06	SESD	12RN
John Deere	7300		G	$7,500	3/06	ECND	MaxEmerge II, 12R-22, liquid, lift assist, new 150 monitor, mounted tanks, John Blue squeeze pump
John Deere	7300		G	$8,000	11/06	NWMN	MaxEmerge vacuum, 12R-30, vertical fold, JD 250 monitor, lift assist, corn and bean plates
John Deere	7300		G	$8,100	2/06	SWNE	8RN, vacuum, Red Ball fertilizer unit, KMC roto-tiller
John Deere	7300		G	$8,500	3/06	NWMN	MaxEmerge, 12R-23, Lock 'N Loads, insecticide, lift assist
John Deere	7300		F	$8,500	1/06	SWNE	MaxEmerge 12R-30, Sunco fertilizer, Groff openers
John Deere	7300		G	$9,000	2/06	NECO	8R corn, trash whips
John Deere	7300		G	$12,500	11/06	ECND	Vacuum, 12R-22, dual lift assist, plumbed for liquid fertilizer, 250 monitor, field ready
John Deere	7300		G	$14,000	12/06	SEMN	12R-30, Rawson cart
John Deere	7300		G	$15,500	11/06	SCNE	MaxEmerge, vacuum, 12R-30, liquid fertilizer, box extensions, Orthman bar and markers, JD 250 monitor
John Deere	7300		E	$17,500	12/06	SCMN	12R-30
John Deere	7300	1990	G	$4,250	12/06	NENE	Corn seed meters, markers, insect boxes
John Deere	7300	1992	G	$7,600	2/06	ECKS	MaxEmerge 8R
John Deere	7300	1993	G	$3,000	6/06	NWKS	MaxEmerge II VacuMeter, 6R, Acra Plant
John Deere	7300	1997	E	$7,200	1/06	SCNE	8R-30 MaxEmerge II, monitor, insect boxes, Yetter trash whippers, all plates
John Deere	7300	1997	G	$12,000	4/06	NWMN	MaxEmerge, 12R-22 lift assist, herbicide, Lock 'N Loads, JD 250 monitor, hopper extension
John Deere	7300	1998	E	$61,000	2/06	WCMN	24R-22, Moore stackable bar, corn, beet and bean plates
John Deere	DB66	2004	E	$95,000	2/06	NEND	36R-22 MaxEmerge, front-fold vacuum meter, 1.6-bu. boxes, hyd. drive, 1,000 gal. on board, liquid fertilizer tank, Gandy orbit air herbicide, insecticide
John Deere	NA		G	$11,000	3/06	SWMN	24R-22 vacuum
John Deere	NA		G	$16,000	11/06	ECND	24R-22, MaxEmerge II units on TFI stacking bar, 4 lift assists, insecticide, variable-rate drive, GreenStar monitor
John Deere	NA		G	$34,000	12/06	WCMN	24R-22 Moore Built stack fold, MaxEmerge II plus units, variable-rate drive, 1.6 boxes

Planters

Make	Model	Year	Cond.	Price	Sale	Location	Comments
John Deere	NA	1998	G	$24,500	12/06	WCMN	24R-22, K&M vertical fold, variable-rate drive, 1.6 boxes
John Deere	NA	2002	G	$45,000	2/06	NWMN	24R-22, MaxEmerge plus units, DT2200 Wilrich front fold bar
Kinze	2000		G	$8,250	1/06	WCIL	6R-30, insecticide, liquid fertilizer, no-till
Kinze	2000		E	$10,500	2/06	SENE	6R/11R split row, reconditioned
Kinze	2500		G	$8,500	8/06	SCMI	8R-30 corn planter, no-till, liquid & dry fertilizer, monitor, transport
Kinze	2500		G	$22,000	3/06	NWIL	8/15 split row
Kinze	2500	2000	G	$25,000	1/06	NWKY	8R, splitters, liquid fertilizer, cleaner wheels
Kinze	2600	1997	E	$27,500	9/06	WCIA	12/23 split row, hyd. fold, precision corn units, 3000 monitor, like new
Kinze	2600	1998	E	$34,000	12/06	SWMI	16R-30, factory monitors, liquid feed, monitors
Kinze	3000		G	$16,500	1/06	NEIN	6/11 split-row
Kinze	3200	2005	E	$31,250	1/06	WCIL	12R-30, Econofold, no-till coulters, residue managers, Regent insect tank, has only planted 600 acres of corn
Kinze	3200	2005	E	$35,000	12/06	SEIA	12R, hyd. flex Econofold, no-till coulters, KP MII monitor, radar, insecticide
Kinze	3500		G	$26,000	2/06	WCIL	8R-15 split row interplant, monitor
Kinze	3500		G	$27,000	8/06	ECNE	8R/15R interplant, no-till coulters, trash whippers, liquid fertilizer, monitor, box extensions, 8 extra boxes without extensions
Kinze	3600		F	$25,500	4/06	SEPA	12R no-till corn, liquid fertilizer, electric monitor
Kinze	3600	2000	G	$45,500	1/06	NWIL	12/23 interplant, insect boxes
Kinze	3600	2001	G	$45,000	9/06	SWIA	16/31, insecticide, one year on Tru V's & no-till coulters, KPM II monitor, always shedded, field ready
Kinze	3600	2001	G	$51,000	1/06	SWOH	12/23, interplants
Kinze	3600	2002	G	$52,000	2/06	NWIL	12/23 interplant, no-till coulters
Kinze	3600	2003	G	$54,000	12/06	WCIA	12/23, corn & bean, coulters, Smart Box insecticide, less than 2,000 acres
Kinze	NA		G	$4,500	11/06	SWOH	4R corn planter, poly boxes, Dickey-john monitor
Kinze	NA		G	$12,000	9/06	WCND	24R-30 folding planter, ripple coulters, Regent chemical inject, seed firmers
Kvernland	UN3200		F	$500	2/06	WCME	4R
Milton	NA		F	$1,100	3/06	NCCO	8R-30, set up on 4×7 bar 2-2¼ bars
Moore Built	NA		G	$9,000	8/06	NECO	50' 7×7 double bar stack, fold planter bar
New Idea	9800		G	$6,000	3/06	WCMN	8R-30, dry fertilizer, insecticide
New Idea	NA		F	$650	2/06	SWIN	4R no-till corn, Kinze planting units, monitor
Nodet Gougis	NA		F	$1,250	7/06	NWMN	24R-22, Corey Welding transport bar, insecticide, 300-gal. tank, liquid drop, beet plates
Nodet Gougis	NA		F	$1,750	7/06	NWMN	24R-22, Swenson transport & bar, insecticide, 300-gal. tank, liquid drop, beet plates
White	5100		F	$450	10/06	WCWI	4R-38, no-till, air corn, liquid fertilizer
White	5100		F	$700	3/06	NCIN	4R-36, liquid fertilizer, insecticide, monitor
White	5100		P	$975	2/06	WCIA	8RW, vertical fold
White	5100		F	$1,000	8/06	NCOH	6R-30, dry fertilizer, insecticide, monitor, bean plates
White	5100		F	$1,000	11/06	WCMN	8R-30, liq. fertilizer, hd openers, wing fold
White	5100		G	$1,100	2/06	NEIA	4RW, very nice
White	5100		F	$1,200	3/06	WCMI	6RN, liquid, monitor
White	5100		G	$1,300	8/06	NCOH	4R-38, air, no-till planter, dry insecticide, markers

Planters

Make	Model	Year	Cond.	Price	Sale	Location	Comments
White	5100		G	$1,800	7/06	NCIA	12R-30 pull, monitor, insecticide, corn and bean plates
White	5100		F	$1,800	12/06	SEMN	12R-30, vertical fold, liquid fertilizer
White	5100		G	$2,000	2/06	WCNE	6R-30, air, pt
White	5100		G	$3,700	8/06	NENE	12R-30, vertical fold, dry fertilizer, insecticide boxes, bean plates, milo plates, (2) sets of corn plates, population monitor
White	5100		G	$4,000	2/06	WCIA	8RW, 7R unit splitter, vertical fold, monitor
White	5100		G	$4,750	8/06	NCOH	13R no-till planter, dry insecticide, markers, 6R planter, 7R splitter
White	5100		G	$5,100	2/06	NCOH	6R-30, air, corn, frame mounted, no-till coulters, liquid fertilizer attachment that was never used
White	5100		F	$5,200	2/06	WCMN	16R-30, 800 acres on rebuild, row units
White	5100		G	$7,500	3/06	NWOH	6R-30, 6900 Series 7R splitter, dry fertilizer, corn, vacuum, 3-pt.
White	5700		F	$2,000	1/06	SESD	6RN
White	6100		E	$6,750	3/06	NCIL	6R-30, insecticide
White	6100		G	$7,100	3/06	NWIL	6R
White	6100		G	$17,250	2/06	ECNE	12R-30, 6300 splitter
White	6100	1996	G	$12,300	12/06	NCIL	12R-30, insecticide boxes, trash wheels, Kelderman fold
White	6100	1997	G	$19,500	3/06	SEND	Wing fold, 12R-30, Rawson variable rate control, dry fertilizer, liquid in furrow drop, Martin trash whippers, hyd. or PTO pump control, monitor, 2 seasons on seed disks, corn, soybean and edible bean plates
White	6138		G	$10,000	3/06	ECNE	8R-36, vertical fold, insecticide, herbicide, liquid fertilizer, trash wipers, duo-rate, angled press wheels, monitor
White	6180		G	$22,000	2/06	NCIL	16R, Dawn trash whipper, insecticide
White	6180		G	$24,000	12/06	SCMN	16R-30, liquid fertilizer
White	6342	1999	F	$16,250	2/06	ECNE	12R-30, 13R-split row, folding
White	6700		F	$3,000	3/06	NCCO	8R vacuum, Smart Boxes, Yetter trash whips
White	6700	1999	G	$9,000	11/06	ECND	Vacuum, 12R-22, Lock 'N Loads, gauge wheels, lift assist, monitor
White	6706		G	$2,100	11/06	NEKS	6R-30
White	6818	2001	E	$10,700	1/06	WCIL	15' no-till , 6R-30 or 18R-10, no-till coulters, central fill
White	6824	1998	E	$10,000	1/06	WCIL	20' air, 8R-30 or 24R-10 rows, on-till coulters, center fill auger
White	8100	2002	G	$13,500	8/06	NEKS	6R-30, monitor, one owner
White	8108	2005	E	$15,800	2/06	WCIL	8R-30 rigid frame, no-till coulters, 360 acres, like new
White	8180	2004	G	$16,000	1/06	SESD	Hyd. fold, 8R-30", insecticide, spider wheels, no-till, planted only 400 acres

Plows

The single most amazing piece of equipment I saw sell in 2006? That's easy. Hands down, it was the IHC 800 12-18 plow sold December 1, 2006, on a super farm auction in west-central Minnesota. What did it bring? Try $32,000. I kid you not. The auctioneer took 10 calls on the plow the afternoon before the auction. He was hoping things would break right and it would go for $25,000. That's the thing with auctions – sometimes stuff sells for less than you think it should, other times more.

Plows

Make	Model	Year	Cond.	Price	Sale	Location	Comments
Baker	NA		G	$3,500	1/06	WCTX	5 bottom, disks, moldboards
Case	700		G	$6,000	8/06	NCIA	6-20 semi mount, spring reset
Case	7000		G	$600	4/06	NCOK	7-bottom moldboard plow, cyl., semi-mounted, some welds
Case	7000		G	$600	4/06	NCOK	7-bottom moldboard, no welds, semi mount
Case IH	145		F	$2,500	3/06	NCCO	4-18 spinner
Case IH	145		F	$3,000	1/06	NCCO	4-18 spinner
Case IH	165		P	$5,000	1/06	NCCO	5-16 spinner
Case IH	165		P	$5,800	2/06	NCCO	5-18 spinner
Case IH	165		G	$6,500	2/06	NECO	Onland 5-18
Case IH	700		G	$2,600	5/06	SEND	Auto reset, 7-18, high clearance, NH$_3$
Case IH	700		G	$4,300	2/06	NCIL	On land, 7-18, auto reset
Ford	142	1978	G	$200	12/06	SWMI	3 bottom
Ford	145		G	$800	9/06	NECO	5-bottom spinner, 3-pt.
Harrell	3606		G	$1,300	9/06	NECO	8 bottom, 3-pt.
Harrell	3606		G	$3,250	10/06	NECO	8 bottom, switch, 3-pt.
Hutchmaster	14'		G	$650	8/06	NEKS	Rolling
Hutchmaster	NA		G	$2,600	1/06	ECNE	Rolling, 23¾" blades, 11L-15 tires, SN 14-334
IHC	140		P	$600	1/06	NCCO	4-16 spinner
IHC	140		P	$750	1/06	NCCO	4-18 spinner
IHC	140		G	$950	2/06	NECO	39188
IHC	140		G	$1,200	9/06	NECO	4 bottom, 3-pt.
IHC	140		G	$1,400	10/06	NECO	4-bottom spinner
IHC	145		G	$1,000	1/06	NECO	3-pt., 4 bottom, spinner
IHC	145		G	$1,100	3/06	NCCO	
IHC	145		G	$1,300	9/06	NECO	4 bottom, 3-pt.
IHC	155		G	$850	1/06	WCNE	4 bottom, 3-pt., spinner
IHC	155		G	$2,600	2/06	NECO	4 bottom, spinner
IHC	155		G	$4,100	1/06	NCCO	5-16, spinner
IHC	165		P	$1,500	1/06	NCCO	4-18 spinner
IHC	510		F	$350	3/06	NWPA	5 bottom
IHC	540		G	$100	8/06	NEIA	4 bottom
IHC	540		F	$110	2/06	SEIA	4 bottom
IHC	540		G	$150	8/06	ECNE	4 bottom, harrow, shedded
IHC	540		F	$1,000	1/06	NEIA	
IHC	550		F	$135	1/06	NWIL	14"
IHC	550		F	$140	8/06	NCIA	5-16
IHC	550		F	$150	9/06	SCMN	5 bottom, trip
IHC	550		G	$150	1/06	WCIL	5 bottom
IHC	550		F	$180	11/06	NEKS	3-14, 2-pt
IHC	550		F	$190	11/06	NEKS	5-16, 2-pt
IHC	550		G	$200	1/06	ECNE	
IHC	550		G	$225	11/06	SWIA	
IHC	550		G	$275	1/06	NEMO	5 bottom
IHC	555		G	$550	3/06	ECNE	5 bottom
IHC	700		F	$100	3/06	ECNE	6 bottom
IHC	700		F	$250	8/06	SEPA	3 bottom, auto reset, semi-mounted
IHC	700		G	$300	3/06	SWOH	7-16, semi mount
IHC	700		G	$350	3/06	NWMN	8-16, trip beam, coulters
IHC	700		G	$900	7/06	ECND	Auto reset trailing, 8-16

Plows

Make	Model	Year	Cond.	Price	Sale	Location	Comments
IHC	700		G	$1,200	6/06	WCMN	7-18 auto reset, pt
IHC	700		G	$1,400	2/06	SCMI	8 bottom, on land hitch
IHC	700		E	$1,925	8/06	ECIL	7-18 on land, auto reset
IHC	700		G	$2,800	3/06	SEND	High clearance, 8-18, NH_3, single coulter
IHC	700		G	$4,200	8/06	WCMN	8-18, on land, pt
IHC	710		F	$75	8/06	NEKS	5 bottom
IHC	710		F	$125	12/06	NCIA	5 bottom
IHC	710		G	$150	8/06	WCIA	5-18, coulters
IHC	710		P	$250	3/06	SWMN	6-16, for parts
IHC	710		F	$250	3/06	WCMN	4-18 auto reset, semi-mounted
IHC	710		G	$850	3/06	SEMN	5-18, auto reset, 3-pt.
IHC	710		G	$850	8/06	WCMN	5-18, auto reset
IHC	710		F	$950	3/06	NWPA	5 bottom, auto reset
IHC	720		F	$200	9/06	SEIA	5 bottom, moldboard
IHC	720		G	$280	2/06	ECIL	5-18, toggle trip, earlier model
IHC	720		G	$350	7/06	NCIA	4-16 toggle trip, gauge wheel
IHC	720		G	$350	8/06	SCMN	4 bottom
IHC	720		E	$400	1/06	WCIL	5-18, early model
IHC	720		G	$475	8/06	NCIA	5-18 toggle trip
IHC	720		G	$500	3/06	NWIL	5 bottom
IHC	720		G	$500	3/06	SCIN	5-18 auto reset
IHC	720		G	$550	8/06	SCMN	5 bottom
IHC	720		G	$600	8/06	NCIA	6-18 toggle trip, spring loader coulters
IHC	720		G	$600	3/06	NEMI	5-bottom toggle trip
IHC	720		G	$900	3/06	NCIL	5-18, toggle trip, drag
IHC	720		P	$900	2/06	SCNY	6 bottom, spring reset
IHC	720		G	$950	12/06	NWIL	5-16 trip bottom
IHC	720		G	$1,050	8/06	NCIA	6-18 auto reset
IHC	720		G	$1,125	9/06	SCMN	4-18, new moldboards
IHC	720		G	$1,350	3/06	NCIL	4-18, auto reset
IHC	720		G	$1,400	3/06	SWMN	6-18, auto reset
IHC	720		G	$1,500	8/06	WCIA	6-18, auto reset
IHC	720		G	$1,650	3/06	SEMN	6 bottom, 18", 3-pt. on-land hitch, auto reset, 22" ripple coulters
IHC	720		G	$2,100	11/06	NCOH	5-18, auto reset, 3-pt. category
IHC	720		G	$2,400	8/06	NCIA	6-20 on-land hitch, auto reset, new mini moldboards
IHC	720		E	$2,950	11/06	SENE	6 bottom, shedded, used very little
IHC	720		G	$3,000	2/06	SCMI	7-18, later model 720, on-land hitch
IHC	720		G	$4,900	3/06	SWMN	12-18, on land
IHC	720	1980		$500	2/06	SWOH	6-16, toggle trip, 200 acres on moldboards & slides
IHC	730		G	$950	2/06	ECMN	5-bottom adjust-a-width semi auto
IHC	735		F	$900	1/06	WCIL	6-bottom variable-width
IHC	735		G	$1,050	8/06	NEIL	5-bottom variable-width, modern toggle
IHC	770		F	$350	10/06	NCND	6-16, slat moldboard, auto reset
IHC	770		G	$1,400	3/06	NWMN	6 bottom, auto reset
IHC	800		F	$450	7/06	NEND	8-18 auto reset
IHC	800		G	$2,500	7/06	NEND	12-18 auto reset, slat bottom
IHC	800		G	$4,300	12/06	WCMN	9 bottom
IHC	800		G	$6,000	1/06	NEIN	9 bottom, auto spring reset

Plows

Make	Model	Year	Cond.	Price	Sale	Location	Comments
IHC	800		G	$12,500	8/06	WCMN	9-18, flex pull, black springs, full set of coulters
IHC	800		E	$32,500	12/06	WCMN	12-18, auto reset, center pivot duals, coulters, approximately 2,000 acres
John Deere	2600		G	$450	3/06	SEIA	6 bottom
John Deere	2600		G	$575	6/06	NCIL	5-bottom variable width
John Deere	2600		G	$600	3/06	NCIL	5-20 variable width
John Deere	2700		G	$1,200	11/06	SCMN	Variable bottom
John Deere	2800		F	$450	4/06	WCMN	4 bottom, good moldboards, coulters, been in fire
John Deere	2800		F	$475	8/06	NCIA	7 bottom
John Deere	2800		G	$550	8/06	NCIA	4 bottom, hyd. adjustable, coulters, toggle trip
John Deere	2800		E	$1,200	2/06	SEMI	6-bottom variable width
John Deere	2800		G	$1,500	7/06	WCMN	8-bottom, variable width
John Deere	2800		G	$1,700	3/06	NWIL	5 bottom
John Deere	2800		G	$1,900	11/06	WCMN	5 bottom, includes pallet of new wear parts
John Deere	2800		G	$1,900	1/06	SCMN	5-bottom variable width
John Deere	2800		G	$2,500	8/06	NCIA	6-bottom auto reset
John Deere	2800		G	$2,600	8/06	NWIL	7 bottom
John Deere	2800		G	$3,000	8/06	NCIA	6-bottom hyd. adjustable, toggle trip, spring loader coulters
John Deere	2800		G	$3,100	2/06	WCMN	7-bottom variable width, coulters,
John Deere	2810		G	$5,100	3/06	SCIN	7 bottom, variable width on land
John Deere	2810		G	$5,900	11/06	NCOH	7 bottom, hyd. widths adjustable on land, 3-pt.
John Deere	3100		F	$150	4/06	NESD	5-16 semi mount, IHC 7' 620 press drill, spoke press wheels
John Deere	3100		G	$400	9/06	NWMN	10-16, two 5 bottoms, tandem hitch, slat bottom trip beam
John Deere	3100		E	$600	3/06	NCOK	6-bottom moldboard
John Deere	3100		G	$750	3/06	ECND	Trip beam, 10 bottom, two 5-16's
John Deere	3200		F	$450	7/06	NWMN	Auto reset, 6-16, tandem hitch
John Deere	3600		G	$1,100	6/06	NWMN	Moldboard, 8-16, toggle trip
John Deere	3600		G	$2,000	4/06	ECND	Auto reset, 7 bottom, variable width
John Deere	3600		G	$2,800	2/06	SEKS	6 bottom
John Deere	3700		G	$5,000	4/06	NEND	Auto reset, 10-18, hinged, levelers
John Deere	3700		G	$16,500	11/06	NWMN	Auto reset, 12-18
John Deere	3710		G	$7,500	8/06	WCMN	9 bottom, coulters
John Deere	3710		G	$8,000	12/06	SCMN	8 bottom
John Deere	3710		G	$11,250	7/06	WCMN	9 bottom, 1 coulter
John Deere	3710		E	$19,750	3/06	SEMN	10 bottom flex, on-land drawn, cushion ripple coulters, auto resets, looks new
John Deere	3710	1992	E	$15,000	1/06	SCKS	10-bottom adjustable one owner, shedded
John Deere	3710	1999	E	$16,500	1/06	SCKS	10-bottom adjustable, one owner, shedded
John Deere	4600		G	$600	5/06	SCCA	5-bottom rollover
John Deere	8350		G	$1,100	1/06	NECO	4 bottom, 3-pt, spinner
John Deere	8450		G	$1,350	2/06	NECO	4 bottom, 3-pt, spinner
John Deere	965		G	$3,100	3/06	NECO	5 bottom
John Deere	975		G	$3,900	12/06	SWWI	5-20, bidirectional
John Deere	995		G	$8,000	1/06	WCCA	6-bottom switch
Melroe	903		G	$750	4/06	NEND	Auto reset moldboard, 8-18
Melroe	903		G	$1,900	3/06	ECND	Auto reset, 8×18", 1 coulter
MF	57		F	$375	1/06	WCNE	4 bottom
MF	57		G	$1,000	1/06	NECO	5 bottom
MF	570		G	$1,100	9/06	NECO	5-bottom spinner, 3-pt.

Plows

Make	Model	Year	Cond.	Price	Sale	Location	Comments
MF	570		G	$1,450	2/06	NECO	5 bottom, 3-pt., spinner
MF	570		G	$1,850	1/06	WCNE	3-pt., 5 bottom, spinner
White	508		F	$600	1/06	SCMI	4×16, semi mount
White	508		G	$700	3/06	ECMI	4-16, auto spring reset, semi mounted
White	549		G	$325	12/06	SCNE	5-18, semi-mounted steerable
White	549		G	$1,500	12/06	SCNE	5-16, on-land hitch
White	588		G	$650	3/06	NCIN	5-18, auto reset
White	588		F	$700	11/06	WCMN	6 bottom, semi mount on land
White	588		F	$1,100	7/06	WCMN	Auto reset, 5 bottom, coulters, like new
White	598		F	$600	1/06	SCMI	6 bottom, variable width
White	598		G	$2,300	7/06	NCIL	5 bottom, variable width, auto reset
Wilrich	2900		G	$3,000	7/06	WCMN	10 bottom, auto reset, coulters

Notes

Rakes

Another category I love. No big deal, right? Take 20-year-old rakes, like New Holland 56s, for example. Just figure they're worth, say, $400, right? Wrong. Check out our auction prices.

See how in 2006 they sold for between $275 on the low side up to a high of $1,200. Average sale price = $738. Why sell for $400 when they're worth $700 or more?

Rakes

Make	Model	Year	Cond.	Price	Sale	Location	Comments
Allis-Chalmers	7'		G	$230	6/06	NCIA	2- wheel PTO hay
Allen	8827		G	$6,100	2/06	WCNE	V-rake, twin basket, hyd. drive
Befco	NA		G	$750	12/06	NWIL	8-wheel, hyd. fold
Case	NA		G	$900	10/06	SCMI	5-bar hay
Columbia	TR79		G	$1,500	3/06	WCMN	9-wheel
Darf	NA		F	$400	5/06	SCCA	16-wheel V
Darf	NA		F	$400	5/06	SCCA	16-wheel V
Gehl	217		G	$900	8/06	NCMI	7-wheel
Gehl	219		G	$500	5/06	SEND	Side, 7-wheel
Gehl	418		F	$800	1/06	NEIN	Tandem
Gehl	418		F	$1,850	8/06	NWIL	V
Gehl	520	2005	E	$5,100	3/06	NENE	Hyd. fold wheel
Gehl	600	2004	E	$7,800	12/06	WCMN	12-wheel V
Gehl	700	2003	G	$10,750	3/06	ECMI	Double 11 hay, hyd. fold
Gehl	9-wheel		G	$1,525	3/06	SEND	9-wheel finger
H&S	10-wheel		G	$2,000	2/06	NEIN	10-wheel V
H&S	10-wheel		E	$2,900	12/06	ECIL	New CR 10-wheel, kicker, hyd. fold
H&S	10-wheel		G	$3,700	12/06	NWMO	
H&S	12-wheel		E	$4,100	9/06	WCOH	Bi-fold
H&S	12-wheel		G	$4,800	12/06	SEMN	Bi-fold
H&S	12-wheel		E	$6,600	12/06	ECMO	New BF12HC high capacity
H&S	12-wheel	2004	E	$6,100	8/06	NEIA	12-wheel high capacity
H&S	14-wheel		G	$3,500	1/06	WCNE	Pt
H&S	NA		F	$1,600	1/06	SWNE	Bi-fold, BE12HC
Hesston	16-wheel		G	$4,800	3/06	NENE	V, one owner
Hesston	5-wheel		F	$150	9/06	NWIL	5-big wheel
John Deere	640		G	$425	4/06	NEND	Left-hand side delivery
John Deere	640		G	$450	4/06	NEND	Left-hand side delivery
John Deere	640		G	$600	8/06	NCIA	
John Deere	640		G	$675	5/06	SWWI	Hay
John Deere	640		G	$700	3/06	NCWI	Hay, front dolly wheel, rubber-mount teeth
John Deere	640		G	$750	11/06	SEIA	4-bar side
John Deere	640		G	$850	2/06	ECMN	Front dolly
John Deere	640		G	$1,400	1/06	NCCO	
John Deere	640		G	$2,500	1/06	SEPA	Transport
John Deere	660		G	$1,400	1/06	NEIN	
John Deere	670		G	$650	4/06	NWSD	9.5' side, new teeth
John Deere	670		G	$1,800	12/06	WCIA	5 bar, dolly wheel
John Deere	694		P	$450	10/06	SEMN	Rough
John Deere	700		G	$2,900	8/06	NECO	Twin
John Deere	702		G	$4,300	2/06	SCMI	10-wheel carted, center wheel
John Deere	704		G	$3,500	3/06	ECKS	Wheel
John Deere	704		E	$5,250	3/06	NWIL	12-wheel
John Deere	704	2000	E	$6,250	12/06	WCIA	12-wheel
John Deere	705		G	$7,900	1/06	NCCO	Twin V
John Deere	894A		F	$325	6/06	SWMN	
John Deere	896A		F	$225	11/06	ECNE	
Kelderman	10-wheel		G	$1,000	8/06	ECIA	V, pt, hyd. fold
Kelderman	10-wheel		G	$1,400	10/06	NCKS	5-wheel each side, V hay

Rakes

Make	Model	Year	Cond.	Price	Sale	Location	Comments
Kuhn	GA7301		E	$12,700	6/06	SCMN	Double wheel rotary hay
M&W	12-wheel		G	$4,250	2/06	SENE	DF-12, wheel, hyd. fold
MF	36		G	$1,000	7/06	WCOH	Side delivery
New Holland	254		G	$600	9/06	NEIN	Tedder
New Holland	256		G	$700	3/06	NEKS	
New Holland	256		G	$750	11/06	WCSD	Rolabar side
New Holland	256		G	$850	8/06	SETN	
New Holland	256		G	$950	8/06	SWWI	
New Holland	256		G	$950	8/06	SWWI	Dolly wheel
New Holland	256		F	$950	3/06	SEPA	
New Holland	256		G	$950	11/06	SENE	5 bar, ground driven, shedded
New Holland	256		G	$1,050	8/06	SEPA	Rolabar
New Holland	256		G	$1,100	3/06	NEOH	
New Holland	256		G	$1,250	12/06	WCMI	5-bar hay
New Holland	256		G	$1,400	1/06	WCIL	5-bar hay
New Holland	256		G	$1,900	12/06	SWIL	
New Holland	256		G	$1,900	1/06	NEIN	
New Holland	256		G	$2,300	12/06	SEIA	Hay, dolly wheel
New Holland	256		G	$2,650	11/06	SWOH	Rolabar side delivery
New Holland	258		F	$300	1/06	WCTX	Rolabar
New Holland	258		G	$600	11/06	SWIA	
New Holland	258		F	$1,025	4/06	SCMN	Rubber teeth
New Holland	258		G	$1,075	3/06	NWIL	Dolly
New Holland	258		G	$1,150	4/06	SEMI	5-bar
New Holland	258		G	$1,200	4/06	WCSD	Side delivery
New Holland	258		G	$1,250	3/06	NEKS	
New Holland	258		G	$1,400	1/06	NEIN	
New Holland	258		E	$1,600	9/06	NEIN	
New Holland	258		G	$1,700	10/06	NCWI	Side
New Holland	258		G	$1,700	12/06	NEMO	5-bar hay, dolly wheel
New Holland	258		G	$1,800	9/06	NECO	5-bar, pull type, hyd. drive
New Holland	258		E	$2,400	8/06	NWIL	No dolly wheel
New Holland	258		F	$2,750	1/06	NCIL	Dolly wheel
New Holland	260		G	$1,325	3/06	NEKS	
New Holland	260		G	$1,900	8/06	SETN	Dolly wheel
New Holland	260		G	$2,700	12/06	SWWI	Rubber teeth, no dolly
New Holland	260	1989	G	$2,300	11/06	WCMN	9.5', left hand
New Holland	55		F	$400	3/06	SEPA	Rubber tooth
New Holland	55		G	$450	2/06	WCNE	5-bar, pt, ground drive
New Holland	55		F	$575	3/06	NWIL	Two wheel hay
New Holland	55		G	$600	4/06	NEND	Left-hand side delivery
New Holland	55		G	$600	4/06	NEND	Left-hand side delivery
New Holland	55		F	$775	2/06	NWIL	Rolabar
New Holland	55		G	$1,800	2/06	SWIN	Rolabar, front dolly wheels
New Holland	56		F	$275	9/06	SCNE	Side delivery
New Holland	56		G	$425	4/06	NEND	Left-hand side delivery
New Holland	56		G	$450	3/06	ECMN	Rolabar, +10% buyers premium
New Holland	56		F	$450	2/06	SWNE	Side delivery
New Holland	56		G	$500	12/06	SCNE	Side delivery

Rakes

Make	Model	Year	Cond.	Price	Sale	Location	Comments
New Holland	56		G	$650	10/06	WCWI	Side
New Holland	56		G	$800	3/06	NWIL	
New Holland	56		F	$875	1/06	SCMI	5-bar hay
New Holland	56		G	$975	2/06	SWPA	Side
New Holland	56		G	$1,100	11/06	NEOH	
New Holland	56		G	$1,150	1/06	NEIN	
New Holland	56		F	$1,200	1/06	NEIA	Dolly wheel
New Holland	56B		G	$900	6/06	NCPA	56B, bean
New Holland	58		G	$650	3/06	SEMN	Side
New Holland	HT154	2004	F	$7,300	2/06	NEIA	2004 model, 14-wheel, used 1 season, heavily used, some welds on it
New Holland	HT154		G	$8,000	12/06	SEMN	Wheel
New Idea	5-wheel		F	$375	7/06	NWIL	Pt
Panarama	NA		G	$2,050	1/06	WCIL	8-wheel hay
Rossi	NA		G	$1,650	3/06	WCMN	10-wheel, pt
Rossi	NA		G	$1,700	4/06	SWIN	8-wheel
Sitrex	10-wheel		F	$1,000	11/06	NEIA	10-wheel butterfly
Sitrex	10-wheel		G	$2,000	2/06	NEIN	
Sitrex	12-wheel		E	$4,350	3/06	NEKS	
Sitrex	16-wheel		G	$4,600	9/06	NEIA	
Sitrex	9-wheel		E	$1,150	9/06	SCMN	Three tire, pt, new, demo, 62 acres
Sitrex	U400		F	$500	8/06	WCIL	Twin rotor hay
Tonutti	9-wheel		G	$2,000	3/06	NESD	
Tonutti	10-wheel		F	$325	1/06	WCNE	On cart
Tonutti	10-wheel		F	$325	1/06	WCNE	On cart
Tonutti	10-wheel		F	$450	4/06	NWSD	V, 3-pt.
Tonutti	10-wheel		F	$950	12/06	SEMN	10-wheel, RCS
Tonutti	RCS12		F	$2,300	2/06	NCCO	Double V, 12-wheel
Vermeer	10-wheel		G	$2,800	3/06	NCCO	V
Vermeer	NA		G	$1,800	8/06	SETN	Hay tedder, pt
Vermeer	R23		E	$1,300	3/06	WCKS	Twin S
Vermeer	R23		G	$5,100	12/06	NEMO	Twin
Vermeer	R23		G	$6,000	3/06	SEMN	Twin, 23' raking width, hydraulic fold and narrow
Vermeer	R23A		G	$8,300	2/06	ECNE	Hyd. driven folding hay
Vermeer	R24A		G	$7,000	12/06	NENE	Hyd fold, hyd. drive
Vermeer	R24A		E	$10,500	4/06	WCWI	Twin, new in 2005
Vermeer	R9B		G	$1,300	2/06	NWSD	Side, left-hand delivery, hyd. driven
Vermeer	WR22		G	$1,600	12/06	SEMN	10-wheel
Vermeer	WR22		G	$2,000	12/06	NEMO	10-wheel
Vermeer	WR24		E	$3,050	12/06	SEIA	12-wheel V, like new
Vicon	6-wheel		F	$475	7/06	SEND	
Vicon	6-wheel		G	$1,050	3/06	SEND	New teeth
Vicon	8-wheel		F	$525	4/06	WCSD	Side
Walton	NA		G	$1,100	3/06	NEKS	Tedder

Rotary Hoes

One of the most common pieces of farm equipment I've watched sell thousands of times over the past 17 years? The JD 400 rotary hoe. Just look at all of them listed here.

Sale prices from a low of $90 all the way up to $4,750 that a buyer paid for a 2003 model 30-foot JD 400 in like-new condition on an auction in south-central Kansas.

Rotary Hoes

Make	Model	Year	Cond.	Price	Sale	Location	Comments
Case IH	181		F	$150	8/06	NWIL	16', 3 pt.
Case IH	181		G	$650	11/06	SCIL	30', folding hoe
Case IH	181		G	$1,300	3/06	SEMN	15', high-residue wheels, used only on 140 acres total
Case IH	181	1995	E	$2,700	8/06	ECIL	30', hyd. fold wings
Case IH	181 MT		G	$4,100	2/06	NWIA	30', 3 pt.
IHC	30'	1984	G	$1,100	3/06	SEND	3 pt.
John Deere	400		F	$90	3/06	NCIA	15'
John Deere	400		G	$100	4/06	SEMI	15'
John Deere	400		F	$100	6/06	NWKS	3 pt.
John Deere	400		P	$100	1/06	NWIL	15'
John Deere	400		F	$115	3/06	NCIL	21', end transport
John Deere	400		F	$125	3/06	NENE	
John Deere	400		G	$125	1/06	WCNE	21', 3 pt.
John Deere	400		F	$125	1/06	NEMO	15'
John Deere	400		F	$130	8/06	NCIA	8R-30, transport
John Deere	400		F	$140	8/06	NCOH	15', 3 pt. hoe
John Deere	400		F	$150	3/06	ECNE	3 pt.
John Deere	400		F	$175	2/06	NWIL	20'
John Deere	400		F	$200	3/06	NWKS	20'
John Deere	400		G	$200	8/06	SCMN	30', 3 pt., transport
John Deere	400		G	$200	8/06	WCIL	20'
John Deere	400		F	$220	3/06	ECIA	
John Deere	400		G	$220	3/06	WCKS	
John Deere	400		F	$225	2/06	ECMN	20', 3 pt.
John Deere	400		F	$250	3/06	SWNE	30', 3 pt., transport
John Deere	400		F	$250	4/06	NENE	3 pt., 6R-30
John Deere	400		F	$250	2/06	NECO	16', 3 pt
John Deere	400		G	$250	12/06	WCMI	16'
John Deere	400		F	$250	2/06	NWIN	30' hyd. fold
John Deere	400		F	$275	1/06	NWIL	30', end transport
John Deere	400		F	$300	3/06	ECNE	3 pt.
John Deere	400		G	$300	3/06	SCIN	3 pt.
John Deere	400		G	$300	9/06	NCIA	20'
John Deere	400		G	$325	3/06	WCMN	20'
John Deere	400		G	$325	3/06	NCIN	15'
John Deere	400		G	$340	1/06	WCIL	30', transports
John Deere	400		F	$350	1/06	NECO	20', 3 pt.
John Deere	400		G	$350	1/06	NECO	21', 3 pt.
John Deere	400		G	$350	3/06	NCIA	20' hoe, gauge wheels
John Deere	400		F	$400	2/06	WCKS	30', 3 pt.
John Deere	400		G	$400	2/06	SCKS	22'
John Deere	400		G	$400	1/06	NWIL	30'
John Deere	400		G	$450	8/06	ECNE	15', shedded
John Deere	400		G	$475	3/06	NENE	21'
John Deere	400		G	$500	8/06	WCKS	
John Deere	400		F	$500	9/06	NECO	30', 3 pt., wing fold
John Deere	400		G	$500	1/06	WCNE	21', 3 pt.
John Deere	400		F	$525	1/06	NWIL	30', end transport
John Deere	400		F	$600	1/06	NCCO	8R

Rotary Hoes

Make	Model	Year	Cond.	Price	Sale	Location	Comments
John Deere	400		G	$650	12/06	SEMN	
John Deere	400		E	$700	2/06	SEMI	
John Deere	400		G	$725	1/06	SWOH	
John Deere	400		G	$750	2/06	ECIL	30', end transport
John Deere	400		G	$925	8/06	NCIA	12R-30 flat fold
John Deere	400		F	$1,100	2/06	NWMN	44', folding
John Deere	400		G	$2,600	11/06	SCNE	40', 3 section, 3 pt., hyd. fold
John Deere	400		G	$2,900	8/06	NCIA	30' flat-fold hoe, 4-gauge wheels
John Deere	400		G	$2,900	2/06	NWIL	30', 3 pt., flat fold
John Deere	400		G	$3,000	12/06	NCIA	30' fold
John Deere	400		G	$3,300	12/06	SEIA	32', fold, 3 pt.
John Deere	400		G	$3,600	2/06	NCIL	40', flat fold
John Deere	400		G	$3,800	3/06	SWKS	40', hyd. fold
John Deere	400		E	$4,500	3/06	SEIA	30' flat fold
John Deere	400	1974	F	$125	4/06	WCMN	20'
John Deere	400	2003	E	$4,750	1/06	SCKS	30', hyd. fold, used very little, 150 acres, shedded, bought new
Kewanee	470		G	$800	1/06	NWIA	25', flat fold, 3 pt.
M&W	1815		G	$400	3/06	ECMI	6R, 3 pt.
M&W	1821		F	$200	2/06	ECIL	21', end transport
M&W	1925		G	$1,000	2/06	SCMI	25'
M&W	1930		F	$550	12/06	NWIL	30', 3 pt., hyd. fold
M&W	1930		E	$1,150	1/06	WCIL	Hyd. flat fold
M&W	30'		E	$3,300	2/06	ECNE	
Phoenix	NA	2004	E	$21,000	12/06	SWIA	53' front fold, hyd. gauge wheel package, low acres
Yetter	21'		G	$1,100	4/06	NWMN	3 pt.
Yetter	30'		G	$750	3/06	NEND	Flat fold
Yetter	30'		G	$2,000	3/06	ECND	Flat fold, gauge wheels, cab guard, less than 500 acres
Yetter	3415		E	$225	9/06	WCOH	Rolling hoe
Yetter	3415		G	$450	11/06	NCOH	15'
Yetter	3421		F	$250	3/06	WCMN	20'
Yetter	3421		G	$500	2/06	WCNE	21', 3 pt.
Yetter	3421		G	$800	4/06	ECND	21', cab guard, gauge wheels
Yetter	3530		G	$1,500	11/06	NWMN	30'
Yetter	3541		F	$3,000	2/06	WCIL	40'
Yetter	3546		G	$6,000	12/06	WCMN	46' flat fold
Yetter	3546		G	$8,200	3/06	SWMN	46', flat fold, trash cleaners, mini-till
Yetter	3546		E	$8,500	12/06	WCMN	46' flat fold
Yetter	3580		P	$900	2/06	WCIL	30'
Yetter	40'		G	$4,000	11/06	ECND	Flat fold
Yetter	46'		G	$5,000	3/06	NWMN	Flat fold, 4-gauge wheels

Skid Steer Loaders

"I wonder what this thing would sell for in a different part of the country?" I love that question. Check out the Bobcat 763 skid steers in this section (Bobcats are listed under "Melroe"). See the Melroe Bobcat 763s that sold in California, Florida, Indiana, Minnesota, North Carolina, North Dakota, Pennsylvania, Tennessee, and Texas.

Skid Steer Loaders

Make	Model	Year	Hrs.	Cond.	Price	Sale	Location	Comments
ASV	4520		1,781	G	$11,500	8/06	SEPA	Rubber tracked, JD diesel, roll cage
ASV	4520	1998	1,800	G	$13,500	12/06	ECMN	OROPS
ASV	RC50	2003	2,075	G	$13,500	9/06	NEIN	Crawler, Cat diesel, 50 hp.
Case	1810B			F	$1,850	3/06	SWNE	42" bucket, Tecumseh gas engine, 9.50-15 tires
Case	1816B		820	G	$2,750	6/06	SCMN	34" bucket
Case	1816C		2,163	F	$2,900	8/06	WCMN	Uniloader, Onan twin cylinder
Case	1816C		3,182	F	$4,000	3/06	NWOH	Gas, 3' bucket
Case	1818	1993	778	G	$4,000	5/06	SCMI	Gas, 4' & 3' buckets, 3' manure tine bucket
Case	1825B		1,279	G	$7,200	3/06	SEIA	Uniloader
Case	1830			G	$3,700	3/06	NCIA	Hydro, 54" bucket
Case	1830		3,989	G	$4,000	3/06	WCMN	5' material bucket, pallet forks
Case	1830		1,895	G	$7,000	8/06	SCMN	
Case	1835B			G	$5,000	3/06	NWIL	Diesel
Case	1835C			G	$5,000	8/06	SECA	
Case	1840			G	$6,000	10/06	NCWI	Diesel, roll cage, aux. hyd., LP bucket, hd tires
Case	1840			G	$6,600	8/06	NWIL	Diesel
Case	1840		1,862	G	$7,000	8/06	SETN	Gp bucket
Case	1840			G	$8,000	11/06	SWCA	Diesel, canopy
Case	1840			G	$8,700	8/06	WCTX	Diesel, roll cage, aux. hyd., gp bucket
Case	1840			G	$8,750	3/06	NWIL	Diesel
Case	1840		1,838	G	$9,200	9/06	SEIA	Uniloader
Case	1840			G	$9,400	3/06	NCMN	
Case	1840		1,375	G	$9,500	6/06	SCMN	72" material bucket, 54" manure bucket
Case	1840		1,700	G	$9,650	8/06	NWIL	Diesel
Case	1840	1986	3,823	G	$7,900	2/06	NECO	5' bucket
Case	1840	1991		G	$8,000	9/06	NECO	10 hours on OH, diesel, roll cage, 5' bucket
Case	1840	1998	3,200	G	$9,400	8/06	NWIL	Diesel
Case	1840	1998	939	G	$12,600	3/06	SEIA	Uniloader
Case	1840	2001	624	G	$15,500	9/06	NEMO	Uniloader, 5' bucket, aux. hyd., 10-16.5 tires
Case	1845			G	$5,000	11/06	SWCA	4-in-1 bucket
Case	1845			G	$6,000	12/06	SEMN	
Case	1845			G	$7,250	3/06	ECIN	Diesel, canopy
Case	1845B			G	$5,000	6/06	NEIN	
Case	1845B			F	$5,300	3/06	NWIL	Diesel
Case	1845C			G	$5,500	11/06	SWCA	Diesel, canopy
Case	1845C			G	$5,750	11/06	SWCA	Canopy
Case	1845C			G	$6,500	6/06	ECSD	
Case	1845C			G	$7,000	9/06	NEIN	Diesel, cab
Case	1845C			G	$7,250	9/06	WCTX	Diesel, roll cage, hyd.
Case	1845C			G	$8,000	9/06	WCTX	Diesel, aux. hyd.
Case	1845C			G	$8,500	10/06	WCFL	Diesel, roll cage, aux. hyd., low-profile bucket
Case	1845C			G	$10,000	8/06	NWIL	Diesel
Case	1845C			G	$12,500	3/06	NWIL	Diesel
Case	1845C		1,632	G	$13,500	8/06	NWOH	Diesel, 6' bucket
Case	1845C	1989	4,500	G	$7,200	9/06	NEIN	Diesel, repainted
Case	1845C	1990		G	$7,800	3/06	ECIN	Diesel, bucket, forks, cab
Case	1845C	1991	1,500	G	$10,250	11/06	SWIA	Diesel, 72" quick-attach bucket
Case	1845C	1992		G	$7,000	3/06	ECMI	New paint
Case	1845C	1994		G	$8,000	3/06	ECMI	Front hyd.

Skid Steer Loaders

Make	Model	Year	Hrs.	Cond.	Price	Sale	Location	Comments
Case	1845C	2000		G	$11,500	8/06	SECA	
Case	1845C	2001		G	$8,400	8/06	WCTX	Diesel, roll cage, aux. hyd., gp bucket
Case	40XT		1,200	G	$13,500	3/06	NWIL	Diesel
Case	40XT	2002		G	$14,000	1/06	WCOH	Diesel, roll cage, aux. hyd.
Case	40XT	2003		G	$14,000	1/06	WCOH	Diesel, roll cage, aux. hyd.
Case	420	2005		E	$22,000	1/06	WCOH	Rubber tracked, diesel, roll cage, aux. hyd., LP bucket
Case	440	2006		E	$23,500	9/06	NEIN	High flow aux. hyd., ride control, low-profile bucket
Case	450	2005		G	$19,000	3/06	ECIN	Diesel, canopy, gp bucket
Case	450	2005		G	$20,000	3/06	ECIN	Diesel, canopy, gp bucket
Case	570		3,789	G	$16,500	9/06	SECA	
Case	570		5,817	G	$17,500	9/06	SECA	
Case	570	2000	2,032	G	$22,000	9/06	SECA	
Case	600			G	$5,000	8/06	SWWI	Skid King, 453 Detroit engine, Allison transmission, engine OH
Case	75XT			G	$10,500	8/06	WCTX	Diesel, roll cage, aux. hyd., gp bucket
Case	75XT		983	G	$17,000	8/06	SETN	Loegering tracks, gp bucket
Case	75XT	1999	1,221	G	$12,750	7/06	WCMN	Dirt bucket, side windows, heater, no door
Case	85XT			G	$0	12/06	SWWI	No sale at $13,500 – wanted $15,500
Case	85XT			G	$9,250	12/06	SEND	Aux. hyd.
Case	85XT	2002		G	$9,750	11/06	SCCA	
Case	90XT		600	G	$15,000	8/06	NWIL	Diesel
Case	90XT	1999	2,400	G	$10,500	8/06	NWIL	Diesel
Case	95XT			G	$9,500	10/06	NCWI	Diesel, roll cage, aux. hyd., gp bucket
Case	95XT	1998	724	G	$24,500	11/06	ECND	Dirt bucket
Case	95XT	2000		G	$16,000	1/06	WCOH	Diesel, aux. hyd., roll cage, gp bucket
Case	95XT	2000		G	$16,000	1/06	WCOH	Diesel, roll cage, aux. hyd., gp bucket
Case	95XT	2002		G	$18,500	1/06	WCOH	Diesel, roll cage, aux. hyd., bp bucket
Case	95XT	2002		G	$18,500	1/06	WCOH	Diesel, roll cage, aux. hyd., gp bucket
Caterpillar	216		274	G	$14,000	12/06	NEMN	
Caterpillar	226	2000	1,672	G	$11,000	11/06	SCND	Dirt bucket, diesel, new tires
Caterpillar	226	2002	302	G	$15,000	3/06	NCNE	60" bucket, 3-cyl. diesel engine, aux. hyd., LSW265-521 MHS tires
Caterpillar	226	2002		G	$17,000	10/06	WCFL	Diesel, enclosed cab, heat, aux. hyd.
Caterpillar	226	2003		G	$13,000	10/06	NCWI	Diesel, enclosed cab, heat, aux. hyd., LP bucket
Caterpillar	226	2003	697	G	$15,500	7/06	ECNY	Diesel, roll cage, aux. hyd.
Caterpillar	226	2004	201	G	$18,000	7/06	ECNY	Diesel, roll cage, aux. hyd.
Caterpillar	226	2004		G	$18,000	11/06	SCCA	Turbo, aux. hyd.
Caterpillar	226	2005		G	$19,500	7/06	ECNY	Diesel, cab, heat, aux. hyd., low-profile bucket
Caterpillar	226	2005		G	$19,500	7/06	ECNY	Low-profile bucket, diesel, aux. hyd.
Caterpillar	232	2003	425	G	$16,500	11/06	SCCA	
Caterpillar	232	2005		G	$16,500	8/06	SEPA	Roll cage, diesel, aux. hyd., gp bucket
Caterpillar	236			G	$8,500	9/06	NEIN	Canopy
Caterpillar	236			G	$17,000	8/06	WCTX	Aux. hyd., diesel, roll cage
Caterpillar	236	2000		G	$16,000	7/06	ECNY	Diesel, aux. hyd., LP bucket, roll cage
Caterpillar	236	2002	980	G	$16,000	2/06	WCSD	Cab, heat
Caterpillar	236	2002		G	$16,500	1/06	WCNH	Diesel, roll cage, aux. hyd., gp bucket
Caterpillar	236	2002		G	$16,500	1/06	WCNH	Diesel, roll cage, aux. hyd., gp bucket
Caterpillar	236	2003		G	$16,500	1/06	WCNH	Diesel, roll cage, aux. hyd., gp bucket
Caterpillar	236	2003		G	$16,500	1/06	WCNH	Diesel, roll cage, aux. hyd., gp bucket

Skid Steer Loaders

Make	Model	Year	Hrs.	Cond.	Price	Sale	Location	Comments
Caterpillar	236	2003		G	$17,500	1/06	WCNH	Diesel, roll cage, aux. hyd., gp bucket
Caterpillar	236	2004		G	$18,000	1/06	WCNH	Diesel, enclosed cab, aux. hyd.
Caterpillar	236	2004		G	$18,000	1/06	WCNH	Diesel, enclosed cab, aux. hyd., gp bucket
Caterpillar	236	2004		G	$18,500	1/06	WCNH	Diesel, enclosed cab, aux. hyd., gp bucket
Caterpillar	236	2005		G	$21,500	7/06	ECNY	Diesel, aux. hyd. low-profile bucket
Caterpillar	242	2003	1,153	G	$13,000	12/06	ECMN	Closed cab, heat
Caterpillar	242	2004		G	$15,000	10/06	SCPA	Diesel
Caterpillar	246			G	$14,000	7/06	ECNY	Diesel, roll cage, aux. hyd.
Caterpillar	246			G	$14,000	9/06	WCTX	Diesel, roll cage, aux. hyd., gp bucket
Caterpillar	246			G	$16,000	9/06	SCMN	
Caterpillar	246			G	$17,500	7/06	ECNY	Diesel, roll cage, aux. hyd.
Caterpillar	246	2000		G	$1,200	8/06	WCTX	Roll cage, diesel, aux. hyd.
Caterpillar	246	2003		G	$14,000	8/06	SECA	
Caterpillar	246	2003	1,398	G	$15,000	11/06	SECA	Bucket, canopy, aux. hyd.
Caterpillar	246	2003	1,398	G	$15,000	11/06	SECA	Bucket, canopy, aux. hyd.
Caterpillar	246	2003	1,830	G	$16,000	5/06	ECMI	Bucket, diesel
Caterpillar	246	2003	1,398	G	$16,000	11/06	SECA	Bucket, canopy, aux. hyd.
Caterpillar	246	2003		g	$18,000	1/06	WCNH	Diesel, roll cage, gp bucket
Caterpillar	246	2003		G	$18,000	1/06	WCNH	Diesel, roll cage, aux. hyd., gp bucket
Caterpillar	246B	2004		G	$16,500	8/06	WCTX	Diesel, roll cage, aux. hyd., gp bucket
Caterpillar	246B	2004	561	G	$19,000	8/06	SEPA	Diesel, roll cage, aux. hyd., gp bucket
Caterpillar	246B	2004		G	$19,000	10/06	WCFL	Diesel, roll cage, aux. hyd., gp bucket
Caterpillar	247			G	$11,000	9/06	WCTX	Diesel, rubber tracked, aux. hyd., roll cage
Caterpillar	247			G	$14,000	8/06	SECA	
Caterpillar	247			G	$14,000	8/06	SECA	
Caterpillar	247		2,100	G	$17,500	8/06	SETN	Teeth, cab, air, gp bucket
Caterpillar	247	2004	1,342	G	$16,000	11/06	SCCA	
Caterpillar	247	2005	450	G	$26,000	11/06	WCMN	247B, track skid steer, CAH, aux. hyd.
Caterpillar	248B	2003	700	G	$18,000	9/06	NEIN	Steel tracks
Caterpillar	252			G	$14,000	8/06	WCTX	Diesel, roll cage, aux. hyd., gp bucket
Caterpillar	257			G	$14,000	9/06	WCTX	Rubber tracked, diesel, roll cage, aux. hyd.
Caterpillar	257			G	$18,000	9/06	WCTX	Diesel, roll cage, aux. hyd.
Caterpillar	257	2003	652	G	$22,500	11/06	SECA	Bucket, canopy, aux. hyd.
Caterpillar	257	2004		G	$27,000	9/06	ECMN	257B, CAH, aux. hyd.
Caterpillar	262		400	G	$15,500	8/06	SEPA	Turbo, fair rubber
Caterpillar	262	2004	757	G	$19,000	5/06	ECMI	Diesel, hyd. quick disconnect
Caterpillar	267B	2006		E	$43,750	12/06	WCMN	Full CAH, hyd. quick-tach, multitool control, 18" tracks, 72" dirt bucket
Caterpillar	277	2001		G	$19,500	8/06	WCTX	Diesel, roll cage, aux. hyd.
Caterpillar	277	2001		G	$24,000	3/06	ECIN	Diesel, canopy
Caterpillar	277	2003	1,240	G	$30,000	11/06	SECA	Bucket, aux. hyd., canopy
Caterpillar	277	2004		G	$32,000	7/06	ECNY	Rubber tracked, diesel, roll cage, gp bucket
Daewoo	2060		1,247	G	$10,600	9/06	SCNE	2060XL, diesel engine, 6' bucket, aux. hyd.
Gehl	2500			G	$2,300	8/06	SETN	
Gehl	3410		931	G	$5,400	11/06	SEIA	
Gehl	3825		1,350	F	$7,900	2/06	NENE	
Gehl	4610			G	$3,000	10/06	SEMN	
Gehl	4610	1989	4,300	G	$4,000	12/06	NWWI	40 hp., gas, 1,150-lb. lift
Gehl	4625			G	$6,300	6/06	NEIN	Bucket

Skid Steer Loaders

Make	Model	Year	Hrs.	Cond.	Price	Sale	Location	Comments
Gehl	4625			F	$8,000	3/06	SEPA	Average rubber
Gehl	4625			G	$9,500	8/06	SEPA	Good rubber
Gehl	4635			G	$6,050	9/06	SCMN	4635SX, diesel, bucket
Gehl	4635		3,096	G	$10,000	2/06	SCNY	
Gehl	4635		2,026	G	$11,500	2/06	SCNY	
Gehl	4635	1999	1,447	G	$10,500	5/06	SWCA	Canopy
Gehl	4835SXT	2001		G	$6,500	9/06	WCTX	Diesel, roll cage
Gehl	4840	2004	505	G	$16,250	5/06	SWCA	Canopy
Gehl	4840	2004		G	$16,500	11/06	SWCA	Canopy
Gehl	5625		2,384	G	$6,500	5/06	SWCA	Canopy
Gehl	5625			G	$7,000	3/06	NCMN	
Gehl	5625			G	$7,700	3/06	NCMN	
Gehl	5635			G	$7,800	3/06	NCMN	
Gehl	5635			G	$8,500	3/06	NCMN	Cab
Gehl	5635DXT			G	$11,300	9/06	SCMN	Diesel, bucket
Gehl	5635	1998		G	$6,750	12/06	SEMN	SXT
Gehl	6635		900	F	$16,500	3/06	SEPA	Series II, fair rubber
Gehl	7600		1,600	G	$24,000	3/06	SEPA	2 spd., average rubber
Hydra Mac	2650			F	$4,950	12/06	NWIL	Diesel
Hydra Mac	2650			G	$7,500	2/06	WCMN	
Hydra Mac	NA			G	$1,700	11/06	WCMN	Onan engine
Hydra Mac	NA			G	$3,000	8/06	NCIA	
Hydra Mac	NA		4,988	G	$5,500	4/06	WCWI	1,000 hours on new Isuzu diesel engine, material, tine buckets
JCB	170		113	G	$12,000	8/06	WCTX	Diesel, roll cage, gp bucket
JCB	170		62	G	$12,000	8/06	SEPA	Diesel, roll cage, aux. hyd.
JCB	170		206	G	$13,500	8/06	WCTX	Diesel, roll cage, aux. hyd., gp bucket
JCB	170		155	G	$13,500	8/06	WCTX	Diesel, roll cage, aux. hyd., gp bucket
JCB	170			G	$18,500	10/06	WCFL	Diesel, roll cage, aux. hyd., gp bucket
JCB	170	2005	203	G	$10,500	9/06	WCTX	Diesel, roll cage, aux. hyd., gp bucket
JCB	170	2005	219	G	$13,500	10/06	WCFL	Diesel, roll cage, aux. hyd., gp bucket
JCB	170	2005		G	$13,500	10/06	SCPA	
JCB	185		2,045	G	$10,750	9/06	NEIN	
John Deere	170			F	$2,400	8/06	WCMN	New gear Case, 65 hp., Wisconsin engine, bucket
John Deere	170			F	$7,000	4/06	SEND	Skid loader, backhoe attachment
John Deere	240			G	$7,000	9/06	WCTX	Diesel, roll cage, aux. hyd., gp bucket
John Deere	240		3,200	G	$8,650	8/06	NWIL	Series II, diesel
John Deere	240			F	$9,200	4/06	SEPA	Poor rubber
John Deere	240		1,161	G	$9,500	9/06	SECA	
John Deere	240			G	$11,000	7/06	WCCA	Bucket, canopy
John Deere	240		175	G	$13,000	2/06	WCMN	No cab, 66" low-profile bucket, almost new
John Deere	240	1999	2,206	G	$10,000	11/06	SECA	60" bucket, canopy, aux. hyd.
John Deere	240	1999	1,241	G	$10,500	11/06	SCND	Bucket, Texana forks, diesel
John Deere	240	2001	343	G	$15,500	5/06	ECNE	60" bucket, aux. hyd., 10-16.5 NHS tires
John Deere	240	2002		G	$8,250	1/06	WCNH	Diesel, roll cage, aux. hyd., gp bucket
John Deere	240	2002	1,189	G	$11,500	9/06	NEIN	Diesel, new tires, canopy, gp bucket
John Deere	240	2003	2,600	E	$9,600	1/06	SCMI	72" material bucket
John Deere	250		3,031	G	$10,000	11/06	SECA	Bucket, canopy, aux. hyd.
John Deere	250			G	$10,800	8/06	SEPA	Average rubber

WHAT'S IT WORTH?

Skid Steer Loaders

Make	Model	Year	Hrs.	Cond.	Price	Sale	Location	Comments
John Deere	250		405	G	$18,250	12/06	ECMN	EROPS, heat, rubber tracks
John Deere	250	1999		G	$11,500	12/06	SEND	Aux. hyd.
John Deere	250	2001		G	$9,500	1/06	WCCA	
John Deere	250	2003		G	$12,500	7/06	ECNY	Series II, diesel, roll cage, aux. hyd., gp bucket
John Deere	250	2004	100	G	$18,250	2/06	SWNE	Series II, JD 72" gp bucket, 12-16.5 rubber, rear weights, aux. hyd.
John Deere	260			F	$11,250	8/06	SEPA	Fair rubber
John Deere	260		5,250	G	$12,100	7/06	SEND	
John Deere	260		2,000	F	$12,100	1/06	SEPA	Average rubber
John Deere	260	2000		F	$10,900	1/06	NEIN	
John Deere	260	2000	2,190	G	$11,250	8/06	SETN	Gp bucket
John Deere	260	2000	1,700	G	$13,250	12/06	WCMN	2 spd., new short block, tires good
John Deere	260	2001	345	G	$14,000	12/06	NWWI	69 hp., 2,400-lb. lift
John Deere	270	2003	1,400	G	$16,500	7/06	WCMN	Series II, cab kit, heat, air, 2 spd., 84" material bucket, new tires
John Deere	280			G	$22,500	3/06	NCUT	
John Deere	317	2005	535	G	$15,500	11/06	SCCA	Aux. hyd.
John Deere	317	2005		G	$18,750	11/06	SWCA	Cab, air
John Deere	317	2005	24	G	$19,000	8/06	SETN	72" bucket
John Deere	320		139	G	$18,500	3/06	NCUT	
John Deere	320			G	$20,000	8/06	SEPA	Average track
John Deere	320	2005	140	G	$18,100	8/06	NWIL	Diesel
John Deere	325	2005	258	G	$22,000	12/06	NWWI	70 hp., 2,500-lb. lift
John Deere	5575	1997		G	$8,000	11/06	SWCA	Canopy
John Deere	7775	1997		G	$7,500	11/06	SWCA	Canopy
John Deere	7775	1997	1,630	G	$9,100	12/06	NWWI	49 hp., 1,705-lb. lift
Melroe	220		900	G	$23,000	3/06	SEPA	A220, Bobcat, CAH, power attachment, average rubber, 30-day warranty
Melroe	220	2004		G	$26,000	1/06	WCNH	Turbo diesel, CAH, sweeper, bucket
Melroe	2410			G	$4,000	9/06	SECA	
Melroe	2410			G	$9,000	9/06	SECA	
Melroe	310			F	$2,750	3/06	NWOH	Bobcat, gas, 3' bucket, tach says 843 hours
Melroe	310			G	$3,900	3/06	ECNE	Bobcat, Kohler gas engine, 40" bucket
Melroe	313		381	G	$5,700	7/06	ECIL	Bobcat, 40" quick-attach bucket, manure tines, Kubota diesel engine, original tires
Melroe	453			G	$4,250	9/06	SECA	
Melroe	453			G	$4,500	9/06	SECA	
Melroe	453			G	$4,500	9/06	SECA	
Melroe	453			G	$6,000	9/06	SECA	
Melroe	453	1999	1,350	G	$4,000	5/06	SWCA	Canopy
Melroe	453	1999		G	$5,000	1/06	WCOH	Kubota diesel, roll cage, aux. hyd.
Melroe	453	1999		G	$5,000	1/06	WCOH	Kubota diesel, roll cage, aux. hyd.
Melroe	463			G	$5,750	5/06	SWCA	Canopy
Melroe	542B		750	G	$4,750	3/06	NWIL	Diesel
Melroe	542B		490	G	$6,350	3/06	NWIL	Diesel
Melroe	543			G	$4,400	10/06	WCFL	
Melroe	543B		1,571	F	$6,300	2/06	NENE	Bobcat, Kubota diesel
Melroe	553			G	$7,500	12/06	SEMN	Bobcat
Melroe	600			F	$1,400	6/06	NWMN	Bobcat, 610 engine, propane, quick-tach bucket

Skid Steer Loaders

Make	Model	Year	Hrs.	Cond.	Price	Sale	Location	Comments
Melroe	642			G	$5,750	11/06	SCCA	Gas
Melroe	642	1982		G	$5,500	11/06	SCSD	Bobcat, 40 hours on new engine, aux. hyd., new tires
Melroe	642	1986	3,618	G	$6,000	2/06	ECIL	Bobcat, 60" bucket, fork bucket sold separate for $450
Melroe	643			G	$5,500	1/06	WCOH	Diesel, roll cage
Melroe	643			G	$5,500	1/06	WCOH	Diesel, roll cage, aux. hyd.
Melroe	722			G	$3,750	11/06	SWCA	Canopy
Melroe	742B			G	$5,250	11/06	SWCA	Dual fuel, canopy
Melroe	742B			G	$5,500	12/06	NWWI	Bobcat, 36-hp. gas, 1,300-lb. lift
Melroe	743			G	$3,800	3/06	SCIN	
Melroe	743			G	$4,000	1/06	WCCA	
Melroe	743		3,800	F	$4,900	12/06	WCMN	Bobcat, cab and heat
Melroe	743			G	$5,000	7/06	ECNY	Diesel, roll cage, gp bucket
Melroe	743			G	$6,000	3/06	ECMI	
Melroe	743			G	$6,600	10/06	NCND	Bobcat
Melroe	743			G	$7,500	8/06	WCMN	Bobcat, bucket, diesel
Melroe	743	1988	3,800	F	$5,750	8/06	WCMN	Bobcat, bucket, diesel
Melroe	743	1988	2,166	G	$8,000	5/06	SEND	Bobcat, aux. hyd., bucket, grapple
Melroe	743	1988	2,711	G	$8,000	9/06	NEND	Bobcat
Melroe	743B			F	$4,000	11/06	SETN	Bobcat
Melroe	743B			G	$6,000	11/06	SWCA	Canopy
Melroe	743B			G	$6,800	11/06	ECIL	Bobcat
Melroe	743B			G	$7,000	8/06	NWIL	Bobcat, diesel
Melroe	743B	1995		G	$6,250	7/06	ECNY	Diesel, roll cage, aux. hyd.
Melroe	751			G	$5,000	9/06	SECA	
Melroe	751			G	$6,500	1/06	WCCA	
Melroe	751		1,689	G	$7,950	1/06	SCTN	Bobcat
Melroe	753			G	$5,250	3/06	WCWA	
Melroe	753			G	$6,100	6/06	NEIN	
Melroe	753			G	$6,600	3/06	SCIN	
Melroe	753			F	$6,700	3/06	SWOH	Bobcat, diesel, cage circa 1990
Melroe	753		2,150	G	$7,000	1/06	SCTN	Bobcat
Melroe	753			G	$7,300	3/06	NWIL	Diesel
Melroe	753		2,150	G	$7,700	1/06	SCTN	Bobcat
Melroe	753		2,444	G	$8,500	9/06	WCWI	Bobcat, quick-tach bucket
Melroe	753			G	$8,500	8/06	SCNE	Bobcat, 60" bucket, 1 hyd.
Melroe	753		4,780	G	$8,700	1/06	NEIN	Bobcat, diesel
Melroe	753		2,100	G	$9,000	3/06	NWIL	Diesel
Melroe	753			G	$9,000	1/06	WCCA	
Melroe	753	1990	2,894	G	$7,900	3/06	WCMN	Bobcat, bucket,
Melroe	753	1998		G	$10,500	11/06	SWCA	Canopy
Melroe	753	1999	2,100	G	$8,600	8/06	NWIL	Bobcat, diesel
Melroe	753	2000		G	$10,000	1/06	WCOH	Diesel, roll cage, aux. hyd.
Melroe	753	2000		G	$10,000	1/06	WCOH	Diesel, roll cage, aux. hyd., 66" bucket
Melroe	753F			G	$9,500	7/06	ECNY	Diesel, enclosed cab, aux. hyd.
Melroe	763			G	$5,250	5/06	SWCA	Canopy
Melroe	763			G	$6,500	8/06	WCNC	
Melroe	763			G	$7,500	1/06	WCCA	
Melroe	763			G	$7,750	9/06	WCTX	Diesel, roll cage, aux. hyd., gp bucket
Melroe	763		1,847	G	$8,250	5/06	SWCA	Canopy

Skid Steer Loaders

Make	Model	Year	Hrs.	Cond.	Price	Sale	Location	Comments
Melroe	763			G	$8,250	9/06	NEIN	Canopy
Melroe	763			G	$9,500	11/06	SWCA	Canopy
Melroe	763			G	$9,500	9/06	SECA	High flow
Melroe	763			F	$9,600	1/06	SEPA	Bobcat, previous rental unit, poor rubber
Melroe	763		2,002	G	$10,500	5/06	SWCA	Canopy
Melroe	763		1,123	G	$10,750	5/06	WCMN	Bobcat, aux. hyd., bucket, no cab
Melroe	763		1,083	G	$10,750	8/06	SETN	Gp bucket
Melroe	763		2,950	G	$11,750	8/06	SETN	Gp bucket
Melroe	763	1997	1,500	G	$8,000	3/06	SCIN	
Melroe	763	1997	2,031	G	$12,600	3/06	SEND	Bobcat, 66" dirt bucket, Kubota diesel engine, cab, heat
Melroe	763	1999		G	$7,000	8/06	WCTX	Diesel, roll cage, aux. hyd., gp bucket
Melroe	763	1999		G	$7,350	8/06	WCTX	Diesel, roll cage, aux. hyd.
Melroe	763	1999		G	$7,500	8/06	WCTX	Diesel, roll cage, aux. hyd., gp bucket
Melroe	763	1999		G	$7,750	8/06	WCTX	Diesel, roll cage, aux. hyd., gp bucket
Melroe	763	1999		G	$7,750	8/06	WCTX	Diesel, roll cage, aux. hyd., gp bucket
Melroe	763	1999		G	$8,000	8/06	WCTX	Diesel, roll cage, aux. hyd.
Melroe	763	1999	2,500	G	$8,000	9/06	NEIN	Diesel, canopy, gp bucket
Melroe	763	1999	1,900	G	$8,100	9/06	NEIN	Diesel, canopy, gp bucket
Melroe	763	1999		G	$8,500	10/06	WCFL	Bobcat, roll cage, aux. hyd., gp bucket
Melroe	763	2000		G	$6,500	9/06	WCTX	Diesel, roll cage, aux. hyd.
Melroe	763	2000		G	$7,500	8/06	WCTX	Diesel, roll cage, aux. hyd., gp bucket
Melroe	763	2000		G	$7,500	8/06	WCTX	Diesel, aux. hyd., gp bucket
Melroe	763	2000	1,285	G	$10,000	10/06	WCFL	Bobcat, roll cage, aux. hyd., gp bucket
Melroe	763	2001		G	$11,000	11/06	SWCA	Canopy
Melroe	763	2001		G	$11,500	11/06	SWCA	Canopy
Melroe	763	2002		G	$12,000	9/06	NEIN	Aux. hyd., low-profile bucket
Melroe	763	2003		G	$10,000	10/06	SCPA	
Melroe	763	2003		G	$12,000	10/06	SCPA	
Melroe	773			G	$7,250	3/06	ECIN	Canopy
Melroe	773		6,233	G	$7,900	3/06	WCMN	Bobcat, diesel, quick-tach
Melroe	773			G	$8,750	8/06	WCTX	Diesel, roll cage, aux. hyd., gp bucket
Melroe	773		2,249	G	$10,000	9/06	SECA	
Melroe	773			G	$10,400	3/06	NWIL	Diesel, new tires, air
Melroe	773		1,900	G	$11,300	2/06	NCIL	Bobcat, bucket
Melroe	773		906	G	$12,200	5/06	WCMN	Bobcat, aux. hyd., forks, bucket, hyd. quick-tach, no cab
Melroe	773	1998		G	$8,300	3/06	SCIN	
Melroe	773	2000	595	G	$11,500	10/06	WCFL	Bobcat, diesel, roll cage, aux. hyd., gp bucket
Melroe	773	2000	2,000	G	$12,500	8/06	WCMN	Bobcat, turbo, cab enclosed w/ heat, bucket, G Series
Melroe	773	2001	400	G	$15,500	3/06	SCIN	500K Series, air
Melroe	773	2001		G	$15,500	9/06	NEIN	Aux. hyd., canopy
Melroe	773	2001	1,258	G	$16,000	8/06	ECIA	Bobcat, diesel, turbo
Melroe	773	2002		G	$12,500	10/06	WCFL	Kubota diesel, roll cage, aux. hyd.
Melroe	773F	1999		G	$12,500	9/06	NEIN	Aux. hyd., low-profile bucket, canopy
Melroe	7753		3,980	G	$9,250	5/06	SWCA	Cab
Melroe	843			G	$4,500	9/06	SECA	
Melroe	843			G	$5,000	9/06	NWTN	Gp bucket
Melroe	843			G	$5,500	11/06	SWCA	Canopy
Melroe	843			G	$6,250	12/06	NEMN	
Melroe	843			G	$8,000	5/06	SWCA	Grapple bucket, canopy

Skid Steer Loaders

Make	Model	Year	Hrs.	Cond.	Price	Sale	Location	Comments
Melroe	843			G	$9,250	12/06	NEMN	
Melroe	843			G	$9,700	3/06	NENE	Bobcat, bucket, new engine, 12-16.5 tires
Melroe	843	1989		G	$7,500	3/06	ECMI	Diesel, front hyd., new paint
Melroe	843	1998		G	$5,500	8/06	SECA	
Melroe	853			G	$6,000	3/06	ECIN	Diesel, canopy
Melroe	853			G	$6,000	9/06	NEIN	Canopy
Melroe	853			G	$6,500	11/06	SWCA	Canopy
Melroe	853		5,541	G	$6,750	11/06	SWCA	Canopy
Melroe	853			G	$7,000	7/06	ECNY	Gp bucket, diesel, roll cage, aux. hyd.
Melroe	853			G	$7,200	7/06	SEND	Bobcat
Melroe	853		3,529	G	$7,650	8/06	NWOH	Bobcat, diesel, 6' bucket
Melroe	853			G	$7,800	7/06	SEND	Bobcat
Melroe	853			G	$8,300	3/06	NWIL	Diesel
Melroe	853	1991	2,800	G	$8,700	8/06	NWIL	Bobcat, diesel
Melroe	853	1994		G	$9,000	1/06	NECO	5' bucket, roll cage
Melroe	853H			G	$6,750	11/06	SWCA	Canopy
Melroe	863			G	$6,250	6/06	NEIN	
Melroe	863		801	G	$6,250	12/06	NEMN	
Melroe	863		1,823	G	$7,500	12/06	NEMN	
Melroe	863			G	$7,750	9/06	NEIN	
Melroe	863			G	$7,800	3/06	SCIN	High flow
Melroe	863		1,297	G	$9,750	1/06	SCTN	Bobcat, gp bucket
Melroe	863			G	$10,000	10/06	WCFL	Bobcat, diesel, roll cage, aux. hyd., gp bucket
Melroe	863			G	$10,500	11/06	SCCA	
Melroe	863		1,485	G	$11,000	8/06	SETN	Gp bucket
Melroe	863		2,250	G	$12,000	3/06	NWIL	Diesel
Melroe	863			G	$13,000	11/06	SWCA	Canopy
Melroe	863			G	$13,500	10/06	WCFL	Bobcat, diesel, roll cage, aux. hyd., low-profile bucket
Melroe	863			G	$14,250	3/06	NWIL	Diesel
Melroe	863	1997		G	$11,500	11/06	SWCA	Canopy
Melroe	863	1999	3,056	E	$10,000	8/06	NWOH	Bobcat, diesel, 6' bucket
Melroe	863	1999		G	$11,000	8/06	NWIL	Bobcat, diesel
Melroe	863	2000	1,599	G	$11,250	11/06	SCCA	Aux. hyd.
Melroe	863	2001	3,596	G	$11,500	5/06	SWCA	Canopy
Melroe	863	2001	1,588	G	$12,000	8/06	WCTX	Diesel, roll cage, aux. hyd., lights, gp bucket
Melroe	863	2004		G	$9,250	5/06	SWCA	Canopy
Melroe	864		7,130	G	$12,500	12/06	NEMN	
Melroe	864			G	$13,500	12/06	ECMN	No door, closed cab, heat, turbo
Melroe	864	1999		G	$13,000	8/06	SECA	Rubber tracked
Melroe	864	2000		G	$13,000	11/06	SWCA	Poly tracks, canopy
Melroe	864	2000		G	$15,500	7/06	ECNY	Rubber tracked, diesel, roll cage, aux. hyd.
Melroe	864	2001	1,250	G	$18,000	7/06	ECNY	Rubber tracked, diesel, 18" tracks
Melroe	873		3,382	G	$8,500	12/06	NEMN	
Melroe	873			F	$9,900	3/06	SEPA	Bobcat, turbo, fair rubber
Melroe	873		2,717	G	$11,000	8/06	SETN	Gp bucket
Melroe	873			G	$11,000	12/06	NEMN	
Melroe	873	1999		G	$7,500	8/06	WCTX	Diesel, roll cage, aux. hyd., gp bucket
Melroe	873	1999	1,353	G	$13,000	5/06	ECMI	Diesel, bucket
Melroe	873	2000		G	$10,000	9/06	NWTN	Gp bucket, cab, air

Skid Steer Loaders

Make	Model	Year	Hrs.	Cond.	Price	Sale	Location	Comments
Melroe	873	2000	2,730	G	$14,000	8/06	SETN	CAH, gp bucket, 2 spd.
Melroe	873	2001		G	$12,000	9/06	NEIN	Cab, air, gp bucket, hd tires
Melroe	873	2001	2,477	G	$12,750	5/06	SWCA	Canopy
Melroe	875C			F	$8,200	8/06	SEPA	Bobcat, fair rubber
Melroe	943			G	$8,500	11/06	SECA	Canopy, gp bucket
Melroe	953			G	$8,000	9/06	NEIN	Aux. hyd., float tires, 3,000-lb. capacity
Melroe	963			G	$11,000	9/06	WCTX	Diesel, roll cage, aux. hyd., gp bucket
Melroe	M500			F	$1,200	12/06	WCMN	Bobcat
Melroe	S130	2004	500	G	$11,500	9/06	NEIN	Aux. hyd., low-profile bucket, canopy
Melroe	S130	2004	50	E	$16,800	12/06	WCIA	Bobcat, like new, 62" bucket
Melroe	S185		3,300	G	$12,000	12/06	WCMN	Bobcat, turbo
Melroe	S185			G	$14,250	3/06	NWIL	Diesel
Melroe	S185	2003		G	$13,000	8/06	WCTX	Roll cage, aux. hyd., gp bucket
Melroe	S185	2005	84	G	$22,750	11/06	WCMN	Bobcat, turbo, full cab kit, cab heat, power Bob-Tach, hand/foot controls, front aux. hyd., one owner
Melroe	S300	2003	1,353	G	$22,500	5/06	SWCA	High flow, canopy
Melroe	S300	2004		G	$18,000	11/06	SWCA	Cab, air
Melroe	S300	2004		G	$18,500	10/06	WCFL	Diesel, enclosed cab, aux. hyd.
Melroe	T190		2,418	G	$12,500	12/06	ECMN	OROPS, aux. hyd.
Melroe	T190	1800		F	$14,800	1/06	SEPA	Bobcat, cab, air, rubber tracked
Melroe	T190	2000		G	$18,000	11/06	SWCA	Poly tracks, canopy
Melroe	T190	2001	1,550	G	$14,000	11/06	WCMN	Bobcat, enclosed cab, heat, power Bob-Tach, tracks, belts 25%
Melroe	T190	2002		G	$17,000	7/06	ECNY	Rubber track, diesel, enclosed cab, gp bucket
Melroe	T190	2002	2,490	G	$19,000	5/06	SWCA	Poly tracks, canopy
Melroe	T190	2004		G	$19,000	11/06	SWCA	Poly tracks, canopy
Melroe	T200			G	$15,000	9/06	NEIN	Track loader, canopy
Melroe	T200		2,600	G	$17,750	8/06	SEPA	Bobcat, turbo, CAH, average tracks
Melroe	T200		1,750	G	$18,500	12/06	NEMN	
Melroe	T200	2000		G	$17,000	8/06	SECA	Rubber track
Melroe	T200	2000	2,958	G	$19,000	5/06	SWCA	Poly tracks, cab, air
Melroe	T200	2002		G	$14,500	9/06	WCTX	Rubber tracked, diesel, roll cage
Melroe	T200	2002		G	$17,500	10/06	WCFL	Bobcat, diesel, roll cage, aux. hyd.
Melroe	T200	2002		G	$17,500	11/06	SWCA	Poly tracks
Melroe	T200	2004		G	$14,000	11/06	SWCA	Poly tracks
Melroe	T200	2004		G	$19,000	11/06	SWCA	Poly tracks
Melroe	T250			G	$19,500	10/06	SWOH	Rubber-tracked Bobcat, turbo diesel, EROPS, 17" rubber tracks, gp bucket
Melroe	T250	2004		G	$20,000	10/06	WCFL	Bobcat, diesel, rubber tracked, roll cage, aux. hyd., LP bucket
Mustang	1000			F	$1,000	8/06	NWIL	Gas
Mustang	2040	1999		G	$5,000	11/06	SWCA	Canopy
Mustang	2050	2001	1,200	G	$8,350	3/06	NWIL	Diesel
Mustang	2070		1,940	G	$10,000	7/06	SEND	
Mustang	2070	2002	75	E	$10,000	3/06	ECIN	Diesel, aux. standard hyd. at 22 gallons per minute
Mustang	2074			G	$8,000	1/06	WCCA	
Mustang	330			G	$2,900	8/06	NCIA	22 hp., engine replaced, cylinders rebuilt
Mustang	345			G	$4,500	6/06	NCIA	4-cyl. Ford industrial engine, 55" quick-tach bucket, cage w/ cab enclosure

Skid Steer Loaders

Make	Model	Year	Hrs.	Cond.	Price	Sale	Location	Comments
Mustang	930A		1,500	G	$4,100	3/06	NWIL	Diesel
Mustang	960			G	$4,750	9/06	NEIN	Diesel
New Holland	180B			G	$10,750	12/06	SWWI	
New Holland	445			G	$3,000	3/06	NWIL	Gas
New Holland	455			G	$4,000	7/06	ECNY	Diesel, roll cage, aux. hyd., gp bucket
New Holland	455			G	$4,950	8/06	NWIL	200 hours on engine, gas
New Holland	553			P	$4,650	11/06	NEIA	Rough
New Holland	L553		1,443	G	$4,250	8/06	SCMI	6' bucket
New Holland	L553		3,758	G	$7,500	6/06	NCPA	One owner, Kubota diesel, bucket, hay spear, 10×16.5 rubber
New Holland	L555			F	$3,600	3/06	SEIA	68" bucket, hay stabber
New Holland	L555			G	$5,250	11/06	SWCA	Canopy
New Holland	L555			G	$5,700	12/06	SEMN	
New Holland	L665	1994		E	$9,700	3/06	NEKS	
New Holland	L783	1998		G	$6,600	12/06	SEMN	
New Holland	L865			G	$5,750	3/06	ECMI	16 hp., 10'6" reach
New Holland	L865		1,500	F	$9,300	1/06	SEPA	High flow, average rubber
New Holland	L985	1999		G	$12,250	8/06	SEPA	Super Boom, poor rubber
New Holland	LS125	2003	2,371	G	$3,000	1/06	NECO	4' bucket, roll cage
New Holland	LS150	2001	1,625	G	$10,000	8/06	SETN	Gp bucket
New Holland	LS160			F	$11,500	9/06	NCOH	Skid steer loader, 6' material bucket, 66" manure fork, less than 2,200 hours, needed rubber
New Holland	LS160		1,365	G	$11,500	11/06	WCMN	Hyd. mounted plate, suspension seat, turn signals, block heater
New Holland	LS160		1,370	G	$11,750	6/06	SCMN	Poor tires
New Holland	LS170		1,771	G	$13,500	11/06	WCMN	Cab, heat, suspension seat, turn signals
New Holland	LS170	2000	1,638	G	$13,900	12/06	SEIA	Turbo
New Holland	LS170	2005	220	G	$16,000	7/06	ECNY	Diesel, enclosed cab, heat, weight kit, gp bucket
New Holland	LS180			F	$11,000	1/06	SEPA	2 spd., average rubber
New Holland	LS180		910	G	$15,000	11/06	WCMN	2 spd., suspension seat
New Holland	LS180			G	$15,000	11/06	SETN	Turbo
New Holland	LS180	1999		G	$13,250	8/06	SEPA	Diesel, aux. hyd.
New Holland	LS180	1999		G	$15,000	7/06	ECNY	Diesel, enclosed cab, heat, aux. hyd.
New Holland	LS180	2003	881	E	$21,000	2/06	SCPA	2 spd.
New Holland	LS185	2005	219	G	$26,000	12/06	NENE	72" bucket
New Holland	LS190		1,100	G	$12,200	8/06	SEPA	Fair rubber, 2 spd.
New Holland	LS190			F	$13,100	3/06	SEPA	2 spd., average rubber
New Holland	LS190	2001		G	$11,000	8/06	SEPA	NH diesel, roll cage, high-flow aux. hyd.
New Holland	LX565			G	$7,000	7/06	ECNY	Diesel, roll cage, gp bucket
New Holland	LX656			G	$8,250	1/06	WCOH	Diesel, roll cage, OROPS
New Holland	LX665			G	$8,500	9/06	NWTN	Gp bucket
New Holland	LX665		991	G	$16,750	2/06	WCOH	Diesel, dirt bucket
New Holland	LX885			G	$7,250	10/06	SWOH	Turbo diesel, ROPS, roll cage, aux. hyd., rear counterweight
New Holland	LX885	1995	4,035	G	$11,500	12/06	NWWI	Cab, heat, 600 hours on new engine
New Holland	LX885	1996		G	$550	11/06	SWCA	Canopy
New Holland	LX985			G	$8,000	11/06	SETN	60" bucket
New Holland	LX985			G	$11,500	8/06	SEPA	Super Boom, average rubber
Scat Trak	1500C	1999		G	$8,000	10/06	WCFL	Diesel, roll cage, aux. hyd.
Scat Trak	1500C	2000	1,326	G	$10,500	5/06	SWCA	Canopy

Skid Steer Loaders

Make	Model	Year	Hrs.	Cond.	Price	Sale	Location	Comments
Scat Trak	1700C			G	$7,000	3/06	ECIN	Diesel
Scat Trak	1750	2000		G	$12,500	5/06	SWCA	Canopy
Scat Trak	2000		1,780	G	$9,750	9/06	SECA	
Scat Trak	2000	1999	1,600	G	$10,000	12/06	SEND	Diesel, aux. hyd.
Takuchi	TL-26	2000		G	$11,500	11/06	SWCA	Canopy, poly tracks
Thomas	153		409	G	$6,550	9/06	SCMN	Full cab
Thomas	173			G	$6,750	11/06	SCCA	

Notes

Soil Movers

Moving dirt. A big job that requires the right piece of equipment. From little 10- to 12-foot land planes up to 18-yard rigs, check out what various makes and models of used soil movers are worth.

WHAT'S IT WORTH?

Soil Movers

Make	Model	Year	Cond.	Price	Sale	Location	Comments
Ashland	646477	2000	E	$24,000	4/06	ECND	Hyd. push-off scraper, 13 yard, 21.5-16.1 front flotation tires, 18.4-26 diamond rears
Ashland	3.5 yard		G	$2,300	3/06	ECND	Scraper
Ashland	4.5 yard		G	$4,000	4/06	SEND	Scraper
Ashland	8 yard		G	$5,000	3/06	NEND	Hyd. dump scraper
Ashland	8 yard		G	$5,700	3/06	NWMN	Scraper
Ashland	6 yard		P	$500	4/06	ECND	Scraper, 6 yard, needs repair
Ashland	18 yard	2005	E	$38,000	12/06	WCMN	18-yard dirt scraper, hyd. push-off, direct mount
Caterpillar	60		G	$10,500	4/06	NWMN	10-yard scraper, hyd. pushoff
Caterpillar	60		G	$14,000	3/06	SEIA	Dirt scraper, hyd. unload
Caterpillar	613B		G	$17,000	9/06	NEIN	Scraper, canopy, 23.5-25 tires
Country Welding	NA		G	$5,800	12/06	ECNE	14' box scraper, 4-wheel lift
Crown	NA		G	$4,000	12/06	SEND	6-yard scraper
Eversman	10'		F	$300	2/06	NECO	Front and rear dollies, pt
Eversman	10'		F	$375	1/06	NECO	
Eversman	2.5 yard		G	$1,500	3/06	ECND	Scraper
Eversman	2400		G	$2,000	4/06	NWMN	Land leveler, converted to hd 3-pt. blade
Eversman	2400		F	$8,100	2/06	NCCO	Land plane
Eversman	250		F	$2,800	12/06	NWIL	8' dirt scraper
Eversman	3212		F	$400	1/06	NCCO	Land plane, steel front wheels
Eversman	3212		F	$750	1/06	NCCO	Land plane
Eversman	3212		F	$900	3/06	NCCO	Land plane
Eversman	3212		F	$1,200	2/06	NCCO	Land plane
Eversman	329		F	$225	2/06	NECO	10', front & rear dollies
Eversman	4 YD		G	$3,400	7/06	NEND	Scraper
Eversman	4512		P	$700	1/06	NCCO	Land plane
Eversman	650		G	$4,800	3/06	NEKS	6 yard scraper
Eversman	NA		G	$900	3/06	ECND	Land leveler
Eversman	NA		G	$2,600	2/06	NECO	3½-yard front dollies
Eversman	700		G	$6,500	8/06	WCIL	700-lb. dirt scraper
Farmhand	NA		G	$2,400	4/06	NWSD	3.5-yard soil mover earth scraper, hydraulics, extra axle
Hammerback	NA		G	$2,700	3/06	ECND	Hammerback welding 15' box scraper, one owner
Hammerback	NA		G	$3,300	3/06	NEND	14' trailing box scraper
John Deere	10'		F	$100	3/06	SWNE	Box scraper
John Deere	1940		G	$1,700	3/06	NWMN	Land plane
John Deere	1940		G	$4,000	4/06	WCMT	Land plane, 12' cut
John Deere	7000		G	$3,700	9/06	SEIL	6.5-yard scraper
John Deere	930		G	$1,800	1/06	WCNE	Land plane, 12', pt, harrow
John Deere	935		G	$1,175	1/06	NCCO	Land plane
John Deere	935		G	$1,400	2/06	NECO	12' land plane
Kuntz	NA		G	$9,000	9/06	SEIL	Kuntz 8½-yard scraper, front dolly wheels
Leon	NA		G	$16,000	6/06	NWMN	9-yard field scraper, hyd. push off
Letourneau	12 yard		G	$7,000	11/06	ECND	LP converted to direct-mount scraper, new paint, 12-14 yard
Letourneau	11 yard		G	$8,000	3/06	NWMN	11-yard converted field scraper
Lorenz	L10800	2004	E	$12,250	12/06	WCMN	10-yard dirt scraper, hyd. push off
Midland	6 yard		G	$4,200	7/06	NWMN	Scraper
Midland	M86		G	$5,900	4/06	ECND	7-yard scraper
Midland	4 yard		F	$1,100	3/06	NCND	4-yard scraper
Miskin	NA		F	$700	7/06	NWMN	Land plane, 16' bucket

Soil Movers

Make	Model	Year	Cond.	Price	Sale	Location	Comments
Reitan	NA	2004	G	$2,900	11/06	ECND	12' box blade, trailing, hyd. tilt option
Reynolds	12C		G	$11,500	7/06	WCTN	
Reynolds	14C		G	$16,500	7/06	WCTN	Dirt scoop
Reynolds	14C		G	$16,750	7/06	WCTN	Dirt scoop
Reynolds	14C		G	$17,500	7/06	WCTN	Dirt scoop
Reynolds	14C		G	$20,500	7/06	WCTN	Dirt scoop
Reynolds	14C		G	$20,500	7/06	WCTN	Dirt scoop
Reynolds	14C		G	$21,000	7/06	WCTN	Dirt scoop
Reynolds	14C		G	$21,000	7/06	WCTN	Dirt scoop
Reynolds	14C		G	$21,000	7/06	WCTN	Dirt scoop
Reynolds	14C	1998	G	$23,500	9/06	NEIN	Pull scraper
Reynolds	17C		G	$19,000	7/06	WCTN	Dirt scoop
Reynolds	17C		G	$21,000	7/06	WCTN	Dirt scoop
Reynolds	NA		G	$7,500	8/06	SCFL	17-yard dirt pan
Rowse	2 yard		G	$1,000	3/06	NWKS	2-yard dirt scraper, one owner
Rowse	7.5 yard		G	$5,500	1/06	SCNE	7.5-yard soil mover, front dolly wheels, very clean
Soilmover	12'		G	$1,200	2/06	WCNE	Box blade, pt
Soilmover	500RF		G	$6,000	12/06	SCNE	5 yard, hyd. eject
Soilmover	90E		G	$4,100	12/06	ECNE	Paddle scraper, 1,000 PTO, hyd. push off, rebuilt gear boxes, 46-16 aircraft tires
Soilmover	3 yard		F	$2,400	11/06	WCMN	3-yard dirt scraper
Soilmover	5 yard		G	$2,700	2/06	WCNE	5-yard earth mover, dolly front, pt
Soilmover	5 yard		G	$3,900	12/06	WCIA	5-yard dirt scraper
Strobel	NA		G	$10,700	8/06	ECNE	8-yard soil mover, 40×14 & 15×22.5 rubber
Tucker	10'		G	$1,250	6/06	NWIL	Dirt mover
Westendorf	NA		E	$2,000	4/06	NWSD	Landscraper, used very little

Notes

WHAT'S IT WORTH?

Sprayers

Every size and shape of sprayers – we've got sale prices on them, from little sprayers that ATVs pull to the big self-propelled rigs. I've felt for years that used sprayer values tend to be very volatile compared to other types of farm equipment. Remember a couple years ago when the price of self-propelled sprayers shot up 25% due to the soybean rust scare? All of a sudden, RoGators & Patriots were selling for $10,000 to $25,000 more at auction.

Sprayers

Make	Model	Year	Hrs.	Cond.	Price	Sale	Location	Comments
Ag Chem	1,000 gal.			G	$2,100	3/06	SWNE	Pull-between trailer, hyd. hoses to rear, Ag Industries piston pump, one owner
Ag Chem	1803	1992	5,367	G	$9,000	2/06	WCMN	Liquid, 3208 Cat, 18 spd., 1,750-gal. stainless tank, 80' hyd. fold booms
Ag Chem	1803	1994	6,803	G	$6,500	2/06	WCMN	3-wheel floater, 8-ton dry box, Airmax 60' booms, hyd. fold, Cummins 8.3, 250-hp., 18-spd. trans., flip tarp, auto rate controller, foamer
Ag Chem	2,200 gal.	1993		P	$2,900	6/06	NCIA	Ag-Gator, 4 injection shanks, 5.7-liter Cummins, 10 spd., 28,000 miles, cab damage
Ag Chem	400 gal.			F	$100	11/06	SWIA	Stainless steel tank, 40' boom, ace pump
Ag Chem	400 gal.			F	$300	3/06	SWMN	Pickup sprayer, 45' manual booms, Raven monitor, 5-hp. Honda engine
Ag Chem	400 gal.			G	$1,150	3/06	NWOH	#302, 45' boom, single axle
Ag Chem	500 gal.			F	$600	3/06	SWMN	Pickup sprayer, 45' folding booms, Raven monitor, foam marker
Ag Chem	502			G	$3,000	12/06	NEMO	500 gal., pt, foam markers, 48' booms
Alloway	300 gal.			F	$350	7/06	NWMN	24R-22 band
Alloway	500 gal.			F	$450	11/06	NWMN	Band, 12R-30, hyd. pump, triple nozzle, lift assist, hyd. fold
Alloway	500 gal.			G	$500	3/06	NWMN	Band, 36R-23, Red Ball monitor, hyd. lift assist
Alloway	500 gal.			G	$2,900	3/06	NCCO	12R-30 or 12R-22 band
Alloway	750 gal.			F	$250	4/06	WCMN	Pup Spray caddy, 90' manual fold boom, hyd. tip height control, electric controls for boom
Almaco	NA			G	$900	12/06	NCIA	Front mounted 12R spray bander
Apache	560		1,360	G	$39,000	2/06	SEKS	500-gal. poly tank, 60' hyd. adjustable booms, foamer
BB	NA	2002		G	$9,000	8/06	ECNE	60' boom, pt, Tee Jet controller, foam marker, self-level boom, single tall tires, 120" centers
Bestway	1,000 gal.			G	$900	3/06	NEIA	Foamer, Raven monitor
Bestway	1,000 gal.			F	$3,250	1/06	WCIL	60' booms
Bestway	1,000 gal.			G	$5,000	2/06	NWKS	60' boom, hyd. fold, Ace poly tank, foam markers, dripless nozzles
Bestway	1,000 gal.			G	$7,000	4/06	NCSD	Field Pro III, 1,000 gal., 60', joystick, Raven 440 hyd. drive
Bestway	1,000 gal.			G	$10,500	12/06	SEIA	Field Pro II, 60' boom, RHS MKR-5000 marking system, Raven SCS sprayer control, tank rinse & flush system, monitor, 12.4-38 tires
Bestway	1,000 gal.			G	$14,000	11/06	NCIN	Field Pro II, 60' hyd. booms, Raven controller, used 2 seasons
Bestway	1,200 gal.	2003		G	$18,000	3/06	SEIA	Field, GPS receiver, mapping capability, lightbar, 80' booms, hyd. pump, chemical inductor, rinse tank, triple nozzle
Bestway	1,200 gal.	2004		E	$26,500	1/06	SCNE	Field Pro III, 1,200 gal., 80' boom sprayer, Outback guidance & mapping
Bestway	500 gal.			F	$150	8/06	NCIA	Middleman
Bestway	500 gal.			G	$2,300	1/06	WCIL	Walking tandems, 60' booms
Bestway	500 gal.			F	$2,750	8/06	NEIA	45' boom, hyd. pump
Bestway	750 gal.			F	$400	3/06	NCIA	Spray caddy, hyd. pump, 3 hyd., castor wheels
Bestway	750 gal.			F	$1,000	1/06	WCIL	Set up to pull in front of planter (Kinze 2000 6R-30 planter)
Bestway	750 gal.			F	$1,275	2/06	WCIL	Tandem axle, 45 boom, Micro Trac monitor
Bestway	750 gal.			G	$2,900	3/06	NCNE	Tandem axle, pt, 45' manual fold front booms, hyd. pump, foam marker

Sprayers

Make	Model	Year	Hrs.	Cond.	Price	Sale	Location	Comments
Bestway	750 gal.	1994		G	$3,000	8/06	ECIL	Walking tandem, poly tank, 45' booms, foamer, pump, controls
Bestway	800 gal.			G	$1,350	3/06	NCIA	800-gal. Bestway caddy, 47' JD boom from 6,000 JD high-clearance, hyd. pump, 18.4-26 tires
Big A	2600	1981		G	$8,500	8/06	WCIL	Floater, Cummins diesel, liquid
Big John	200 gal.			G	$500	3/06	ECNE	Pasture sprayer, pump
Blumhardt	1,000 gal.			G	$1,200	4/06	WCSD	Pull through, rigged to spread fertilizer & used as nurse tank for sprayer, hyd. pump, adjustable axles
Blumhardt	1,000 gal.			G	$5,100	2/06	NEIN	ST300, Trail Master sprayer, foamer, 90' boom, tandem axle
Blumhardt	1,000 gal.			F	$8,200	1/06	NWIL	62' boom, hyd. pump, Dickey-john radar control
Blumhardt	500 gal.			F	$275	6/06	NWIL	Pickup sprayer, foamer, Micro Trac 300 monitor
Blumhardt	500 gal.			G	$600	12/06	WCMN	Pickup field sprayer
Blumhardt	500 gal.			F	$1,200	2/06	ECIL	40' booms, hyd. pump, foam markers, Dickey-john monitor
Blumhardt	500 gal.			F	$2,000	11/06	NEND	60' sprayer, 3 pt., poly tank, hyd. pump, hyd. boom lift
Blumhardt	600 gal.			G	$900	12/06	WCMN	Pickup sprayer, 66' booms, Honda GX240 engine
Blumhardt	750 gal.			G	$1,000	12/06	WCMN	Alloway spray pump, 750-gal. tank, 88' spray boom, pt
Brandt	QF1000	1996		G	$7,000	6/06	NWMN	Broadcast sprayer, 120', Hiniker 8150 spray rate/speed control monitor system
Brittonya	500 gal.			G	$2,100	4/06	NWMN	36R band
Brittonya	500 gal.			G	$2,600	3/06	NEND	3 pt. band, 16R-30 or 24R-30, band broadcast & control, hyd. or PTO drive
Brittonya	750 gal.			G	$2,900	4/06	NWMN	36R band sprayer, band and broadcast, hyd. drive
Broyhill	400 gal.			F	$300	6/06	NWKS	36' boom, hyd pump, 3 pt.
Cagle	500 gal.	1992		G	$2,500	5/06	SCMI	Tandem axle, foamer, 45' boom
Case IH	4260	1999	3,593	G	$66,500	8/06	WCIL	Cummins diesel, hydrostatic trans., 1,200 gal., ss liquid system, 30" centers, foam marker, Raven 460 controller
Case IH	SPX4260	2002	885	E	$120,000	12/06	WCMN	Patriot, AIM Command, 90' boom, foam marker, Raven controller, 1,250 stainless tank, adj. axles, rinse tank
Century	500 gal.			F	$150	5/06	SCMI	Tank, trailer
Century	500 gal.			F	$500	3/06	NWOH	Single axle, foamer, 45' boom
Century	500 gal.			G	$525	3/06	NEIA	Foamer, Raven monitor
Century	500 gal.			G	$1,200	8/06	NCIA	Pull, 45' boom, foamer, hyd. pump
Century	500 gal.			G	$2,700	1/06	SWOH	45' booms
Century	500 gal.			G	$4,500	3/06	ECNE	45' boom, pt, vertical lift, adjustable axles, Ace hyd. pump, wash tank, Tee Jet controller
Century	NA			G	$550	1/06	SCNE	55' spray boom, 3 pt.
Chem Farm	500 gal.			G	$475	8/06	NCOH	In between, ss
Continental	500 gal.			F	$125	1/06	SWOH	Field
Continental	NA			F	$665	3/06	NCOK	35', PTO driven
Demco	1,000 gal.			G	$10,750	2/06	ECMN	HTH 1,000 gal., hyd. pump, rinse tank, Raven SCS 440 monitor, 12×38 rubber, 60' boom, sharp
Demco	150 gal.			G	$1,600	3/06	NWOH	ATV, motor, 18' boom
Demco	150 gal.			G	$1,600	3/06	NWOH	ATV, 30' boom, foamer
Demco	300 gal.			G	$700	2/06	NWIN	3 pt., 30' boom
Demco	500 gal.			F	$200	9/06	NCIA	Pull, 45' boom, PTO pump
Demco	500 gal.			F	$800	5/06	SCMI	45' boom, single axle
Demco	500 gal.			G	$1,650	8/06	NECO	TMC 500 gal., 45' booms
Demco	500 gal.			G	$1,800	12/06	NWOH	Field, 45' booms, foamer, older model

Sprayers

Make	Model	Year	Hrs.	Cond.	Price	Sale	Location	Comments
Demco	750 gal.			G	$2,100	12/06	WCMI	60' boom, ground-driven pump
Demco	750 gal.			G	$3,200	2/06	SEIN	45' booms, foamer, Hiniker controls
Demco	HP600	1995		G	$2,100	1/06	NWIA	4-wheel trailing sprayer, 45' hyd. boom, Jet nozzles, Lil' Thumper piston pump
Elk Creed	NA			G	$1,100	8/06	NEKS	3 pt. caddy
Fast	1,000 gal.			G	$2,200	12/06	WCMN	#500, 80' pt, 440 Raven controller
Fast	1,000 gal.			F	$9,000	6/06	SCMN	Poly tank crop sprayer, 90' hyd. folding booms, foam markers, rinse tank, Raven SCS440 monitor
Fast	7000			G	$11,000	1/06	SCMN	1,000-gal., 60' hyd. boom, Raven 440 monitor
Fast	900 gal.			G	$4,750	2/06	WCMN	Inside mounted ss tanks for Cat 765 tractor, hyd. pump, Raven SCS 450 monitor, ss rinse tank
Fast	NA	1997		G	$7,700	3/06	NWIL	90' boom
Flexi-Coil	50			G	$1,100	3/06	ECND	System 50, 650-gal. pull sprayer, 72', hyd. pump, foam markers, rinse tank, on/off boom control
Flexi-Coil	55			F	$700	8/06	WCMN	60'-650 poly, wind screens
Flexi-Coil	65			F	$1,000	3/06	WCMN	120', Flexi-Coil accurate flow control, 1,000 gal.
Flexi-Coil	65			F	$1,500	9/06	NEND	Field, 120' booms, 1,000-gal. tank
Flexi-Coil	65			G	$1,800	11/06	NWMN	120', pt, dual wind screen, dual nozzle, 1,000-gal. tank
Flexi-Coil	65			F	$3,600	11/06	NEND	90', foam marker, 750-gal. tank
Flexi-Coil	650 gal.			F	$900	7/06	NWMN	60', hyd. pump, boom control, windscreens
Flexi-Coil	67	2004		G	$17,500	4/06	NWMN	90' hyd. booms, 3 twist nozzles, all hyd. pump, 1,200-gal. tank, Raven full control, variable-rate monitor
Flexi-Coil	800 gal.	1991		G	$6,100	4/06	WCMB	Canadian sale, poly tank, centrifugal pump, Peacock markers
Flexi-Coil	System 62			F	$900	4/06	NEND	1,000-gal. tank, pt, PTO pump, Raven monitor
Flexi-Coil	System 62			G	$1,000	6/06	NWMN	90', 500-gal. tank, Raven spray control system
Ford	L9000	1994		G	$39,000	8/06	WCIL	Floater, dry
Great Plains	750 gal.	2001		G	$7,500	12/06	NWMO	16.9-28 tires, 60' boom, hyd. pump, 750-gal. tank
Great Plains	NA			G	$3,100	3/06	ECNE	Custom spray application system, 3 pt. mounted, 60' booms
Gemline	300 gal.			F	$350	4/06	NWMN	Briggs motor
Geo. White	300 gal.			F	$300	3/06	NWOH	Foamer
H&S	1,000 gal.	2003		G	$13,500	6/06	NWMN	60R dual manifold band/broadcast sprayer
H&S	1,500 gal.	2002		G	$21,000	2/06	NWMN	132', straddle duals, 650 Raven monitor, rinse tank, hyd. pump, quart triple nozzle, hyd. fold, variable rate
H&S	300 gal.	1989		F	$500	7/06	SEND	60' boom
H&S	500 gal.			G	$2,250	3/06	ECND	Band, 16R-30, Red Ball monitor
Hagie	284	2003	974	G	$64,000	12/06	SWMI	800 gal., air ride, all WD, 80' booms, foam, fully loaded, air, cab, Outback GPS
Hagie	437			F	$1,000	8/06	NCIA	High-clearance sprayer, 50' boom
Hardi	1,000 gal.			F	$1,300	7/06	SEND	60' suspended boom, poly tank, PTO, triple nozzle, foam markers, hyd. fold, adjustable axles at 88" tandems
Hardi	1,000 gal.			G	$1,300	5/06	WCMN	53' boom, John Blue ground-drive pump, hyd. agitating pump, Hiniker pump
Hardi	1,000 gal.			G	$3,200	3/06	NCOH	Foam markers, 60' booms, monitor
Hardi	1,000 gal.			G	$4,900	7/06	NWMN	66', pt, PTO high-pressure pump
Hardi	1,100 gal.	2003		G	$24,000	3/06	NWIL	NaviGator, trailer sprayer, 90' boom
Hardi	100 gal.			G	$825	2/06	SEMI	3 pt., 20' booms
Hardi	500 gal.			G	$2,250	6/06	NWIL	40' booms, pt

Sprayers

Make	Model	Year	Hrs.	Cond.	Price	Sale	Location	Comments
Hardi	500 gal.	1989		G	$3,500	8/06	NCIA	Tandem pull, 60' boom, hyd. raise and lower, 4 section, electric shutoffs
Hardi	800 gal.			G	$3,300	2/06	NCIL	60' boom
Hardi	950			G	$9,000	12/06	NWIL	60' boom
Hardi	NA			F	$200	3/06	NEMI	40' boom
Hardi	NA			G	$900	3/06	NCIL	NK600, 3 pt., PTO 160-gal. fence line sprayer
Hardi	TR 1000			F	$1,300	9/06	NEND	Foam markers
Hardi	TR 1000			G	$1,500	3/06	NWOH	1,000 gal., foamer, tandem
Hardi	TR 1000			G	$4,100	4/06	ECND	1,000 gal., pt, 60', high-pressure PTO pump, triple nozzle bodies, hyd. up/down, folding boom, adjustable tandem axle, variable-rate control
Hardi	TR 500			F	$1,250	7/06	SEND	45' boom, pt, PTO, 500-gal. tank, single axle, boom control monitor
Hardi	TR 500			G	$2,200	8/06	NCOH	500-gal. tandem axle spreader, 40' hyd. self-leveling booms, foam markers
Hardi	TR 500			G	$2,300	4/06	NEIA	45', foamer
Hardi	TR 500			G	$3,400	3/06	NCIL	500 gal., 45' boom
John Deere	250			G	$700	4/06	ECND	Spray cart, tow between, hyd. pump
John Deere	4700	1998	2,873	G	$67,500	3/06	ECND	CAH, foam marker, rinse tank, 750-gal. stainless tank, 90' boom, 5 nozzle bodies, one owner
John Deere	4700	1998	2,040	G	$80,000	3/06	NESD	GreenStar ready, 750 gal., ss tank, 90' boom, new JD foamer
John Deere	4700	2000	1,782	G	$79,500	12/06	SEMN	GreenStar, hyd. tread adjustment, traction control, 800-gal. ss tank, 90' booms, foam marker, 20" nozzle spacing
John Deere	4710		1,200	G	$100,000	12/06	SCMN	
John Deere	4710	2004	650	G	$112,750	12/06	SEMN	800-gal. ss tank, 90' boom, radar, hyd. tread adjustment
John Deere	4720	2005	313	G	$129,000	8/06	SCNE	90' self-propelled high clearance, 800-gal. poly tank, hyd. tread adjustable, onboard air induction system, foam markers
John Deere	4720	2005	355	E	$143,000	11/06	ECND	90' booms, ss 800-gal. tank, triple nozzles, bottom fill, rinse tank, foam markers, GreenStar SF2 controller w/ autosteer
John Deere	535			F	$750	5/06	WCMN	350-gal. tank
John Deere	535			G	$800	3/06	NEKS	On trailer
John Deere	600			F	$1,700	11/06	NCKY	High Boy, 12R boom
John Deere	6000			G	$1,500	5/06	SCCA	High Cycle, 8R-38
John Deere	6000			G	$2,000	8/06	SCFL	9,174 miles
John Deere	6000			G	$2,800	3/06	SEIA	3-wheel, air, 60' boom
John Deere	6000			G	$6,500	7/06	WCCA	High cycle
John Deere	6000			G	$9,750	8/06	NCIA	High clearance, cab, air, 60' Hagie boom, cushion front end
John Deere	734			F	$1,550	3/06	ECIL	High cycle, 3-cyl. gas, 3-wheel sprayer, 9.5×36, hyd. fold & height
John Deere	NA			G	$165	4/06	ECNE	Lawn & garden, gas motor
Keller	500 gal.			G	$1,700	4/06	SEND	24R
Keller	500 gal.			G	$3,000	3/06	ECND	36R band
Keller	NA			F	$800	11/06	NWMN	Band, 36R-30
King	500 gal.			F	$500	7/06	NWMN	Band, 24R-22, hyd. pump
Koyker	300 gal.			G	$2,100	11/06	SENE	3 pt., pasture, poly tank, 40' manual fold booms
Kuker	200 gal.			F	$400	2/06	NCIN	3 pt., 27' booms

Sprayers

Make	Model	Year	Hrs.	Cond.	Price	Sale	Location	Comments
Kuker	300 gal.			G	$700	2/06	SCKS	40' boom
Kuker	500 gal.			G	$400	3/06	NWKS	40' manual fold boom, foam marker, PTO pump
Kuker	500 gal.			F	$1,600	3/06	NCCO	40' booms
Loral	1,500 gal.	1994	3,055	G	$10,000	2/06	WCMN	DT466, auto trans.
Loral	3000	1996	3,648	G	$26,000	11/06	ECND	DT466 diesel, auto, Airmax 5 box, 60' booms
Loral	Magnum	1986		G	$8,000	8/06	WCIL	Floater, diesel, liquid
Marflex	400 gal.			G	$1,200	3/06	NWMN	Pickup sprayer, 50', midmount, Honda 8 hp., on/off 3-boom control
Marflex	500 gal.	1993		G	$2,400	3/06	ECND	76' pt sprayer, skid mount capabilities, tandem axle, hyd. pump, hyd. boom lift, 500-gal. tank, mix tank, bottom fill, one owner
Melroe	103			F	$650	9/06	NWMN	Spra-Coupe, 56'
Melroe	103			G	$750	3/06	NCND	Spra-Coupe, 135-gal. tank, 50' boom
Melroe	104			G	$450	3/06	ECND	Spra-Coupe, 20" spacing
Melroe	104			G	$600	3/06	ECND	Spra-Coupe, 20" spacing
Melroe	115			F	$400	11/06	NWMN	Spra-Coupe, cab, fan, Quick Jet nozzles, 200-gal. tank
Melroe	115			G	$750	3/06	NEND	Spra-Coupe, cab, 60', Quick Jet nozzles, 20" space
Melroe	115			G	$1,000	4/06	SEND	Spra-Coupe, MT3000 monitor system
Melroe	115	1980	1,060	G	$600	7/06	SEND	Spra-Coupe, 50' booms
Melroe	116			G	$4,800	4/06	WCSD	Spra-Coupe, 50', VW gas engine, tow hitch
Melroe	116		579	E	$9,000	7/06	SEND	Spra-Coupe, 60', 20" spacing, electric boom lift
Melroe	215		1,274	G	$1,900	4/06	NWMN	Spra-Coupe, cab, fan, liquid cooled, 30" space, adjustable rear axle, 200-gal. tank, Quick Jet nozzles
Melroe	215	1979		G	$700	7/06	SEND	Spra-Coupe, foam marker
Melroe	216		1,178	G	$8,500	2/06	NCKS	Spra-Coupe, 60'
Melroe	220		3,659		$4,200	2/06	WCME	Spra-Coupe
Melroe	3630	1994		G	$29,000	1/06	NWKY	Spra-Coupe, 60' boom
Mertz	3250	1990		F	$5,000	8/06	WCIL	Floater, diesel, liquid ss tank
Mertz	4250	1992		G	$6,500	8/06	WCIL	Floater, Cummins 400-hp. diesel, dry
Miller	NA			G	$7,000	3/06	SEMN	60', 3-pt. sprayer boom, foam markers, triple-nozzle system, hydraulic adjustment, Raven 440 computer monitor system
Miller Pro	500 gal.			G	$3,800	9/06	WCWI	Field, foam markers, floating booms
Miller Pro	300 gal.			G	$3,300	4/06	WCWI	3 pt., 300 gal.
NYB	400 gal.			G	$2,600	3/06	ECND	60' midmount boom sprayer, hyd. boom lift, Honda 8 hp., Quick Jet nozzles, mounted 3000 monitor on 1976 Chevy Scottsdale, 400, automatic, 4WD, 63K actual miles
NYB	500 gal.			G	$3,300	4/06	NWMN	Skid mount, poly tank
NYB	NA			G	$6,000	2/06	NWMN	100', front fold, 650 monitor, foam markers, 3 pt.
PK	500 gal.	1999		G	$1,000	2/06	WCIL	40'
Pleasure P.	1,000 gal.			G	$4,000	3/06	NEND	Tow-between caddy, enamel tank, hyd. drive, 21.5-16.1 singles, Raven 440 control
Pleasure P.	750 gal.	1992		G	$2,750	3/06	NEND	Suspended boom, all hyd. booms, 2-pt. attachment w/ dolly, electric shut off, twin nozzle, Raven SCS440 control
Pleasure P.	NA			G	$900	4/06	NWMN	ATV sprayer, 33' boom, gas engine, pump needs work
Red Ball	1,000 gal.			E	$12,500	2/06	NWIN	#665, 60' self-leveling boom, foamer, inductor and rinse, Raven 440 monitor, 2 years old, like new

Sprayers

Make	Model	Year	Hrs.	Cond.	Price	Sale	Location	Comments
Red Ball	660			G	$12,500	3/06	NENE	60' hyd. fold booms, pt, RDM Products custom-built frame, 1,000-gal. tank, 320/85R38 tires, Tee Jet 844 monitor, rinse tank, quick fill
Red Ball	680	2000		G	$16,000	4/06	NWMN	80', pt, 1,000-gal. tank, foam markers, 450 Raven auto, controller, radar, rinse tank, 12.4-42 singles, adjustable axle, hyd. pump, triple nozzle body, bottom fill
Red Ball	680	2001		G	$13,750	5/06	WCMN	1,350-gal. tank, 90', Raven 450, Hypro hyd. pump, foam marker
Red Ball	680	2001		G	$14,900	5/06	WCMN	1,350-gal. tank, 80', Raven 450, Hypro hyd. pump, 2 pt. hitch, foam marker
Red River	1,000 gal.			G	$1,600	3/06	NWMN	Chemical caddy, ground-drive pump, gas 2" adjustable pump, flotation tires
RoGator	554	1997	3,772	G	$30,000	8/06	WCIL	Cummins diesel engine, 500-gal. ss liquid system, 60/80' booms, 20" centers, foam marker, poly rinse tank, Raven SCS 460 controller
RoGator	664	1994	4,332	G	$28,500	8/06	WCIL	Cummins diesel engine, air, AM/FM, 600-gal. poly liquid system, 60/80' booms, foam marker, hyd. adjustable axles, Raven monitor
RoGator	664	1994		G	$31,000	12/06	NENE	600-gal. ss tank, 60' booms, foam markers
RoGator	854		3,500	G	$65,000	2/06	ECNE	
RoGator	854	1995	3,720	G	$48,000	3/06	ECNE	4-wheel post sprayer, 5.9-liter Cummins turbo diesel, cab, air
RoGator	854	1996	2,934	E	$67,500	2/06	WCIL	60/80' booms, triple nozzle bodies, 1,000-gal. ss tanks, 14.9R-46 tires, foam markers, radar, Mid-Tech arc 6,000 monitor, 5.9L engine
RoGator	854	2001	2,700	G	$0	9/06	SWIA	No sale at $57,000, 60/90 booms, 800-gal. tank, inductor, Cummins, triple nozzles, Raven 505661
Silver Wheels	NA	1999	3,200	G	$29,000	8/06	WCIL	Floater, center ride, Cat 3176 diesel, Allison MD, air, 2,000-gal. ss liquid system, 75' booms, 3-section shutoff
Simpson	1,000 gal.			G	$1,800	2/06	NWKS	1,000-gal. poly tank, pt, walking tandem axles, PTO pump, electric controls, foam marker kit, inductor cone tank, rinse tank, shedded
Snyder	500 gal.			G	$1,400	3/06	NCIL	PTO, 36' boom
Spray-Air	1,200 gal.			G	$6,250	4/06	SEND	88', pt, on Pleasure Products cart
Spray-Air	3200	2000		G	$19,500	3/06	NCND	96' Trident boom, pt, full hyd. air assist, second boom, triple nozzle body, 800-gal. poly tank, rinse tank, foam markers, boom tip wheels
Sprayer Spec.	NA	2006		E	$8,000	12/06	SWIA	Sprayer Specialties, 1,600-gal. bottom sump, tandem axle nurse trailer, brakes, lights, Honda 5.5 hp., bottom fill, tongue jack, 30' discharge, shut-off, high speed tires, brand-new – never used
Summers	1,000 gal.			G	$3,100	7/06	NEND	90' pt, 15-gal. mix cone
Summers	1,000 gal.			G	$20,000	4/06	NESD	2002 model, pt, 90' booms, 200-gal. rinse tank, foam markers, Raven 460 monitor
Summers	1,000 gal.	1998		G	$3,750	7/06	SEND	132', 200-gal. rinse tank, windscreens, double nozzle, Raven SCS440 flow control, 14.9-38 singles
Summers	500 gal.	1996		G	$2,500	11/06	ECND	Pickup sprayer, 80' midmount booms, 500-gal. poly tank, Honda 8 hp., Raven control and radar

Sprayers

Make	Model	Year	Hrs.	Cond.	Price	Sale	Location	Comments
Summers	500 gal.	2004		G	$3,300	9/06	WCND	3 pt. sprayer, 66' boom, triple nozzle, hyd. pump and boom lift, 500-gal. tank, bottom fill, foam markers, Raven 440 control w/ radar
Summers	NA			G	$15,750	10/06	NCND	90'
Summers	NA			F	$475	5/06	SEND	60' pickup style, Raven monitor
Summers	NA			F	$1,100	7/06	SEND	60', 3 pt., MT3000 controller, radar, hyd. pump
Summers	NA	1997		G	$6,700	4/06	ECND	3 pt., 60'-90' booms, lift assist, windscreens, 500-gal. tank, hyd. pump, twin nozzle bodies, Raven SCS440 radar, monitor
Terragator	1603	1991		F	$6,500	8/06	WCIL	Floater, diesel, dry spreader
Terragator	1603	1994		G	$19,750	8/06	WCIL	Floater, Cat 3208 diesel, Allison automatic 2-spd. aux. trans., air, 1,600-gal. ss liquid system, 60/80' booms, 4-section shutoff
Terragator	1603T	1991		F	$5,000	8/06	WCIL	Floater, diesel, dry Loral box
Terragator	1603T	1992	5,932	F	$3,250	11/06	ECNE	Cat 3208 diesel, 10 speed, 1,600-gal. ss liquid system, 60/80' booms, 60" spacing, stainless steel chemical inductor
Terragator	1603T	1992		F	$6,500	8/06	WCIL	Floater, Cat diesel, liquid
Terragator	1603T	1992		F	$10,000	11/06	ECNE	Cat 3208 turbo diesel, 10 spd., 1,600-gal. ss liquid system, 60' booms, 60" spacings, 3" load, ss foam marker tank, Raven 460 monitor
Terragator	1603T	1995		G	$0	2/06	ECIL	No sale at $12,000 - wanted $15K, 60' liquid system, 1,600-gal. ss tank, foam and rinse tank, Dickey-john monitor
Terragator	1803	1991	5,000	G	$9,500	8/06	WCIL	Floater, diesel, dry spreader
Terragator	1803	1992		F	$7,500	8/06	WCIL	Floater, diesel, liquid
Terragator	1803	1992	5,500	F	$9,500	8/06	WCIL	Floater, diesel, liquid
Terragator	1803	1992		G	$12,500	8/06	WCIL	Floater, diesel, liquid
Terragator	1803	1992	5,200	G	$13,750	8/06	WCIL	Floater, diesel, liquid
Terragator	1803	1993		F	$4,000	11/06	ECNE	Cab & chassis, Cat 3208 diesel, 18-spd. trans., air brakes
Terragator	1803	1993		F	$6,500	8/06	WCIL	Floater, cab, chassis only, diesel
Terragator	1803	1996		G	$7,000	8/06	WCIL	Cab, chassis only, diesel, 6CTA Cummins diesel, Allison automatic, 2-spd. aux. trans., AM/FM
Terragator	1803	1996	4,810	F	$12,000	11/06	ECNE	Cat 3208T diesel, Allison automatic, 1,800-gal. ss liquid system, 80' booms, 60" nozzle spacings, poly rinse tank
Terragator	1803	1998		G	$30,000	2/06	WCIL	2020 stainless steel dry box
Terragator	1844	1994		G	$8,500	8/06	WCIL	Floater, diesel, dry
Terragator	1903	1996	4,653	F	$5,500	11/06	ECNE	Cab & chassis, Cat 3176 diesel, 18-spd. Torq Boost trans., Falcon I controller, 60% rubber
Terragator	1903	1996		G	$11,000	8/06	WCIL	Dry selection, diesel
Terragator	1903	1997		G	$18,500	8/06	WCIL	Dry selection, diesel
Terragator	8103	1998		G	$47,000	11/06	ECNE	JD diesel engine, Terra-Shift trans., new, 1,800-gal. ss liquid system, 70' booms, 30" nozzle spacings
Top Air	1,000 gal.			F	$1,400	8/06	NWIL	Pt
Top Air	500 gal.			G	$1,150	3/06	NEIA	Tandem axle, 45' boom, Raven 440 monitor, foamer, PTO pump
Top Air	500 gal.			G	$2,600	3/06	NWOH	45' boom, tandem axle
Top Air	500 gal.			G	$5,000	4/06	SEMI	45' boom, foamer, tandem axle
Top Air	750 gal.			F	$3,250	2/06	WCIL	40' self-leveling boom, pt, foam markers

Sprayers

Make	Model	Year	Hrs.	Cond.	Price	Sale	Location	Comments
Top Air	750 gal.			G	$3,800	3/06	NCIA	Pull sprayer, tandem axle, 60' boom, hyd. raise and lower, hyd. fold, PTO pump
Top Air	750 gal.			G	$4,700	2/06	NWOH	45' boom, foamer, monitor, tandem
Top Air	750 gal.			G	$4,750	2/06	SCMI	45' booms, tandem, PTO pump, electric shut-off, one owner
Top Air	750 gal.	1994		F	$4,750	11/06	WCMN	60', walking tandem, Micro Trak monitor, nozzles
Top Air	NA			G	$1,300	8/06	WCIL	#35, 40'
Top Air	NA			G	$2,750	3/06	NWIL	90' boom
Top Air	TA1600	2005		G	$20,500	8/06	WCMN	90', 320/46 duals, Raven 454 monitor, foam markers
Tyler	3300	1998	3,350	G	$20,500	8/06	WCIL	Titan 3300, floater, 3208 Cat diesel, GPS ready, new Raven servo valve, New Leader L3020 G4 ss dry spreader box, Raven 660 monitor
Tyler	3300	1998	2,470	E	$52,000	11/06	ECNE	Cat 3208 diesel, 6-spd. auto., 1,800-gal. ss liquid system, 75' booms, 30" nozzle spacings, 3" load, 24,342 miles, always shedded
Tyler	4330	1996	2,470	G	$45,000	11/06	ECNE	3208 Cat diesel, 6-spd. auto., rebuilt two years ago for $9K, 2003 New Leader 3020 G4 painted ss dry spreader bed, 35,137 miles, always shedded
Tyler	Patriot XL	1995	3,540	G	$27,000	8/06	WCIL	90' booms, JD diesel, hydro. trans., AM/FM, 750-gal. poly sphere liquid system, 15" centers, foam marker
Tyler	Patriot XL	1996	3,550	G	$28,500	8/06	WCIL	60' boom, JD diesel engine, hydro. trans., AM/FM, 700-gal. poly sphere liquid system, 15" centers, foam marker, hyd. adjustable axles, Dickey-john controller
Tyler	Patriot XL	1997		G	$31,000	8/06	WCIL	75' booms
Tyler	Patriot XL	1997	3,700	G	$36,000	8/06	WCIL	75' boom, JD diesel engine, hydro. trans., AM/FM, 750-gal. poly sphere liquid system, 15" centers, foam marker
Walsh	300 gal.			F	$175	3/06	NWOH	
Walsh	500 gal.			G	$500	5/06	WCMN	45'
Wiley	300 gal.			F	$2,000	2/06	NCCO	200-gal. drop nozzle, 42' booms
Willmar	765	1994	3,482	G	$23,000	3/06	ECIL	60' booms, 600-gal. poly tank
Willmar	765	1994	2,897	G	$24,000	3/06	ECIL	60' boom, 600-gal. ss tank
Willmar	765	1996	2,653	G	$27,500	3/06	ECIL	Air ride, 60' boom, 600-gal. poly tank, foamer and rinse tank
Zimmerman	175 gal.			G	$575	4/06	SEPA	Poly, 3 pt., PTO pump

Notes

Stalk Choppers

I have to wonder, with more corn acres being planted in 2007, will there be increased demand to acquire good-condition used stalk choppers?

It would seem so. If that's the case, better be plugged into what these things have been selling for to know for sure what they are currently worth.

WHAT'S IT WORTH?

Stalk Choppers

Make	Model	Year	Cond.	Price	Sale	Location	Comments
Alloway	20'		G	$1,700	8/06	NECO	3-pt., flail shredder
Alloway	20'		G	$2,900	4/06	NWMN	3 pt.
Alloway	20'		G	$3,400	8/06	WCMN	Pt
Alloway	21'	2003	G	$6,400	3/06	NWMN	Woods/Alloway
Alloway	22'		G	$1,500	1/06	WCNE	PTO, pt
Alloway	22'		F	$2,000	7/06	NWMN	Flail shredder, 3 pt.
Alloway	22'		G	$2,200	8/06	WCMN	
Alloway	22'		G	$3,000	7/06	NWMN	Flail shredder, 3 pt.
Alloway	22'		G	$5,250	2/06	NWMN	3 pt. shredder
Alloway	24'		G	$4,000	3/06	NWMN	Trailing or 3-pt. shredder, steel flails
Artsway	20'		G	$1,700	3/06	ECNE	Shredder
Artsway	240B		G	$4,600	8/06	NCIA	8R-30 flail stalk cutter
Balzer	1500		G	$4,200	3/06	WCMN	15'
Balzer	20'		G	$4,000	8/06	WCMN	Shredder, pt, good knives
Balzer	2000		G	$1,900	12/06	SCMN	
Balzer	2000		G	$4,200	3/06	WCMN	20'
Balzer	2000		G	$5,700	11/06	WCMN	20', pt, new hammers last fall
Balzer	NA		G	$5,500	3/06	NCIA	8R-30 flail
Besler	NA		E	$3,200	1/06	NECO	3 pt, 6R30"
Besler	NA		G	$5,600	1/06	NECO	12R rolling
Besler	NA		G	$6,000	3/06	SWNE	12R-30, 3 pt., hyd. fold, rolling
Brady	144		F	$525	3/06	NCWI	
Brady	16'		F	$300	2/06	WCNE	Fl-12, PTO, pt
Brady	1680		G	$1,050	8/06	NCIA	6R-30
Brady	2400		G	$1,400	3/06	SWNE	20', 1,000 PTO
Buffalo	NA		G	$800	3/06	NWKS	8R
Bush Hog	10'		G	$1,100	8/06	NCNE	
Hawkbilt	4144		F	$500	3/06	ECIA	
Hiniker	1700		F	$900	12/06	SCMN	Flail shredder
Hiniker	1700		G	$1,300	7/06	NCIA	6R-30 flail stalk cutter
Hiniker	1700		G	$3,900	8/06	WCIA	6R
Hiniker	5600		G	$4,250	9/06	NECO	6R-30, PTO, pt
IHC	50		G	$550	11/06	WCSD	Stalk shredder, one owner
IHC	50		G	$1,050	4/06	SCMN	540 PTO, nice
IHC	50		G	$3,000	3/06	NCIL	15', new knives
IHC	60		G	$850	9/06	NECO	6R-30, PTO, pt
John Deere	120		G	$3,000	3/06	NCNE	20' flail shredder, 4 wheels, one owner
John Deere	120		G	$5,500	3/06	ECMI	8R, completely reconditioned
John Deere	120	1992	G	$2,400	4/06	ECND	Shredder, pt, 20', 1,000 PTO, steel flails
John Deere	220		F	$1,700	8/06	WCMN	Constant velocity, PTO shaft, new knives
John Deere	220		G	$3,900	12/06	WCMN	20', 4 wheels, high speed
John Deere	220		G	$6,200	3/06	SWMN	20', high speed, 4 tires
John Deere	220		G	$9,000	2/06	SCMI	High-speed shredder, end transport, hard surface knives, 8R
John Deere	220	2002	G	$9,000	3/06	NENE	High-speed flail shredder, 1,000 PTO, 4 tires
John Deere	220	2003	G	$6,000	8/06	WCMN	20' chopper, high speed
John Deere	27		F	$800	3/06	NCCO	6R
John Deere	27		F	$1,150	8/06	SEMN	
John Deere	27		F	$1,700	6/06	WCMN	
John Deere	27		F	$2,500	6/06	SWMN	6R

Stalk Choppers

Make	Model	Year	Cond.	Price	Sale	Location	Comments
John Deere	27		G	$2,550	1/06	SCMN	6R-30
John Deere	27		G	$2,800	8/06	NCIA	Flail stalk cutter, 4 wheels
John Deere	27		G	$3,750	8/06	NCIA	6R-30 flail stalk cutter, 4 wheels
John Deere	27	1974	G	$2,950	4/06	WCMN	Four wheels, disk hitch
John Deere	520	2005	E	$14,900	3/06	SEMN	Flail stalk shredder, 20', 1,000 PTO, 4 transport wheels
Loftness	15'		G	$2,700	12/06	SEMN	
Loftness	20'		G	$1,700	1/06	WCNE	PTO
Loftness	20'		P	$2,200	6/06	SCMN	Rough, stalk shredder, 3 pt., lift-assist wheels
Loftness	22'		F	$900	8/06	WCMN	
Loftness	22'	2005	E	$7,500	2/06	WCMN	2 pt.
Loftness	240		E	$16,000	2/06	WCIA	20' stalk shredder
Loftness	25'	2002	G	$6,200	8/06	WCMN	14/22 or 8/36 chopper, 90% knives
Loftness	30'		G	$13,000	8/06	NECO	Flail shredder
Loftness	360		G	$6,800	12/06	SCMN	
Lundell	15'		G	$1,650	8/06	ECNE	Flail shredder, pt, used very little, shedded
MC	144SB		G	$3,300	8/06	SCMI	14'
MC	15'		G	$3,800	1/06	NWIA	
MC	180SB		G	$1,650	3/06	ECNE	15', 1,000 PTO
MC	180SB		G	$1,800	7/06	NCIL	15'
MC	180SB		G	$7,250	4/06	WCWI	
MC	180SB	1990	G	$4,100	12/06	NWIL	Flail shredder
MC	NA		G	$1,350	12/06	NCIA	6R
MC	NA		G	$3,000	8/06	NCIA	6R-30
MC	NA		G	$3,300	11/06	SCNE	8R-30 flail shredder
MC	NA		G	$4,800	8/06	NCIA	6R-30 flail
MC	NA	2003	G	$7,800	8/06	NCIA	8R-30
Rhino	SR18		G	$6,750	6/06	NWKS	Rotary stalk shredder, mulching blades
Schultz	15'		G	$2,000	8/06	WCIA	New knives
Strobel	NA		G	$3,700	11/06	SCNE	12R-30 rolling stalk cutter, 3 pt., hyd. fold
Sunmaster	12'		F	$500	11/06	WCMN	
Sunmaster	15'		F	$950	9/06	SCMN	FK180M, 4 wheels

Notes

WHAT'S IT WORTH?

Swathers

Or windrowers as they are referred to more often in some parts of the country. Either way, we've got you covered with sale prices here. Where a swather sells at auction can play a big part in what it sells for. Do swathers sell for more money in Western states like Wyoming, Montana, Kansas, and Colorado? Dive into our data and find out.

Swathers

Make	Model	Year	Hrs.	Cond.	Price	Sale	Location	Comments
Case	8210	1992		G	$2,900	3/06	NWMN	21', bat reel
Case IH	4000			G	$1,550	11/06	SCSD	Windrower, 19.5' draper head
Case IH	721			G	$1,100	3/06	ECND	Auto fold pt, 21', bat reel
Case IH	721			G	$1,750	7/06	SEND	Pt
Case IH	721			G	$2,600	4/06	NESD	21', pt, kept inside, still has paint on guards
Case IH	725			G	$1,700	10/06	NCND	25', pt
Case IH	725			G	$2,750	3/06	NCND	25', pt, auto fold, bat reel
Case IH	725			G	$3,600	3/06	ECND	25', pt, auto fold, bat reel
Case IH	730			F	$950	10/06	NCND	Auto fold, 30'
Case IH	730			G	$4,200	4/06	SWMB	Canadian sale, MacDon pick-up reel, plastic teeth
Case IH	730			G	$4,200	4/06	WCMN	Canadian sale, pt, plastic teeth
Case IH	8220			G	$1,750	4/06	NWMN	21', pt, hyd., bat reel
Case IH	8220			G	$4,000	3/06	NCND	25', pt, auto fold, bat reel
Case IH	8220			G	$4,900	10/06	NCND	Auto-fold swather, finger reel
Case IH	8220			F	$5,900	11/06	NEND	25', pt, auto fold, finger reel
Case IH	8220	1998		G	$5,000	6/06	NWMN	25', finger reel, light kit, less than 1,500 acres of use
Case IH	8820			F	$5,900	11/06	NEND	25', pt, auto fold, finger reel
Case IH	8830		590	E	$13,500	8/06	NEIA	SP Haybine, 12' head, like new
Case IH	8840			G	$11,000	3/06	NCUT	Windrower
Case IH	8870			G	$15,000	8/06	SCNE	SP, 16' auger hay header, 2,409 header hours, 3,184 engine hours
Case IH	WDX1101		1,700	E	$27,000	3/06	WCKS	Self-propelled, 18' header
Case IH	WDX1701			E	$53,000	6/06	SCMN	Windrower, like new, bought new in 2003, 16' RDX161 rotary head, cab, power unit
Gehl	2650	1982	7,174	G	$4,900	2/06	WCNE	Cab, 14' auger head, diesel
Hesston	500			F	$500	11/06	NCKS	SP swather
Hesston	6400			F	$700	2/06	NWSD	Cab, 18' draper grain head
Hesston	6450	1982		G	$2,500	7/06	SEND	15' draper head, pickup reel, double drive
Hesston	6450	1982	1,447	G	$4,500	5/06	SEWY	Cab, gas, 14' draper head
Hesston	6550	1984	2,012	G	$6,500	5/06	SEWY	Cab, gas, 16' auger
Hesston	6600			G	$6,300	8/06	NEKS	SP swather, diesel, cab, 14' head
Hesston	6600			F	$9,000	3/06	NCCO	Gas windrower
Hesston	6600	1978		G	$2,000	1/06	WCNE	Gas, cab, 12' auger
Hesston	6650			F	$4,700	3/06	NCUT	Windrower, 16' platform
Hesston	6655	1986		F	$1,700	3/06	NWKS	SP, 14' cutting width, 4-cyl. diesel, 16' auger
Hesston	8200			G	$11,000	3/06	WCMN	Hydro, Fiat diesel, 14' auger head
Hesston	8200	1994	400	G	$23,500	3/06	NCCO	
Hesston	8450	2000	2,053	G	$26,000	3/06	SWKS	SP windrower, 18' head
Hesston	8450	2003	642	E	$46,000	5/06	SEWY	Cab, 16', double auger
Hesston	8550	2003	1,280	G	$37,000	3/06	NCCO	15' rotary disk head
IHC	4000	1976		G	$1,100	4/06	ECND	SP swather, open station, 19.5', bat reel
IHC	4000	1980		F	$1,350	5/06	SEWY	Gas, cab, 12', double auger
IHC	4000	1988		E	$7,600	3/06	ECND	SP swather, 19.5', cab, 6 cyl., hyd. drive, rear weights, bat reel
IHC	5000			G	$5,200	3/06	NEND	SP swather, 25', cab, bat reel, platform stabilizer wheels
IHC	5000	1979		G	$2,800	2/06	NCKS	14' swather, hyd., 100 hours on OH
IHC	5000	1980		G	$1,600	5/06	SEWY	Diesel, cab, 14' auger
IHC	730			G	$1,500	1/06	NECO	30', pt, draper, PTO
John Deere	2280	1980		G	$13,100	2/06	NCCO	Diesel, 14'

Swathers

Make	Model	Year	Hrs.	Cond.	Price	Sale	Location	Comments
John Deere	2320			G	$4,100	2/06	ECMN	12' draper head, conditioner
John Deere	2320	1982		G	$2,200	11/06	NWMN	SP swather, cab, air, gas engine, 21' table, MacDon finger reel, bat reel
John Deere	240			F	$1,000	4/06	NENE	Swather
John Deere	2420	1980	2,376	F	$9,800	2/06	NCCO	Windrower, diesel, 14' head
John Deere	2420	1983	2,431	G	$9,300	6/06	ECND	25', cab, air hydro, bat reel, platform gauge wheels
John Deere	3830			G	$9,100	8/06	NECO	
John Deere	3830	1990	2,800	F	$15,100	2/06	NCCO	Windrower, 16' head
John Deere	4890			G	$18,000	11/06	SECA	JD 890 power reverse, 16' sickle head
John Deere	4890		1,107	G	$22,000	3/06	NCUT	Windrower, 16' platform
John Deere	4890	1997	2,400	G	$24,000	1/06	NCCO	16' head
John Deere	4890	1997	1,399	G	$28,000	3/06	SWKS	SP windrower, rebuilt w/ 890 power reverse, 16' head
John Deere	4890	1997	2,100	E	$29,000	11/06	SCSD	SP windrower, 18' auger head, power reverse
John Deere	4890	1999	1,130	G	$22,000	8/06	SCNE	Windrower, 890 16' hay header, 883 header hours
John Deere	4890	1999	2,612	G	$28,750	2/06	SENE	SP windrower, 1,893 sep. hours
John Deere	4895	2004	805	G	$39,000	3/06	SWKS	SP windrower, 645 header hours
John Deere	490			F	$75	5/06	SEND	21', pt
John Deere	4990		1,170	G	$34,000	3/06	NCUT	Windrower, 16' disk head
John Deere	580			G	$500	3/06	NWMN	18', bat reel, pt
John Deere	580			F	$650	7/06	NEND	25', pt
John Deere	590			F	$1,300	11/06	NWKS	Draper swather, 36'
John Deere	590			G	$1,700	7/06	NEND	Auto fold, pt, 25'
John Deere	590			G	$1,750	3/06	ECND	Auto fold, 21' pt, 540 PTO, low rpm conversion, bat reel, single owner
John Deere	590			G	$2,250	9/06	NECO	30' draper head, pt
John Deere	590			G	$3,400	4/06	NEND	Auto fold, pt, 30' hd Pitman drive, 3-rib tires, Tiger Jaw pickup teeth
John Deere	590			G	$3,600	6/06	NWSD	Pull-type swather
John Deere	590	1988		G	$2,000	4/06	ECND	Auto fold, 21', bat reel
John Deere	590	1988		G	$2,000	4/06	ECND	Auto fold, 21', bat reels
John Deere	590	1990		F	$1,800	4/06	NEND	Auto fold, pt, 25', bat reel
John Deere	590	1992		G	$1,600	3/06	NEND	Auto fold, pt, 25', bat reel
John Deere	590	1992		G	$1,600	3/06	NEND	Auto fold, pt, 25', bat reel, 2 on this sale – each sold for $1,600
John Deere	800			P	$75	4/06	NESD	SP swather, 18' platform, needs work
John Deere	800			P	$200	10/06	SEMN	SP swather, 12' draper head, for parts
John Deere	800			G	$450	3/06	NCND	SP swather, 18', slant 6
John Deere	800			F	$600	5/06	SEND	14', SP, water cool engine
John Deere	800			G	$1,250	10/06	SEMN	SP, 12' draper head
John Deere	830			F	$1,550	2/06	NECO	Gas, 14' auger
Lockwood	835			F	$400	3/06	NEMI	Windrower
MacDon	21'	1994		G	$2,000	7/06	SEND	Auto fold swather, MacDon finger reel
MacDon	21'	1995		E	$4,400	4/06	NWMN	Auto fold, pt, low acres
MacDon	9300			G	$11,000	5/06	SCCA	MacDon 920 14' auger header
MacDon	9350	2000	946	E	$42,000	4/06	NEND	SP swather, turbo diesel, two spd. hydro cab, tow bar, MacDon 972 harvest head, 25', finger reel
MacDon	9350	2001	1,511	G	$21,000	3/06	SWKS	Turbo windrower, 920 18' head, 21.5l-16.1SL fronts, 16.5L-16.1

Swathers

Make	Model	Year	Hrs.	Cond.	Price	Sale	Location	Comments
MacDon	9350	2001		G	$26,000	3/06	SWKS	Turbo windrower, 18' 920 head, 21.5L-16.1 fronts, 16.5L-16.1SL rear
MacDon	9350	2001	503	E	$41,000	2/06	WCNE	16' auger head, diesel, cab
MacDon	9352	2002	1,002	E	$57,500	9/06	NECO	Cab, #922 16' auger, diesel
MacDon	960			G	$12,000	4/06	WCMB	Canadian sale
MacDon	972	2002		E	$13,500	9/06	NECO	30' draper head, transports, off MacDon 9352 swather
MF	220	1997	637	G	$36,500	4/06	WCMB	Canadian sale, pt, universal reel pickup
MF	775			G	$1,000	4/06	NWSD	SP, cab, hydrostatic, new sections
MF	775			G	$4,000	2/06	WCME	
New Holland	1100	1980	1,587	F	$3,000	2/06	WCNE	14' auger, cab with ½ the glass, gas
New Holland	1116			G	$6,100	11/06	WCSD	Speedrower SP auger windrower, 6' conditioner
New Holland	114			F	$850	2/06	NECO	14' auger, hydro swing
New Holland	116			F	$1,100	2/06	NECO	14' auger, hydro swing
New Holland	1495	1978		F	$1,600	5/06	SEWY	Gas, cab, 12'
New Holland	1495	1984		F	$1,300	6/06	NECO	12' Haybine, cab, gas
New Holland	1495	1984		F	$8,300	1/06	NCCO	
New Holland	2216			F	$2,750	8/06	NECO	16' bidirectional head, conditioner & adapter
New Holland	2450	1994	873	E	$36,000	4/06	WCMT	Self-propelled windrower, cab, air, radio, Ford diesel, hydro trans., 16.9-24 drive tires, 14' head, like new
New Holland	2550		2,420	G	$18,000	8/06	SCNE	SP windrower, 16' auger hay header
OMC	18'			F	$1,500	7/06	SEND	Pt
OMC	260			F	$900	7/06	SEND	Self-propelled swather, 16.5', bat reel
OMC	265	1982		F	$1,300	5/06	SEWY	Cab, gas, 12' auger
OMC	280			G	$1,200	8/06	WCMN	Cab, hydro drive, 14', head finger reel
Premier	1900			G	$2,100	7/06	SEND	25', auto fold
Premier	1900			G	$6,300	4/06	WCSD	
Premier	1900	1996		G	$1,750	7/06	SEND	25', pt
Premier	1900	1997		G	$2,750	7/06	SEND	25', finger reel
Premier	1900	1997			$6,400	11/06	NWMN	Auto fold, pt, 25', finger reel
Premier	3000	1994		G	$1,750	7/06	SEND	Windrower
Premier	NA	1994		F	$1,500	9/06	WCND	Auto fold, pt, 30' bat reel
Premier	10			P	$50	4/06	SWSD	Older, pt, 18', good canvas
Versatile	10			F	$500	3/06	ECND	24', pt, Johnson auto-fold transport, new canvasses
Versatile	10	1981		G	$800	4/06	ECND	Pt
Versatile	10	1982		G	$400	4/06	ECND	20', pt
Versatile	400			P	$350	7/06	SEND	20', finger and bat reels
Versatile	400			F	$500	4/06	SEND	SP swather, 18'
Versatile	400			G	$650	6/06	NWMN	SP swather, 18', MacDon finger reel
Versatile	400			G	$650	5/06	SEND	20' hydro swather
Versatile	400			F	$800	7/06	SEND	20'
Versatile	400			F	$800	7/06	SEND	Self-propelled, 20'
Versatile	400	1972		G	$1,000	4/06	ECND	SP swather, 18'
Versatile	400	1976		F	$500	7/06	ECND	20' bat reel
Versatile	400	1977		F	$650	7/06	SEND	SP swather, 20', finger reel, cab, air
Versatile	4400			G	$2,500	4/06	NEND	SP swather, 22', double swath, cab, bat reel, Tiger Jaw pickup teeth
Versatile	4400	1980		G	$1,600	3/06	ECND	SP swather, 18' hydrostatic
Versatile	4700	1989		G	$6,000	11/06	ECND	SP

WHAT'S IT WORTH?

Tractors

No old tractors listed here. For those, see the *Rust Book* (**www.rustbook.com**). People often ask, "Hey Pete, what's the hottest thing on the used market?" My reply has been the same over the years: 10- to 20-year-old tractors in very good condition. Want proof? Check out the sale prices on JD 4455s. Deere made this model from 1989 to 1992, so they're 15 to 20 years old. Nice ones with low hours sell at auction for about the same as they sold for brand-new!

Tractors

Make	Model	Year	Hrs.	Cond.	Price	Sale	Location	Comments
Allis-Chalmers	175		4,137	G	$3,650	9/06	SCMN	Diesel, 3 pt., 2 hyd.
Allis-Chalmers	185		1,655	G	$8,600	1/06	NEIN	One owner
Allis-Chalmers	4W305	1984	4,050	G	$26,000	12/06	NWIL	4WD, fully-equipped cab, 1,000 PTO, 4 hyd., 3 pt., new 18.4R-42 tires w/ duals
Allis-Chalmers	5020			G	$3,200	12/06	NWIL	Hyd. front blade, diesel
Allis-Chalmers	5020	1982		G	$2,550	11/06	WCIL	4WD, compact tractor, 3 pt., diesel, 540 PTO, gear drive
Allis-Chalmers	5040	1978		G	$2,700	9/06	NECO	New tach – 4 hours, WF, 3 pt., 2 hyd., no cab, diesel
Allis-Chalmers	5040	1980	2,100	G	$5,300	8/06	ECMI	2WD, diesel, PS, 3 pt., PTO, 1 hyd., 14.9-28 tires, one owner, sharp, last year made
Allis-Chalmers	5050	1977	2,650	G	$4,500	9/06	NEIN	Utility, diesel
Allis-Chalmers	5050	1982	3,183	G	$3,400	12/06	ECMO	2WD
Allis-Chalmers	6060			F	$6,750	3/06	WCMN	Cab, 3 pt., PTO, 2 hyd.
Allis-Chalmers	6060	1981	6,650	G	$9,000	12/06	NWWI	2WD, open station, 18.4-28
Allis-Chalmers	6080			F	$6,100	3/06	WCMN	MFWD, PTO, 3 pt., 3 hyd., AC 460 loader, trans. problems, one owner
Allis-Chalmers	6080			P	$12,000	3/06	WCMN	MFWD, cab, 3 pt., PTO, 3 hyd., AC 460 loader, rough
Allis-Chalmers	6140		879	G	$3,500	9/06	ECMN	3 pt., PTO, turf tires, WF, diesel
Allis-Chalmers	7000			F	$2,200	12/06	SEMN	
Allis-Chalmers	7000			F	$4,450	8/06	NWIL	Diesel
Allis-Chalmers	7000	1979	5,294	G	$4,450	12/06	NEMO	Fully-equipped cab, 2 hyd., complete OH
Allis-Chalmers	7010		3,900	G	$4,300	12/06	NWIL	Diesel, 3,900 hours
Allis-Chalmers	7010	1981	3,700	G	$5,500	11/06	WCIL	Cab, front weights, diesel, 18.4-38 tires
Allis-Chalmers	7010	1981	5,690	G	$8,050	3/06	NENE	PS, 2 hyd., 18.4-38
Allis-Chalmers	7020			G	$0	8/06	NEIA	No sale at $5,500 – wanted $7,500
Allis-Chalmers	7040	1974		G	$3,400	12/06	NWIL	Diesel, cab, new 18.4-38 rear tires, 11:00-16 fronts
Allis-Chalmers	7040	1976	8,826	F	$3,900	2/06	ECIL	Weights, 3 pt., 2 hyd., 540/1,000 PTO, duals
Allis-Chalmers	7040	1976		G	$4,000	11/06	WCIL	Cab, PS, front & rear weights, 540/1000 PTO, 2 hyd., 18.4-38 tires, diesel
Allis-Chalmers	7045		4,863	F	$5,700	9/06	NWIL	Cab, WF, weights, diesel
Allis-Chalmers	7045		4,822	G	$6,500	8/06	NCIA	Cab, air, PS, 3 pt., 2 hyd., front rock box, axle duals
Allis-Chalmers	7045	1979	7,000	G	$3,900	6/06	ECSD	PS, CAH
Allis-Chalmers	7045	1979		G	$7,500	8/06	WCMN	2WD, diesel, 20.8-38, complete OH at 4,800 hours, 3 pt., PTO, 2 hyd., front weights, CAH, one owner
Allis-Chalmers	7050			G	$12,000	3/06	NEMO	2WD, cab, Westendorf TA-46 loader
Allis-Chalmers	7060	1975	5,698	G	$8,200	2/06	NWKS	Less than 1,000 hours on OH
Allis-Chalmers	7060	1976		G	$5,200	3/06	NENE	2 hyd., 20.8-38
Allis-Chalmers	7060	1976	4,430	G	$5,400	12/06	NWIL	Cab, new 20.8R-38 tires, diesel
Allis-Chalmers	7060	1978	3,000	G	$6,300	8/06	NCOH	CAH, PS, 3 hyd., duals
Allis-Chalmers	7060	1979	4,848	G	$7,900	3/06	NENE	18.4R-42 with 20.8-38 axle-mount duals, 2 hyd., 540/1,000 PTO, 11:00-16 front tires (1 year), stadium lights, new AC pump
Allis-Chalmers	7080			G	$1,750	6/06	ECSD	CAH, needs engine work
Allis-Chalmers	7080			F	$6,000	3/06	NCMN	
Allis-Chalmers	7580			F	$2,750	3/06	NCUT	4WD
Allis-Chalmers	7580			G	$8,250	12/06	SCQB	Canadian sale, 4WD, Cummins L10, cab, air, 3 pt., 4 hyd., converts to $7,201 U.S.
Allis-Chalmers	7580	1981	3,249	F	$10,000	2/06	ECIL	4WD, 3 pt., 1,000 PTO, 3 hyd., duals
Allis-Chalmers	8010	1983	7,897	G	$14,300	3/06	NENE	MFWD, diesel, cab, 16.9-38 tires

WHAT'S IT WORTH?

Tractors

Make	Model	Year	Hrs.	Cond.	Price	Sale	Location	Comments
Allis-Chalmers	8050		6,400	G	$21,000	4/06	NEND	MFWD, CAH, PS, 3 pt., PTO, 3 hyd., 18.4-42 duals (75% rubber), 14.9-28 fronts
Allis-Chalmers	8050	1981		F	$5,000	8/06	NEKS	2WD
Allis-Chalmers	8050	1981	4,451	G	$13,500	2/06	NWKS	2WD, PS, less than 1,000 hours on OH
Allis-Chalmers	8070			G	$6,000	5/06	SCCA	MFWD, front weights, cab, air, 3 pt, PTO, rear weights, 2 hyd.
Allis-Chalmers	8550	1981	3,595	E	$13,000	8/06	ECIL	4WD, CAH, less than 100 hours on new tires dualed, 325 hp., 3 hyd., 3 pt., PTO, quick hitch
AGCO	6670	1991	2,330	G	$13,000	12/06	ECMO	MFWD, CAH, AGCO 340 loader
AGCO	6690			G	$14,500	8/06	SCNE	2WD, Westendorf TA 26 loader, quick-attach bucket, cab, 3 pt., PTO, 2 hyd., 18.4-38
AGCO	6690	1995	300	E	$23,000	3/06	NEMO	MFWD, ROPS, AGCO loader, one owner
AGCO	8360	1997	1,582	G	$57,000	8/06	NCIA	Star 4WD, cab, air, 855 Cummins, 360 hp., Easton Fuller trans., 24.5-32 duals, 4 hyd., bareback
AGCO	8610	1997	2,710	G	$28,000	3/06	NWIL	MFWD, fully-equipped cab, 540/1000 PTO, 3 pt. hitch, with 884 loader, diesel
AGCO	8785	2000	1,000	G	$40,500	12/06	NCOH	MFWD, deluxe cab, 3 hyd., 18.4-34 Michelin rubber & clamp-on spacer duals, 14.9-28 front, SN J244014
AGCO	9435	1994	3,018	G	$25,000	3/06	NENE	MFWD, diesel, cab, like-new rubber, PS, front weights
AGCO	9455	1995	1,340	E	$32,500	7/06	ECIL	2WD, 32 speed, duals
AGCO	9455	1995	1,379	E	$35,000	3/06	NWOH	MFWD, cab, 15 front weights, 3 hyd., quick hitch, snap-on duals
AGCO	9655	1996	1,400	E	$32,500	8/06	ECIL	2WD, CAH, 3 hyd., PS, quick hitch
AGCO	9670	1994		G	$20,200	12/06	NCIL	MFWD, PS
AGCO	9670	1994	1,284	G	$33,000	6/06	NWIL	MFWD, 18.4R-42, hub duals, 16.9R-28 fronts, 3 hyd., 10 front weights
AGCO	9675	1996	3,219	G	$35,000	8/06	NEKS	MFWD, 18.4R-42 duals, 16.9R-28 fronts, 1,000 PTO, 15 front end weights, shedded, one owner
AGCO	9675	1997	1,520	E	$38,000	8/06	ECIL	MFWD, CAH, like new, dual rears, PS, quick hitch, 3 hyd.
AGCO	DT160	2002		E	$53,000	3/06	NWIL	MFWD, fully-equipped cab, 18-speed ps, 540/1,000 PTO, 3 pt., 4 hyd., 15 front weights, 480/80R42 tires, axle duals, warranty to 10/06
AGCO	DT180	2001	829	E	$49,000	3/06	NWIL	MFWD, fully equipped cab, 18-speed ps, 1,000 PTO, 3 pt., 4 hyd., 15 front weights, 18.4R-46 rear axle duals, 380/85R34 front, front fenders
AGCO	DT225	2004	420	E	$81,000	3/06	SEMN	MFWD, duals, deluxe cab, 3 pt., PTO, 14-front weights, 18-speed ps, shuttle shift, 4 hyd.
AGCO	RT115	2002		G	$54,100	8/06	NEKS	MFWD, Cummins B5.9A, 540/1,000 PTO, Quickie Q970 loader w/ 8' bucket and 4-tine grapple fork, 18.4R-38, 14.9R-28 front, one owner, shedded
AGCO	RT120	2004	379	E	$47,000	12/06	NCOH	MFWD, deluxe cab, air ride seat, 540/1,000 PTO, 18.4-34 Michelin radials, 3 hyd.
AGCO	RT120	2004	480	E	$49,000	3/06	NENE	MFWD, diesel, one owner, like new, cab, 12-front suitcase weights, Michelin 480/80R42 tires
Belarus	420A		455	G	$36,000	9/06	NWTN	4WD
Belarus	820			G	$5,000	12/06	SCQB	Canadian sale, MFWD, cab, 3 pt., PTO, 4 cyl., converts to $4,365 U.S.
Belarus	822	1991	958	F	$3,600	5/06	SEWY	MFWD, cab, diesel, Belarus loader
Belarus	825	1989	2,050	F	$2,600	12/06	NWWI	MFWD, cab, 16.9-38

Tractors

Make	Model	Year	Hrs.	Cond.	Price	Sale	Location	Comments
Belarus	825	1989	790	G	$7,200	12/06	NWWI	MFWD, Allied 594 loader
Belarus	925		322	G	$8,500	2/06	WCIL	Turbo, MFWD, fully equipped cab, 2 hyd., loader
Buhler	2160	2005	290	G	$59,500	2/06	NWIL	2WD, fully equipped cab, 18-speed PS, 3 hyd., 3 pt., front & rear weights, duals
Buhler	2180	2004	372	E	$53,000	12/06	NCIL	Genesis II, 18 speed (runs 26 mph) full-front weights, maximum back weights, 18.4R-42 tires w/ duals, 3 hyd., 3 pt., PTO
Buhler	2425	2002	2,111	G	$87,500	4/06	NEND	4WD, 12 speed, 4 hyd., performance monitor, 850/65R/38 duals, weights
Carraro	9400 TRG			G	$8,500	7/06	WCCA	Front weights, 3 pt., PTO, 2 hyd.
Case	1130			G	$9,500	8/06	NWOH	Kelly B10A backhoe, 3 pt., PTO, L108 loader
Case	1390			G	$1,500	1/06	WCCA	Mudder, 3 pt., PTO, 2 hyd
Case	1490			G	$3,000	7/06	WCCA	Cab, 3 pt., PTO, 1 hyd
Case	1490			F	$6,700	3/06	NCCO	
Case	1490			F	$8,750	3/06	NCMN	GB loader
Case	1570			F	$4,700	3/06	NCMN	
Case	1570		5,800	F	$6,750	6/06	NWMN	3 pt., hyd, PTO w/ Leon 808 loader
Case	1570	1977	6,000	G	$9,600	4/06	SWSD	Agri-King, diesel, cab, air, radio, 3 pt., 2 hyd., 1,000 rpm, 20.8-38, good rear tires & duals
Case	2090		3,761	F	$8,000	3/06	NCUT	
Case	2090		4,524	G	$8,700	3/06	WCMN	Cab, PS, 2 hyd., hub duals, rock box
Case	2090	1974	7,229	G	$6,500	2/06	SEIA	Fully-equipped cab, 2 hyd., axle-mount duals
Case	2290	1978	4,752	F	$6,000	9/06	NWIL	Cab, WF, weights, diesel
Case	2290	1979		F	$5,300	8/06	WCIL	
Case	2290	1979	5,570	F	$5,600	3/06	SEIA	Red, PS, air, cab, hub-mount duals
Case	2290	1981	1,857	E	$15,000	9/06	NCIA	Cab, air, PS, 2 hyd., front rock box, quick coupler, long axles
Case	2290	1981	2,860	G	$15,000	8/06	WCIL	
Case	2290	1982	5,125	F	$8,250	1/06	NCCO	Axle duals, 3 hyd., 540/1,000 PTO, one owner
Case	2294		4,500	G	$12,000	4/06	NEND	CAH, 3 pt., PTO, 4 hyd., 18.4-34 duals (80% rubber), one owner
Case	2294	1984	4,739	G	$19,000	3/06	SEND	12-speed ps, 3 hyd., 3 pt., 540/1,000 PTO, differential lock, 18.4-42 singles (90%)
Case	2294	1985	5,896	G	$15,000	2/06	WCNE	Diesel, 2WD, 3 pt., cab, duals
Case	2294	1985	3,459	G	$19,500	2/06	WCMN	CAH, MFWD, hub duals
Case	2390	1978	4,575	F	$6,700	2/06	WCIL	Fully-equipped cab, 3 hyd.
Case	2390	1981	8,100	F	$5,900	3/06	NWKS	3 pt., PTO, duals
Case	2390	1982	7,046	E	$11,500	3/06	NCOK	160 hp., 12 speed, 3 pt., PTO, 3 hyd., duals, tires good
Case	2394			G	$13,500	4/06	SCMN	2WD, hub duals, sharp
Case	2470		5,000	F	$4,400	3/06	NWIL	3 pt., PTO
Case	2470	1973	9,839	G	$3,200	4/06	NWMN	Traction King, CAH, 12-speed ps, 2 hyd., 18.4-34 duals
Case	2470	1976	4,335	G	$4,100	9/06	NECO	Leon 10' dozer, cab, no 3 pt., 2 hyd., diesel
Case	2590			F	$4,250	7/06	WCMN	Duals, weights
Case	2590	1979	5,927	G	$12,500	3/06	SEIA	1,200 hours on engine and trans. OH, 3 hyd., axle-mount duals
Case	2590	1980	4,200	G	$7,200	8/06	WCIL	
Case	2590	1981	4,998	G	$8,250	5/06	SEWY	Diesel, cab, front weights
Case	2590	1982	5,085	G	$10,250	8/06	NCIA	Cab, air, PS, front weights, 2 hyd., quick coupler w/ 10-bolt duals, engine OH 80 hours ago

WHAT'S IT WORTH?

Tractors

Make	Model	Year	Hrs.	Cond.	Price	Sale	Location	Comments
Case	2590	1982	4,700	G	$11,200	2/06	NCIL	Cab, 3 hyd., 18.4R-42, duals
Case	2590	1982	4,214	G	$14,000	3/06	NCND	CAH, 12-speed ps, 3 hyd., 3 pt., 1,000 PTO, front suitcase weights, 380R90-46 cast duals, 90% rubber, one owner
Case	2590	1983		G	$18,500	2/06	SEIL	Clean, 2WD, 20.8-38, duals
Case	2594			F	$7,000	12/06	NWWI	2WD
Case	2670			F	$3,200	8/06	NCIA	4WD, cab, air, PTO, 3 pt., 4 hyd., duals
Case	2670			G	$7,000	10/06	WCWI	225 hp., 4WD w/ duals all around, 3 pt. hitch, 1,000-rpm PTO
Case	2670	1976	7,640	G	$8,000	3/06	NECO	4WD, PS, 3 pt., PTO, 4 hyd., 18.4-34, duals, 1,280 hours on engine & trans. OH
Case	2670	1977	4,443	F	$2,500	9/06	NWIL	4WD, 3 pt., OH trans., diesel
Case	2670	1978		F	$6,000	3/06	NWKS	4WD, 1,167 hours on engine OH, 4-speed ps, 20.8-38, duals, 3 pt., PTO
Case	2870			G	$4,250	8/06	SCMI	4WD, cab, 3 hyd., 3 pt., bad tranny, tach shows 2,242 hours
Case	2870	1977	4,200	G	$7,000	3/06	SWOH	4WD, PS, no PTO
Case	2870	1979	8,037	G	$8,500	3/06	NCND	4WD, CAH, 12-speed PS, 4 hyd., new 20.8-34 inside tires, 20.8-34 outside, 30% rubber, wide space duals, 1,500 hours on complete engine OH, 500 hours on front differential OH, one owner
Case	3294	1984		F	$9,800	3/06	ECKS	MFWD, 3 pt., PTO
Case	3394	1987	3,663	G	$28,500	12/06	NWOH	MFWD, 24-speed, PS, radar, cab, air, duals
Case	4494			F	$12,500	3/06	SEIA	4WD
Case	4690		4,244	G	$6,500	8/06	SCMI	4WD, cab, 4 hyd., 3 pt., axle duals
Case	4690		2,988	G	$9,500	8/06	SCMI	4WD, cab, 4 hyd., 3 pt., axle duals
Case	4690	1980	7,400	F	$4,750	11/06	ECND	4WD, 4 hyd., 3 pt., PTO, 20.8-34 duals, 2,100 hours on OH
Case	4890		2,461	G	$9,250	8/06	SCMI	4WD, cab, 4 hyd., 3 pt.
Case	4890			G	$18,250	12/06	SEMN	4WD, 3 pt., PTO, duals
Case	570L			G	$12,500	7/06	ECNY	Landscape tractor, diesel, EROPS
Case	570L	1999	3,624	G	$19,500	11/06	SWCA	4×4, Gannon 5-valve rear scraper
Case IH	1896	1986	1,572	G	$17,250	8/06	ECNE	2WD, PS, 18.4-38 rear, 14L-16.1 front tires, 3 hyd.
Case IH	2096			F	$11,800	3/06	NCMN	2WD
Case IH	2096	1987	4,285	G	$19,300	7/06	ECND	2WD, CAH, 3 pt., 540/1,000 PTO, 3 hyd., differential lock, 12 speed, duals
Case IH	2096	1989	4,834	G	$17,250	3/06	NCIA	2WD, cab, PS, 3 hyd., front weights, 540/1,000 PTO, 5.9-liter engine, 18.4-38 axle duals
Case IH	235		1,149	G	$3,900	6/06	SCMN	Compact tractor, ROPS, 3 pt.
Case IH	2394		5,458	G	$15,750	8/06	ECNE	2WD, 3 hyd., 18.4-42 duals
Case IH	2394	1987	7,020	G	$12,000	7/06	ECND	2WD, CAH, 3 pt., PTO, duals
Case IH	2594	1984	5,934	G	$18,250	12/06	NENE	2WD, new motor at 4,300 hours, 2 hyd., quick hitch, 12 front end weights, 18.4R-38, 9-bolt duals, 11:00-16 front tires
Case IH	3394		7,200	F	$13,000	7/06	NWMN	MFWD, 3 pt., hub duals, quad hyd., PTO
Case IH	3394	1986	6,080	F	$8,000	7/06	SEND	MFWD, 24 speed, 3 hyd., 3 pt., PTO, 18.4-38
Case IH	3394	1987	9,000	F	$8,250	8/06	WCMN	MFWD, 14.9-46 duals, 3 pt., PTO, quick coupler
Case IH	3394	1987		G	$15,750	8/06	ECNE	MFWD, 981 hours on new tach, PS, 18.4-42 rear, 18.4-26 front tires, 2 hyd., quick hitch, small 1,000 PTO, 16 front end slimline weights
Case IH	3594	1987	5,880	G	$17,750	1/06	SESD	MFWD, duals, 1987 model, CAH

Tractors

Make	Model	Year	Hrs.	Cond.	Price	Sale	Location	Comments
Case IH	4210	1995		G	$11,900	1/06	NEIN	Tach shows 391, 2WD
Case IH	4694	1986	7,474	G	$7,000	4/06	NCOK	4WD, 3 pt., PTO, quick hitch, 4 hyd., 12-speed trans.,
								1,500 hours on motor, front weights, tires poor
Case IH	485	1985	3,200	G	$5,700	11/06	WCMN	Diesel, 2WD, 45 hp., cab, air, 2 hyd., 3 pt., 540 PTO
Case IH	5120	1990		G	$7,000	7/06	WCCA	Mudder, canopy, creeper gear, 3 pt., PTO
Case IH	5120	1990	3,860	G	$21,000	12/06	WCIA	MFWD, Case IH 520 loader, roll bar, 16.9-34, new tires
Case IH	5130			F	$14,500	3/06	NCUT	MFWD
Case IH	5140	1990		G	$5,500	7/06	WCCA	Mudder, front weights, canopy, creeper gear, 3 pt., 2 hyd.
Case IH	5140	1992		G	$5,500	7/06	WCCA	Mudder, front weights, canopy, creeper gear
Case IH	5140	1992		G	$7,000	7/06	WCCA	Mudder, front weights, canopy, creeper gear
Case IH	5140	1992		G	$7,500	7/06	WCCA	Mudder, front weights, canopy, creeper gear, 3 pt., PTO
Case IH	5220	1995	3,544	G	$26,500	5/06	SCMI	2WD, cab, air, 18.4R-38, 2 hyd., 3 pt.
Case IH	5230			G	$28,500	1/06	SESD	MFWD, CAH, loader
Case IH	5230	1993		P	$2,500	7/06	WCCA	MFWD, front weights, canopy, creeper gear, 3 pt.,
								PTO, 2 hyd., for parts, high crop, front weights, canopy,
								creeper gear, PTO, 2 remotes, 12.4×42, 12.4R54
Case IH	5240			G	$7,500	7/06	WCCA	MFWD, GB loader, roll bar, 3 pt., 2 hyd.
Case IH	5240		5,400	F	$14,600	3/06	SEPA	MFWD, Maxxum, ROPS, PS, average rubber
Case IH	5240		6,867	G	$29,000	4/06	NEND	Maxxum MFWD, CAH, left-hand reverser, 3 pt., PTO, 3 hyd.,
								16.9-38 (50% rubber)
Case IH	5240		5,823	G	$37,000	4/06	NEND	Maxxum MFWD, Case IH 520 quick-tach loader, CAH,
								left-hand reverser, 3 pt., PTO, 2 hyd., 84" bucket,
								4-tine grapple
Case IH	5240	1992	1,650	G	$32,500	10/06	NCWI	MFWD, diesel, high clearance, cab, heat, creeper gear
Case IH	5240	1992	2,689	G	$32,500	1/06	ECIL	MFWD, 100 hp., cab, air, 3 hyd., 18.4-38, 14.9-24 fronts
Case IH	5240	1996	6,153	G	$29,000	2/06	WCMN	MFWD, CAH, PS, 3 hyd.
Case IH	5250			G	$7,500	7/06	WCCA	MFWD, front weights, canopy, 3 pt., PTO
Case IH	5250			F	$20,100	3/06	SEPA	MFWD, Maxxum, CAH, PS, average rubber
Case IH	5250		2,478	E	$38,000	8/06	SCMI	MFWD, cab, 3 pt., 6 front weights, 3 hyd., axle duals
Case IH	5250	1996	2,519	G	$38,000	1/06	WCIL	Maxxum, MFWD, fully-equipped cab, duals, 3 hyd.,
								540/1,000 PTO
Case IH	5250	1996	710	G	$46,000	2/06	WCIL	Maxxum, MFWD, fully-equipped cab, 3 hyd., Case IH 520
								loader w/ joystick controls
Case IH	595			G	$4,500	8/06	WCTX	OROPS, diesel, digging bucket
Case IH	685	1989	440	E	$15,000	8/06	ECMI	One owner, 2WD, diesel, original hours, 61 hp., 1 hyd.,
								3 pt., PTO, PS, open station, radio, like new
Case IH	685	1990		G	$8,400	12/06	ECMO	2WD, Case IH loader, diesel
Case IH	695	1992	1,190	G	$14,000	8/06	SETN	CAH, Bush Hog 2440 GT front loader
Case IH	7110			G	$18,500	3/06	NCMN	2WD
Case IH	7110	1989		G	$23,000	4/06	NCSD	MFWD Magnum, power, air, 3 hyd., 3 pt., 2,000 hours on
								new engine, Woods Dual loader, scoop, grapple
Case IH	7110	1991		F	$14,000	8/06	SEPA	2WD, ROPS, WF, average rubber
Case IH	7110	1991	4,361	G	$30,500	3/06	ECNE	2WD, 18.4R-42, 10-bolt duals, 11L-16.5 front tires, 3 hyd.,
								540/1,000 PTO, 12 front-end weights
Case IH	7120	1989	4,797	G	$30,000	1/06	SWMN	2WD
Case IH	7120	1989	3,345	G	$34,000	3/06	NWIL	2WD, fully-equipped cab, dual PTO, 3 hyd., 3 pt., 12 front
								weights, hub duals
Case IH	7120	1989	2,394	G	$38,500	1/06	ECNE	2WD, 18.4R-42 duals, 3 hyd., dual PTO, 3 pt., PS, quick
								hitch, front end weights

    WHAT'S IT WORTH?

Tractors

Make	Model	Year	Hrs.	Cond.	Price	Sale	Location	Comments
Case IH	7120	1990	5,150	G	$28,000	2/06	NEMO	2WD, 18-speed ps, radar ground speed, 2 hyd., front fenders, OH at 2,960 hours, full set of front weights
Case IH	7120	1990	7,100	G	$29,000	4/06	NCKS	2WD, loader
Case IH	7120	1990	3,780	G	$32,000	1/06	NWKY	2WD, Magnum, duals
Case IH	7120	1990	3,250	G	$37,250	12/06	NWOH	2WD, cab, air, 2 hyd., front weights, duals
Case IH	7120	1991	12,000	F	$21,000	12/06	NWWI	MFWD, 3 hyd., 18.4-42, 12,000 hours
Case IH	7120	1991	4,100	G	$32,750	1/06	NEIN	2WD, 18.4-42, nice
Case IH	7120	1991	4,423	F	$33,000	1/06	NWIL	2WD, 18.4R42 hub duals
Case IH	7120	1991	3,800	G	$38,000	8/06	NCKS	MFWD, one owner
Case IH	7120	1991	2,831	E	$46,000	2/06	SENE	2WD, 3 hyd., duals
Case IH	7120	1992	5,400	G	$41,000	4/06	WCMB	Canadian sale, MFWD, diesel, 18 speed, powershift, 3-spool hyd., 1000/540 PTO, duals
Case IH	7120	1992	1,815	G	$43,500	2/06	SEIL	MFWD, 18.4-42, duals, paint faded, clean
Case IH	7130		9,014	G	$20,000	11/06	SCNE	2WD, 4 hyd., 4 reverse, 18.4R-42 duals, front weights
Case IH	7130		7,307	G	$29,000	6/06	SCMN	MFWD, duals, rock box, 4-speed reverse, radar, complete engine OH at 1,700 hours
Case IH	7130	1988		G	$30,000	11/06	ECND	MFWD, PS, creeper, 3 hyd., 3 pt., PTO, 14.9-46 duals
Case IH	7130	1988	2,742	G	$33,000	3/06	NCCO	MFWD
Case IH	7130	1989	8,235	G	$25,000	4/06	NWMN	MFWD, 18.4-46 band duals, 14.9-30 fronts, suitcase weights
Case IH	7130	1989	8,325	G	$28,500	7/06	SEND	MFWD, CAH, 18-speed ps, 3 pt., PTO, 14.9-46 duals, 14.9-30 fronts
Case IH	7130	1990		F	$11,000	1/06	WCCA	MFWD, front weights, cab, air, 4-speed, 3 hyd.
Case IH	7130	1990		G	$27,500	1/06	NEIN	MFWD, 18.4-42 duals
Case IH	7130	1991		G	$25,000	7/06	WCCA	MFWD, front weights, cab, air, 3 pt., 3 hyd.
Case IH	7130	1991	4,850	G	$37,000	10/06	NCND	MFWD, 3 pt.
Case IH	7130	1991	2,914	G	$47,500	3/06	NCIA	MFWD, cab, PS, 3 hyd., front weights, 1,000 PTO, 4 reverse, 18.4-42 duals
Case IH	7140		7,648	G	$32,000	3/06	NCOH	MFWD, CAH, axle-mount duals, quick hitch, 3 hyd., major OH at 7,104 hours
Case IH	7140	1988	6,200	G	$30,000	1/06	SCNE	MFWD, 18-speed ps, 3 hyd., good 16.9R-28 front, 20.8R-42 rear tires, duals, serviced regularly
Case IH	7140	1989	9,407	G	$21,000	3/06	SEMN	2WD, duals, 10 suitcase weights, 540/1,000 PTO, 3 pt., 3 hyd.
Case IH	7140	1989	10,088	G	$25,000	6/06	NWKS	MFWD, 195 hp., 3 hyd., PTO, 3 pt.
Case IH	7140	1989	5,150	G	$39,500	2/06	NCIL	MFWD, PS, 3 hyd., 18.4R-42, duals
Case IH	7140	1990	5,176	F	$38,500	1/06	NWIL	MFWD, 20.8-42, hub duals, 4 hyd., front weights
Case IH	7140	1991	5,066	G	$40,000	3/06	ECND	MFWD, 18-speed ps, 4 reverse, 4 hyd., 3 pt., quick hitch, front suitcase weights, 18.4-42 press steel duals, 70% rubber, 14.9-30 fronts (75%)
Case IH	7140	1992		P	$9,000	1/06	WCCA	MFWD, front weights, cab, air, 4 speed
Case IH	7140	1992	7,175	F	$26,000	9/06	NEND	MFWD, CAH, 420/80R46 tires & duals, PTO, 3 pt., 4 hyd.
Case IH	7140	1992	2,815	E	$49,250	11/06	SENE	MFWD, Magnum, 18-speed ps, 4-speed reverse, 20.8R-42 rear, 18.4R-26 front, 3 hyd., large 1,000 PTO, 10 front end weights, cab, air, AM/FM/cassette, new batteries, one owner, shedded
Case IH	7150		9,000	P	$27,500	12/06	SWWI	MFWD, rough, cab, air
Case IH	7150	1992	5,409	E	$35,000	2/06	NECO	Axle duals, MFWD

Tractors

Make	Model	Year	Hrs.	Cond.	Price	Sale	Location	Comments
Case IH	7210			F	$19,000	8/06	SWWI	MFWD, cab, air
Case IH	7210	1994	4,138	G	$34,500	2/06	NCCO	18-speed ps, 14.9-46 duals, 14.9-30 fronts
Case IH	7210	1994	1,550	E	$42,000	12/06	WCIA	2WD, 18.4-42 tires, no duals
Case IH	7210	1995	2,459	G	$36,000	1/06	NWIL	2WD, cab, 3 hyd., 12 front weights, 18.4R-42
Case IH	7220	1995	5,650	G	$33,700	6/06	ECSD	MFWD
Case IH	7220	1995	2,630	G	$35,000	8/06	WCIA	2WD
Case IH	7220	1995	2,686	G	$53,500	1/06	NWIL	MFWD, cab, 3 hyd., 12 front weights, 18.4R-42 & hub duals, 14.9-30 fronts
Case IH	7220	1996	2,031	E	$50,000	2/06	NCIL	MFWD, very nice
Case IH	7230	1994	3,110	E	$52,750	12/06	WCIA	MFWD, 18.4-42 tires, no duals
Case IH	7230	1995	2,200	F	$53,750	2/06	ECNE	MFWD, no duals, 3 hyd.
Case IH	7230	1996		F	$23,500	11/06	WCMN	2WD, PS, new 42" rear rubber, front weights
Case IH	7240	1994	4,521	G	$46,000	11/06	ECND	MFWD, 4 hyd., 3 pt., quick hitch, big 1,000 PTO, 18.4-42 duals, 16.9-28 front duals w/ hub spacers, front suitcase weights
Case IH	7240	1995	7,800	G	$30,000	3/06	SEIA	MFWD, 4 hyd.
Case IH	7240	1995	2,262	G	$51,000	5/06	SCMI	MFWD, cab, air 18.4-42 rear duals, 14.9R-30 front duals, 4 hyd., 3 pt., 18 front weights
Case IH	7240	1996	2,744	G	$54,600	12/06	SEIA	MFWD, 18-speed trans., Goodyear 18.4R-42
Case IH	7250	1994	4,400	G	$48,000	1/06	NECO	MFWD, 16-speed ps, 3 pt., PTO, 3 hyd., 18.4R46 duals
Case IH	7250	1996	1,402	E	$75,500	12/06	WCIA	MFWD, 18 front weights, 20.8-42, duals
Case IH	885		2,500	G	$12,250	12/06	NWIL	No cab, 225 loader
Case IH	885			G	$14,500	12/06	SCQB	Canadian sale, MFWD, Case IH 2255 loader, cab, 3 pt., 2 hyd., PTO, converts to $12,657 U.S.
Case IH	885	1986		G	$12,500	8/06	SETN	Case IH 2255 front loader, CAH, 72 hp., 4WD
Case IH	8920	1997	941	E	$60,000	3/06	NWIL	MFWD, fully-equipped cab, dual PTO, 3 hyd., 3 pt., 12 front weights
Case IH	8920	1997	1,316	E	$70,000	1/06	NEIA	MFWD, 3 hyd., 2 PTOs, duals, like new
Case IH	8920	1998	7,338	F	$25,000	1/06	WCTX	MFWD, paint faded, duals, rubber 50%
Case IH	8920	1998	5,214	G	$40,000	4/06	WCWI	MFWD, cab, air, 3 hyd., 3 pt., dual PTO, duals
Case IH	8920	1998	3,148	G	$48,000	3/06	SEMN	MFWD, one owner, 18.4-42 w/ duals, 18-speed ps, 18 front weights, 3 pt., 3 hyd., quick hitch
Case IH	8920	1998	2,896	G	$50,000	8/06	ECNE	MFWD, PS, dual PTO, 3 hyd., radar, 18.4-42 duals, weights, front fenders
Case IH	8920	1999	1,965	G	$48,000	8/06	NCIA	2WD, cab, air, 4 hyd., 18/4 powershift, front weights, quick coupler, wide mirrors, duals
Case IH	8940	1998	2,105	G	$57,000	7/06	NWOH	MFWD, cab, air, 18-speed ps, rice tires, creeper gear, 4 hyd., front weights
Case IH	8940	1998	2,405	G	$58,000	5/06	SCMI	MFWD, cab, 3 pt., 18 front weights, 4 hyd., cab, air, 18.4R-42 duals, 14.9R-30 front duals
Case IH	9110	1989	3,681	G	$39,000	1/06	WCIL	4WD, row crop special, Cummins 350 engine, 3 pt., quick hitch, duals
Case IH	9130	1986	8,000	G	$28,250	5/06	SEND	4WD, row crop special, CAH, PS, 3 hyd., 3 pt., 1,000 PTO, steerable front axle, 18.4-38 duals, 60% rubber
Case IH	9130	1988	5,932	F	$19,700	11/06	NEKS	4WD, powershift trans, 18.4R-38 duals, 3 hyd., bareback
Case IH	9130	1989	7,700	G	$24,000	1/06	NECO	4WD, bareback, row crop special, 3 pt., PTO, 12-speed ps, 18.4-38R
Case IH	9170		5,229	G	$39,000	4/06	NCSD	4WD, PS, 4 hyd., no 3 pt., 20.8R-42
Case IH	9170	1990	5,357	G	$37,000	11/06	NEND	4WD, PS, 4 hyd., 24.5-32 Goodyear duals, 40% rubber

Tractors

Make	Model	Year	Hrs.	Cond.	Price	Sale	Location	Comments
Case IH	9180	1989	3,714	E	$37,500	9/06	WCIA	4WD, new 9280 paint, CAH, AM/FM, 4 hyd., 12-speed ps, duals, like new
Case IH	9230		5,900	F	$39,850	1/06	SESD	4WD, 1994 model, 3 pt., PTO, duals
Case IH	9230	1991	3,280	G	$35,000	7/06	SEND	PS, 4 hyd., return flow, 1,000 PTO, 18.4-38 duals, 65%
Case IH	9230	1993	3,750	G	$34,000	3/06	ECND	4WD, CAH, PS, 4 hyd., return flow, no PTO, 18.4-38 duals
Case IH	9260	1991	2,126	G	$45,500	2/06	ECIL	4WD, hyd. outlets, 18.4R-42, duals, no PTO
Case IH	9270		3,260	G	$55,000	4/06	NEND	4WD, deluxe cab, 12 speed, 4 hyd., 20.8-42 duals, one owner
Case IH	9270	1995	5,212	G	$40,500	3/06	ECND	4WD, 335 hp., 12 speed, 4 hyd., rear weight pkg, 20.8-42 triples (60% rubber), one owner
Case IH	9270	1995	5,313	G	$42,500	11/06	ECND	4WD, 12-speed synchro, 4 hyd., 20.8-42 duals
Case IH	9280	1991	3,964	G	$50,000	11/06	NCIN	4WD, 4 hyd., 12-speed ps
Case IH	9280	1992		F	$36,000	11/06	SCND	4WD, 375 hp., Cummins, 4 hyd.
Case IH	9330			G	$66,250	1/06	SESD	4WD, 1998 model, 3 pt., PTO, duals, low hours, Row Crop Special
Case IH	9330	1996	4,167	G	$60,000	7/06	SEND	4WD, row crop, powershift, 4 hyd., 3 pt., 1,000 PTO, steerable front axles, 14.9-36 duals (75%), complete service records
Case IH	9330	1998	808	G	$64,000	12/06	SCNE	4WD, row crop special, steerable front axle, 18.4-38 tires & duals, PTO, 4 hyd.
Case IH	9350		2,981	G	$50,000	12/06	WCMN	4WD, 2,981 hours showing, row crop special, 4 hyd., 3 pt., 14.9-46 tires
Case IH	9350	1996	3,400	G	$56,750	2/06	WCMN	4WD, 20.8-42, duals, very clean
Case IH	9350	1998	1,500	E	$50,000	7/06	ECIL	4WD, 24 speed, new Cummins M11, 330 Century engine installed at 1,172 hours, remaining warranty on engine is transferable, duals
Case IH	9370		5,185	G	$50,000	2/06	SEKS	4WD, PS, 4 hyd., duals
Case IH	9370	1996	3,364	G	$57,500	4/06	WCSD	4WD, PS, deluxe cab, air seat, OH done 350 hours ago, bareback, 20.8R-42 duals
Case IH	9370	1997	3,750	G	$65,000	3/06	NEKS	Quad trans., 12-speed ps, 4 hyd., 1,000 PTO, 30" belt
Case IH	9370	1998	5,473	G	$53,000	12/06	SEMN	Quad trans., 12 speed, 30" belts
Case IH	9380	1997	4,041	G	$59,000	2/06	WCMN	4WD, 4 hyd., Cummins CN14, rock box, Trelleborg 750-65-38 tires & duals
Case IH	9380	1999	4,600	G	$66,000	10/06	NCND	Quadtrack, 12-speed ps, 400 hp., 1,500 hours on major OH
Case IH	9390	1997	5,255	G	$60,000	12/06	WCMN	4WD, 12 speed, package, 4 hyd.
Case IH	C100		1,087	G	$20,000	11/06	SWOH	2WD, 100 hp., 8 speed, 18.4-30 tires
Case IH	C70	2000	778	G	$21,700	4/06	SWIN	IHC 2255 front end loader with bucket & forks, 2 hyd., 540 & 1,000 PTO, 16.9-30 tires
Case IH	C90		2,240	G	$17,400	12/06	ECIL	MFWD, ROPS, Quicke Q940 hyd. loader w/ quick-attach 7' bucket, pallet & bale forks, shuttle clutch, 18.4-30 tires
Case IH	CX100	2000	2,200	G	$24,000	1/06	NEIN	MFWD, cab, air
Case IH	DX24E		20	E	$9,750	8/06	NWOH	4×4, diesel, 3 pt., PTO, MWX 1605 deck, LX110 loader
Case IH	DX45	2003	275	E	$14,700	7/06	NWIL	Utility, MFWD, diesel, roll bar, hydro, like new
Case IH	JX100		1,480	G	$25,000	9/06	SCMN	JX100U, MFWD, 3 pt., 2 hyd., in-cab valve
Case IH	JX75	2005	172	G	$27,000	9/06	NWTN	4WD, front loader
Case IH	MX110			F	$13,200	8/06	SEPA	MFWD, high clearance, fair rubber
Case IH	MX110		6,000	F	$16,500	1/06	SEPA	MFWD, Maxxum, high clearance, ROPS, creeper, fair rubber
Case IH	MX120		7,234	F	$19,500	12/06	SWWI	MFWD

Tractors

Make	Model	Year	Hrs.	Cond.	Price	Sale	Location	Comments
Case IH	MX120		2,615	G	$33,000	1/06	NCIL	MFWD, CAH, 16-speed ps, 2 hyd., 3 pt., 540/1,000 PTO, clamp-on duals
Case IH	MX120		3,660	E	$39,000	2/06	NCIL	MFWD, 20.8-38 tires, very good
Case IH	MX120	1999	5,700	G	$24,000	11/06	WCMN	2WD, power quad, left-hand reverser, creeper, 3 hyd.
Case IH	MX120	2000	630	G	$49,000	6/06	SCMN	2WD, cab, 12 front weights, 3 hyd., quick hitch, 14.9R-46 factory dual hubs
Case IH	MX135			F	$30,000	12/06	SWWI	MFWD, cab, air, tractor came from California, new tires, duals, front weights, 7,624 hours
Case IH	MX135		6,000	F	$32,000	12/06	SWWI	MFWD
Case IH	MX135	1997	4,400	G	$41,000	2/06	WCMN	MFWD, CAH, hub duals
Case IH	MX135	1998	1,525	E	$46,000	2/06	SENE	2WD, PS, 3 hyd., duals
Case IH	MX135	2000	1,090	E	$37,500	9/06	WCIA	MFWD, CAH, AM/FM, 3 hyd., 12-speed shuttle shift, duals, like new
Case IH	MX135	2001	2,838	G	$51,000	5/06	SCMI	MFWD, Case IH I655 loader, 8' bucket & tongs, cab, 3 pt., 3 hyd.
Case IH	MX190		810	G	$49,250	7/06	SEND	2003 model, Maxxum, MFWD, PS, 4 hyd., 3 pt., 540/1,000 PTO, comfort ride suspension, front suitcase weights, 14.9-36 duals, 14.9-30 fronts
Case IH	MX200	2000	1,270	G	$66,000	3/06	ECNE	MFWD, 18.4R-46 duals, quick hitch, 3 hyd., front fenders, 14.9R-34 fronts
Case IH	MX200	2001	1,800	G	$49,500	1/06	NECO	Deluxe cab, 18-speed PS, 3 pt., PTO, 4 hyd., 480/80R46 duals
Case IH	MX200	2001	766	G	$59,900	1/06	NWIL	2WD, cab, 3 hyd., quick hitch, 10 front weights, 18.4R-46 & hub duals, 11×24 fronts
Case IH	MX200	2001	1,740	G	$65,750	1/06	SESD	MFWD, 46" duals, CAH, 4 hyd.
Case IH	MX200	2002	3,007	G	$54,500	12/06	WCMN	MFWD, 480×50 duals, 380×38 front, 4 hyd., no quick hitch
Case IH	MX210	2006	250	G	$82,500	12/06	SEMN	MFWD, 3 hyd., hd front axle, 10 front weights, duals, warranty until 7/20/08
Case IH	MX220	2000	1,689	G	$62,000	3/06	ECND	MFWD, PS, 4 hyd., power beyond, 1,000 PTO, front suitcase weights, 390/9046 press steel duals, 90% rubber, 14.9-30 fronts (90%), one owner
Case IH	MX230	2005	420	E	$93,400	3/06	WCKS	MFWD, suspension, front axle, duals, warranty, like new
Case IH	MX240		1,700	G	$66,000	3/06	SCID	MFWD
Case IH	MX240		1,800	G	$67,000	3/06	SCID	MFWD
Case IH	MX240		2,134	G	$69,000	12/06	SEMN	MFWD, 480/80R46, front weights, PTO, quick hitch
Case IH	MX240	1999	3,400	G	$46,000	6/06	ECSD	MFWD
Case IH	MX240	1999	2,502	E	$62,000	12/06	ECIL	MFWD, 18.4R46 rear w/ duals, R34 front tires, like new
Case IH	MX240	1999	830	G	$62,500	2/06	WCMN	MFWD, 4 hyd., 380/90R46 duals & triples, 14.9-30 fronts
Case IH	MX240	2001	964	G	$66,000	1/06	SWMN	MFWD
Case IH	MX240	2001	1,703	G	$72,000	12/06	SEIA	MFWD, 18/4 trans., Firestone 18.4R-46, front & rear weights
Case IH	MX240	2001	430	E	$81,500	8/06	NCIA	MFWD, 18/4 PS, duals, axle duals, 500-lbs. in rear weights, 3 hyd., heavy quick coupler, performance monitor, trainer seat, wide mirrors, heated seat, radar, hyd. return, 1,000 PTO
Case IH	MX255	2005	200	G	$82,500	4/06	NEND	MFWD, deluxe cab, 3 pt., quick hitch, leather seats, 5 hyd., 540/1,000 PTO, 380/90/50 duals, front & rear weights
Case IH	MX255	2005		E	$93,000	3/06	NWOH	MFWD, cab, PS, duals front 480/80R46 and rear 380/85-34, 4 hyd., buddy/heated seats

WHAT'S IT WORTH?

Tractors

Make	Model	Year	Hrs.	Cond.	Price	Sale	Location	Comments
Case IH	MX255	2005	3	E	$100,000	1/06	NEIN	MFWD, 480/80R46 duals
Case IH	MX270	2000	2,400	G	$66,000	1/06	NECO	MFWD, 18-speed ps, 3 pt., PTO, 4 hyd., deluxe cab, 18.4R46 duals, front & rear weights
Case IH	MX270	2001	1,351	G	$85,500	3/06	ECNE	MFWD, turbo, PS, cab, air, 4 hyd., 3 pt. w/ dual cylinder lift assist
Case IH	MX270	2002	3,500	G	$66,000	6/06	NWKS	MFWD, 270 hp., 4 hyd., PTO, 3 pt., quick-tach
Case IH	MX270	2002	1,211	G	$79,000	1/06	NEIN	MFWD, 480/80R46 duals
Case IH	MX285	2003		E	$97,500	2/06	NWIA	MFWD, 3 pt., quick hitch, 4 hyd., hub duals, front weights, dual front rubber w/ spacers, loaded, 46" rear rubber
Case IH	MX285	2004	935	G	$90,000	3/06	ECNE	MFWD, 480/80R46 Firestone rear tires w/ duals, 380/85R34 Firestone front w/ duals, 5 hyd., performance monitor, quick hitch, hd drawbar, rear weights, 18 front weights
Case IH	MX285	2004	881	G	$99,000	3/06	ECNE	MFWD, 480/80R46 Firestone rear tires w/ duals, 380/85R34 Firestone front w/ duals, 5 hyd., performance monitor, quick hitch, hd drawbar, rear weights, 10 front weights, front fenders
Case IH	MX285	2005	945	E	$93,000	9/06	NCIA	MFWD, loaded, duals
Case IH	MX285	2005		G	$95,000	4/06	NEND	MFWD, 3 pt., quick hitch, 4 hyd., 1,000 PTO, 480/80R/46 duals, front weights
Case IH	MX90C	2000	2,100	G	$30,000	12/06	SCQB	Canadian sale, MFWD, front loader, joystick, cab, air, 3 pt., 2 hyd., 2-speed PTO, converts to $26,187 U.S.
Case IH	MXM 155		822	E	$50,000	2/06	NCIL	MFWD, like new
Case IH	MXM 155	2005	793	G	$52,000	4/06	WCWI	MFWD, cab, air, 3 hyd., 3-pt. dual PTO, duals
Case IH	MXM190	2003	146	E	$62,000	6/06	SCMN	MFWD, cab, 4 hyd., rock box, 14.9R-46 factory hub duals, 14.9R-30 fronts
Case IH	MXU100		556	E	$25,500	1/06	NCIL	2WD, open station, 2 hyd., 3 pt., 540/1,000 PTO, warranty to 9/27/06
Case IH	STX 325	2003	1,250	G	$93,000	12/06	SCMN	20.8-42 tires, duals
Case IH	STX275	2001	2,392	G	$81,500	1/06	NEIN	4WD, PS, 3 pt., PTO, Accu-Steer
Case IH	STX275	2002	636	E	$92,000	1/06	WCIL	4WD, 480/80R46 axle-mount duals, PTO, 4 hyd.
Case IH	STX375		2,335	G	$88,000	6/06	SCMN	4WD, 710 metric duals, rock box, deluxe cab
Caterpillar	45			G	$27,500	12/06	NWIL	New engine, diesel, 3 pt., PTO, new 24" tracks
Caterpillar	45	1995	4,492	G	$38,000	4/06	SEND	16-speed ps, air, 4 hyd., 3 pt., quick hitch, PTO, radar, new 16" Camoplast directional tracks, 60" spacing
Caterpillar	45	1995	1,830	G	$50,000	8/06	WCMN	16-speed ps, quick hitch, front suitcase weight pkg., 4 hyd., rock box, 24" belts
Caterpillar	45	1997		F	$13,000	3/06	NWKS	25" standard belt, 125-gal. fuel tank, deluxe cab, 15,000-lb. hitch, 80" gauge spacers, quick hitch, mounting kit, 31.2-gpm hyd. pump
Caterpillar	45	2000	2,243	G	$54,000	12/06	NWMO	
Caterpillar	55	1996	5,083	G	$37,500	5/06	WCMN	4 hyd., 88" stance w/ 16" tracks, narrow gauge w/ spacers, front weights
Caterpillar	55	1997	3,314	G	$57,000	3/06	SWMI	Challenger, wide stance 18" extreme service belts, 4 hyd., PTO, 3 pt., 15 weights, radar, front idler
Caterpillar	55	1997	2,056	G	$59,000	3/06	SWMI	Challenger, wide stance 25" belts, 4 hyd., PTO, 3 pt., 15 weights
Caterpillar	55	1998	3,982	G	$42,000	11/06	WCMN	Challenger, 120" spacing, 20" bolts, 4 hyd., 60" undercarriage
Caterpillar	55	1999	1,929	G	$79,000	3/06	SWMI	Challenger, wide stance 25" belts, 4 hyd., PTO, 3 pt., radar

Tractors

Make	Model	Year	Hrs.	Cond.	Price	Sale	Location	Comments
Caterpillar	60			G	$23,000	8/06	SCIL	Canopy
Caterpillar	65	1986	13,661	F	$12,500	3/06	NWKS	Rubber track, 13,661 hours, 3 pt., powertrain trans., rear window wiper, aux. electric circuit, pulley group, ether starting aid, lighting system
Caterpillar	65	1989	5,048	G	$31,250	2/06	NCIL	Challenger, 4 hyd.
Caterpillar	65	1997		F	$20,000	11/06	SCND	Challenger, 300 hp., 3 pt., PS, 4 hyd.
Caterpillar	65A	1987	10,192	F	$17,000	11/06	ECND	CAH, PS, 4 hyd., swing drawbar, 24" belts
Caterpillar	65B		5,000	F	$32,500	1/06	SEPA	Challenger
Caterpillar	65D	1996		G	$34,500	11/06	ECND	CAH, PS, 3306 Cat, 4 hyd., 1,000 PTO, radar, 30" belts
Caterpillar	65E	1999	2,182	G	$65,000	2/06	SCMI	Challenger, new tracks, deluxe cab, 6-disk CD changer, computer data system, 4 hyd., radar
Caterpillar	75			P	$7,000	1/06	WCCA	Front weights, cab, air, 4 hyd.
Caterpillar	75			P	$20,250	12/06	SCMN	Challenger, trans. problems
Caterpillar	75C		8,480	G	$36,000	7/06	SEND	30" belts Chevron drives, 4 hyd., swinging drawbar, 4 hyd., 90% undercarriage
Caterpillar	75C	1995	4,991	G	$58,000	3/06	NCND	CAH, 10-spd. ps, 4 hyd., 30" belts, aux. light pkg., one owner
Caterpillar	75C	1996	6,900	F	$39,000	5/06	ECNE	Challenger, 4 hyd., R134A air, AM/FM radio, new right track
Caterpillar	75D	1997	2,443	G	$48,000	9/06	NEIN	10-spd. powershift, 2-spd. reverse, 4 hyd.
Caterpillar	75E	1998	2,795	G	$74,000	8/06	WCMN	340 hp., 4 hyd., 35" tracks
Caterpillar	75E	2002	2,224	G	$91,500	12/06	NWMO	36" tracks, bareback, 4 hyd.
Caterpillar	85C			G	$34,000	2/06	WCMN	4 hyd. w/ return, 36" tracks, 2,780 hours on engine OH, fresh differential OH w/ complete new pump installed
Caterpillar	85C		4,535	G	$50,000	2/06	NWSD	Challenger, 10-speed PS, 4 hyd., 3176 motor, 375 hp., tracks 30" wide, steerable hitch, one owner, 8-04 changed all oils & filters, new batteries
Caterpillar	85C	1993		F	$30,000	3/06	SEIA	350 hours on complete engine, complete rebuild in 2002
Caterpillar	85C	1994	9,200	F	$27,500	2/06	SEKS	4 hyd., PTO, wide-swing drawbar, 36" bolts
Caterpillar	85C	1994	4,245	F	$45,750	2/06	WCIL	36" tracks, 4 hyd., 10 spd., 2 spd. reverser
Caterpillar	85C	1996	3,230	G	$48,000	12/06	ECMO	Challenger, PS, wide-swing drawbar, 4 hyd., very good 30" tracks, 10 front weights
Caterpillar	95E	2001	3,082	G	$85,000	12/06	SCMN	30" belts
Caterpillar	MT295	2002	267	G	$15,000	11/06	SECA	44 hp., MFWD hydro trans.
Caterpillar	MT297	2005		G	$18,000	11/06	SECA	MFWD, 55 hp., ML 40 front loader
Caterpillar	MT545	2003	805	G	$29,000	11/06	SECA	MFWD, CAH, 3 pt, PTO
Caterpillar	MT565	2003	495	G	$40,000	11/06	SECA	MFWD, weights, CAH, synchro trans
Caterpillar	MT655	2003	1,025	G	$61,000	4/06	NEND	PS, 3 pt., 4 hyd., Datatronics, radar, front weights, front & rear duals, warranty
Caterpillar	MT665	2004	611	G	$85,000	11/06	SECA	MFWD, weights, CAH, 3 pt, PTO
Caterpillar	MT765		1,600	G	$137,000	2/06	WCMN	6 hyd., power beyond, 18" belt, quick hitch, high-output light system, Auto Farm GPS 5001 autosteering system
Caterpillar	MT765	2002	505	G	$60,000	12/06	WCMN	20 suitcase weights
Caterpillar	MT765	2004	536	G	$123,000	3/06	SWMI	Challenger, wide stance 18", extreme service belts, 4 hyd., PTO, 3 pt., 20 front weights, front idler radar
David Bradley	NA			F	$1,000	9/06	ECMI	Belly mower, all original, restored, #917
Deutz Allis	DX130	1980	4,500	G	$7,000	8/06	ECIA	Diesel, fully-equipped cab
Deutz Allis	6260	1986	2,085	G	$10,500	12/06	NWIL	Open station utility w/ Deutz-Allis 456 loader, 6' bucket, 16.9-30 tires, ROPS
Deutz Allis	7085	1987	7,300	P	$6,000	3/06	WCMN	3 pt., PTO, 2 hyd., cab, air
Deutz Allis	7085	1990	3,070	G	$12,000	8/06	ECIA	Westendorf TA-26 loader, diesel, turbo, fully-equipped cab

WHAT'S IT WORTH?

Tractors

Make	Model	Year	Hrs.	Cond.	Price	Sale	Location	Comments
Deutz Allis	DX90		4,169	G	$8,300	1/06	NEIN	Westendorf loader
Fendt	920		1,650	G	$90,000	4/06	SEPA	Vario, MFWD, front PTO, 3 pt., duals
Fendt	924		585	G	$101,000	4/06	SEPA	Vario, MFWD, 4 hyd., 1-year warranty, reverse station, front PTO, 3 pt.
Ford	1100			G	$3,500	8/06	NWOH	4×4, 768 loader, 3 pt., PTO, diesel
Ford	1500		666	G	$2,100	9/06	NWTN	
Ford	1600		1,055	G	$1,700	12/06	NWIL	2WD compact utility tractor, weights, diesel
Ford	1700			G	$1,700		SETN	Diesel
Ford	1700			G	$3,500	11/06	SCCA	Diesel, 3 pt
Ford	1710		1,660	G	$3,300	9/06	NWTN	
Ford	1715			G	$4,350	10/06	SWOH	Compact/utility, 4WD, diesel
Ford	1720			G	$3,500	8/06	WCTX	
Ford	1720		1,943	G	$4,700	9/06	NWTN	ROPS, mowing deck
Ford	1720		1,943	G	$4,700	9/06	NWTN	ROPS, mowing deck
Ford	1920	1995	112	E	$11,500	3/06	NWOH	MFWD, Ford 7108 loader, rollover bar, 3 pt., 555 trans.
Ford	2110			G	$4,750	8/06	SETN	Front loader, 4WD, ROPS, sunshade
Ford	2120			G	$6,000	12/06	SCQB	Canadian sale, 4×4 utility tractor, snowblower, 3 pt., PTO, converts to $5,237 U.S.
Ford	2810			F	$4,500	1/06	SEPA	WF, ROPS, fair rubber
Ford	2910			F	$4,000	1/06	SEPA	2910 LCG, WF, ROPS, fair turf rubber
Ford	3550			F	$4,250	8/06	NWOH	Backhoe & loader
Ford	3600			G	$3,600	9/06	NWTN	
Ford	3910			G	$4,000	8/06	SETN	Diesel
Ford	3910			G	$4,250	8/06	WCTX	Diesel, 3-pt. hitch
Ford	3910			G	$8,000	6/06	NEIN	91" finishing mower
Ford	3910		20	E	$12,200	1/06	SEPA	New, MFWD, front-end loader, new rubber
Ford	3910	1987	1,758	G	$7,700	3/06	ECIL	Ford 7209 loader, 4/2 hi lo, 3 pt., 540 PTO, 1 hyd.
Ford	3930			G	$7,750	3/06	SCIN	Diesel, broom
Ford	3930		803	G	$10,500	8/06	SETN	4WD, ROPS, shuttle shift trans
Ford	4600	1980	2,935	G	$6,000	8/06	SETN	52 hp.
Ford	4610			G	$4,600	9/06	NCMI	2WD, diesel, 3 pt., PTO, new rims & tires all around
Ford	4610			G	$6,800	8/06	SETN	Diesel
Ford	4630	1994		G	$13,500	9/06	NWTN	NH 731 front loader
Ford	4630	1994	1,069	G	$14,000	8/06	SETN	Ford 7310 front loader, ROPS, sunshade, shuttle shift
Ford	540			G	$3,000	8/06	WCTX	Diesel
Ford	5600			F	$5,000	3/06	NWIL	Diesel
Ford	5600		1,123	G	$7,800	9/06	NWTN	ROPS, sunshade
Ford	5610			F	$6,250	3/06	SEPA	2WD, WF, ROPS, good rubber
Ford	5610	1988	3,000	G	$11,250	2/06	SWIN	Dual 200 front end loader w/ pallet & bale fork, diesel, dual power trans., 2 hyd., wheel weights
Ford	6600			G	$4,900	9/06	NWTN	Front loader
Ford	6600			G	$6,500	9/06	NWTN	ROPS
Ford	6600	1979	1,541	E	$8,200	4/06	ECNE	Diesel, one owner, this tractor has only mowed grass
Ford	6600	1979		G	$13,250	12/06	NEMO	2 hyd., 540 PTO
Ford	6600	1980		F	$5,500	9/06	WCOH	Ford 727 loader
Ford	6610			F	$2,500	8/06	SCFL	Loader
Ford	6610			G	$5,000	10/06	WCFL	Diesel
Ford	6610			G	$5,900	10/06	WCFL	3140 loader
Ford	6610			G	$10,000	1/06	NEIN	Series II, cab, nice
Ford	701			G	$2,800	8/06	WCMN	NF, PS, gas, 3 pt., 13.6-28 tires, hyd. loader

Tractors

Make	Model	Year	Hrs.	Cond.	Price	Sale	Location	Comments
Ford	7600			F	$7,500	1/06	SEPA	WF, ROPS, average rubber
Ford	7600	1974	4,300	G	$11,000	3/06	SWIN	Diesel, dual power, load monitor, roll bar canopy, 2-speed PTO, weights, radio, good tires
Ford	7610		1,398	G	$13,000	1/06	NEIN	MFWD, Farmhand quick-tach loader
Ford	7700			G	$8,300	9/06	NWTN	Bush Hog front loader, ROPS
Ford	7700		6,372	G	$9,500	3/06	NCWI	4×4, 3 hyd.
Ford	7700	1979	6,500	G	$9,500	8/06	SWIA	WF, good rubber
Ford	7740			G	$15,000	8/06	SETN	CAH, Bush Hog 2845QT, front loader
Ford	7740		4,356	G	$20,100	11/06	WCSD	Powerstar SLE, MFWD, 85 hp., 3 pt., 4 yard, Woods dual 255 loader, 8' bucket & bale fork
Ford	9700	1975		G	$5,500	7/06	ECND	3 pt., PTO, duals
Ford	9700	1977		G	$11,200	9/06	NWOH	Dual power, cab, air, front weights, duals, 125 hours on complete engine OH
Ford	TW 10	1978	6,792	G	$10,000	3/06	SEMN	2WD, one owner, cab, air, 18.4-38 w/ duals, 3 pt., 2 hyd.
Ford	TW 10	1981	3,252	G	$15,250	2/06	NCOH	Diesel, CAH, 2 hyd., weights, 18.4-38 rubber
Ford	TW 15	1988		G	$17,100	1/06	SESD	2WD, 1988 model
Ford	TW 25			G	$8,250	9/06	NWTN	CAH, duals
Ford	TW 25			G	$11,000	7/06	WCMN	MFWD, cab, AC
Ford	TW 25			F	$13,600	3/06	SEPA	Series II, WF, ROPS, average rubber, 1,000 hours on tach
Ford	TW 25	1987	4,603	G	$25,000	2/06	NCOH	MFWD, CAH, 20.8-38 rubber & axle duals, 3 hyd., standard trans., weights, Series II, diesel
Ford	TW 30		4,219		$5,000	9/06	NWTN	CAH, duals
Ford	TW 30			G	$5,000	11/06	SETN	Rear duals, cab, air
Ford	TW 30		4,219		$5,800	9/06	NWTN	CAH, duals
Ford	TW 30	1983	5,390	F	$6,000	3/06	NEMI	2WD, CAH, 30.5-32 rear flotation tires, new factory engine at 4,000 hours, 3 hyd., dual PTO, one owner
Ford	TW 35		5,330	G	$11,500	10/06	SWOH	4WD, EROPS, 4 spd. trans., rear PTO, 3 rear hyd.
Ford	TW 35		2,908	G	$28,000	12/06	SCMN	MFWD
Ford	TW 35	1989	4,248	E	$16,000	9/06	WCOH	MFWD, Series II, CAH, weights, 3 hyd., less than 1,000 hours on new motor
Ford-NH	4630			G	$7,600	10/06	WCFL	3-pt. hitch
Ford-NH	4835			G	$20,600	8/06	SEPA	MFWD, 7310 loader, CAH, average rubber
Ford-NH	5030	1994	1,140	G	$20,000	3/06	SWIN	MFWD, shuttle shift, roll bar canopy, 2 hyd., Farmhand DXL 740 front end loader w/ material & manure buckets, bale spear
Ford-NH	5640	1997	2,331	E	$20,500	5/06	SEWY	MFWD, cab, 3 pt., 2 hyd., diesel
Ford-NH	6640	1994		F	$8,250	2/06	WCIL	ROPS, 4' side-mount rotary mower
Ford-NH	7635	1997	2,112	E	$23,000	5/06	SEWY	MFWD, front 3 pt., 3 hyd.
Ford-NH	7740	1994	2,800	G	$20,000	12/06	NWMO	2WD, CAH, 3 hyd., dual PTO, 16-speed shuttle, Westendorf 26 loader
Ford-NH	7740 SL			G	$13,500	9/06	NWTN	CAH, 12-spd. shuttle shift
Ford-NH	7740 SL	1994	2,929	G	$18,500	2/06	SWIN	Diesel, cab, weights, good tires, 2 hyd., radio, dual speed PTO
Ford-NH	7840			F	$9,300	1/06	NEIN	MFWD
Ford-NH	7840	1995	3,200	P	$13,000	2/06	WCIL	2WD, fully-equipped cab, Powerstar SL Series, 2 hyd., 3 pt., PTO
Ford-NH	8160	1998	825	G	$44,500	4/06	SEIA	MFWD, PS, one owner
Ford-NH	8210	1984	6,071	F	$7,250	5/06	SEWY	MFWD, Farmhand 1140 loader & grapple, diesel
Ford-NH	8260		2,273	G	$33,500	7/06	WCMN	MFWD, PS, Buhler 795 loader, 18.4-38
Ford-NH	8260	1997	2,885	G	$30,000	8/06	NCMI	MFWD, diesel, CAH, 100 hp., PS, reverser, 4 hyd., 18.4R-38

Tractors

Make	Model	Year	Hrs.	Cond.	Price	Sale	Location	Comments
Ford-NH	8670		900	G	$59,500	12/06	SWWI	MFWD
Ford-NH	8670	1993	5,092	G	$34,000	11/06	NEKS	Super Steer, powershift trans., 4 hyd., 1,000 PTO, 3 pt., 20.8R-38 rear tires, 420/85R28 front, 22 front end weights
Ford-NH	8670	1995	2,100	E	$40,000	7/06	ECIL	MFWD, Super Steer, duals
Ford-NH	8670	1995	2,111	E	$40,000	1/06	WCIL	2WD, PS, 3 hyd., 18.4R-38 duals
Ford-NH	8770	1995	6,100	G	$23,500	8/06	WCMN	2WD, 20.8-38 duals, 3 pt., PTO, front weights, quick coupler
Ford-NH	8770	1995	1,465	E	$50,000	3/06	NWMN	MFWD, CAH, PS, MegaFlow Super Steer, 4 hyd., 3 pt., PTO, front weights, 14.9-46 duals, 14.9-30 fronts, fenders
Ford-NH	8770	1998	5,400	G	$40,500	3/06	SCID	MFWD, Super Steer
Ford-NH	8830	1990		G	$15,500	11/06	WCMN	2WD, PS, 20.8-38 duals, 70% rubber
Ford-NH	8830	1990		G	$33,800	1/06	ECIL	MFWD, 170 hp., cab, air, PS, radar, 3 hyd., weights, 18.4R-42, axle duals, 16.9-28 fronts
Ford-NH	8830	1991	7,200	G	$11,000	11/06	WCMN	2WD, 170 hp., PS, cab, air, 3 pt., PTO, front weights, 18.4-42 duals, new paint
Ford-NH	8870	1996		F	$23,000	12/06	WCMN	MFWD, Super Steer, high hours
Ford-NH	8870	1996	4,450	G	$45,500	3/06	SEND	MFWD, Super Steer, MegaFlow, 4 hyd., 3 pt., PTO, front weights, 18.4-42 press steel duals, 14.9-30 fronts
Ford-NH	8870	1996	2,963	E	$54,000	3/06	SEND	MFWD, Super Steer, MegaFlow, 4 hyd., return flow, 3 pt., quick hitch, front suitcase weights, Firestone 18.4-42 press steel duals (80%), 16.9-28 fronts, front fenders, one owner
Ford-NH	8870	1997	2,700	G	$56,000	3/06	SCID	MFWD, Super Steer
Ford-NH	8870	1999	2,000	G	$58,000	3/06	SCID	MFWD, Super Steer
Ford-NH	8870	2001	1,180	E	$72,500	2/06	ECNE	Super Steer, radar, 4 hyd., MegaFlow hyd.
Ford-NH	8970	1995	6,527	G	$34,000	11/06	ECND	MFWD, PS, 4 hyd., Super Steer, MegaFlow, 3 pt., PTO, 320-90R50 rear press steel duals
Ford-NH	8970	1996	3,540	G	$45,000	4/06	SEMN	Canadian sale, 210 hp., 3-spool hyd. w/ extra flow line, front weights, 1,000 PTO
Ford-NH	9280	1995	3,400	E	$43,500	4/06	SWMB	Canadian sale, 4WD, Cummins 10-litre engine, 12-speed standard trans., 4 hyd., 20.8-38 duals, clamp-on triples available, shedded
Ford-NH	9282		3,708	F	$35,750	3/06	ECKS	4WD
Ford-NH	9282	1996	1,323	E	$48,000	3/06	NWMN	4WD, 12-speed gear, 4 hyd., 20.8-38 duals, one owner
Ford-NH	9480	1994	2,214	E	$61,000	1/06	NWKY	4WD, 3 pt., PTO
Ford-NH	9480	1995	3,244	G	$50,000	2/06	WCIL	4WD, 855 Cummins, 20.8-38 duals, 4 hyd.
Ford-NH	9482		1,575	G	$62,350	3/06	WCMN	4WD, M11 Cummins, 12 spd., 4 hyd., duals, weight pkg.
Ford-NH	9482	1997	4,400	G	$42,000	9/06	NCIA	4WD, duals
Ford-NH	9482	1997	2,097	G	$65,000	12/06	ECIL	4WD, bareback, 20.8R-42, Cummins M11, 4 hyd.
Ford-NH	9680	1994		G	$29,750	8/06	WCMN	4WD, 20.8-42 tires, 4 hyd., PTO, JD financing available
Ford-NH	9682		3,042	G	$51,000	9/06	NEIN	CAH, radio, duals, powershift
Ford-NH	9682	1998	4,422	G	$57,500	4/06	NEND	4WD, 12 speed, 4 hyd., monitor, 710/65R/38 duals, rear weights
Ford-NH	9684	2001	1,287	G	$71,000	4/06	NEND	4WD, front weights, 4 hyd., 710/70R duals, rear weights
Ford-NH	9880	1995	4,270	G	$46,000	7/06	SEND	4WD, 12-speed gear, 4 hyd., 20.8-42 triples
Ford-NH	TC21			G	$1,800	9/06	NWTN	4WD, ROPS
Ford-NH	TC21			G	$3,800	9/06	NWTN	4WD, ROPS
Ford-NH	TC24		402	E	$11,000	8/06	NWOH	12LA loader, 3 pt., PTO, 914A deck
Ford-NH	TC25		780	G	$11,600	8/06	SEMN	7308 loader
Ford-NH	TC33	1999		G	$6,700	12/06	ECMO	MFWD, open, diesel
Ford-NH	TC33D		27	G	$13,400	9/06	NWTN	4WD, NH 14LA front end loader, ROPS

Tractors

Make	Model	Year	Hrs.	Cond.	Price	Sale	Location	Comments
Ford-NH	TC33D			E	$14,600	1/06	SEPA	New, MFWD, 914A belly mower, 7308 loader, ROPS, hydro
Ford-NH	TC33D	2001	516	G	$11,000	12/06	NWMO	2WD, 3-speed hydro, NH 7308 loader w/ stick
Ford-NH	TC33D	2003	651	E	$11,000	2/06	SCPA	Like new, no options
Ford-NH	TC40			G	$14,750	8/06	SEPA	TC40A, MFWD, ROPS, front loader, good rubber
Ford-NH	TC40		150	G	$16,000	3/06	SEPA	MFWD, ROPS, #17LA loader, Super Steer, good rubber
Ford-NH	TC45	2004	308	E	$18,250	3/06	SWIN	MFWD, shuttle shift, roll bar canopy, 2004 Ford-NH 16LA front-end loader, 6' bucket & rear bale spear, all in like-new condition
Ford-NH	TG210		1,151	G	$0	12/06	SWWI	No sale at $74,000 – wanted $74,500, MFWD
Ford-NH	TG230	2003	3,019	G	$69,000	2/06	WCMN	MFWD, 3 pt. w/ quick hitch, 3-shaft PTO, 5 hyd., MegaFlow Super Steer, radar, duals
Ford-NH	TG255	2004	122	E	$90,000	2/06	WCMN	Super Steer, 4 hyd., deluxe cab, duals, 3 pt., differential lock, fenders, radar
Ford-NH	TG285	2004	260	E	$95,000	2/06	WCMN	Super Steer, 4 hyd., deluxe cab, duals, 3 pt., differential lock, fenders, radar
Ford-NH	TL90		1,621	G	$23,500	12/06	SWMI	MFWD, ROPS canopy, diesel, 18.4-34, 2 hyd., with NH 52LA loader w/ 7' material bucket
Ford-NH	TL90		307	G	$31,000	8/06	SETN	CAH, 4WD, NH 52LA front loader
Ford-NH	TL90	2004		G	$16,000	9/06	NWTN	4WD, ROPS, sunshade
Ford-NH	TL90	2004		G	$22,000	9/06	NWTN	CAH, NH 52LA loader
Ford-NH	TM125	2000	2,184	F	$30,500	3/06	WCMN	2WD, 3 pt., PTO, 2 hyd., shuttle trans., 18.4-38
Ford-NH	TM150	2000		G	$36,000	1/06	SESD	MFWD, loaded, 2000 model
Ford-NH	TM150			G	$39,000	11/06	NCKY	MFWD, cab, Ford 7312 front end loader
Ford-NH	TN65			G	$17,500	3/06	NCUT	NH 32LA loader
Ford-NH	TN75S	2001	1,725	G	$17,500	12/06	SEIA	MFWD, open station, Super Steer, creeper gears, shuttle shift, 3 pt., 2 hyd., joystick for loader, front weights
Ford-NH	TS115A		922	G	$42,750	12/06	SWWI	4WD, Westendorf 340 loader
Ford-NH	TS90		793	G	$23,500	7/06	WCMN	MFWD, open station, 3 pt., PTO, Buhler S595 loader, 14.9-24 fronts, 18.4-34 rear
Ford-Vers.	276		5,056	G	$18,750	10/06	NCND	Bidirectional, various heads, 3 pt. on both ends, loader w/ grapple
Ford-Vers.	276	1990	1,840	G	$28,500	6/06	SCMN	Bidirectional 4WD, cab, 3 hyd., 16.9-28 rubber all around
Ford-Vers.	846		4,818	G	$22,000	4/06	NEND	4WD, Designation 6, 12 speed, CAH, 4 hyd., 20.8-38 duals
Ford-Vers.	9030	1994	5,880	G	$28,000	11/06	ECND	Bidirectional, air, front & rear PTO, front & rear 3 pt., loader w/ bucket
Ford-Vers.	976		3,354	G	$33,000	4/06	ECND	Designation 6, duals, 4 hyd., air ride seat
Ford-Vers.	976	1988	8,504	G	$30,000	4/06	ECND	4WD, CAH, 4 hyd., duals
Ford-Vers.	976	1989	7,760	F	$18,500	3/06	NWKS	4WD, Cummins remanufactured motor, 2,500 hours on new motor, 12-speed PS, 24.5-32 tires, 4 hyd., 1,000 PTO, new hinge pins
Ford-Vers.	976	1991	5,020	G	$32,000	11/06	ECND	4WD, 12-speed gear, CAH, 4 hyd., return flow, differential lock front, performance monitor, 20.8-42 duals, annual work check, 1,000 hours on lower end OH, 500 hours on clutch & bearings pump & injector
Ford-Vers.	TV140		5,100	G	$42,000	1/06	SESD	4WD, loader grapple, 3 pt., PTO
Ford-Vers.	TV140	1998	5,082	G	$32,000	3/06	SWKS	Bidirectional MFWD, w/ 7614 loader, 3 hyd., 3 pt., 8' bucket and grapple, 540 front PTO
Ford-Vers.	TV140	1999	5,207	G	$37,500	5/06	SEND	CAH, hydro, front/rear, 3 pt., front/real differential lock, 3 hyd., 2 hyd., 3 pt., PTO, hd 7614 loader, 5-tine grapple

Tractors

Make	Model	Year	Hrs.	Cond.	Price	Sale	Location	Comments
Ford-Vers.	TV140	1999	3,400	G	$49,000	4/06	SEMN	Canadian sale, 540 & 1,000 PTO, Quickie 7614 loader, 8' bucket & pallet fork, 3-pt. hitch, weights
Ford-Vers.	TV140	2000	1,700	G	$42,000	12/06	SCQB	Canadian sale, bidirectional 4WD, 5 hyd., cab, PTO, 3 pt., converts to $36,662 U.S.
Ford-Vers.	TV140	2002	520	G	$53,000	12/06	SCQB	Canadian sale, bidirectional 4WD, 2 hyd., cab, 3 hyd., PTO, 3 pt., 480/85R34 tires, converts to $46,264 U.S.
Ford-Vers.	TV140	2002	755	G	$55,000	2/06	WCIL	Bidirectional 4WD, fully-equipped cab, 3 pt., PTO, Ford-NH 7614 loader, like new
Hesston	1880	1982	5,965	G	$5,500	8/06	NEKS	MFWD, 20.8-38 clamp on duals, 1,000 PTO, Leon 10' hyd. front blade, 3 hyd., one owner
Hesston	666		4,679	F	$5,000	12/06	SEMN	DT, MFWD
Hinomoto	C172			G	$3,500	5/06	SWCA	20 hp., diesel, PTO, 3 pt., front loader
IHC	1086			G	$6,000	2/06	WCME	Cab, 12 front weights
IHC	1086			F	$6,300	3/06	NWIL	Diesel, TA out
IHC	1086		1,332	F	$7,500	4/06	NWKS	2 hyd., 3 pt., 540/1,000 PTO, 4-spd. hydro, 1,332 hours on tach (not actual), runs good
IHC	1086		8,600	F	$8,600	2/06	NWSD	Cab, air, 3 hyd., 3 pt., extra lights, good rubber, 20.8-38
IHC '	1086			G	$8,750	3/06	NWIL	Diesel
IHC	1086			F	$9,100	1/06	SESD	CAH, 3 pt., Farmhand 358 loader grapple
IHC	1086		6,980	F	$10,750	2/06	NENE	2 hyd., 300 hours on OH
IHC	1086		5,841		$11,500	2/06	WCIL	Cab, duals
IHC	1086		527	G	$15,200	9/06	SCMN	CAH, diesel, one owner, 3 pt., 2 hyd., 540/1,000
IHC	1086			G	$15,250	3/06	NCOH	CAH, 1 hour on major OH at 12,387 total hours
IHC	1086	1976	5,095	G	$7,100	3/06	NWOH	Cab, 3 pt., 2 hyd., dual PTO, 8 front weights, snap-on duals
IHC	1086	1977	4,273	G	$11,700	1/06	NWIA	Cab, air ride seat, WF, 3 pt., dual hyd, PTO
IHC	1086	1977	3,270	E	$15,300	3/06	NCIL	CAH, 2 hyd., dual PTO, 18.4-38 axle-mount duals, one owner
IHC	1086	1978	7,092	F	$9,900	1/06	NWIL	18.4R-38 hub duals
IHC	1086	1978	4,665	G	$14,000	12/06	WCIL	Fully-equipped cab, 540/1,000 PTO, 2 hyd.
IHC	1086	1978	4,825	G	$14,100	12/06	WCIL	Fully-equipped cab, 540/1,000 PTO, 2 hyd.
IHC	1086	1979	8,560	G	$4,700	1/06	WCNE	WF, needs glass in cab
IHC	1086	1979	9,700	G	$7,000	7/06	NWMN	CAH, 3 hyd., 3 pt., 540/1,000 PTO, front suitcase weights, 14.9-38 singles
IHC	1086	1979	9,700	G	$7,500	7/06	NWMN	CAH, 3 hyd., 3 pt., front suitcase weights, 540/1,000 PTO, engine OH
IHC	1086	1979	4,700	P	$10,000	2/06	ECNE	
IHC	1086	1979	4,282	G	$13,100	11/06	SCNE	Red power, CAH, 3 hyd., diesel
IHC	1086	1979	5,125	E	$20,500	1/06	NEIA	Red power, WF, 3 pt., 2 hyd., air, 2 PTOs, new BFG
IHC	1086	1980	3,525	G	$11,900	2/06	WCNE	Diesel, cab, 3 pt., front weights
IHC	1086	1981	4,300	G	$13,000	9/06	NEIN	Diesel, factory CAH, duals, good rubber
IHC	1086	1981	5,509	G	$13,700	2/06	NCCO	One owner, cab, air, 3 hyd., 18.4-38, axle duals
IHC	1086	1981	3,766	E	$15,500	2/06	NEMO	Cab, WF, front weights, duals, 2 hyd., 18.4-38 tires, real sharp, clean
IHC	1486			G	$4,750	2/06	WCME	Cab, 12 front weights
IHC	1486			F	$5,100	11/06	WCMN	2 hyd., 3 pt., PTO
IHC	1486			F	$5,200	3/06	SEPA	MFWD, CAH, bad TA, average rubber
IHC	1486			F	$5,700	3/06	NCMN	
IHC	1486		7,800	G	$7,100	12/06	WCMN	Duals, 3 pt., PTO, 2 hyd., cab, one owner
IHC	1486			F	$7,750	8/06	NCIA	Cab, air, front weights, 2 PTO, quick coupler, 2 valves
IHC	1486			F	$8,700	1/06	SESD	CAH, 3 pt.

Tractors

Make	Model	Year	Hrs.	Cond.	Price	Sale	Location	Comments
IHC	1486	1976	4,108	G	$11,600	2/06	WCKS	Cab
IHC	1486	1978	4,788	G	$14,250	2/06	NWIL	Fully-equipped cab, dual PTO
IHC	1486	1979	5,785	G	$8,200	8/06	ECNE	18.4-38 rear tires w/ 10-bolt duals, 11:00-16 front tires, 3 hyd., 540/1,000 PTO, 6 front end weights on bracket, hyd. seat
IHC	1486	1980	4,200	G	$9,400	11/06	SCIL	New air weights, duals
IHC	1486	1981		G	$10,100	8/06	NWOH	Cab, 2 hyd., 3 pt., duals, 1,760 hours on tach
IHC	1486	1981	4,534	G	$13,750	1/06	ECNE	3 pt., 3 hyd., dual PTO, 20.8-38
IHC	1568			G	$10,200	3/06	NWIL	Diesel, duals, weights
IHC	1586			F	$6,500	3/06	SEPA	WF, cab, new TA & clutch, duals, fair rubber
IHC	1586		5,537	F	$6,800	4/06	SWOH	CAH, 18.4-38, bolt-on duals
IHC	1586			F	$7,700	1/06	SEPA	WF, TA not working, fair rubber
IHC	1586			F	$8,250	3/06	NCMN	
IHC	1586			G	$8,500	3/06	NWIL	New TA
IHC	1586			G	$9,750	3/06	NWIL	Diesel, duals, weights
IHC	1586		3,384	G	$9,800	4/06	SWIN	3 hyd., 540 & 1,000 PTO, CAH, 20.8-38 tires
IHC	1586		5,400	G	$10,000	11/06	SCIL	200 hours on OH & new TA, 18.4-42 tires, weights, duals
IHC	1586		5,700	G	$11,500	8/06	NWOH	Cab, duals, 3 pt., 2 hyd.
IHC	1586	1976	7,552	F	$7,300	3/06	NEKS	2 hyd., 18.4-38, 14L-16.1 front tires
IHC	1586	1977		F	$4,000	8/06	NCNE	Duals, $1,500 spent on AC
IHC	1586	1977	4,242	G	$8,000	3/06	NWOH	Cab, 3 pt., 6 front weights, 2 hyd., snap-on duals
IHC	1586	1979	4,691	E	$14,750	8/06	NCIA	New 18.4-38R duals, front rock box
IHC	1586	1981	2,300	E	$15,750	9/06	NCIA	Cab, 18.4R-38 duals
IHC	1586	1981	3,893	G	$16,800	3/06	NCIL	2 hyd., like-new 20.8-38 tires w/ axle-mount duals, one owner
IHC	1600	1977		G	$3,800	2/06	SEIL	5×2 spd., 15' bed & hoist
IHC	184	1986		G	$4,550	3/06	SEND	Cadet Low Boy, w/ 5' mower
IHC	185	1977		G	$3,100	3/06	SEND	Cadet Low Boy w/ 5' mower
IHC	234			G	$3,200	8/06	SCIL	Diesel, hydro trans., F35 60" mower, float tires
IHC	2400		1,799	F	$2,500	1/06	NEIN	Series B
IHC	2500			F	$3,500	3/06	NWOH	Industrial, gas, 3 pt., with 3050 loader, tach says 3,342 hours
IHC	2500			G	$4,000	8/06	SCIL	Cab, painted, yellow
IHC	254			G	$4,050	3/06	NWIL	Diesel, MFWD
IHC	284	1978	1,362	G	$5,000	9/06	NEND	Utility, 3 pt., PTO, 72" belly-mount mower
IHC	3288		5,200	G	$9,400	4/06	SCMN	2WD, 18.4-34, poor paint, good mechanically
IHC	3388		6,044	F	$5,000	8/06	NWIL	2+2, cab, air, 3 pt., 1,000/540 PTO, 3 hyd.
IHC	3388	1981		P	$4,000	8/06	NEKS	2+2, rough
IHC	3488	1984	5,800	G	$13,250	11/06	WCMN	Hydro, 112 hp., cab, air, 3 hyd., 3 pt., 540/1,000 PTO
IHC	354	1972	2,622	F	$750	10/06	NECO	3 pt., WF, gas
IHC	3588	1978		F	$5,500	7/06	SEND	2+2, 4 hyd., 3 pt., PTO, 16.9-38 hub duals, unknown hours (tach changed)
IHC	3588	1979	5,525	F	$5,200	11/06	NEKS	4WD, synchro trans., 18 forward and 8 reverse, 3 pt., 1,000 PTO
IHC	3588	1979	6,328	G	$6,000	9/06	NWMN	2+2, 4WD, CAH, 3 pt., 1,000 PTO, 3 hyd., 18.4-38 (60%), recent rebuild on final drives
IHC	3588	1979	3,615	F	$11,400	1/06	NEIN	
IHC	3588	1981		F	$6,300	3/06	SEND	2+2, recent OH, CAH, 3 pt., 1,000 rpm PTO, 18.4-38 hub duals
IHC	3788			F	$4,200	12/06	SEMN	2+2
IHC	3788		3,529	F	$5,800	10/06	SEMN	2+2, 4WD, 3 pt., 3 hyd., 540/1,000 PTO, good TA

WHAT'S IT WORTH?

Tractors

Make	Model	Year	Hrs.	Cond.	Price	Sale	Location	Comments
IHC	4386	1977	6,358	G	$9,000	12/06	WCIL	4WD, 3 pt., 2 hyd.
IHC	4586	1981	2,432	G	$8,500	9/06	WCOH	4WD, CAH, duals, cab rebuilt, 3 hyd.
IHC	5088			F	$8,750	8/06	SEMN	2WD
IHC	5088	1981	2,155	F	$9,750	3/06	NEKS	18.4-38 clamp on duals, 3 hyd., 3 pt., 540/1,000 PTO, 1,000 rear wheel weights, 7 front end weights, cab redone
IHC	5088	1982	4,042	G	$11,500	2/06	WCKS	Duals, quick hitch
IHC	5088	1983		E	$14,250	3/06	NEKS	Good rubber & paint
IHC	5288		5,478	G	$8,650	11/06	SCNE	2WD, 3 hyd., front weights
IHC	5288	1981	6,218	G	$19,000	1/06	NEMO	
IHC	5288	1983	5,636	G	$16,600	4/06	NWMN	CAH, 18 speed/6 reverse, 3 hyd., power beyond, 3 pt., 540/1,000 PTO, front weights, 14.9-46 press steel duals, 75% rubber
IHC	5488			F	$4,250	1/06	SEPA	WF, poor rubber
IHC	5488		3,543	G	$16,800	6/06	NWIL	Full set of front weights, 3 hyd.
IHC	5488	1984	6,804	G	$14,500	2/06	WCKS	MFWD, duals
IHC	584		3,000	G	$6,100	11/06	NCKY	Diesel
IHC	584		1,800	E	$12,300	12/06	SCIA	Westendorf loader, sharp
IHC	584	1980	2,881	G	$6,300	12/06	ECMO	Loader, 2WD
IHC	6788		5,218	G	$8,800	3/06	NWIL	2+2, duals, diesel
IHC	6788		6,600	F	$10,900	2/06	ECNE	2+2, rubber electric tandem axle, 3 hyd., duals
IHC	684	1984	2,200	G	$11,500	2/06	WCIL	Utility, 540 PTO, 3 pt., IHC 2250 front end loader, material bucket, manure forks
IHC	686			G	$4,600	9/06	NCIA	
IHC	686			F	$6,700	11/06	WCMN	Loader, work orders available
IHC	784			G	$9,900	3/06	NWIL	Utility, IHC 2255 loader, 3 pt., dual PTO, diesel
IHC	786			F	$7,100	1/06	SEPA	WF, good rubber
IHC	786	1981	2,302	E	$13,600	8/06	NWOH	MFWD, cab, 3 pt., 2 hyd.
IHC	884	1984		G	$8,300	1/06	NWKY	Loader
IHC	884	1988	2,900	G	$9,500	8/06	NWIL	IHC 2255 loader, diesel
IHC	886		6,488	F	$5,100	9/06	SCMN	CAH, diesel, 3 pt., 2 hyd., 540/1,000
IHC	886	1981	2,121	G	$13,000	3/06	NWOH	Cab, 3 hyd., 3 pt., 5 front weights, dual PTO, snap-on duals
IHC	986			G	$5,500	9/06	NWTN	Cab, front loader
IHC	986		6,500	F	$9,750	2/06	NENE	3 hyd.
IHC	986		4,796	G	$10,800	10/06	NEIA	Cab, duals
IHC	986		4,065	G	$11,000	4/06	SWIN	CAH, 2 hyd., 540 & 1,000 PTO, 18.4-38 tires
IHC	986		4,900	F	$14,500	3/06	SEPA	WF, cab, average rubber
IHC	986	1973	9,625	F	$5,000	8/06	NWIL	Cab, air, WF, 1,000 and 540 PTO, dual outlets
IHC	986	1976	5,202	G	$10,300	11/06	SCNE	Diesel, CAH, 3 hyd.
IHC	986	1977	8,750	F	$6,300	7/06	SEND	Gear trans., 2 hyd., 3 pt., 540/1,000 PTO, 18.4-38
IHC	986	1977	2,327	E	$17,000	3/06	ECMI	2WD, factory CAH, 18.4-38 axle duals, digital tach
IHC	986	1979	3,944	F	$8,900	1/06	NCCO	Axle duals, 2 hyd., 540/1,000 PTO
IHC	986	1979	6,165	F	$9,800	3/06	NWOH	Cab, 3 pt., dual PTO, 3 hyd.
IHC	986	1979	2,546	E	$15,000	11/06	SENE	Last 1979 model made, 18.4-38 rear, 10:00-16 4 ribbed front tires, 2 hyd., 540/1,000 PTO, 3 pt., front end weight bracket, cab, air, AM/FM, new batteries, shedded
IHC	986	1981	4,367	F	$7,600	9/06	SCMN	Close center hyd.
IHC	Hydro 100		5,117	F	$6,000	2/06	WCIL	Hydro, factory cab, 2 hyd., weak hydro
IHC	Hydro 84		6,300	F	$2,700	8/06	SEPA	Diesel, WF, fair rubber
IHC	Hydro 84		1,600	G	$13,900	1/06	SCMN	Hydro utility, adjustable bar axle, IHC 2250 hydraulic loader

Tractors

Make	Model	Year	Hrs.	Cond.	Price	Sale	Location	Comments
IHC	Hydro 86			G	$8,500	11/06	WCSD	Hydro diesel, one owner, Farmhand F11 loader with bale fork & 8' snow scoop
Iseki	1610			G	$4,250	11/06	SWCA	4WD, loader
John Deere	1050		1,600	F	$5,100	1/06	SEPA	MFWD, fair turf rubber
John Deere	1050		1,600	G	$7,100	8/06	SEPA	2WD, JD 75 loader, WF, ROPS, average rubber
John Deere	1050			G	$9,700	5/06	ECMN	2WD, JD 75 hyd. loader, diesel
John Deere	1050	1983		E	$8,900	10/06	NECO	2WD, JD 75 loader, 6' blade, 3 pt., diesel, tach shows 1,434 hours
John Deere	1070		400	G	$9,950	3/06	SEPA	JD 440 loader, ROPS, turf rubber
John Deere	1250	1984	2,326	G	$8,100	8/06	NCMI	MFWD, JD 3100 hyd. loader, material bucket, ROPS canopy, diesel
John Deere	2040			F	$4,150	1/06	SEPA	WF, average rubber
John Deere	2040			F	$4,400	8/06	SEPA	Diesel, WF, average rubber, ROPS
John Deere	2150			G	$2,850	8/06	WCNC	
John Deere	2155			G	$6,000	8/06	SETN	ROPS
John Deere	2155			G	$6,200	8/06	SETN	ROPS
John Deere	2210		89	G	$10,750	9/06	NEIN	4WD, loader, diesel, hydrostatic trans., JD belly mower, JD 210 loader, 4' box scraper, 4' grader blade
John Deere	2210	2004	33	G	$10,000	2/06	WCOH	MFWD, compact, JD 210 loader
John Deere	2240			G	$2,750	10/06	SWOH	Diesel, 3 pt., gp bucket, manual trans
John Deere	2240			G	$7,850	3/06	NWIL	Diesel
John Deere	2240	1977		G	$8,250	3/06	NWMN	Open station, ROPS, 8 speed, 2 hyd., 3 pt., PTO, quick hitch, front weights, 14.9-38 singles
John Deere	2350			G	$5,200	8/06	SETN	
John Deere	2350			G	$5,500	1/06	WCCA	Front weights, mounted cultivator, canopy, 3 pt, 2 hyd.
John Deere	2350		2,000	F	$10,000	3/06	SEPA	2WD, WF, fair rubber
John Deere	2350			G	$10,500	8/06	SETN	ROPS, canopy
John Deere	2350		4,000	F	$13,000	3/06	SEPA	MFWD, JD 245 loader, ROPS, fair rubber
John Deere	2350	1984	5,000	F	$12,200	2/06	NCCO	2WD, 245 loader, CAH, 2 hyd., 16.9-30 tires
John Deere	2355		6,900	F	$14,750	2/06	SCPA	MFWD, hi/lo, JD 265 loader, open station
John Deere	2355			G	$17,800	8/06	SEPA	520 loader, WF, CAH, fair rubber
John Deere	2440		6,997	G	$7,750	3/06	NCWI	Good rubber, 2 hyd.
John Deere	2440		8,911	F	$9,000	2/06	SCPA	2WD, hi/lo, JD 146 loader
John Deere	2440	1979		G	$10,750	11/06	NCIN	145 loader, open station, 16.9-28 tires
John Deere	2550		10,691	F	$11,000	2/06	SCPA	MFWD, hi/lo, open station, JD 246 loader
John Deere	2550			F	$11,300	1/06	SEPA	2WD, WF, CAH, fair rubber
John Deere	2550			F	$13,700	3/06	SEPA	2WD, WF, CAH, average rubber
John Deere	2550		4,676	G	$17,700	2/06	NEIN	MFWD, open station, JD 245 loader, self-leveling, 2 hyd.
John Deere	2550	1983	7,711	G	$10,750	11/06	WCMN	MFWD, cab, 8-speed synchro trans., 16.9-30 tires
John Deere	2640			F	$2,500	1/06	WCCA	Canopy, 3 pt., 2 hyd.
John Deere	2640			F	$3,500	8/06	SCFL	OROPS
John Deere	2640			G	$5,300	3/06	NEKS	Good rubber
John Deere	2640			G	$7,150	12/06	NWIL	WF, cab, diesel, 4,000 hours
John Deere	2640			F	$8,000	2/06	SCPA	2WD, hi/lo, Tiger stripe
John Deere	2640			G	$9,900	3/06	SCIN	Loader
John Deere	2640			G	$9,900	3/06	SCIN	Loader
John Deere	2750			P	$1,500	1/06	WCCA	Mudder, front weights, canopy, 3 pt., PTO, 2 hyd.
John Deere	2750			G	$10,000	3/06	NWIL	Diesel, MFWD, 245 loader
John Deere	2750			G	$13,100	8/06	SEPA	MFWD, CAH, fair rubber
John Deere	2755			F	$5,000	1/06	WCCA	Mudder, front weights, canopy, 3 pt., 2 hyd.

WHAT'S IT WORTH?

Tractors

Make	Model	Year	Hrs.	Cond.	Price	Sale	Location	Comments
John Deere	2755			F	$6,750	1/06	WCCA	Mudder, front weights, canopy, 3 pt., 2 hyd.
John Deere	2755			F	$8,000	1/06	WCCA	Mudder, front weights, canopy, 3 pt., 2 hyd.
John Deere	2755			F	$8,700	1/06	SEPA	2WD, WF, ROPS, average rubber
John Deere	2755			G	$9,200	3/06	ECIN	Diesel, 3 pt.
John Deere	2755			G	$10,800	10/06	WCFL	
John Deere	2755		3,183	G	$18,500	11/06	SCNE	No cab, 8 speed
John Deere	2755	1990		G	$8,000	7/06	WCCA	Mudder, front weights, canopy, creeper gear, 3 pt., PTO, 2 hyd.
John Deere	2755	1990	3,057	G	$10,500	8/06	SETN	ROPS, sunshade
John Deere	2755	1990		G	$14,000	12/06	SCMN	MFWD
John Deere	2840			G	$3,500	7/06	WCCA	Front weights, canopy, 3 pt., PTO, 2 hyd.
John Deere	2840			G	$5,400	6/06	ECSD	
John Deere	2840	1979	6,335	F	$5,500	11/06	WCMN	2WD, 18.4-34, tach shows 3,335 hours, 6,335 actual hours
John Deere	2840	1979	10,000	G	$7,300	9/06	WCND	10,000+ hours, hyd. shuttle shift, 2 hyd., 3 pt., 540/1,000 PTO
John Deere	2840	1979	1,221	G	$10,500	3/06	NCIL	2 hyd., PTO, 18.4-34
John Deere	2940			G	$12,250	12/06	SEMN	MFWD, ROPS, showing 10,833 hours, 2 hyd., 18.4-34 tires
John Deere	2940		5,539	G	$13,500	2/06	WCMN	MFWD, 3 pt. (never used), PTO, 2 hyd., w/ JD 260 self-leveling quick-tach loader, 84" bucket and grapple assembly, less than 400 hours on PTO and 2 spd. hi/lo
John Deere	2940	1980	6,742	G	$6,000	11/06	WCMN	2WD, 2 hyd.
John Deere	2950			G	$8,750	8/06	SETN	ROPS, sunshade
John Deere	2950			G	$23,000	8/06	SEPA	MFWD, JD 740 loader, average rubber, CAH
John Deere	2950	1984	6,252	G	$9,000	12/06	ECMO	2WD, canopy, hi-low trans.
John Deere	2950	1984	3,265	G	$20,500	3/06	ECIL	MFWD, JD 260 loader, 6' quick-attach bucket, 4' pallet forks, joystick controls, ROPS w/ canopy, front & rear weights, quick hitch
John Deere	2955			G	$12,750	8/06	SEPA	2WD, ROPS, WF, average rubber
John Deere	2955	1987	4,573	G	$25,500	4/06	WCWI	2WD, cab, air, 2 hyd., 3 pt., JD 720 loader
John Deere	2955	1990	6,100	G	$14,500	12/06	NWWI	2WD, JD 265 SL loader, 540/1,000 PTO, 18.4-38
John Deere	301			F	$2,250	8/06	NWOH	Gas, 3 pt., PTO, WF
John Deere	301			G	$2,750	7/06	ECNY	Compact, utility, diesel, roadside sicklebar mower
John Deere	3055		9,397	G	$13,500	6/06	SCMN	2WD, cab, 2 hyd., 3 pt., 540 PTO
John Deere	3055		3,300	F	$16,800	3/06	SEPA	2WD, WF, ROPS, average rubber, hi/low
John Deere	3055	1993	3,716	E	$23,000	11/06	SEIA	2WD, cab, air
John Deere	3150			G	$11,500	10/06	SWOH	MFWD, JD 120 hp., diesel, 3 pt., canopy
John Deere	3150		8,600	F	$23,500	2/06	SCPA	MFWD, 4 post, 10 front weights
John Deere	3155		5,100	F	$19,000	3/06	SEPA	MFWD, CAH, rebuilt hi/low, good rubber
John Deere	3320		400	G	$14,750	8/06	SETN	4WD, CAH
John Deere	4040			F	$6,000	1/06	WCCA	MFWD, front weights, canopy, synchro trans., 3 pt.
John Deere	4040			G	$15,600	3/06	NWIL	Diesel, weights
John Deere	4040		6,635	G	$19,900	1/06	SCMN	PS, cab, diesel, second owner, 3 pt.
John Deere	4040		4,220	G	$23,500	3/06	ECNE	Quad range, 16.9-38, 11l-15 front tires, 2 hyd., rear wheel weights, 6 front end weights, sound guard cab
John Deere	4040	1980	3,394	G	$19,000	8/06	NECO	PS, 3 hyd., 3 pt., PTO, 18.4-38, JD 158 loader
John Deere	4040	1980	5,350	G	$21,000	4/06	WCMT	JD 158 loader w/ 7' bucket, CAH, diesel, 90 hp., 16-spd. quad range, 3 pt., dual PTO, 2 hyd., 18.4-34, long axles
John Deere	4050			G	$18,000	3/06	NCUT	2WD, PS
John Deere	4050	1983		G	$17,500	11/06	SEIA	2WD, cab, air, quad range

Tractors

Make	Model	Year	Hrs.	Cond.	Price	Sale	Location	Comments
John Deere	4050	1983		G	$23,000	8/06	NECO	MFWD, PS, JD 265 loader
John Deere	4050	1985	4,481	G	$22,000	8/06	SETN	CAH, PS
John Deere	4100		907	G	$5,250	11/06	SWCA	4WD, diesel, loader, rear scraper
John Deere	4100		315	G	$6,300	9/06	NWTN	4WD, 60" mower, hydro drive
John Deere	4100		383	F	$6,600	2/06	WCIL	MFWD, ROPS, 3 pt., PTO, JD 410 loader, 54" belly mower
John Deere	410D			G	$7,500	5/06	SWCA	Canopy
John Deere	4110	2002	1,028	G	$7,600	11/06	NEKS	MFWD utility, hydro, 3 pt., 60" belly-mounted mower
John Deere	4115			G	$6,500	9/06	WCTX	Diesel, belly mower, box blade
John Deere	4120		40	G	$19,800	8/06	SEPA	Warranty, 400X front end loader, MFWD, ROPS, good rubber
John Deere	4120	2005	10	G	$14,000	8/06	SCNE	MFWD, 12 spd., ROPS, 3 pt., warranty, 17.5L24 tires
John Deere	4200			G	$7,000	9/06	WCTX	Diesel, 3-pt. hitch, loader
John Deere	4200		507	G	$10,300	12/06	SWWI	JD 420 loader, mower
John Deere	4200		300	G	$12,500	1/06	SEPA	MFWD, JD 430 loader, belly mower, hydro, turf rubber
John Deere	4240		2,132	F	$6,000	8/06	SCFL	OROPS, PS
John Deere	4240			G	$10,000	5/06	SCCA	Front weights, cab, air, PS, 3 pt., PTO, 2 hyd
John Deere	4240			F	$12,000	3/06	NCUT	Quad range
John Deere	4240		4,300	F	$15,400	9/06	NWIL	JD 148 loader, diesel
John Deere	4240		7,300	G	$16,500	2/06	NEIA	Open station
John Deere	4240			E	$17,500	3/06	NEKS	Quad range, good rubber & paint
John Deere	4240		8,900	F	$18,250	2/06	NEIA	Quad range
John Deere	4240		5,769	G	$18,600	3/06	WCMN	Cad, quad range, duals, 2 PTOs, 3 hyd., rock box
John Deere	4240		4,750	G	$18,750	3/06	SENE	Diesel, cab
John Deere	4240		9,598	F	$19,000	10/06	NCKS	Rough appearance, PS, 3 pt., PTO, 2 hyd., JD 158 loader and grapple, 1,000 hours on major OH
John Deere	4240		6,952	G	$20,600	2/06	WCOH	Cab, air, 600 hours on complete OH, axle duals
John Deere	4240	1978		F	$18,000	2/06	NCIL	CAH
John Deere	4240	1978	5,273	G	$18,500	12/06	SCMN	Quad range
John Deere	4240	1978	3,229	G	$26,000	3/06	SWNE	PS, 3 hyd., PTO, JD 158 loader w/ grapple fork, 18.4R-34
John Deere	4240	1979	7,860	P	$11,500	7/06	ECND	3 pt., PTO, 3 hyd.
John Deere	4240	1980	8,500	G	$14,500	7/06	WCMN	Quad range, cab, air
John Deere	4240	1980	7,437	G	$16,700	6/06	ECND	CAH, PS, 2 hyd., 3 pt., 18.4-38 press steel duals, inside weights
John Deere	4240	1980	6,782	G	$18,500	2/06	WCIL	Quad range, sound guard body, 2 hyd., front weights, R134 air, 18.4-38, like-new tires
John Deere	4240	1980	5,070	G	$22,600	12/06	NWIL	Quad range, 3 pt., one owner, duals, wide space
John Deere	4240	1981	6,269	G	$14,850	8/06	WCIL	Quad range, 2 hyd.
John Deere	4240	1981		G	$18,750	9/06	NCIA	Fresh engine OH
John Deere	4240	1982	5,050	G	$23,000	3/06	NCCO	
John Deere	4240	1982	3,183	G	$25,750	2/06	NWIN	Cab, air, PS
John Deere	4250		4,183	G	$24,000	8/06	NWOH	2WD, cab, quick hitch, 3 pt., 2 hyd., quad range, 12 front weights
John Deere	4250		6,794	G	$24,500	4/06	NEND	2WD, PS, 20.8-38 duals
John Deere	4250		4,451	G	$32,000	11/06	SCNE	2WD, quad range, cab, 2 hyd., 18.4-38
John Deere	4250	1983	9,022	G	$24,750	8/06	NCIA	PS, 2WD, cab, air, 2 hyd., quick coupler
John Deere	4250	1986	11,300	G	$22,000	11/06	ECND	MFWD, PS, 3 hyd., 3 pt., 540/1,000 PTO, 60 Series step, 18.4-38 singles
John Deere	4250	1986	5,641	G	$30,000	3/06	ECND	2WD, CAH, 15-speed ps, 3 hyd., 3 pt., PTO, 18.4-38 press steel duals, Michelin radials, 95% rubber

WHAT'S IT WORTH?

Tractors

Make	Model	Year	Hrs.	Cond.	Price	Sale	Location	Comments
John Deere	4250	1987	1,555	E	$44,000	11/06	SENE	2WD, quad range, 3 hyd., 18.4R-38 rear tires, 10:00-16, front, sound guard cab, 8 front end weights
John Deere	4250	1988	6,891	G	$25,500	1/06	NEIN	2WD, cab, air, quad range
John Deere	4255		6,454	F	$11,500	8/06	SCFL	2WD, high crop, cab, PS
John Deere	4255		5,627	F	$15,000	8/06	SCFL	2WD, cab, 20.8×38
John Deere	4255		2,267	F	$16,000	8/06	SCFL	2WD, cab, 20.8×38
John Deere	4255		6,600	F	$27,000	12/06	SWWI	MFWD, quad range
John Deere	4255		6,240	G	$28,500	11/06	SCNE	2WD, cab, quad range, 3 hyd., duals, front weights, quick hitch
John Deere	4255	1989		G	$12,500	7/06	WCCA	Canopy, PS, rear weights
John Deere	4255	1989		G	$12,500	7/06	WCCA	Front weights, canopy, 3 pt., 3 hyd.
John Deere	4255	1990		G	$13,500	7/06	WCCA	MFWD, front weights, cab, air, PS, 2 hyd.
John Deere	4255	1990		G	$13,500	7/06	WCCA	MFWD, front weights, cab, air, PS, 2 hyd.
John Deere	4255	1990		G	$17,500	7/06	WCCA	Front weights, cab, air, PS, 3 pt.
John Deere	4255	1990		G	$17,500	7/06	WCCA	Front weights, cab, air, PS, 3 pt.
John Deere	4255	1990		G	$18,000	7/06	WCCA	Canopy, front weights, PS
John Deere	4255	1990		G	$21,000	7/06	WCCA	Front weights, cab, air, PS, 3 pt.
John Deere	4255	1990		G	$21,000	7/06	WCCA	Front weights, cab, air, PS, 3 pt.
John Deere	4255	1990	3,540	G	$24,750	5/06	SEWY	2WD, JD 265 loader w/ grapple
John Deere	4255	1991	641	E	$56,200	2/06	SWNY	MFWD, PS, 3 hyd., 20.8-38 duals, 14 front weights, 2,000 lbs. in rear weights, radar, quick hitch, like new
John Deere	4300		983	G	$9,500	1/06	SCTN	TLB, 4WD
John Deere	4300	2000		G	$7,000	9/06	WCTX	Diesel, loader
John Deere	4310		800	G	$13,500	3/06	SEPA	MFWD, JD 420 loader, average rubber
John Deere	4400		2,700	F	$6,000	9/06	NCOH	Compact tractor w/ 4WD, 3 pt., PS, aux. hyd.
John Deere	4400			G	$11,600	1/06	SEPA	MFWD, JD 430 loader, good rubber
John Deere	4400		844	E	$21,250	2/06	ECMN	4WD compact, 35 hp., hydro trans., PTO, 3 pt., 72" mower deck, joystick, one owner
John Deere	4410	2003	225	G	$9,750	11/06	NEKS	MFWD, utility, 12.4-24 rear tires, 540 PTO, 3 pt., JD 430 loader
John Deere	4410	2004	297	E	$14,300	12/06	WCMN	MFWD, JD 430 loader, diesel, ROPS, 3 pt.
John Deere	4440			F	$10,900	3/06	SEPA	WF, PS, CAH, average rubber
John Deere	4440			G	$11,000	5/06	SCCA	Front weights, cab, air, PS, 3 pt., rear weights
John Deere	4440			F	$12,000	12/06	NWWI	Open station, quad range
John Deere	4440			G	$14,000	8/06	NWOH	Cab, 3 pt., 2 hyd., quad range
John Deere	4440			G	$14,000	8/06	NWOH	Cab, 3 pt., 2 hyd., quad range, 6 front weights, axle duals, 2,500 hours on OH
John Deere	4440		7,000	P	$15,700	1/06	NEIA	Rough
John Deere	4440		7,790	G	$18,000	3/06	ECND	Quad range, 3 hyd., power beyond, 3 pt., 540/1,000 PTO, 14.9-46 band duals w/ inside cast
John Deere	4440		8,500	G	$23,250	7/06	SEND	Quad range, 3 hyd., 3 pt., hub duals, JD 725 quick-tach loader, joystick control, extra clean
John Deere	4440			G	$26,400	11/06	SCMN	
John Deere	4440		2,231	G	$28,500	8/06	SCMN	540/1,000 PTO, PS, quick hitch, 2 hyd., duals
John Deere	4440	1978		F	$10,000	9/06	SEIA	Quad range, 2 hyd.
John Deere	4440	1978		F	$15,000	12/06	NWWI	PS, $18K spent on reconditioning in 2003, 20.8-38 tires
John Deere	4440	1978	9,825	G	$16,250	3/06	ECMI	CAH, 500 hours on JD OH, 2 hyd., PS, 18.4-38
John Deere	4440	1978	8,492	F	$17,000	3/06	NCCO	8-speed ps, 2 hyd., PTO, purchased as a demo when it had 1,200 hours on it, 18.4-38, axle duals
John Deere	4440	1978	6,357	G	$18,500	2/06	ECIL	Quad range, 18.4-38 duals

Tractors

Make	Model	Year	Hrs.	Cond.	Price	Sale	Location	Comments
John Deere	4440	1978	6,727	G	$21,000	4/06	WCMT	CAH, 130-hp. diesel engine, 16-speed quad range, 3 pt., dual PTO, 2 hyd., 18.4-38 duals, 12 front weights
John Deere	4440	1978	5,600	G	$22,500	4/06	SEMI	Cab, PS, 3 pt., 2 hyd., 20.8-38
John Deere	4440	1978		G	$24,750	2/06	SENE	PS, 3 hyd., 3 pt., 1,157 hours on complete engine & trans. OH, front fenders, 6 front weights, 18.4R-38 (70%), 50 Series front end lights
John Deere	4440	1978	2,743	G	$25,000	1/06	WCIL	Duals, 8-speed PS, 2 hyd., 3 pt.
John Deere	4440	1978	6,611	E	$28,500	12/06	WCIA	OH at 6,034 hours, PS, 18.4R-38, axle duals
John Deere	4440	1979		G	$14,000	7/06	SEND	HFA, quad range, CAH, 3 hyd., 3 pt., PTO, 826 hours on complete OH, 16.9-38
John Deere	4440	1979		F	$15,500	1/06	NEIN	Cab, air, quad range
John Deere	4440	1979	4,149	G	$17,400	12/06	ECIL	Cab, PS, 18.4-38, axle duals, front & rear weights, quick hitch
John Deere	4440	1979	7,272	G	$17,750	3/06	ECNE	PS, 2 hyd., 3 pt., R134 air (new in 2005), AM/FM, 18.4-38 tires
John Deere	4440	1979	5,760	G	$18,750	1/06	WCIL	Cab, quad shift, axle-mount duals, 3 hyd., 3 pt., quick hitch
John Deere	4440	1979	5,366	G	$19,900	9/06	ECNE	Quad range, 2 hyd., 540/1,000 PTO, near-new 18.4-38 rear tires, 9-bolt hubs and duals, 11:00-16 front, 12 front weights
John Deere	4440	1979	8,338	E	$21,000	3/06	WCKS	3,000 hours on 50 Series motor, PS, 3 pt., 2 hyd., PTO, Westendorf BT TA 76 front end loader w/ bucket, joystick, bale fork, grapple fork
John Deere	4440	1979	5,165	G	$21,000	12/06	ECIL	Cab, air, weights, 18.4R-38, JD axle duals
John Deere	4440	1979	8,600	G	$21,250	3/06	SESD	OH 400 hours ago
John Deere	4440	1979	10,572	G	$22,500	3/06	NECO	3,500 hours on OH, quad range, 3 pt., PTO, 3 hyd., new 18.4R-38 tires, duals
John Deere	4440	1980	11,000	G	$11,800	7/06	NWMN	CAH, quad range, 3 hyd., 3 pt., 540/1,000 PTO, quick hitch, power beyond, 14.9-46 band duals, front tank, front suitcase weights
John Deere	4440	1980	3,287	G	$15,000	3/06	NEMI	Hyd. MFWD, new rear and new fronts, duals, quad range, 220-gal. saddle tanks
John Deere	4440	1980	8,140	G	$18,400	1/06	SESD	Quad range, CAH
John Deere	4440	1980	4,300	G	$23,000	12/06	WCMN	PS, 18.4-38, 3 pt., PTO, 2 hyd., CAH, one owner
John Deere	4440	1980	9,086	F	$25,000	2/06	NCCO	1,000 hours on OH, 14.9-46, axle duals
John Deere	4440	1980	5,825	G	$26,500	2/06	SCKS	20.8-38, clamp-on duals, 2 hyd., 11.00-16 front tires, front-mounted fuel tank, 3 pt., drawbar
John Deere	4440	1980	1,156	E	$37,000	8/06	ECNE	Actual hours, quad range, 18.4-38, 2 hyd., 3 pt., joystick loader controls (loader sold separately), 2 sets of rear wheel weights, one owner
John Deere	4440	1981	7,700	G	$17,000	5/06	WCMN	Std. front, quad range, 3 pt., PTO, 18.4-38
John Deere	4440	1981		G	$19,500	3/06	NENE	600 hours on engine OH, PS, 2 hyd., 3 pt., AM/FM, R134A freon
John Deere	4440	1981	4,559	G	$24,300	3/06	NCIA	Cab, quad range, 2 hyd., power beyond, quick coupler, front weights, 18.4-38 duals
John Deere	4440	1981	6,600	G	$27,500	11/06	ECNE	Very clean, PS, 3 hyd., lift assist, quick hitch, front weights, front fenders, 3 sets of rear weights, good 18.4-38 tires, axle duals sold separately
John Deere	4440	1981	3,498	E	$32,250	7/06	SEMN	Quad range, axle duals, new tires, JD quick hitch, cherry condition
John Deere	4440	1981	2,481	E	$34,250	2/06	SWNY	PS, 2 hyd., 6 rear weights, 10 front weights, quick hitch

WHAT'S IT WORTH?

Tractors

Make	Model	Year	Hrs.	Cond.	Price	Sale	Location	Comments
John Deere	4440	1982	5,200	P	$10,100	8/06	NECO	Quad range, 3 pt., 2 hyd., PTO, 18.4-38
John Deere	4440	1982		G	$19,750	1/06	NEIN	Cab, air, quad range
John Deere	4440	1982		G	$20,000	11/06	SCNE	Cab, 3 hyd., quad range, 18.4-42 duals
John Deere	4440	1982	4,000	G	$20,750	3/06	NWIL	Diesel, cab, weights, synchro, new paint, duals
John Deere	4440	1982	4,555	G	$22,000	8/06	WCKS	Quad range
John Deere	4440	1982		E	$22,000	8/06	ECIA	Super sharp, actual hours unknown, quad range, diesel, WF, factory cab, 2 hyd., isocouplers, 18.4-42, extended axle
John Deere	4440	1982	9,000	G	$26,000	1/06	NCCO	Engine OH about 1,500 hours ago, 2 hyd., 3 pt., PTO
John Deere	4440	1982	3,217	E	$32,500	7/06	SEMN	Quad range, axle duals, cherry condition
John Deere	4450			G	$17,000	7/06	ECNY	Diesel, cab, air, front weights
John Deere	4450			G	$17,500	5/06	SCCA	MFWD, front weights, cab, air, PS, PTO, 3 hyd.
John Deere	4450		2,000	F	$18,100	3/06	SEPA	2WD, duals, average rubber
John Deere	4450			P	$21,000	1/06	NEIA	2WD, cab, rough, tires bald
John Deere	4450		4,425	G	$27,500	12/06	SEMN	2WD, quad range, front weights
John Deere	4450	1983	9,550	G	$17,000	7/06	NWMN	2WD, CAH, quad range, 3 hyd., power beyond, 3 pt., 540/1,000 PTO, 14.9-46 band duals, front tank & suitcase weights
John Deere	4450	1983	10,000	F	$19,500	12/06	WCMN	2WD, PS, 3 hyd., PTO
John Deere	4450	1983	8,500	G	$21,500	2/06	SWNE	2WD, PS, 3 pt., 3 hyd., 540 & 1,000 PTO, 18.4R-38, duals, 1,500 lbs. in rear weights, 8 front weights
John Deere	4450	1983	8,300	G	$24,000	4/06	WCMN	2WD, quad range, 2 hyd., 18.4R-38, duals, 540/1,000 rpm
John Deere	4450	1983	4,424	G	$34,000	4/06	SEMI	2WD, cab, 2 hyd., front fenders, 20.8-38
John Deere	4450	1984	2,400	E	$35,750	8/06	NWIL	2WD, diesel, weights
John Deere	4450	1985	10,000	P	$16,500	7/06	ECND	MFWD rough, PS, 3 pt., PTO, front weights, band duals
John Deere	4450	1985	6,608	G	$23,500	3/06	ECNE	2WD, quad range, cab, 3 hyd., 3 pt., 10-bolt hub-mount duals
John Deere	4450	1985	10,161	G	$31,250	3/06	NENE	MFWD, 15-speed ps, 18.4R-42, 10-bolt duals, 3 hyd., front fenders, 12 front end weights, rear wheel weights, lift assist, recent engine work, R134A air
John Deere	4450	1986	8,056	G	$22,000	8/06	NCIA	2WD, cab, air, quad range, 2 hyd., power beyond, 18.4-38
John Deere	4450	1986	4,324	G	$27,500	2/06	WCIL	2WD, quad range, 3 hyd., 3 pt., front & rear weights, 2 PTOs, duals
John Deere	4450	1988	3,963	G	$33,500	8/06	WCIL	2WD, one owner, 3 hyd., quick hitch, PS
John Deere	4455			G	$19,000	7/06	ECNY	4WD, 150 hp., cab, air, front weights, 6 outlets
John Deere	4455			G	$29,100	8/06	SEMN	2WD, PS, JD 148 loader, joystick
John Deere	4455	1987	5,250	G	$41,000	2/06	NWIN	MFWD, cab, air, PS, duals
John Deere	4455	1987	1,081	E	$53,500	2/06	SWNY	MFWD, 3 hyd., 20.8-38, no duals, PS, no rear weights, 14 front weights, quick hitch
John Deere	4455	1989	5,000	F	$25,500	9/06	SEIA	MFWD, PS
John Deere	4455	1989	7,545	G	$27,000	6/06	NCIA	2WD, cab, air, PS, 3 hyd., quick coupler
John Deere	4455	1989		G	$31,000	12/06	ECMO	MFWD, PS, front fenders, 2 hyd., duals
John Deere	4455	1989	5,086	E	$45,000	3/06	SEIA	MFWD, PS, 2 hyd., performance monitor
John Deere	4455	1990	8,500	G	$24,000	7/06	WCMN	2WD, quad range
John Deere	4455	1990	4,781	G	$35,500	4/06	WCMN	2WD, 3 pt., 2 PTOs, 540/1,000 CAH, rock box, radar, 18.4R-38 duals, PS, one owner
John Deere	4455	1990	4,488	G	$37,000	2/06	WCIL	2WD, 18.4R-42 duals, radar, quad range, 3 hyd., quick hitch
John Deere	4455	1991	8,750	G	$27,500	5/06	WCMN	2WD, 3 hyd., PS, 3 pt., PTO, 18.4-42 hub duals, 90% rubber
John Deere	4455	1991	5,166	G	$28,500	3/06	NWMN	2WD, PS, 3 hyd., 540/1,000 PTO, 46" duals

Tractors

Make	Model	Year	Hrs.	Cond.	Price	Sale	Location	Comments
John Deere	4455	1991	4,900	G	$29,700	3/06	SCIA	2WD, PS, nice
John Deere	4455	1991	3,663	G	$32,200	8/06	NEIL	2WD, quad range, no duals or quick hitch, shoup steps, 18.4-38
John Deere	4455	1991	6,575	G	$35,000	2/06	WCKS	2WD, PS, 3 pt., pt, quick hitch, duals, JD 265 loader, joystick
John Deere	4455	1991	4,550	G	$41,000	12/06	WCMI	2WD, weights, 3 hyd., 15 speed, 140 hp.
John Deere	4455	1991	4,600	E	$41,500	1/06	NEIN	MFWD, cab, air, PS, 18.4-42, very nice
John Deere	4455	1991	6,643	G	$41,750	2/06	SCPA	2 hyd., no duals, 20.8-38 tires, 10 front weights, radar, 2WD
John Deere	4555			G	$31,000	3/06	SWMN	MFWD, CAH, PS, 15 speed, 4 hyd., power beyond, radar, quick hitch, PTO, rock box, hub duals
John Deere	4555	1989	4,144	G	$30,000	3/06	NCIL	2WD, quad range, 3 hyd., 18.4-42, axle duals
John Deere	4555	1989	3,510	G	$33,000	2/06	ECIL	2WD, SN 1407, quad range, 3 hyd., 18.4R-42 duals
John Deere	4555	1990	5,965	G	$26,000	11/06	SCNE	2WD, 15-speed PS, 3 hyd.
John Deere	4555	1990	5,891	G	$26,000	1/06	WCNE	42" rear tires, front weights
John Deere	4555	1990	5,550	G	$32,000	3/06	NEOH	MFWD, radar, weights, quick tach, duals
John Deere	4555	1990	5,680	G	$33,000	11/06	NWMN	MFWD, 15-speed PS, 3 hyd., power beyond, 1,000 PTO, 3 pt., quick hitch, 18.4-42 press steel duals (60%), 16.9-28 fronts, fenders, front suitcase weights
John Deere	4555	1990	2,302	E	$41,250	8/06	NCIA	2WD, PS, radar, quick coupler, 3 hyd., axle duals, front weights
John Deere	4555	1991	4,042	G	$41,700	11/06	ECNE	2WD, always shedded, 15-speed PS, GPS radar, 3 hyd., lift assist, quick hitch, front fenders, front weights, 500 lb. each rear wheel weights, 18.4-42 duals, clean
John Deere	4560			F	$21,000	12/06	SEMN	MFWD, PS, 18.4-38
John Deere	4560			G	$27,000	3/06	WCMN	2WD, PS, 3 hyd., 3 pt., PTO, light pkg., 18.4-46 press steel duals
John Deere	4560	1992	8,300	G	$27,250	12/06	WCMN	2WD, PS, 3 pt., PTO, quick hitch, duals
John Deere	4560	1992	7,435	G	$32,000	4/06	SEND	MFWD, 15-speed ps, air, 3 hyd., 3 pt., quick hitch, PTO, radar, 14.9-46 rear, press steel duals, 14.9-30 fronts, 50% rubber, front weights, fenders
John Deere	4560	1992	4,150	G	$41,000	1/06	NCCO	MFWD, 3 hyd., 3 pt., PTO, one owner
John Deere	4560	1993	7,166	G	$36,000	3/06	NCCO	MFWD, PS, 3 pt., quick hitch, PTO, 4 hyd., 14.9-30 fronts, 14.9-46 rears, duals
John Deere	4600			G	$10,900	12/06	SCMN	Compact tractor, deck
John Deere	4640			P	$5,000	1/06	WCCA	Cab, PS, 3 pt., PTO, 2 hyd
John Deere	4640			G	$5,600	8/06	SETN	CAH
John Deere	4640		6,693	P	$7,300	9/06	SEIL	As is, will not shift, quad range, 3 pt., quick hitch, front & rear weights, 18.4R-42 axle duals
John Deere	4640			F	$10,750	8/06	SEPA	CAH, weights, duals, average rubber
John Deere	4640		9,844	F	$13,000	8/06	WCMN	Quad range, 3 hyd., 18.4-42
John Deere	4640			G	$14,400	7/06	ECIL	Quad range, air, 2 hyd., front and rear weights, quick hitch, 2,673 hours on new engine and rear, 18.4R-42
John Deere	4640		7,288	G	$15,500	3/06	SWMN	CAH, PS, 3 hyd., 3 pt., PTO, hub duals
John Deere	4640		3,230	E	$17,500	3/06	WCKS	3 pt., PTO, quad range, PTO, axle duals, rear end OH
John Deere	4640			G	$18,000	11/06	SCMN	
John Deere	4640		8,845	G	$18,000	10/06	NCKS	PS, 3 pt., PTO, 3 hyd., inside rears, front tires like new, less than 300 hours on underhaul
John Deere	4640			G	$18,000	3/06	NWIL	Diesel, weights, duals
John Deere	4640			G	$18,750	12/06	SEMN	PS, 2 hyd., quick hitch

Tractors

Make	Model	Year	Hrs.	Cond.	Price	Sale	Location	Comments
John Deere	4640		4,917	G	$20,800	1/06	WCIL	18.4/42 tires, quad range, SN 22631
John Deere	4640		6,400	E	$23,000	4/06	NCSD	3 hyd., 3 pt., quick hitch, 116 hours on new tach, quad range
John Deere	4640		5,624	G	$23,000	1/06	SCMN	1980 model, PS, loaded, one owner
John Deere	4640		5,177	G	$24,500	8/06	SCMN	PS, 10-bolt duals
John Deere	4640	1978		F	$8,800	7/06	WCMN	Hyd., MFWD, quad range, duals, quick hitch, 1,000 PTO
John Deere	4640	1978	8,775	F	$10,000	11/06	ECND	MFWD, CAH, quad range, 3 hyd., 3 pt., PTO, 20.8-38 band duals
John Deere	4640	1978		F	$12,700	1/06	SCNE	Quad range, 3 hyd., 6 front weights, new 18.4-42, duals, accessory powerstrip
John Deere	4640	1978	11,620	G	$13,500	2/06	NECO	Quad range, duals, 2,500 hours on OH, 11,620 total hours
John Deere	4640	1978	6,778	G	$18,000	8/06	NWIA	Cab, 18.4-38 axle-mount duals, OH at 5,000 hours, nice
John Deere	4640	1979		F	$12,000	11/06	NEKS	PS, duals, 3 hyd., 3 pt., quick hitch
John Deere	4640	1979	7,600	G	$13,500	2/06	NECO	Axle duals, 4 hyd, front weights
John Deere	4640	1979	5,206	G	$16,000	3/06	NCIL	Quad range, 2 hyd., 20.8-38
John Deere	4640	1979	5,602	G	$25,200	9/06	NENE	Quad range, 20.8-38, 10-bolt duals, 14L-16.1 front tires, 3 hyd., JD quick hitch, 1,000 PTO, sound guard cab, one owner, shedded
John Deere	4640	1980	6,902	G	$13,500	3/06	WCIL	Quad range, 20.8-38, duals, shedded
John Deere	4640	1980	5,522	F	$14,700	12/06	ECIL	Quad range, 18.4-38, axle duals, 3 hyd., front & rear weights, quick hitch
John Deere	4640	1980		G	$15,750	2/06	WCMN	PS, 18.4-42, duals
John Deere	4640	1981		F	$10,000	8/06	NECO	3 hyd., 3 pt., PTO, 18.4-38, duals
John Deere	4640	1981	9,980	G	$15,500	2/06	NWMN	Hyd. MFWD, quad range, 3 hyd., power beyond, 3 pt., quick hitch, PTO, 14.9-46 rears on step-up rims, 50% rubber, 11.25×28 mono rib fronts
John Deere	4640	1981	7,846	G	$16,000	2/06	SCMI	One owner, cab, 12 front weights, 2 hyd., quick hitch, quad range, 18.4R-42, axle duals, just back from winter JD dealer service program
John Deere	4640	1981	4,521	G	$25,600	7/06	NCIL	2 hyd., 20.8-38 axle duals, PS, $7,443 spent on OH
John Deere	4640	1982	8,179	G	$16,000	8/06	ECNE	PS, Goodyear 20.8-38 tires w/ 8-bolt hubs & duals, 11:00-16 front tires, long axles, 2 hyd., sound guard cab, complete OH at 5,700 hours
John Deere	4640	1982	4,254	E	$25,000	2/06	WCIL	Quad range, sound guard body, 20.8-38 duals, 2 hyd., front & rear weights, quick hitch, sharp
John Deere	4640	1982	3,094	G	$26,700	2/06	NCIN	Factory 18.4R-42 duals, quad range, hd quick hitch
John Deere	4650			G	$16,000	12/06	NWWI	MFWD, duals, 2940 MFWD, open station, reconditioned
John Deere	4650		9,700	F	$20,750	4/06	NCKS	MFWD, 15-speed ps
John Deere	4650			F	$21,500	1/06	NEIN	2WD
John Deere	4650		2,825	G	$34,400	6/06	NWIL	MFWD, full set of front weights, duals, quick hitch
John Deere	4650		3,068	G	$38,000	7/06	WCMN	MFWD, PS, 18.4-42 duals
John Deere	4650	1983	7,400	G	$21,750	7/06	NWMN	MFWD, CAH, PS, 3 hyd., power beyond, 3 pt., quick hitch, 1,000 PTO, 14.9-46 press steel hub duals, front suitcase weights
John Deere	4650	1984	5,700	G	$27,000	5/06	SEWY	MFWD, JD 280 loader & grapple, diesel
John Deere	4650	1984		G	$27,000	7/06	SEND	MFWD, PS, 3 hyd., power beyond, 3 pt., quick hitch, 1,000 PTO, 14.9-46 press steel duals (70%), front fenders & suitcase weights, 60 Series step aux. lights
John Deere	4650	1984	4,844	G	$28,300	2/06	ECIL	CAH, PS, 4 hyd., 3 pt., PTO, quick hitch, duals
John Deere	4650	1984	9,200	G	$30,500	11/06	SWIA	MFWD, 3 hyd., clean, 18.4-42, duals

Tractors

Make	Model	Year	Hrs.	Cond.	Price	Sale	Location	Comments
John Deere	4650	1985	5,985	G	$23,000	7/06	NCIA	2WD, cab, air, quad range, 3 hyd., front weights, PTO, quick coupler, 18.4-42
John Deere	4650	1985		G	$24,200	1/06	NEIN	MFWD, PS, 18.4-42 duals
John Deere	4650	1985	4,015	G	$31,000	2/06	SWOH	2WD, 3 hyd., 20.8-38, duals, 15-speed ps, 16 front weights, rear weights, quick hitch, exterior lights
John Deere	4650	1985	3,983	G	$35,750	1/06	WCIL	MFWD, fully-equipped cab, axle duals, 2 hyd., quick hitch
John Deere	4650	1986	12,869	G	$21,500	3/06	NCCO	2WD, PS, 3 pt., quick hitch, PTO, 3 hyd., 14.9-46, duals, recent underhaul
John Deere	4650	1986	8,317	P	$22,000	8/06	NECO	Rough, MFWD, 3 hyd., 3 pt., PTO, 20 front weights, rear weights, 18.4-42, duals
John Deere	4650	1986	8,711	G	$24,000	3/06	NCCO	MFWD, PS, 3 pt., quick hitch, PTO, 3 hyd., power beyond, 16.9-28 fronts, 18.4-42 rears, duals
John Deere	4650	1986	8,750	G	$24,750	3/06	NEND	MFWD, CAH, 15-speed PS, 3 hyd., power beyond, rear inside weights, 3 pt., quick hitch, PTO, 18.4-42 press steel duals, front fenders, suitcase weights, 16.9-28 fronts
John Deere	4650	1987	9,267	G	$30,000	3/06	NEND	MFWD, PS, 3 hyd., 3 pt., quick hitch, 1,000 PTO, 14.9-46 press steel duals, new inside rubber, new 14.9-30 fronts w/ fenders, greenlighted, extensive service records
John Deere	4650	1987	8,728	G	$30,000	1/06	WCNE	MFWD, duals, front weights
John Deere	4650	1987	5,300	G	$30,750	3/06	NCIL	MFWD, PS, 3 hyd., 20.8-38, axle duals
John Deere	4650	1988		G	$26,000	11/06	NEND	MFWD, PS, 3 hyd., 3 pt., 18.4-42 press steel duals, 14.9-30 fronts, suitcase weights
John Deere	4650	1989	4,170	G	$38,000	12/06	NWIL	2WD, PS, one owner, 3 pt., quick hitch, 3 hyd.
John Deere	4755			G	$37,500	12/06	SEMN	MFWD
John Deere	4755			G	$39,000	4/06	NEND	MFWD, front weights, 14.9-46 duals
John Deere	4755	1989	8,094	F	$19,000	8/06	NECO	2WD, PS, 3 hyd., 3 pt., PTO, quick hitch, 20 front weights, 18.4-42, duals
John Deere	4755	1989	8,450	F	$21,750	2/06	NCCO	2WD, PS, 3 hyd., quick hitch, power beyond, 18.4-42, axle duals
John Deere	4755	1991	7,966	F	$29,000	2/06	WCIL	MFWD, 3 hyd., PS, weights, quick hitch
John Deere	4755	1991	3,584	G	$32,600	2/06	WCIL	2WD, quad range, 3 hyd., 3 pt., 18.4-42 duals
John Deere	4760	1992	8,000	G	$33,000	7/06	WCMN	MFWD, duals, 42" rubber
John Deere	4760	1993	7,105	G	$34,000	4/06	SEND	MFWD, 15-speed PS, air, 3 hyd., 3 pt., quick hitch, PTO, radar, $13,000 in trans. work 11/05, 12.4-54 rears, steel press duals, 9.5-44 fronts, 50% rubber, front weights
John Deere	4840			G	$6,500	5/06	SCCA	Cab, air, PS, 3 pt., quick hitch, PTO, rear weights
John Deere	4840			P	$6,500	1/06	WCCA	Front weights, cab, air, PS, 3 pt., quick hitch
John Deere	4840			G	$7,500	5/06	SCCA	Cab, air, PS, 3 pt., PTO, weights, 3 hyd.
John Deere	4840			F	$9,500	9/06	NCIA	3 hyd., 20.8-38
John Deere	4840			F	$14,000	8/06	SCNE	2WD, weights, CAH, PS, 3 pt., PTO, 3 hyd., 18.4-42 duals
John Deere	4840		7,250	G	$14,500	3/06	NWIL	Axle duals, one owner
John Deere	4840		9,222	G	$16,800	3/06	SWNE	PS, newer 50 Series motor, 3 hyd., 20 front weights w/ cast duals, 18.4R-42, quick hitch, 20 front end weights
John Deere	4840		8,172	G	$17,000	4/06	WCSD	PS, quick-tach 3 pt., 3 hyd., 1,000 PTO, front weights, 20.8R-38 factory duals (90%)
John Deere	4840	1978		F	$10,000	7/06	SEND	CAH, PS, 3 hyd., 3 pt., 1,000 PTO, wide space duals, aux. lights
John Deere	4840	1978	9,440	G	$13,200	11/06	NWKS	Recent OH
John Deere	4840	1978	3,129	F	$13,500	3/06	SWNE	PS, 2WD, 18.4R-38, cast duals, rear wheel weights

WHAT'S IT WORTH?

Tractors

Make	Model	Year	Hrs.	Cond.	Price	Sale	Location	Comments
John Deere	4840	1978	4,652	F	$14,000	12/06	ECIL	PS, 18.4R-38 w/ axle duals, front & rear weights, quick hitch
John Deere	4840	1979		G	$11,000	11/06	WCMN	3 pt., PTO, 20.8-38 hub duals
John Deere	4840	1979	5,740	G	$23,500	11/06	NCIN	8-speed PS, 3 hyd., 20.8-38 axle duals
John Deere	4840	1980	5,800	G	$20,000	3/06	NCIL	3 hyd., PS, quick hitch, 18.4-42, axle duals
John Deere	4840	1981	7,700	G	$12,250	7/06	SEND	PS, 3 hyd., 3 pt., quick hitch, 1,000 PTO, radar, differential lock
John Deere	4840	1981		F	$13,500	10/06	SEMN	
John Deere	4840	1981		F	$15,000	3/06	NCNE	300 hours on complete engine OH, 3 hyd., AM/FM, quick hitch, 1,000 lb. rear wheel weights, 8 front end weights, 20.8R-38 w/ 10-bolt duals
John Deere	4840	1981	2,928	E	$17,000	3/06	WCKS	50 Series engine, PS, 3 pt., 3 hyd., quick hitch, PTO, duals
John Deere	4840	1982		G	$8,000	4/06	NCOK	PS, 3 pt., PTO, quick hitch, 3 hyd., duals, front weights, 1,000 PTO
John Deere	4840	1982		G	$15,250	3/06	NWKS	EROPS, PTO, 3 hyd., PS, rear duals
John Deere	4850		8,400	F	$18,000	8/06	WCMN	MFWD, 18.4-42 duals, 3 hyd., 3 pt., PTO, ps
John Deere	4850		7,642	G	$21,500	11/06	WCMN	2WD, PS, 18.4-42 duals
John Deere	4850		7,642	G	$23,500	7/06	WCMN	2WD, PS, 18.4-42 duals
John Deere	4850			G	$26,500	12/06	SEMN	MFWD, PS, front weights, 20.8R-38
John Deere	4850			G	$31,500	7/06	ECIL	MFWD, PS, air, 3 hyd., front and rear weights, quick hitch, Firestone 10-ply 18.4R-42 axle mount duals, 18.4-26 front
John Deere	4850		4,246	G	$36,500	2/06	WCMN	MFWD, CAH, 15-speed ps, 3 hyd., quick hitch, hub duals, 14 suitcase weights
John Deere	4850	1983	9,300	G	$20,500	7/06	NWMN	MFWD, CAH, PS, 3 hyd., power beyond, 3 pt., quick hitch, 1,000 PTO, 14.9-46 press steel duals, front suitcase weights
John Deere	4850	1983	9,246	G	$20,500	11/06	ECND	MFWD, 15-speed ps, 3 hyd., power beyond, 3 pt., quick hitch, front fenders, weights, 18.4-42 cast duals
John Deere	4850	1983	9,100	G	$23,400	7/06	NWMN	MFWD, CAH, PS, 3 hyd., power beyond, 3 pt., quick hitch, 1,000 PTO, 18.4-42 cast hub duals, front suitcase weights
John Deere	4850	1983	7,406	G	$27,500	3/06	NECO	MFWD, 3,200 hours on OH, PS, 3 pt., PTO, 3 hyd., 18.4-42, duals
John Deere	4850	1984	8,845	G	$30,500	6/06	NWMN	MFWD, 15-speed ps, 3 pt., PTO, 3 hyd., power beyond, 14.9R-46 duals, 3,200 hours on engine major OH
John Deere	4850	1984	4,342	G	$33,000	1/06	WCIL	MFWD, 16-speed ps, triples, front axle extensions, 3 hyd., 3 pt.
John Deere	4850	1985	8,544	F	$16,500	3/06	NCKS	2WD, 3 pt., duals
John Deere	4850	1985	9,500	G	$22,750	7/06	NWMN	MFWD, CAH, PS, 3 hyd., power beyond, 3 pt., quick hitch, 1,000 PTO, 14.9-46 press steel hub duals, 60 Series step
John Deere	4850	1988	1,137	G	$18,000	2/06	NECO	2,200 hours on rebuild, 4 hyd., axle duals
John Deere	4850	1988	3,850	G	$24,000	1/06	WCIL	2WD, duals, 16-speed PS, 3 hyd., new engine has approximately 2,000 hours
John Deere	4850	1988	7,632	G	$27,000	6/06	NWMN	MFWD, 15-speed PS, 3 pt., PTO, 3 hyd., power beyond, front weights, 14.9R-46 duals
John Deere	4850	1988	6,130	G	$30,400	8/06	NCIA	MFWD, 15-speed PS, fast hitch, duals, weights
John Deere	4850	1988	2,730	E	$53,000	8/06	WCKS	2WD, PS, quick hitch, 18.4-42 tires
John Deere	4850	1989	6,558	G	$32,500	2/06	NWOH	MFWD, CAH, quick hitch, PS, 8 front weights, 18.4-46 axle duals, 3 hyd.
John Deere	4955			G	$26,000	5/06	SCCA	Front weights, cab, air, PS, 3 pt., PTO
John Deere	4955		9,000	F	$28,000	3/06	NCUT	MFWD, 46" duals

Tractors

Make	Model	Year	Hrs.	Cond.	Price	Sale	Location	Comments
John Deere	4955		3,654	G	$44,000	11/06	NCOH	MFWD, PS, duals, PTO, quick hitch, 3 hyd.
John Deere	4955	1989	9,217	F	$18,000	8/06	NECO	MFWD, 3 hyd., 3 pt., PTO, quick hitch, radar, 20 front weights, 3 sets of 450-lb. rear weights, 14.9-46 duals
John Deere	4955	1989		G	$26,000	11/06	NWKS	MFWD
John Deere	4955	1989	9,090	F	$28,900	3/06	ECNE	MFWD, duals, 3 hyd., 14' Leon dozer to sell separate
John Deere	4955	1989	3,298	E	$45,000	8/06	WCKS	2WD, PS, quick hitch, 18.4-42 duals
John Deere	4955	1990	4,840	F	$37,000	3/06	SWNE	MFWD, 15-speed PS, 3 hyd., PTO, 18.4-46, 14.9-30 front tires, front end weights, rear wheel weights
John Deere	4955	1990	5,759	G	$37,500	8/06	NCIA	MFWD, cab, air, PS, 3 hyd., quick coupler, front tank and weights, duals
John Deere	4955	1991	8,971	F	$25,000	8/06	NECO	2WD, 3 pt., PTO, quick hitch
John Deere	4955	1991	9,775	G	$31,000	3/06	SEMN	MFWD, 20.8-42 w/ duals, 95% rubber, front weights, 15-speed PS, new JD at 6,275 hours, trans. rebuilt at 6,500 hours
John Deere	4960			G	$27,000	8/06	SEPA	MFWD, CAH, average rubber
John Deere	4960		6,200	F	$27,500	3/06	NWKS	MFWD, PS, 18.4R-42 duals, 3 hyd.
John Deere	4960		2,000	F	$37,000	3/06	SEPA	MFWD, CAH, duals, average rubber
John Deere	4960		4,945	G	$50,000	3/06	SWMN	MFWD, CAH, PS, 4 hyd., radar, quick hitch, hub duals
John Deere	4960		3,603	E	$60,500	4/06	NESD	MFWD, 15-speed PS, 4 reverse, PTO, 4 hyd., 3 pt., axle duals, front fenders, quick-tach, kept inside
John Deere	4960		2,630	G	$62,000	11/06	SCMN	MFWD, PS
John Deere	4960	1992		G	$22,000	7/06	WCCA	Front weights, cab, air, PS, 3 pt.
John Deere	4960	1992		G	$25,000	7/06	WCCA	Front weights, cab, air, PS, 3 pt.
John Deere	4960	1992	8,800	G	$26,500	8/06	WCMN	MFWD, PS, 20.8-42, duals, 3 pt., 3 hyd., front fenders
John Deere	4960	1992		G	$36,000	3/06	SEIA	MFWD, 3 hyd., front fenders
John Deere	4960	1993	7,849	G	$36,000	2/06	NWMN	MFWD, 15-speed PS, 3 hyd., power beyond, PTO, front suitcase weights, 14.9-46, 14.9-30 fronts
John Deere	4960	1993	3,800	G	$55,200	2/06	WCIL	MFWD, duals, quick hitch
John Deere	4960	1993	3,167	G	$60,000	2/06	ECIL	MFWD, SN 4713, 18.4-46 duals, tires were 50% or less
John Deere	4960	1994		G	$22,000	7/06	WCCA	MFWD, front weights, cab, air, PS, 3 pt.
John Deere	4960	1994		G	$25,000	7/06	WCCA	MFWD, front weights, PS, 3 pt., 3 hyd.
John Deere	4960	1994		F	$32,250	1/06	NEIN	MFWD, high hours
John Deere	5105	2002	650	G	$10,300	11/06	NEKS	Utility, 2WD, synchro trans. w/ 8 forward and 4 reverse, 2 hyd., 540 PTO, 3 pt.
John Deere	5200		1,843	G	$7,250	8/06	SETN	ROPS, sunshade, ROPS
John Deere	5200		·	G	$8,500	8/06	SETN	ROPS
John Deere	5220		800	G	$13,800	8/06	SEPA	2WD, JD 521 loader, WF, ROPS, average rubber
John Deere	5220		448	G	$31,000	3/06	NCCO	MFWD, GB loader
John Deere	5300		334	G	$9,500	8/06	SETN	JD 521 loader, ROPS
John Deere	5300	1994		G	$11,000	9/06	NWTN	Woods, 1020 loader
John Deere	5300	1997	2,211	G	$13,750	8/06	SETN	CAH, synchro trans.
John Deere	5310	1998		G	$12,500	12/06	ECMO	MFWD, open
John Deere	5310	1998	1,987	G	$13,000	8/06	SETN	JD 520 loader, sunshade, 55 hp.
John Deere	5310	2000	1,515	G	$21,000	8/06	NECO	MFWD, 500 Series loader, cab, air, 2 hyd., 3 pt., PTO, 16.9-30 tires
John Deere	5310	2001	3,210	G	$18,000	12/06	SEIA	MFWD, open station, 3 pt., 2 hyd., Power Reverser, creeper gears
John Deere	5320			G	$21,000	8/06	SCNE	MFWD, JD 541 loader w/ joystick control, 3 pt., PTO, 2 hyd., left-hand reverser, 14.9-28 rear

Tractors

Make	Model	Year	Hrs.	Cond.	Price	Sale	Location	Comments
John Deere	5325		299	E	$20,750	12/06	ECMO	MFWD
John Deere	5325	2005	107	E	$0	2/06	ECIL	No sale at $28,000 – wanted $30,000, sync shuttle, 3 pt., 2 hyd., PTO, ROPS w/ JD 542 quick-tach loader
John Deere	5400			G	$8,000	11/06	SWCA	4WD, diesel
John Deere	5400			G	$11,500	7/06	WCCA	Front weights, 6 spd. creeper, 3 pt., PTO
John Deere	5400			G	$13,750	12/06	ECMO	JD 540 loader
John Deere	5420	2000	1,768	G	$18,250	8/06	SETN	4WD, ROPS
John Deere	5420	2004	772	G	$19,000	8/06	NECO	2WD, cab, air, 2 hyd., 3 pt., PTO, 16.9-30 tires
John Deere	5420	2004	364	G	$25,500	12/06	NWMO	CAH, MFWD, 3 hyd.
John Deere	5425		65	G	$41,000	8/06	SETN	4WD, CAH, JD loader
John Deere	5425	2006		G	$22,500	12/06	ECMO	MFWD, 3 hyd., 16.9-30 rear
John Deere	5500	1996		G	$14,500	7/06	WCCA	MFWD, JD 540 front loader, 3 pt., PTO, rear weights, 1 hyd.
John Deere	5510			G	$9,000	8/06	SETN	ROPS
John Deere	5510			G	$10,000	7/06	WCCA	Front weights, canopy, 3 pt., 3 hyd.
John Deere	5510			G	$12,000	7/06	WCCA	Front weights, mudder, canopy, 3 hyd.
John Deere	5510		2,719	G	$20,000	8/06	SETN	4WD, ROPS, JD 541 loader
John Deere	5510			G	$21,500	1/06	WCCA	MFWD, front weights, Power Reverser, canopy, 3 pt., 3 hyd.
John Deere	5510		1,390	G	$23,100	9/06	SEIL	MFWD, roll bar, Power Reverser, 3 hyd. w/ attached 541 hyd. loader and 6' bucket, 16.9-30 tires, weights
John Deere	5510	1997	1,220	G	$22,250	3/06	NEMO	MFWD, open ROPS, JD loader, one owner
John Deere	5510	1998		G	$19,500	7/06	WCCA	MFWD, JD 540 front loader, canopy, 3 pt., 3 hyd.
John Deere	5510	2002		G	$15,500	11/06	SECA	MFWD, canopy, 3 pt., PTO, 3 hyd.
John Deere	5520		1,901	G	$24,000	8/06	SETN	CAH, 4WD, shuttle
John Deere	5520	2002	656	E	$28,000	11/06	SEIA	MFWD, ROPS, canopy, Power Reverser, JD 541 quick-tach loader w/ joystick control and 6' bucket
John Deere	5525	2005	336	G	$26,750	12/06	NWMO	MFWD, 12-speed Power Reverser, vertical exhaust, 3 hyd., front weight bracket, mechanical hitch, 480/80R/30 rear tires
John Deere	6110		5,397	F	$4,100	3/06	NCUT	MFWD, power quad
John Deere	6200	1992	4,500	G	$19,000	12/06	NWWI	2WD, power quad, 18.4-26
John Deere	6210		1,600	G	$22,000	8/06	SEPA	2WD, CAH, fair rubber
John Deere	6210	2002	1,268	E	$25,000	3/06	NWOH	2WD, cab, 2 hyd., 3 pt., quad shift, like new
John Deere	6220			G	$43,500	3/06	NCUT	MFWD, power quad, rev.
John Deere	6220	2002	1,337	G	$35,500	3/06	NCCO	MFWD, power quad, shuttle, cab, 3 pt., quick hitch, 3 hyd., PTO, 12.4-28 fronts, 16.9-38 rears
John Deere	6300	1995		G	$9,000	7/06	WCCA	Push bumper, front weights, canopy, creeper gear, 3 pt., PTO
John Deere	6310	1999		G	$23,500	12/06	SCQB	Canadian sale, MFWD, cab, 3 pt., 3 hyd., PTO, converts to $20,513 U.S.
John Deere	6310	1999	1,850	G	$29,750	12/06	NWWI	2WD, open station, power quad, 540/1,000 PTO, 18.4-38
John Deere	6310	2000	1,148	G	$29,000	12/06	SCQB	Canadian sale, MFWD, cab, 3 pt., 3 hyd., PTO, converts to $25,314 U.S.
John Deere	6320	2004	660	G	$44,000	12/06	SCQB	Canadian sale, MFWD, cab, air, 24-speed autoquad, 3 hyd., 2-speed PTO, 3 pt., converts to $38,408 U.S.
John Deere	6320	2004	573	G	$44,000	12/06	SCQB	Canadian sale, MFWD, cab, air, 24-speed autoquad, 3 hyd., 2-speed PTO, 3 pt., converts to $38,408 U.S.
John Deere	6320	2004	566	G	$44,000	12/06	SCQB	Canadian sale, MFWD, cab, air, 24-speed autoquad, 2 hyd., 2-speed PTO, 3 pt., converts to $38,408 U.S.
John Deere	6320	2004	390	G	$46,000	12/06	SCQB	Canadian sale, MFWD, cab, air, 24-speed autoquad, 2 hyd., 2-speed PTO, 3 pt., converts to $40,153 U.S.

Tractors

Make	Model	Year	Hrs.	Cond.	Price	Sale	Location	Comments
John Deere	6320	2004	434	G	$46,000	12/06	SCQB	Canadian sale, MFWD, cab, air, 24-speed autoquad, 2 hyd., 2-speed PTO, 3 pt., converts to $40,153 U.S.
John Deere	6400			F	$12,500	3/06	NCUT	MFWD, open station, loader
John Deere	6400		3,800	F	$13,800	1/06	SEPA	MFWD, ROPS, average rubber
John Deere	6400			G	$17,750	8/06	SEMN	MFWD
John Deere	6400		8,000	F	$20,000	1/06	NEIA	MFWD, loader
John Deere	6400			G	$25,000	5/06	SWCA	4WD, diesel, PTO, 3 pt., 1 hyd., cab, air
John Deere	6400	1993		G	$17,500	7/06	WCCA	Mudder, push bumper, front weights, canopy
John Deere	6400	1994		G	$12,500	7/06	WCCA	Front weights, cab, air, 3 pt., PTO
John Deere	6400	1994		G	$12,500	7/06	WCCA	Front weights, cab, air, 3 pt., PTO
John Deere	6400	1994		G	$16,500	7/06	WCCA	Mudder, push bumper, front weights, canopy
John Deere	6400	1994	3,200	G	$23,000	2/06	WCMN	2WD, power quad, CAH
John Deere	6400	1994	4,644	G	$33,500	1/06	NEIN	MFWD, JD 640 loader, cab, air, power quad
John Deere	6400	1994	830	E	$43,500	8/06	NEIA	MFWD, JD 640 loader w/ joystick, one owner, power quad, very very clean
John Deere	6400	1995	1,993	P	$14,250	8/06	NECO	2WD, rough, cab, air, 2 hyd., 3 pt., PTO, 18.4-38 tires, with JD 620 loader & grapple
John Deere	6400	1995		G	$16,500	7/06	WCCA	Mudder, push bumper, front weights, canopy
John Deere	6400	1995	1,745	G	$41,000	11/06	NCOH	MFWD, power quad trans., 3 pt. quick hitch, 3 hyd.
John Deere	6400	1996		G	$10,000	7/06	WCCA	Mudder, push bumper, front weights, canopy
John Deere	6400	1996		G	$16,500	7/06	WCCA	Mudder, push bumper, front weights, canopy, creeper gear
John Deere	6400	1996		G	$17,500	7/06	WCCA	Mudder, push bumper, front weights, canopy
John Deere	6403			G	$25,000	3/06	NCUT	MFWD, open station, new, full factory warranty
John Deere	6403	2004	159	E	$23,000	3/06	NWOH	2WD, utility, 2 hyd., 9 spd., 540 PTO, roll bar, like new
John Deere	6405			G	$8,900	8/06	SEPA	2WD, WF, ROPS, average rubber
John Deere	6405		5,900	G	$11,250	8/06	SEPA	2WD, WF, average rubber, ROPS, synchro
John Deere	6405		370	G	$31,000	12/06	WCMN	2WD, JD 620 loader, synchro plus trans.
John Deere	6410		2,510	G	$25,000	8/06	SCFL	Cab, MFWD
John Deere	6410			G	$29,000	1/06	SEPA	MFWD, CAH, good rubber
John Deere	6410	1999		G	$32,000	12/06	NWMO	18.4-38 rear tires, 2WD, power quad, deluxe exhaust, cold package, JD 620 loader
John Deere	6410	2000	1,150	G	$38,500	3/06	SCIN	95 hp., 620 loader, joystick, extra front grill
John Deere	6410	2000	2,817	E	$42,000	11/06	SEIA	MFWD, cab, air, power quad, w/ JD 640 quick-tach loader w/ joystick control and 6' bucket
John Deere	6410	2000	1,200	E	$48,750	3/06	NEMO	MFWD, JD 640 loader
John Deere	6415	2005	270	E	$43,000	2/06	NCIL	MFWD, JD 640 loader, bucket, quick-tach, bale spear sold separate
John Deere	6420		3,606	G	$30,000	8/06	SETN	Cab, air, heat, power quad trans., left-hand reverser
John Deere	6420		3,658	G	$33,500	8/06	SETN	4WD
John Deere	6420			G	$35,000	8/06	SETN	CAH, 4WD
John Deere	6420			G	$37,000	3/06	SEPA	MFWD, CAH, good rubber, low hours, weights
John Deere	6420		700	G	$42,500	3/06	SEPA	MFWD, CAH, good rubber
John Deere	6420		455	G	$59,000	4/06	WCWI	MFWD, power quad, left-hand reverse, cab, air, 2 hyd., 3 pt., PTO, joystick w/ JD 640 self-leveling loader w/ 8" bucket
John Deere	6420	2004	544	G	$47,000	12/06	SCQB	Canadian sale, MFWD, cab, air, 24-speed autoquad, 2 hyd., 2-speed PTO, 3 pt., converts to $41,026 U.S.
John Deere	6420	2004	540	G	$47,000	12/06	SCQB	Canadian sale, MFWD, cab, air, 24-speed autoquad, 2 hyd., 2 speed PTO, 3 pt., converts to $41,026 U.S.
John Deere	6420	2004	511	G	$47,000	12/06	SCQB	Canadian sale, MFWD, cab, air, 24-speed autoquad, 3 hyd., 2-speed PTO, 3 pt., converts to $41,026 U.S.

Tractors

Make	Model	Year	Hrs.	Cond.	Price	Sale	Location	Comments
John Deere	6420	2004	437	G	$47,000	12/06	SCQB	Canadian sale, MFWD, cab, air, 24-speed autoquad, 2 hyd., 2 speed PTO, 3 pt., converts to $41,026 U.S.
John Deere	6420	2004	810	G	$48,000	12/06	SCQB	Canadian sale, MFWD, cab, air, 24-speed autoquad, 3 hyd., 2-speed PTO, 3 pt., converts to $41,899 U.S.
John Deere	6420	2004	465	G	$52,500	12/06	SCQB	Canadian sale, MFWD, cab, air, 24-speed autoquad, 3 hyd., 2 speed PTO, 3 pt., converts to $45,827 U.S.
John Deere	6420	2005		G	$42,900	12/06	NWMO	MFWD, 3 hyd., 16/16 PQ plus, adjustable rear wheels, deluxe exterior, air comfort seat
John Deere	650			G	$1,800	8/06	NWIL	5' blade, diesel
John Deere	650			G	$2,100	11/06	SWCA	4WD, diesel, PTO, canopy
John Deere	650			G	$2,600	8/06	SEPA	WF, average turf rubber
John Deere	650		1,600	F	$3,200	1/06	SEPA	WF, belly mower, average turf rubber
John Deere	6603	2004	58	E	$33,000	2/06	WCOH	Sold new in 2005, air, cab
John Deere	670			G	$6,350	9/06	NWTN	4WD, ROPS, JD 60" front loader
John Deere	6715	2005	18	E	$49,000	6/06	ECND	MFWD, CAH, 3 pt., 3 hyd., joystick, power quad, left-hand reverser, looks new, 18.4-38, one owner
John Deere	7200			F	$11,000	8/06	SCFL	MFWD, 3 hyd.
John Deere	7200	1995	4,744	G	$25,000	12/06	SEMN	MFWD, open station, ROPS, JD 740 loader, 2 hyd., 3 pt., PTO, 18.4-38, power quad
John Deere	7200	1995	2,400	G	$37,250	12/06	NWWI	2WD, JD 725 loader, joystick, power quad
John Deere	7210	1998	4,515	G	$36,000	11/06	WCMN	MFWD, power quad, radar, 2 hyd., 3 pt., quick hitch, 540/1,000 PTO, 18.4-38 hub duals, 75% insides, 13.6-28 fronts, front fender, K&M box
John Deere	7210	2001	2,400	G	$40,300	12/06	NWWI	MFWD, power quad, new 18.4-38
John Deere	7220		2	G	$32,000	8/06	SCFL	Two post roll guard
John Deere	7220	2004	1,600	G	$52,500	12/06	NWWI	MFWD, power quad, 540/1,000 PTO, 18.4-38
John Deere	7320		369	G	$64,000	3/06	NCUT	Power quad, reverse, joystick, air seat, factory warranty until July of 2007
John Deere	7320	2003	1,596	G	$56,000	12/06	NWMO	MFWD, 480/80/38 rear tires, 380/85/28 front tires, 16-speed power quad plus, 3 hyd., deluxe exhaust, fender, JD 741 loader
John Deere	7320	2004	758	E	$53,000	3/06	NWOH	MFWD, cab, power quad, 3 hyd., quick hitch, 480/80-38 rears
John Deere	7320	2004	150	G	$54,500	12/06	NWMO	CAH, MFWD, 16-speed power quad, deluxe exterior
John Deere	7400		1,603	F	$16,500	8/06	SCFL	High crop, 2WD
John Deere	7400	1994		G	$20,000	11/06	SECA	MFWD, cab, air, power quad trans., front fenders, PTO, 3 pt.
John Deere	7400	1994		G	$24,000	7/06	WCCA	MFWD, cab, air, radio, power quad trans.
John Deere	7400	1995	3,672	G	$34,500	2/06	SCMI	2WD, new rear duals 18.4-38, quick hitch, power quad, radar
John Deere	7400	1996		G	$19,500	11/06	SECA	MFWD, cab, air, power quad trans., 3 pt., PTO
John Deere	7400	1996	9,350	G	$28,500	8/06	NCMI	MFWD, diesel, JD 740 loader, CAH, PS, 100 hp., 18.4R-38, 2 hyd.
John Deere	7405		7,400	G	$20,500	3/06	NCUT	MFWD, open station, power quad, rev., JD 740 loader
John Deere	7405		4,500	F	$20,750	3/06	SEPA	2WD, ROPS, good rubber
John Deere	7405	1999		G	$17,500	7/06	WCCA	Power quad trans., canopy, 3 pt, 3 hyd
John Deere	7410	1997		G	$34,000	11/06	ECND	MFWD, CAH, power quad, 3 pt., PTO, fresh transmission OH, Allied 795 quick-tach loader, bucket, bale forks, hyd. grapple attachment and JD joystick
John Deere	7410	1997	4,093	G	$41,000	3/06	NCCO	MFWD
John Deere	7410	1997	3,100	G	$45,000	1/06	NCCO	MFWD, 18.4-38 rear, 16.9-26 fronts, power quad, 3 hyd., radio

Tractors

Make	Model	Year	Hrs.	Cond.	Price	Sale	Location	Comments
John Deere	7410	1998	8,006	F	$42,000	2/06	SCNY	MFWD, JD 741 loader, power quad, standard cab, 2 hyd., 18.4-38
John Deere	7410	1998	3,200	G	$45,000	12/06	NWWI	MFWD, power quad, 540/1,000 PTO, 18.4-38 duals
John Deere	7410	1998	1,605	G	$45,000	2/06	SCMI	MFWD, 18.4-38 duals, quick hitch, radar, power quad, Performance Monitor
John Deere	7410	1998	6,050	E	$45,000	2/06	NEIN	MFWD, JD 740 loader, self-leveling, power quad, reverser, CAH, 3 hyd., right-hand door
John Deere	7410	1999	3,037	G	$48,750	2/06	SCPA	2WD, 2-door cab, corner exhaust, 3 hyd., no weights
John Deere	7410	2001	1,575	G	$43,000	12/06	NWWI	2WD, 20-speed PS, 18.4-38
John Deere	7420	2004	1,326	G	$56,000	7/06	WCMN	MFWD, 20-speed power quad, 3 hyd., joystick, air seat 540/540E/1,000 PTO, 18.4-38 rear, 14.9-28 front
John Deere	7420	2005	1,236	G	$61,000	12/06	WCMN	MFWD, 20-speed power quad, 3 hyd., JD 741 loader w/ joystick
John Deere	7420	2006	315	E	$66,500	12/06	WCMN	MFWD, 3 pt., PTO, 4 hyd., ITV command arm trans., quick coupler, deluxe cab, front fenders
John Deere	7510		1,323	G	$54,000	9/06	WCWI	MFWD, 20 speed, power quad, right-hand door, fully loaded w/ JD 740 loader, one owner
John Deere	7510	2000	1,829	G	$60,500	12/06	NEMO	MFWD, quad range, 3 hyd., complete with JD 740 loader, 8' bucket
John Deere	7510	2000	1,550	E	$75,000	12/06	SWIA	MFWD, 20-speed power quad w/ reverser, deluxe cab, 3 hyd., 3 pt., quick hitch, 540/1,000 PTO, 18.4-42 singles, front weight bracket, front fenders
John Deere	7510	2001		G	$30,000	11/06	SECA	MFWD, cab, air, 3 pt, PTO
John Deere	755	1987	1,163	G	$4,650	12/06	SEIA	3 pt., 540 PTO, 72" deck, manual
John Deere	7600	1993	3,519	E	$42,500	3/06	NEIA	2WD, one owner, diesel, fully-equipped factory cab, SN H001819, power quad, 18.4-38 with fluid
John Deere	7610	1997	2,200	G	$42,000	9/06	SEIA	16-speed power quad, 3 hyd., front. fenders
John Deere	7610	1998	3,175	G	$51,000	12/06	NWMO	MFWD, 18.4-38 rear tires, power quad, front fenders, 540 PTO, 2 hyd.
John Deere	7610	1998	3,535	G	$51,500	12/06	NWMO	MFWD, 18.4×38 rear tires, 16-speed power quad, fenders, 1,000 PTO, 3 hyd., JD 740 loader & bucket
John Deere	7610	1998	850	G	$55,000	1/06	SWOH	2WD, CAH, power quad, bolt-on duals
John Deere	7610	2000		G	$44,000	8/06	SCNE	2WD, 8 front weights, CAH, power quad, 3 pt., PTO, 3 hyd., 18.4-38
John Deere	7610	2000	1,220	E	$49,000	2/06	SEMI	2WD, 2 hyd., 18.4-38
John Deere	770			G	$6,200	3/06	SEPA	ROPS, good turf rubber, rotary mower
John Deere	7700	1993	2,211	G	$26,000	8/06	SEMN	MFWD, PS
John Deere	7700	1995		G	$24,000	11/06	SECA	Front & rear weights, cab, air, PS, 3 pt., quick hitch, PTO
John Deere	7700	1995	6,140	G	$29,000	4/06	NWMN	2WD, 3 hyd., power beyond, 540/1,000 PTO, radar, 14.9-46 hub duals, 60% rubber, diesel
John Deere	7700	1996	970	E	$51,500	2/06	SEMI	MFWD, 3 hyd., 18.4R-42, duals, quick hitch
John Deere	7700	1997		G	$31,000	12/06	WCMN	MFWD, PS, 14.9-46 tires
John Deere	7710			F	$26,000	12/06	SWWI	2WD, cab, air, tach shows 3,000 but was broken so hours unknown
John Deere	7710		4,249	G	$36,000	8/06	SCFL	Cab, air, MFWD, PS
John Deere	7710	1997	2,025	G	$57,500	3/06	SCIA	2WD, power quad, 18.4-38, one owner
John Deere	7720			G	$72,000	4/06	SEPA	MFWD, JD 746 loader, 20-speed power quad, 800 Series loader hook up, GreenStar ready
John Deere	7720	2004		G	$60,000	12/06	WCMN	2WD, 3 hyd., 20 speed, right-hand door, Active Seat

WHAT'S IT WORTH?

Tractors

Make	Model	Year	Hrs.	Cond.	Price	Sale	Location	Comments
John Deere	7800			F	$18,000	8/06	SCFL	ROPS, 2WD
John Deere	7800			F	$22,500	8/06	SCFL	Cab, air, MFWD
John Deere	7800		5,573	F	$25,000	8/06	SCFL	Cab, air, MFWD
John Deere	7800		4,609	G	$28,000	8/06	SCFL	Cab, MFWD, power quad, 20.8×38
John Deere	7800			G	$30,500	12/06	SEMN	MFWD, PS, 12 front weights, 3 hyd., 18.4R-42
John Deere	7800		7,044	G	$37,000	3/06	WCMN	MFWD, CAH, PS, 3 hyd., hub duals, quick hitch, rock box
John Deere	7800	1993	2,540	G	$36,000	7/06	SEND	2WD regular front, power quad, 3 hyd., 3 pt., quick hitch, 540/1,000 PTO, press steel duals
John Deere	7800	1993	4,400	E	$40,500	2/06	NEIN	MFWD, PS, CAH, 3 pt., 3 hyd., axle duals
John Deere	7800	1993	5,200	G	$40,500	3/06	NWMN	MFWD, power beyond, quick hitch, 14.9-46 duals, 320/85R34 fronts w/ fenders, set of suitcase weights
John Deere	7800	1993	5,044	G	$42,000	2/06	NECO	MFWD, PS, 14.9R-46 duals
John Deere	7800	1994	4,800	G	$43,500	10/06	NCND	MFWD, duals, 3 pt., PS
John Deere	7800	1994	3,900	E	$44,410	8/06	ECNE	2WD, 18.4-42 duals, weights, power quad, 3 hyd., just been through local dealer inspection program
John Deere	7800	1994	4,846	G	$44,500	12/06	WCMN	MFWD, 19-speed PS, 3 hyd., duals, 3 pt., PTO
John Deere	7800	1994	2,820	G	$47,000	1/06	NWIL	2WD, axle duals
John Deere	7800	1995	3,816	G	$41,300	8/06	WCKS	2WD, power quad, quick hitch, joystick w/ JD 725 loader, 6' bucket, no duals
John Deere	7800	1995	3,887	G	$44,000	1/06	SCKS	2WD, 18-speed PS, 18.4R42 tires w/ 10-bolt duals, 1100-16 4 rib front tires, 3 hyd., 3 pt., quick hitch, 10 front end weights, rear weights, SN 11565, shedded
John Deere	7800	1997		G	$25,000	11/06	SECA	MFWD, front, weights, cab, air, radio, PS, 3 pt., PTO
John Deere	7800	1997		G	$25,000	11/06	SECA	MFWD, front weights, cab, air, PS, 3 pt., PTO, quick hitch
John Deere	7800	1998		G	$25,000	11/06	SECA	MFWD, front weights, cab, air, PS, 3 pt., quick hitch
John Deere	7810			F	$27,300	12/06	SWWI	MFWD, cab, air, new tires, 8,600 hours
John Deere	7810			G	$41,000	8/06	SCFL	PS, MFWD, 20.8×38
John Deere	7810		2,904	G	$51,000	8/06	SCFL	Cab, MFWD, 20.8×38 w/ duals
John Deere	7810	1997	3,156	E	$49,500	2/06	SCMN	2WD, 420/80R-46 rubber & duals, 3 hyd., lift assist
John Deere	7810	1997	2,921	G	$50,300	12/06	SCNE	2WD, CAH, 4 hyd., 18.4-42 tires, duals, 20 front weights, power quad
John Deere	7810	1997	4,500	G	$56,000	1/06	NCCO	MFWD, radar, performance monitor, 14.9-46 duals, power quad, 3 hyd., air seat
John Deere	7810	1997	3,797	G	$57,000	12/06	NWMO	CAH, new 18.4-42 rear tires, new 14.9-38 front tires, 19-speed ps, MFWD, 3 hyd., side exhaust, quick hitch, JD 740 loader w/ joystick
John Deere	7810	1997	2,200	G	$59,800	1/06	WCIL	MFWD, duals
John Deere	7810	1997	745	G	$60,000	2/06	SEIL	
John Deere	7810	1997	2,881	G	$62,500	2/06	SESD	MFWD, PS, 3 hyd., 42" tires/duals
John Deere	7810	1997	2,280	E	$67,000	2/06	SEMI	MFWD, 3 hyd., 18.4R-42, duals, quick hitch
John Deere	7810	1998	1,300	E	$56,000	3/06	NEIA	2WD, one owner, fully-equipped factory cab, SN P013824, PS, 18.4-42 duals, diesel
John Deere	7810	1998	1,870	E	$62,000	11/06	WCIA	2WD, PS, deluxe cab, one owner, 14.9R-46, factory duals & weights
John Deere	7810	1999		G	$59,500	3/06	NEMI	MFWD, CAH, 150 hp., power quad 16, 3 hyd., 18.4R-42 axle duals, 14.9-30 fronts, one owner
John Deere	7810	2000	1,446	G	$70,500	1/06	NWIL	MFWD, 18.4-42, hub duals, power quad, 5 speed, front weights, front. fenders, wheel weights, 3 hyd., quick hitch

Tractors

Make	Model	Year	Hrs.	Cond.	Price	Sale	Location	Comments
John Deere	7810	2001	3,772	F	$51,000	2/06	SCNY	MFWD, 3 hyd., PS, standard cab, no weights, 20.8-38 duals
John Deere	7810	2002	2,400	G	$63,500	1/06	NEIN	MFWD, cab, air, power quad, 18.4-42, nice
John Deere	7810	2003	990	E	$63,000	2/06	SCWI	2WD, PS, right-hand door, 3 hyd., front weights, 18.4-42 axle duals, deluxe cab, very nice
John Deere	7820			G	$88,000	4/06	SEPA	MFWD, 7-month warranty, GreenStar ready, IVT trans., 1,200 hours warranty, GreenStar ready, 1,000/540 PTO, 3 hyd., deluxe comfort package
John Deere	7820	2004	1,150	G	$72,000	12/06	NWWI	MFWD, power quad, 3 hyd., 480/90R42, no duals
John Deere	7820	2004	870	G	$79,500	3/06	NENE	MFWD, quad trans., left-hand reverser, 480/80R42 rear tires, 10-bolt duals, 420/85R28 front tires, 4 hyd., 540/1,000 PTO, always shedded
John Deere	7820	2004		G	$80,000	7/06	WCCA	Front weights, cab, air, power quad, left-hand reverser, quick hitch, PTO, 3 hyd.
John Deere	7820	2004	1,114	G	$81,000	8/06	WCMN	MFWD, 18.4-46, duals, field vision, 3 hyd.
John Deere	7820	2005	1,150	G	$80,250	12/06	NWWI	MFWD, power quad, loaded, duals
John Deere	7920	2004	1,030	E	$88,500	3/06	NWOH	MFWD, cab, IVT trans., duals, 3 hyd. buddy seat, quick hitch, weights, GreenStar ready
John Deere	7920	2005	988	G	$91,000	12/06	WCMN	MFWD, IVT, auto track, 4 hyd., duals
John Deere	7920	2006	209	E	$97,750	12/06	WCMN	MFWD, IVT transmission, triple-link front suspension, 380/90R/50 duals, 380/85R34 fronts w/ fenders, hd lighting, multi PTO, 3 pt. lift assist, quick coupler, 4 hyd., rock box w/ weight bracket, GreenStar ready
John Deere	8100		5,366	G	$39,250	7/06	WCTN	MFWD, 18.4×42R duals
John Deere	8100		8,846	G	$43,000	3/06	NCUT	MFWD, 46" duals
John Deere	8100		2,110	G	$74,000	4/06	NESD	MFWD, 16 speed ps, 4 reverse, 3 pt., 4 hyd., 3 pt., radar, deluxe cab, axle duals, quick-tach, kept inside
John Deere	8100	1995	5,650	G	$45,000	12/06	SCMN	MFWD, 14.9-34 tires
John Deere	8100	1995		G	$47,000	3/06	SWMI	MFWD, PS, 4 hyd., 3 pt., PTO, front weights, 480/80R46 tires
John Deere	8100	1995	3,866	E	$56,000	1/06	NWIA	MFWD, 3 hyd., front weights
John Deere	8100	1995	1,537	G	$65,000	3/06	SCIA	MFWD, dual PTO, 18.4-42 duals, weights, 3 hyd.
John Deere	8100	1996	3,267	G	$49,750	12/06	SCMN	MFWD
John Deere	8100	1996	4,268	G	$53,000	12/06	SCMN	MFWD
John Deere	8100	1996	4,218	G	$57,000	12/06	SCMN	MFWD, fenders, 18.4-46 tires
John Deere	8100	1996	2,743	G	$61,000	12/06	NCIA	MFWD, 18.4-42 duals, 3 hyd.
John Deere	8100	1996	2,159	G	$62,000	2/06	ECMN	MFWD, 1,000 rpm, 3 hyd., power beyond, rock box, cab, PS, 14.9R-46, factory duals
John Deere	8100	1997	12,800	F	$28,000	8/06	NECO	2WD, 3 hyd., 3 pt., quick hitch, PTO, 18.4R-46, duals
John Deere	8100	1997	6,374	F	$42,500	3/06	WCMN	MFWD, 18.4-42 duals, front fenders, 3 pt., quick coupler, 3 hyd., PTO, rock box
John Deere	8100	1998	1,108	E	$65,000	2/06	ECMN	MFWD, one owner, Goodyear DT800 320/90R50 triples, 5 hyd., 540/1,000 PTO, 3 pt., performance monitor,
John Deere	8100	1999	4,100	G	$55,000	3/06	SCID	MFWD
John Deere	8100	1999	3,750	G	$63,500	3/06	SCID	MFWD
John Deere	8100T	1998		P	$28,000	11/06	ECND	CAH, PS, 4 hyd., 3 pt., PTO, 16" belts, hours unknown
John Deere	8100T	1998	2,947	G	$48,500	12/06	SCMN	Tracks
John Deere	8110	2000	3,006	E	$63,500	2/06	NWMN	MFWD, deluxe cab, 4 hyd., 3 pt., PTO, 380/90R50 rear hub duals, 14.9-R34 fronts, front fenders

Tractors

Make	Model	Year	Hrs.	Cond.	Price	Sale	Location	Comments
John Deere	8110	2000	1,570	G	$69,750	11/06	WCMN	MFWD, PS, 3 hyd., 3 pt., quick hitch, 540/1,000 PTO, K&M rock box, 18.4-46 hub duals, 85% rubber, 14.9-34 fronts, front fenders, one owner
John Deere	8110	2000	1,925	G	$71,000	2/06	ECMN	MFWD, PS, 420/80R-46 duals, 320/85R-34 fronts, cab, quick hitch, 1,000 rpm, 4 hyd., rock box
John Deere	8110	2001		G	$50,000	8/06	SCNE	2WD, 3 pt., PTO, 4 hyd., 520/85R42 duals, 11R24.5 front
John Deere	8120	2002	1,300	G	$78,000	2/06	WCIA	MFWD, 3 hyd., 3 pt., PTO, 30-gpm hyd. pump, 18.4-46 duals
John Deere	8120	2002	1,057	G	$81,500	12/06	NCIA	MFWD, 18.4-46 duals, 3 hyd., front weights
John Deere	8120	2002	2,012	E	$82,500	2/06	NWMN	MFWD, 5 hyd., 3 pt., PTO, 380/90R50, hub duals, autosteer ready
John Deere	8120	2003	1,020	E	$87,500	12/06	SWIA	MFWD, PS, 3 hyd., deluxe cab, Active Seat, GreenStar ready, 3-pt. quick hitch, 1,000 PTO, Firestone 18.4-46 press steel duals
John Deere	8120	2004	97	G	$93,750	2/06	WCIL	MFWD, deluxe cab w/ Active Seat, radar, 3 hyd., duals, quick hitch, like new
John Deere	8120	2005	290	G	$95,000	7/06	SEND	MFWD, PS, deluxe cab, 3 hyd., 3 pt., PTO, 18.4-46 press steel duals, 14.9-34 fronts
John Deere	8120T	2002	900	G	$69,000	12/06	NWWI	Track tractor, 80" space, 24" belts, deluxe cab, GMP pump, radar
John Deere	8120T	2002	2,700	G	$75,000	12/06	SCMN	120" stance, 16" belts
John Deere	8200	1995	6,023	G	$37,500	2/06	WCMN	Reg. 2WD front, power shift, 3 hyd., 3 pt., 1,000 PTO, press steel duals
John Deere	8200	1995	6,083	G	$38,250	7/06	SEND	2WD, PS, 3 hyd., 3 pt., quick hitch, 1,000 PTO, 14.9-R-46 duals
John Deere	8200	1995	4,620	G	$47,500	7/06	SEND	MFWD, PS, 3 hyd., power beyond, 3 pt., quick hitch, radar, 1,000 PTO, 18.4-42 press steel duals
John Deere	8200	1995	4,600	G	$57,500	3/06	SESD	MFWD, 3 hyd., 18.4-46 duals, front weights
John Deere	8200	1995	3,700	G	$59,750	12/06	NWWI	MFWD, 18.4R-46 duals
John Deere	8200	1996	2,600	G	$58,000	7/06	WCMN	MFWD, duals
John Deere	8200	1997	3,000	G	$59,000	7/06	SEND	MFWD, 4 hyd., deluxe cab, 3 pt., PTO, front weights, fenders, 14.9-46 metric size
John Deere	8200	1997	4,900	G	$61,000	3/06	ECNE	MFWD, 16-speed ps, 480/80R46 rear tires, duals, 10" spacers, 380/85R34 fronts, 3 hyd., quick hitch, 12 front end weights, cab, radar
John Deere	8200	1997	2,191	G	$75,750	8/06	NCIA	MFWD, 16/4 power shift, 3 hyd., quick coupler, front weights, radar, mirrors, rear wipers, bolt duals
John Deere	8200	1997	1,257	E	$77,500	3/06	NEIA	MFWD, one owner, fully-equipped factory cab, SN P011797, PS, 18.4-46 plus duals
John Deere	8200	1998	4,200	G	$58,000	1/06	NCCO	MFWD, 18.4-46 rear, duals, 16.9-30 fronts, PS, 3 hyd., quick hitch, clevis hitch, radio
John Deere	8200T	1998	3,575	G	$47,500	12/06	WCMN	16" tracks, PS, 4 hyd., PTO, 3 pt., front weights, 24"
John Deere	8220		250	E	$90,000	12/06	SWMI	MFWD, 18.4-46, duals, quick attach, full hydraulics, full weights, very clean
John Deere	8220	2002		G	$58,000	8/06	SCNE	2WD, deluxe cab, 3 pt., PTO, 4 hyd., GreenStar ready, JD Active Seat, 18.4-46 duals, 14L-16 front, 12 front weights
John Deere	8220	2002	1,050	G	$87,500	12/06	NWWI	MFWD, remaining 5-year/5,000-hour warranty, 20.8-42 w/ duals, deluxe cab, 4 hyd., 540 PTO

Tractors

Make	Model	Year	Hrs.	Cond.	Price	Sale	Location	Comments
John Deere	8220	2004	950	G	$87,500	11/06	ECND	MFWD, CAH, PS, 4 hyd., large hyd. pump, 3 pt., PTO, high-intensity lights, 380R50 press steel duals
John Deere	8220	2004	1,295	G	$87,500	12/06	SCMN	MFWD, duals
John Deere	8220	2004	293	E	$95,000	8/06	WCMN	MFWD, custom deluxe cab, 4 hyd., 480/46 duals
John Deere	8220	2004	560	G	$95,000	12/06	WCMN	MFWD, deluxe cab, 3 hyd., duals, high-intensity lighting, Active Seat
John Deere	8220	2005	179	E	$97,500	12/06	WCMN	MFWD, 4 hyd., 380/90RR50, Active Seat, buddy seat, front fenders, rock box, high-intensity lighting, 3 pt., PTO
John Deere	8220T	2004	315	G	$95,000	11/06	ECND	Deluxe cab, PS, 4 hyd., 3 pt., PTO, high-intensity lights, 42-gpm pump, 24" belts set at 80"
John Deere	8300		4,479	G	$42,000	8/06	SCFL	Cab, MFWD, 18.4×46 duals
John Deere	8300		5,569	G	$50,000	7/06	WCTN	MFWD, 18.4×46R duals
John Deere	8300	1995	4,757	G	$42,750	8/06	NECO	2WD, 4 hyd., 3 pt., PTO, radar, front weights, rear weights, 18.4R-46 duals
John Deere	8300	1995	5,000	G	$49,000	12/06	SEMN	MFWD
John Deere	8300	1995	3,840	G	$50,000	5/06	WCKS	MFWD, duals
John Deere	8300	1995	4,300	G	$50,000	8/06	SCNE	MFWD
John Deere	8300	1995	4,320	G	$55,000	2/06	SWNE	MFWD, 15-speed PS, 3 pt., quick hitch, 4 hyd., large 1,000 PTO, 380/85R front, 18.4R-46 rear w/ hubs & duals
John Deere	8300	1995	3,700	G	$58,750	1/06	NEIN	MFWD
John Deere	8300	1995	3,218	G	$63,000	2/06	SWNE	MFWD, 4 hyd., 18.4R-46, duals, 14.9R-34 front tires, 1,000 PTO, 3 pt., quick hitch, one owner, JD guidance system
John Deere	8300	1995	1,720	G	$67,500	1/06	NWIL	MFWD, axle duals
John Deere	8300	1995	1,602	E	$76,000	2/06	SCMN	MFWD, 18.4R-46, duals, 16.9R-30 fronts, 20 weights, wheel weights, 3 hyd. w/ return, all updates
John Deere	8300	1996	4,196	G	$62,000	3/06	NEND	MFWD, deluxe cab, 16-speed PS, 4 hyd., 3 pt. quick hitch, 1,000 PTO, 14.9-46 hub duals (75%), rear wheel weights, front suitcase weights, fenders, 14.9-30 fronts (80%), greenlighted
John Deere	8300	1996	2,749	G	$68,000	3/06	SEMN	MFWD, 18.4-46 w/ duals, 70% rubber, front weights, 3 pt., quick hitch, 3 hyd., very clean
John Deere	8300	1997	3,025	G	$67,000	2/06	WCMN	MFWD, 3 pt., 3 hyd., 14.9R-46 duals & triples, 14.9-30 fronts
John Deere	8300	1997		G	$68,000	8/06	SCNE	MFWD, 3 pt., quick hitch, PTO, 5 hyd., 18.4-46 duals, 14.9R34 front, rear wheel weights
John Deere	8300	1997	3,800	G	$70,000	2/06	NWIN	MFWD, front weights, quick coupler, tires 70%, nice clean tractor
John Deere	8300	1997	2,990	G	$76,000	12/06	NCIA	MFWD, 18.4-46 duals, 4 hyd., front & rear weights, one owner
John Deere	8300	1998	3,400	G	$47,500	6/06	ECSD	Duals
John Deere	8300	1998	3,028	G	$68,750	3/06	NCIA	MFWD, PS, 3 hyd., quick coupler, 18.4-46 duals, 14.9-34 front tires, front fenders and weights
John Deere	8300	1998	2,600	G	$71,500	12/06	NCIA	MFWD, 18.4-46 duals, 4 hyd.
John Deere	8310	2001	2,489	G	$75,000	12/06	WCMN	MFWD, 4 hyd., deluxe cab, duals
John Deere	8310	2001	2,700	G	$76,000	9/06	SWIA	MFWD, one owner, fully loaded, radar, 4 hyd., front 3 pt., 18.4-42 duals, 14.9-34 front tires, extra clean
John Deere	8320	2002		G	$83,000	8/06	SCNE	MFWD, deluxe cab, 3 pt., quick hitch, PTO, 4 hyd., 18.4-46 duals, 420/90R-30 front, front fenders, 12 front weights

Tractors

Make	Model	Year	Hrs.	Cond.	Price	Sale	Location	Comments
John Deere	8320	2002	1,227	G	$91,000	3/06	NENE	MFWD, 780/80R46 rear tires, 10-bolt duals, 380/85R34 front tires, 4 hyd., power beyond, quick hitch, 12 front weights, 1,000 lbs. in rear weights, GreenStar ready, one owner
John Deere	8320	2002	1,764	G	$93,000	11/06	SCNE	MFWD, 16 speed, 4 hyd., implement management system, climate control, performance monitor, GreenStar ready, front, rear weights, duals
John Deere	8320	2003		E	$94,000	1/06	SCNE	MFWD, CAH, 16-speed PS, monitor, 4 hyd., 3 pt. quick hitch, 1,000 PTO, axle mount duals, weights
John Deere	8320	2003	575	E	$110,500	4/06	NWKS	MFWD, GreenStar ready, 215 hp., 4 hyd., 3 pt., PTO, 14.9-34R front duals, 18.4R-46 rear duals
John Deere	8320	2004	508	G	$105,000	12/06	SCMN	MFWD, AutoTrac ready, duals
John Deere	8320	2004	1,050	G	$110,000	12/06	NWMO	CAH, MFWD, 4 hyd., 480/80R/46 rear tires, 40/90R30 front tires, deluxe cab, radar, GreenStar, fenders
John Deere	8320	2005	730	G	$104,000	11/06	SCNE	MFWD, 16 speed, 4 hyd., Active Seat, implement management system, climate control, performance monitor, GreenStar ready, front and rear weights, duals
John Deere	8400		5,963	G	$42,500	3/06	NCUT	MFWD, 42", duals
John Deere	8400		6,800	F	$46,500	12/06	SWWI	MFWD
John Deere	8400	1996	7,474	F	$40,000	3/06	NESD	MFWD, 46" tires w/ duals
John Deere	8400	1996	4,632	G	$60,000	3/06	SWKS	MFWD, 16-speed PS, 4 hyd., large 1,000 PTO, 18.4R-46 duals, 16.9R-30 fronts, 20 front weights
John Deere	8400	1996	3,976	E	$71,750	4/06	NWMN	MFWD, CAH, deluxe cab, field cruise, PS, 3 hyd., 3 pt., quick hitch, 18.4-46 steel press duals, 16.9-30 fronts, front fenders, suitcase weights
John Deere	8400	1996	2,585	G	$75,000	11/06	NCIN	MFWD, 4 hyd., 20.8-42 axle duals
John Deere	8400	1997	8,310	G	$51,000	9/06	WCND	MFWD, 16-speed PS, deluxe cab, 4 hyd., 3 pt., 1,000 PTO, rear weight pkg., front suitcase weights, radar, 380R/90/50 press steel duals
John Deere	8400	1997	5,909	G	$52,000	2/06	SEKS	MFWD, duals, 6 hyd.
John Deere	8400	1997	4,287	G	$67,000	4/06	ECND	MFWD, deluxe cab, 16-speed PS, 4 rev., 4 hyd., 3 pt., quick hitch, 540/1,000 PTO, rear inside weights, front suitcase weights, 18.4-46 press steel duals (50% rubber)
John Deere	8400	1997	2,713	G	$73,000	2/06	SCMI	MFWD, new engine (new injectors and turbo charger by JD equipment, London, OH), 20.8-46 duals, 5 hyd., power beyond, buddy seat, fender flashers, radar, quick hitch, PS
John Deere	8400	1998	5,265	G	$66,900	2/06	WCKS	MFWD, PS, duals, quick hitch
John Deere	8400	1998	3,109	G	$72,000	2/06	SWNE	MFWD, 4 hyd., 18.4R-46, duals, 14.9R-34 front tires, 1,000 PTO, 3 pt., quick hitch, JD Auto Trac guidance system
John Deere	8400	1998	3,276	G	$80,000	12/06	ECNE	MFWD, new 18.4R-42 w/ 10-bolt duals, 14.9R-34 front, 4 hyd., quick hitch, 1,000 lb. rear wheel weights, 20 front end weights, front fenders, performance monitor, radar
John Deere	8400	1998	1,048	E	$93,500	3/06	SEMN	MFWD, 3 pt., 3 hyd., duals, deluxe cab, looks new
John Deere	8400T		5,102	F	$30,000	3/06	NCUT	30" belts
John Deere	8400T		2,800	G	$63,000	3/06	WCMN	Radar, 16" belts for 20" rows, full suitcase weights, GreenStar auto steer ready
John Deere	8400T	1998		G	$22,500	7/06	WCCA	Front weights, cab, air, 3 pt., quick hitch, 3 hyd
John Deere	8400T	1998	28,335	G	$67,000	2/06	NWMN	5 hyd., 3 pt., PTO, new 16" tracks, auto steer ready
John Deere	8410		3,700	G	$74,000	2/06	WCMN	MFWD, deluxe cab, 3 pt., quick hitch, PTO, 4 hyd., 8 front weights, duals

Tractors

Make	Model	Year	Hrs.	Cond.	Price	Sale	Location	Comments
John Deere	8410		3,518	G	$74,000	2/06	WCMN	MFWD, deluxe cab, 3 pt. w/ quick hitch, PTO, 4 hyd., 8 front weights, duals
John Deere	8410	2000	3,470	G	$78,000	11/06	ECND	MFWD, CAH, PS, 4 hyd., 3 pt., 1,000 PTO, 14.9-46 duals, 14.9-30 fronts, radar, front fenders, front weights
John Deere	8410	2001	4,080	G	$75,000	3/06	ECND	MFWD, front weights, 3 pt., 3 hyd., PTO w/ duals
John Deere	8410	2001	1,059	E	$88,000	11/06	NWMN	MFWD, 16-speed PS, 3 hyd., 3 pt., quick hitch, 1,000 PTO, deluxe cab, 480-46 press steel duals, 90% rubber, rear weight pkg., 380-85-34 fronts, fenders, front suitcase weights, one owner
John Deere	8410T		5,850	F	$55,000	11/06	ECND	Track tractor, 16" tracks 70%, 5 hyd., front weights, auto-steer equipped
John Deere	8410T	2000	2,680	G	$67,000	8/06	SCNE	Deluxe cab, 3 pt., quick hitch, PTO, 4 hyd., GreenStar ready, 16" tracks, 120" wide gauge, front weights
John Deere	8410T	2000	1,861	G	$95,000	2/06	WCIL	Deluxe cab, comfort pkg., 4 hyd., quick hitch, 30" belts, wide track, radar, field office
John Deere	8420	2002		G	$80,000	8/06	SCNE	MFWD, deluxe cab, 3 pt., quick hitch, PTO, 4 hyd., 18.4R46 factory duals, 16.9R30 front, 12 front weights, fenders, rear wheel weights
John Deere	8420	2002	1,507	G	$92,000	2/06	SCNY	MFWD, 3 hyd., PS, front & rear weights, 20.8-42 duals
John Deere	8420	2002	826	E	$112,500	1/06	NWIA	MFWD, diesel, PS, 4 hyd., GreenStar ready, extra light kit, front weights, 3 pt., like new
John Deere	8420	2003	2,149	G	$84,000	8/06	SCNE	MFWD, deluxe cab, 3 pt., quick hitch, PTO, 4 hyd., 480/80R46 rear duals, 420/90RX30 front, fenders, rear wheel weights
John Deere	8420	2003	3,420	G	$85,500	11/06	ECND	MFWD, CAH, PS, 4 hyd., 3 pt., quick hitch, 1,000 PTO, instructional seat, radar, AutoTrac ready, front suitcase weights, rear weights, front fenders, 380/90-50 metric duals, 380-85-34 fronts
John Deere	8420	2003	2,560	G	$87,000	12/06	SEND	MFWD, deluxe cab, comfort pkg., 3 pt., PTO, 4 hyd., duals
John Deere	8420	2003	2,700	G	$89,000	3/06	SCID	MFWD
John Deere	8420	2003	2,919	G	$90,000	12/06	WCKS	MFWD, implement, GreenStar ready, 480/80R50 tires, duals, weights, 420/85R34 fronts w/ fenders, weight bracket, 4 hyd., 1,000 PTO, buddy seat, AM/FM radio/CD player
John Deere	8420	2003	1,518	G	$110,000	11/06	SCNE	MFWD, 16 speed, 4 hyd., Active Seat, implement management system, GreenStar ready, performance monitor, duals, front and rear weights
John Deere	8420	2005	1,500	G	$115,000	11/06	SCNE	MFWD, 16 speed, 4 hyd., Active Seat, implement management system, climate control, GreenStar ready, performance monitor, duals, front. and rear weights
John Deere	8420	2005	405	G	$115,000	12/06	WCMN	MFWD, 380/90R50 duals, 320/85R38, 4 hyd., 3 pt., PTO, quick coupler, high-intensity lights, buddy seat
John Deere	8420	2005	455	E	$115,000	12/06	SWIA	MFWD, PS, deluxe cab, GreenStar ready, buddy seat, active seat, high intensity lights, side lights, climate control option, 4 hyd., 3 pt., quick hitch, 1000 PTO

Tractors

Make	Model	Year	Hrs.	Cond.	Price	Sale	Location	Comments
John Deere	8420	2005	175	E	$125,750	12/06	WCMN	MFWD, high-intensity lighting, deluxe comfort guard cab, GreenStar ready, independent link suspension, PS, multi-PTO, 3 pt. w/ lift assist, quick coupler, 4 hyd., power beyond, rock box, front weight, extra light package, new in November 2005
John Deere	8420	2005	245	E	$127,000	12/06	WCMN	MFWD, rock box, deluxe comfort guard cab, 4 hyd., independent link suspension, GreenStar ready, powershift, multi PTO, 3 pt. w/ lift assist, quick coupler, power beyond, high-density lighting
John Deere	8420T		1,400	G	$90,000	12/06	SWMI	Tracks, 235 hp., one owner, quick-attach PTO, 12 front weights, 4 hyd.
John Deere	8420T	2002	2,326	G	$79,000	8/06	SCNE	Deluxe cab, 3 pt., PTO, 5 hyd., GreenStar, 120" wide gauge, 16" tracks, front weights
John Deere	8420T	2003	3,300	G	$76,500	12/06	WCMN	16", 5500 tracks 80%, new mid rollers, 4 hyd., PS, 3 pt., front weights, autosteer ready, extended warranty available
John Deere	8420T	2003	1,400	G	$95,000	12/06	SEND	Wide stance, 120", deluxe cab, comfort pkg., 3 pt., PTO, 4 hyd.
John Deere	8420T	2004	1,510	G	$97,500	11/06	ECND	CAH, PS, 4 hyd., 3 pt., PTO, high-intensity lights, 16" belts
John Deere	8440	1980	5,750	G	$12,000	11/06	WCMN	4WD, 3 pt., PTO, 850 hours on OH
John Deere	8440	1981	9,508	G	$7,000	2/06	NECO	Axle duals, 4 hyd, 3 pt
John Deere	8440	1981	3,799	G	$17,000	3/06	SWNE	4WD, quad range, 18.4-38, cast duals, PTO, 3 hyd., 12' dozer blade, 3 hyd.
John Deere	8440	1982	8,400	G	$15,750	3/06	NWMN	4WD, 1,000 hours on 50 Series engine, 3 pt., PTO, 3 hyd., 18.4-38 duals, 90% rubber
John Deere	8450			F	$13,500	4/06	NEND	4WD, PTO, 3 hyd., 18.4-38 duals
John Deere	8450	1982	8,414	G	$10,250	7/06	SEND	4WD, CAH, quad range, 3 hyd., 1,000 PTO, 18.4-38 press steel duals
John Deere	8450	1982	4,091	G	$30,500	2/06	SCMI	4WD, power beyond, PTO, quick hitch
John Deere	8450	1984	8,800	G	$11,500	6/06	ECND	4WD, CAH, 3 hyd., no PTO, inside weights all around, 20.8-34 press steel duals
John Deere	8450	1984		F	$15,500	12/06	NWWI	4WD, 3 hyd., fresh engine OH, 18.4-38, duals
John Deere	850		4,900	F	$3,800	1/06	SEPA	WF, belly mower, average turf rubber
John Deere	8520	2002	3,800	G	$89,000	12/06	WCMN	MFWD, new 18.4-46 duals, Active Seat, 4 hyd., warranty up to 5,000 hours
John Deere	8520	2002	807	E	$112,000	8/06	WCIL	MFWD, like new, loaded, deluxe cab, quick hitch, 520/85R46 duals, one owner
John Deere	8520	2002	700	G	$127,000	1/06	NEIN	50" rear duals, front duals
John Deere	8520	2005	843	G	$125,000	8/06	SCNE	MFWD, independent link suspension, deluxe cab, active seat, Xenon lights, 3 pt., PTO, 4 hyd., rear duals, front duals, warranty
John Deere	8520	2005	177	E	$135,000	8/06	NECO	MFWD, 5 hyd., 3 pt., PTO, 22 front weights, rear weights, 420/85R34 & 710/70R42 tires w/ front & rear duals
John Deere	8520T			G	$64,000	1/06	WCCA	Front weights, cab, air, side weights, 3 pt.
John Deere	8520T	2003	2,020	G	$90,000	4/06	NWMN	5 hyd., 3 pt., PTO, 16" tracks, autosteer ready, 16" tracks set at 88", 80%
John Deere	8520T	2004	993	G	$111,000	8/06	SCNE	Deluxe cab, 3 pt., quick hitch, PTO, 4 hyd., return line, 120" wide gauge, 16" tracks, 22 front weights
John Deere	8520T	2004	688	G	$120,000	12/06	WCMN	18" wide, quick coupler, 4 hyd., buddy seat, front weights, GreenStar ready

Tractors

Make	Model	Year	Hrs.	Cond.	Price	Sale	Location	Comments
John Deere	855		1,201	G	$5,700	3/06	WCMN	Utility, ROPS, hydrostatic, 3 pt., belly mower
John Deere	855		800	E	$8,800	3/06	NEKS	72" mower deck, one-year-old JD 420 loader
John Deere	855	1993	537	G	$11,500	8/06	SETN	JD 70A front loader, 72" midmounted mower, 4WD, hydro trans., ROPS
John Deere	8560			F	$24,000	8/06	SCNE	4WD, Degelman 12' dozer, extension, 6-way blade, 24 speed, 3 hyd., silage rack, 20.8-38 duals
John Deere	8560			F	$29,000	8/06	SCNE	4WD, 24 speed, 3 hyd., 18.4-42 duals
John Deere	8560		1,599	G	$47,000	8/06	SCMN	24 spd., 3 hyd, block heater, bareback
John Deere	8560	1990	8,600	G	$22,000	7/06	SEND	4WD, 24 speed, 4 hyd., differential lock, 18.4-38 duals
John Deere	8560	1990		F	$23,000	2/06	ECKS	4WD
John Deere	8560	1990	5,671	F	$24,000	3/06	NWKS	4WD, 12 speed, hubs and duals, recent OH
John Deere	8560	1990	4,231	G	$39,500	3/06	NESD	4WD, 24 speed, quad, 3 hyd., radar, hub duals
John Deere	8570	1995	1,922	E	$63,000	3/06	ECND	4WD, 24 speed, 4 hyd., 1,000 PTO, new Titan 18.4-38 tires press steel hub duals, one owner
John Deere	8640			F	$5,700	8/06	NECO	4WD
John Deere	8640			F	$7,000	8/06	SCNE	4WD, quad range, 3 pt., PTO, 3 hyd., 18.4-38 duals
John Deere	8640		7,583	G	$17,000	4/06	WCSD	4WD, 1,000 PTO, 3 pt., radio, air, axle duals w/ JD 12' dozer, 50 Series engine
John Deere	8640	1981	9,100	F	$6,500	7/06	SEND	4WD, CAH, quad range, 3 hyd., PTO, 20.8R-38
John Deere	8640	1981	5,886	F	$10,100	1/06	NEIN	4WD, PTO
John Deere	8640	1981	5,710	G	$15,000	3/06	NWKS	4WD, quad range, 18.4-38, 10-bolt duals, 3 hyd., 3 pt., quick hitch, PTO, AM/FM radio, air
John Deere	8640	1981	9,950	G	$16,750	3/06	NEKS	4WD, 3 pt., 1,000 PTO, JD 12' dozer blade, 2,155 hours on new tach, 18.4-38, duals
John Deere	8640	1982	9,600	G	$8,750	4/06	NEND	4WD, 16-speed quad range, 3 hyd., PTO, 20.8-38 press steel duals
John Deere	8640	1982	10,000	G	$10,000	4/06	NEND	4WD, 16-speed quad range, 3 hyd., PTO, 20.8-38 cast duals, extensive reconditioning 2,500 hours ago
John Deere	8640	1982	6,900	G	$14,000	3/06	NCNE	4WD, single stick quad, 20.8-38, 9-bolt duals, 3 hyd., 3 pt., PTO
John Deere	8650			G	$10,000	5/06	SCCA	Cab, air, 3 pt., PTO, 3 hyd., 20.8×42 duals
John Deere	8650			F	$13,500	9/06	NCIA	4WD, shows 7,850 hours, 3 hyd., quick hitch, 20.8-38 tires
John Deere	8650	1982		G	$17,000	11/06	NEND	4WD, 4 hyd., 1,000 PTO, recent JD rebuild, 20.8-38-steel press hub duals, recent engine & clutch
John Deere	8650	1983	6,000	G	$16,750	8/06	NECO	4WD, 3 hyd., new 20.8-42 duals
John Deere	8650	1983	8,300	G	$19,000	2/06	WCKS	4WD, duals, 3 pt., PTO, quad range
John Deere	8650	1983	3,717	G	$40,000	12/06	WCMI	4WD, bareback, 3 hyd., quad shift, new Michelin 520/85R38 w/ inner rim cast weights, duals, cab
John Deere	8650	1984	5,650	F	$10,000	7/06	SEND	4WD, quad range, 4 hyd., 20.8-38 cast duals
John Deere	8650	1986	7,914	G	$20,000	3/06	NEND	4WD, CAH, 16-speed trans., 4 hyd., differential lock, rear inside weights, 20.8-38 press steel duals, 2,500 hours on engine OH
John Deere	8650	1987	6,481	G	$30,750	11/06	WCMN	4WD, 3 hyd., K&M rock box, Firestone 520/85R38 tires, 90% rubber, all around cast duals
John Deere	870			G	$10,500	11/06	SCCA	4WD, Rhino, 5' deck
John Deere	8760		10,700	G	$36,000	12/06	NENE	3 pt., PTO, triple hyd., Degelman 14' dozer
John Deere	8760			G	$50,000	8/06	SCNE	4WD, 24 speed, 3 pt., PTO, 3 hyd., 20.8-42 duals
John Deere	8760	1989	6,600	G	$27,500	8/06	WCMN	4WD, 4 hyd., 24.5-32 tires, 12 speed, JD financing
John Deere	8760	1989	8,935	F	$28,000	3/06	SWKS	4WD, 24 speed, 275 hours on out of frame OH, differential lock, 3 hyd., 3 pt., quick hitch, duals

Tractors

Make	Model	Year	Hrs.	Cond.	Price	Sale	Location	Comments
John Deere	8760	1989	2,671	G	$57,000	3/06	ECIL	4WD, air, 4 hyd., 24 speed, radar, bareback, 20.8R-38 Firestone 8-ply w/ matching axle duals
John Deere	8760	1990	9,876	G	$25,500	11/06	ECND	4WD, CAH, 24 speed, 3 hyd., differential lock, 20.8-42 duals
John Deere	8760	1990	6,865	G	$32,000	3/06	SWKS	4WD, 24 speed, 3 hyd., bareback, 20.8R-38 duals
John Deere	8760	1990	5,733	G	$34,000	3/06	NWMN	4WD, 12 speed, 4 hyd., Goodyear 20.8-42 (80% rubber)
John Deere	8760	1991	6,503	G	$33,000	12/06	WCMN	4WD, 20.8-42 duals, 4 hyd., 24 speed, radar, perfect monitor, rock box
John Deere	8770		2,624	G	$67,000	1/06	SCMN	4WD, 3 pt.
John Deere	8770	1993	6,167	G	$39,000	3/06	NEND	4WD, CAH, 24 speed, differential lock, 4 hyd., in/outside rear weights, 20.8-38 press steel duals
John Deere	8770	1993	2,605	G	$58,000	3/06	NENE	4WD, 24 speed trans., 20.8R-42, 10-bolt duals, 4 hyd., 2,000 lbs. in rear wheel weights, bareback, radar, AM/FM
John Deere	8770	1994	4,271	G	$48,000	4/06	ECND	4WD, CAH, 12 speed, 4 hyd., 20.8-42 press steel duals, 85% rubber
John Deere	8770	1995	4,800	G	$41,250	4/06	SCKS	Quad range trans., duals, 3 hyd., bareback
John Deere	8770	1995	4,178	G	$52,000	2/06	SCKS	4WD, quad range, 20.8-42, duals, 3 hyd.
John Deere	8770	1995	2,725	E	$53,500	1/06	WCIL	4WD, 18.4-42 duals, 3 hyd., bareback
John Deere	8770	1996	5,152	G	$42,000	4/06	NWMN	4WD, 24 speed, 4 hyd., radar, 520/85R42 duals
John Deere	8850			F	$15,500	8/06	SEMN	4WD, PTO
John Deere	8850	1982	7,150	G	$23,500	12/06	ECNE	4WD, 18-speed power quad, 2-speed reverse, Michelin 20.8R-38, 4 hyd., large 1,000 PTO, 3 pt., quick hitch, sound guard cab
John Deere	8850	1984	10,000	P	$5,100	3/06	NWKS	4WD, 24 speed, rebuilt V-8, bareback w/ duals, PTO, rebuilt engine
John Deere	8850	1984	10,300	F	$12,500	11/06	ECND	4WD, CAH, 16 speed, quad range, 4 hyd., 20.8R-42 duals
John Deere	8850	1985	6,891	G	$24,000	11/06	NWMN	4WD, 16 speed, 4 hyd., return flow, 1,000 PTO, 20.8-42 cast duals
John Deere	8850	1987	7,859	G	$22,000	11/06	NWMN	4WD, 16 speed, 4 hyd., 20.8-42 cast triples
John Deere	8870	1995	5,957	G	$42,000	3/06	NWKS	4WD, 24 speed, 3 pt., 4 hyd., hubs and duals, differential locks
John Deere	8870	1996	3,263	G	$58,200	12/06	ECIL	4WD, 3 pt., 24 speed, like new 18.4R-42 tires w/ duals, 4 hyd., very sharp
John Deere	8960			G	$33,000	8/06	SCNE	4WD, 24 speed, 4 hyd., 24.5-32 tires
John Deere	8960	1989	8,700	F	$29,000	11/06	ECND	4WD, CAH, 24 speed, differential lock, 20.8-42 duals
John Deere	8960	1989	8,371	G	$35,000	11/06	NWKS	4WD
John Deere	8960	1989		G	$40,000	12/06	SEND	4WD, 24 speed, differential lock, radar, performance monitor, weight pkg, 8,000 hours with 3,000 hours on complete engine major OH
John Deere	8960	1992	8,056	G	$34,000	6/06	NWMN	4WD, 24 speed, 3 hyd., 20.8R-42 triples
John Deere	8960	1992	2,822	G	$64,250	2/06	ECMN	4WD, 20.8-42, factory duals, 4 hyd., bareback, 24 speed, weights, cab
John Deere	8960	1993	7,075	G	$47,500	11/06	ECND	4WD, 12 speed, 4 hyd., aux. return, differential lock, radar, 20.8-42 triples
John Deere	8960	1993	7,445	G	$50,500	11/06	ECND	4WD, 12 speed, 4 hyd., aux. return, differential lock, radar, BF Goodrich 20.8-42 on factory triples, 80% rubber
John Deere	8970	1993	3,900	G	$65,000	4/06	NEND	4WD, 24 speed, 4 hyd., radar, 20.8-42 triples
John Deere	8970	1994	7,200	F	$38,000	7/06	SEND	4WD, CAH, 24 speed, 4 hyd., 800-70/32 duals
John Deere	8970	1994	4,220	G	$60,500	12/06	WCMN	4WD, 24 speed, 3 hyd., differential lock, radar

Tractors

Make	Model	Year	Hrs.	Cond.	Price	Sale	Location	Comments
John Deere	8970	1996	5,920	G	$53,000	10/06	NCND	4WD, 12 speed, 400-hp. Cummins power, 4 hyd., BF Goodrich 20.8R42 triples
John Deere	9100	1997	1,724	E	$51,000	4/06	SEND	4WD, 18.4R-42D duals, 3 hyd., single owner, like new
John Deere	9100	1997	4,470	G	$57,000	12/06	SCMN	4WD, 24 speed, duals
John Deere	9100	1997	3,515	G	$57,500	3/06	NWKS	4WD, 24 speed, differential lock, 3 hyd., hubs and duals
John Deere	9200		6,424	G	$45,000	8/06	SCFL	4WD, 24 speed, 3 pt., duals
John Deere	9200	1998	2,410	G	$79,500	12/06	WCMN	4WD, 4 hyd., radar, 1,000 PTO, 3 pt., quick coupler, 24/6 manual shift
John Deere	9200	2000	2,333	G	$75,250	8/06	NECO	4WD, 24 speed, 4 hyd., 20.8-42 duals
John Deere	9220	2003	982	G	$97,000	1/06	SCKS	4WD, 4 hyd., 520/85R42 tires w/ 10-bolt duals, 3,000 lbs. in rear weights, exterior working lights, AM/FM, Air-ride deluxe cab, JD Active Seat, SN 11001, bought new, shedded
John Deere	9220	2003	809	G	$106,000	1/06	SCKS	4WD, 4 hyd., 520/85R42 tires w/ 10-bolt duals, 3,000 lbs. in rear weights, exterior working lights, AM/FM, air, deluxe cab, JD Active Seat, SN 11002, bought new, shedded
John Deere	9220	2004	1,173	G	$95,000	3/06	SWKS	4WD, 24 speed, warranty through March 2006, AutoTrac ready, 4 hyd., no PTO, 3 pt. w/ quick hitch, differential lock, comfort, sound guard cab, Active Seat, 520/85R42 duals
John Deere	9220	2004	289	E	$140,000	3/06	NESD	PS, PTO, 42" tires w/ duals, autosteer ready, differential lock, 78 gpm, hyd. pump, 5 hyd., 3 pt., quick hitch, PTO, factory warranty until 5/06
John Deere	9220	2005	570	G	$126,000	12/06	WCMN	4WD, PTO, high-intensity lights, Active Seat, 5 hyd..
John Deere	9300	1997		G	$57,500	8/06	SCNE	4WD, 24 speed, 4 hyd., return line, 710/70R38
John Deere	9300	1998	3,136	G	$75,000	2/06	SESD	4WD, 24 speed, 4 hyd., bareback, weight pkg., 710 metric tire/duals
John Deere	9300	1998	2,655	G	$80,000	3/06	NEND	4WD, deluxe cab, 24 speed, 4 hyd., rear wheel weight pkg., one owner, 710/38 metric duals (70%)
John Deere	9300	2000	1,400	G	$96,000	1/06	NEIN	4WD, super sharp
John Deere	9300	2001	3,200	G	$79,000	4/06	NEND	4WD, 24 speed, 4 hyd., differential lock
John Deere	9300	2001	1,720	G	$84,500	3/06	NWMN	4WD, 24 speed, radar, 4 hyd., 710/70R38 metrics (80%)
John Deere	9320	2002	1,501	G	$89,000	3/06	NWKS	4WD, 12 speed, 3 hyd., 620/70R42 hub duals, rear weights
John Deere	9320	2004	495	G	$122,000	12/06	NWMO	480/80R/46 duals, 16-speed ps, 4 hyd., bareback
John Deere	9320T	2003	1,797	G	$102,000	12/06	WCMN	PS, 30" tracks, 4 hyd., deluxe cab, front weights
John Deere	9400		5,652	G	$40,000	7/06	WCTN	4WD, duals
John Deere	9400		3,095	G	$78,000	3/06	SWMN	4WD, cab, 24 speed, 4 hyd.
John Deere	9400	1997	6,512	G	$43,000	3/06	NWKS	4WD, 24 speed, 18.4-42 duals, 3 hyd., bareback
John Deere	9400	1997	11,000	G	$60,000	4/06	NEND	4WD, PS
John Deere	9400	1997		G	$76,000	4/06	NEND	4WD, 24 speed, 4 hyd., differential lock, radar, 20.8-42 triples
John Deere	9400	1997	3,227	G	$77,500	12/06	WCMN	4WD, 4 hyd., 710/70R38, radar, 24 speed
John Deere	9400	1997	1,245	E	$111,500	3/06	SEMN	4WD, 3 pt., 3 hyd., Clevis hitch, duals, super clean
John Deere	9400	1998	5,250	G	$72,000	6/06	NWMN	4WD, deluxe cab, 24 speed, PTO, 4 hyd., 20.8R-42 triples
John Deere	9400	1998	3,800	G	$72,500	3/06	WCMN	4WD, 4 hyd., 18.4-46 triples
John Deere	9400	1998	4,104	G	$78,500	11/06	ECND	4WD, 24 speed, 4 hyd., 20.8-42 factory triples, rear wheel weight pkg.
John Deere	9400	1998	4,860	G	$80,000	4/06	ECND	4WD, CAH, 24 speed, 4 hyd. return flow, deluxe cab, field office, differential lock, Goodyear 710-70-38 metric duals
John Deere	9400	1998	2,272	G	$95,000	2/06	WCIL	4WD, deluxe cab, 24/6 speed trans., duals, radar, 4 hyd., front & rear weights, 710/70R38 tires & duals

WHAT'S IT WORTH?

Tractors

Make	Model	Year	Hrs.	Cond.	Price	Sale	Location	Comments
John Deere	9400	1998	1,481	E	$97,500	2/06	ECMN	4WD, one owner, quad range, 12 speed, 4 hyd., performance monitor pkg., deluxe cab
John Deere	9400	1999	8,791	F	$39,000	10/06	SEMN	4WD, duals
John Deere	9400	1999	3,178	G	$86,000	4/06	NWMN	4WD, CAH, 24 speed, 4 hyd., field office, field cruise, Trelleborg 750-65-38 duals (wide space), 90% rubber, full weight pkg.
John Deere	9400	2001		G	$84,500	3/06	SWKS	4WD, 24 speed, 4 hyd., bareback, 710/70R42 duals, wheel weights front & back
John Deere	9400	2001	912	G	$100,000	3/06	SWNE	4WD, 24 speed, 4 hyd., 710/70R42 duals, bareback
John Deere	9400	2001	2,320	E	$101,000	11/06	ECND	4WD, 24 speed, 4 hyd., field office, buddy seat, 20.8-42 factory triples, weight pkg., GreenStar ready
John Deere	9400	2001	1,024	E	$104,000	4/06	NEND	4WD, CAH, 425 hp., 24 speed, 4 hyd., return flow, field cruise and office, deluxe cab, mirrors, performance monitor, Goodyear DT820 wide space metric duals (80%), inside weights, rear weights
John Deere	9400T	2001	2,163	G	$90,000	12/06	WCMN	36" tracks, radar, warning lights, AutoTrac ready, 4 hyd., 24 speed
John Deere	9420			G	$86,000	7/06	WCTN	4WD, duals, dirt moving pkg.
John Deere	9420		3,549	G	$90,000	7/06	WCTN	4WD, duals
John Deere	9420			G	$98,000	7/06	WCTN	4WD, duals, dirt moving pkg.
John Deere	9420	2003	3,605	G	$93,000	11/06	ECND	Deluxe cab, comfort pkg., light pkg., 24-speed PowerSync trans., radar, differential lock, hd axles, 800 metric duals
John Deere	9420	2003	3,431	G	$93,500	11/06	ECND	Deluxe cab, comfort pkg., light pkg., 24-speed PowerSync trans., radar, differential lock, hd axles, 800 metric duals
John Deere	9420	2003	3,436	G	$95,000	11/06	ECND	Deluxe cab, comfort pkg, 24-speed PowerSync trans., radar, differential lock, hd axles, 800 metric duals
John Deere	9420	2003	3,067	G	$111,000	11/06	ECND	Deluxe cab, comfort pkg., light pkg., 24-speed PowerSync trans., radar, differential lock, hd axles, 800 metric duals
John Deere	9420	2005	2	E	$158,000	3/06	NESD	24 speed, 46" tires w/ triples, autosteer ready, 4 hyd., 48-gpm hyd. pump, front & rear weights, factory warranty
John Deere	9420T	2006	560	E	$142,000	12/06	WCMN	30" tracks, 4 hyd., PTO, GreenStar ready, autosteer ready, front weights
John Deere	950		365	G	$5,600	3/06	ECIL	3-cyl. diesel, 3 pt., PS, 12.4-28 tires
John Deere	950	1983	5,294	G	$3,200	8/06	SETN	28 hp., ROPS, power steering
John Deere	9520		1,360	G	$130,000	12/06	WCMN	PS, rear weights, 4 hyd.
John Deere	9520	2002	1,899	E	$121,000	4/06	NWMN	CAH, 18-speed PS, 4 hyd., differential lock, field cruise, return flow, autosteer ready, metric wide space duals, inside weights all around, rear suitcase weight pkg., Firestone 800R38 metric wide space duals
John Deere	9520	2002	2,769	G	$121,000	12/06	SEMN	4WD, PS, deluxe cab, GreenStar, 4 hyd., rear weight pkg., 800/70R38 w/ duals
John Deere	9520	2002	1,600	G	$136,000	12/06	SCMN	
John Deere	9520	2005	404	G	$159,000	12/06	WCMN	4WD, PS, 1 yr. warranty remaining, 4 hyd., GreenStar ready
John Deere	9520	2005	301	G	$161,000	12/06	SCMN	
John Deere	9520T	2002	1,750	G	$0	11/06	ECND	No sale at $110K, CAH, deluxe cab, PS, 4 hyd., high-intensity lights, wide swing drawbar, 36" belts
John Deere	9520T	2002	2,550	G	$117,000	12/06	SCMN	36" belts, wide swing
John Deere	9520T	2002	943	G	$119,000	12/06	NWMO	36" tracks, GreenStar, radar, 26 front weights
John Deere	955		236	G	$8,000	1/06	WCIL	4WD, 72" belly mower, front weights
John Deere	955	1998	305	G	$9,750	11/06	NEKS	4WD utility, hydro trans., 540 PTO, 3 pt., JD 420 loader

Tractors

Make	Model	Year	Hrs.	Cond.	Price	Sale	Location	Comments
John Deere	9620T	2006	250	E	$185,500	12/06	WCMN	36" tracks, 26 front weights, buddy seat, radar, extremity lights, hd drawbar support, deluxe comfort cab, autosteer ready, warranty, full package side weights
John Deere	970			G	$12,500	12/06	SCMN	2WD, JD 440 loader
John Deere	990	2004	102	E	$14,100	12/06	ECMO	MFWD, JD 430 loader
Jinma	284			G	$3,450	9/06	NEIN	4WD, loader, diesel
Kubota	2150		817	E	$9,300	8/06	NWOH	4×4, diesel, LA350A loader, 3 pt., PTO, 60" deck
Kubota	2500			G	$2,500	7/06	WCCA	3 pt., PTO
Kubota	4610	2000		G	$6,250	10/06	WCFL	Compact/utility, 4WD, diesel, OROPS
Kubota	B1550		948	G	$3,300	9/06	NWTN	4WD, ROPS
Kubota	B1550		500	G	$8,800	3/06	SEPA	MFWD, loader, diesel, hydro, rotary mower, turf rubber
Kubota	B1750			G	$1,500	7/06	WCCA	MFWD, canopy, 3 pt., PTO
Kubota	B21			G	$7,000	8/06	WCTX	4WD, diesel, box blade, front loader, 3 pt. hitch
Kubota	B21	2000		G	$15,500	3/06	WCWA	Utility tractor, 4WD, gp bucket, backhoe, canopy
Kubota	B2100		3,623	G	$1,100	11/06	SWCA	4WD, diesel, rear scraper, PTO, 3 pt.
Kubota	B2400	2000		G	$7,750	3/06	WCWA	4WD, gp bucket, 3 pt. hitch
Kubota	B2410		771	G	$7,000	9/06	NWTN	4WD, 60" deck
Kubota	B2410	2004		G	$4,500	1/06	WCOH	ROPS, diesel, hyd. drive trans., 3 pt.
Kubota	B7100		720	G	$1,350	9/06	NWTN	4WD
Kubota	B7200		1,254	G	$4,000	2/06	NCIN	4WD, compact, hydrostatic
Kubota	B7200			G	$5,250	11/06	SCCA	Loader, diesel, 3 pt., PTO
Kubota	B7400		40	E	$7,300	1/06	SEPA	New, MFWD, belly mower, turf rubber
Kubota	B8200			G	$1,800	9/06	NWTN	HST tractor, 60" deck
Kubota	B8200			G	$3,500	9/06	NWTN	HST tractor, 60" deck
Kubota	B8200			G	$7,000	9/06	NEIN	Utility, 4WD, hydro, 3 pt., PTO
Kubota	BX2200			G	$3,700	8/06	WCTX	Diesel, ROPS, belly mower
Kubota	BX2200			G	$4,500	9/06	WCTX	4WD, diesel, ROPS, front loader
Kubota	BX2200			G	$5,500	9/06	NWTN	Hydrostatic drive, 4WD, ROPS
Kubota	BX2200			G	$6,300	8/06	WCTX	Landscape tractor, 4WD, diesel, ROPS, front loader
Kubota	BX2230		65	G	$7,900	9/06	NWTN	4WD, Kubota LA211 front loader, 60" mowing deck
Kubota	L1501		10	G	$3,200	5/06	SWCA	PTO, 3 pt.
Kubota	L175		1,872	G	$1,700	5/06	SWCA	Utility, diesel, 4-speed trans., PTO, 3-pt. hitch, turf tires, mower attachment
Kubota	L225			G	$600	10/06	WCFL	Diesel
Kubota	L2250			G	$4,500	8/06	WCTX	Diesel, 4WD, 3 pt.
Kubota	L2350			G	$1,950	9/06	NWTN	
Kubota	L2350			G	$2,300	9/06	NWTN	
Kubota	L245		1,520	G	$3,100	8/06	SETN	4WD
Kubota	L245		300	G	$6,750	5/06	SWCA	4WD, 4×4, 25 hp., diesel, PTO, 3-pt. hitch, front loader, rear scraper box
Kubota	L245		500	F	$7,000	3/06	SEPA	L245H, WF, high clearance, diesel, cultivators
Kubota	L2500		992	G	$3,400	9/06	NWTN	4WD, ROPS
Kubota	L2500	2002	210	G	$9,250	1/06	WCCA	4WD, loader
Kubota	L260	1975		G	$1,600	6/06	NECO	2WD, 3 pt., PTO, diesel
Kubota	L285		788	G	$2,300	8/06	SETN	Diesel
Kubota	L285		620	G	$3,750	11/06	SWCA	Diesel, front bucket, PTO, 3 pt.
Kubota	L2850			F	$3,400	11/06	SETN	
Kubota	L2900			G	$3,500	7/06	WCCA	Dowdy's push blade, roll bar
Kubota	L-3010			G	$10,500	9/06	NWTN	4WD, Kubota LA482 front end loader
Kubota	L3450			G	$6,300	9/06	NWTN	4WD, ROPS, sunshade, front loader

WHAT'S IT WORTH?

Tractors

Make	Model	Year	Hrs.	Cond.	Price	Sale	Location	Comments
Kubota	L35			G	$10,000	8/06	WCTX	4WD, diesel, ROPS, digging bucket, gp bucket
Kubota	L3600		1,579	G	$7,100	9/06	NWTN	4WD, ROPS
Kubota	L3710			G	$5,200	10/06	WCFL	3-pt box blade
Kubota	L3710		2,300	G	$10,250	8/06	SEPA	GST, MFWD, ROPS, average rubber
Kubota	L3750			G	$6,000	7/06	WCCA	Low-Pro, 3 pt., PTO
Kubota	L4200			G	$5,200	9/06	WCTX	Diesel, loader
Kubota	L4200		1,362	G	$8,700	8/06	SETN	4WD, ROPS, sunshade shuttle shift
Kubota	L4200	1997		G	$17,000	12/06	SCQB	Canadian sale, 4×4, utility tractor, reverse plow, glide shift trans., cab, 2 hyd., 3 pt., converts to $14,839 U.S.
Kubota	L4300			G	$10,000	9/06	WCTX	Diesel, loader
Kubota	L4310			G	$18,250	8/06	SEPA	LA682 front end loader, MFWD, CAH, average rubber
Kubota	L4350	1993	523	G	$8,800	12/06	NWMO	4×4, 4-speed hi lo shuttle, 17.4-24 rear tires
Kubota	M110			G	$19,000	8/06	WCTX	4WD, cab
Kubota	M4900			G	$12,750	9/06	NWTN	ROPS, sunshade, Westendorf TA180 loader
Kubota	M4900			G	$14,500	8/06	SETN	ROPS
Kubota	M5700			G	$9,200	9/06	NWTN	ROPS, sunshade, shuttle shift
Kubota	M6030		1,790	G	$10,000	8/06	SETN	ROPS, 4WD, shuttle shift
Kubota	M6800		390	G	$20,000	11/06	SWOH	MFWD, Kubota LA1162 front loader, gravel & manure buckets, 6.9-30 tires
Kubota	M6950			G	$6,500	9/06	NWTN	4-post ROPS, canopy
Kubota	M8200		580	G	$23,500	8/06	SEPA	MFWD, LA1251 front end loader, CAH, hydro shuttle, average rubber
Kubota	M9000		1,850	G	$25,500	8/06	SEPA	MFWD, LA1251 front end loader, CAH, new rubber, power shuttle
Kubota	M9000		1,064	G	$27,000	8/06	SETN	CAH, 4WD, Bush Hog front loader
Kubota	R400			G	$8,750	3/06	NEMI	Compact 4×4 end loader, ½-yard bucket, 2,300 on chassis, 5 hours on new crate Kubota engine
Leyland	272			P	$1,750	5/06	SEWI	Turbo, needed mechanical work
Long	2460		245	G	$6,500	8/06	SETN	Sunshade, Bush Hog 2426 front loader
Long	910			P	$250	10/06	SEMN	Bad engine, needs new engine, 3 pt., 540 PTO, for parts, some pieces missing
McCormick	CX100	2004	600	G	$26,250	1/06	SEPA	2WD, WF, Quickie Q720 front-end loader, CAH
MF	1010			G	$650	9/06	WCTX	Diesel, belly mower
MF	1020			F	$1,300	1/06	WCCA	MFWD, roll bar
MF	1020			G	$3,000	7/06	WCCA	MFWD, push blade, roll bar, 3 pt.
MF	1085			F	$2,000	8/06	SEPA	WF, CAH, fair rubber, 1,600 hours on tach
MF	1085	1973		G	$3,000	2/06	WCKS	3 pt., PTO
MF	1135		5,985	G	$3,500	10/06	SEMN	
MF	1135		3,915	G	$7,000	3/06	ECIA	Late 1977 or early 1978 model, diesel, cab, real clean, 18.4R-38 tires
MF	1135		3,795	G	$7,300	8/06	NWOH	Cab, 2 hyd., 3 pt., duals
MF	1135	1976	4,805	G	$6,400	2/06	WCNE	Diesel, 3 pt., cab
MF	1135	1976	3,123	G	$8,300	6/06	NWMN	CAH, 3 pt., PTO, 2 hyd., front weights, 16.9-38 duals
MF	1205		347	G	$4,400	8/06	SETN	4WD, ROPS, mower deck
MF	1528	2005	46	E	$13,500	9/06	NEMO	MFWD, 1520 loader, ROPS, hydro, 3 pt., PTO, 2 hyd., 12.5/30&25×8.5-14 tires, like new
MF	230			G	$5,500	11/06	SWCA	Diesel, PTO, 3 pt.
MF	2300		100	G	$5,700	8/06	SEPA	4WD, ROPS, good turf rubber
MF	231		1,277	g	$5,000	8/06	SETN	ROPS
MF	231			G	$6,000	11/06	ECIL	Diesel utility tractor

Tractors

Make	Model	Year	Hrs.	Cond.	Price	Sale	Location	Comments
MF	231			G	$7,600	8/06	NWOH	3 pt., PTO
MF	2315			G	$7,250	3/06	ECIN	Diesel, 3 pt.
MF	243		600	G	$6,800	1/06	SEPA	WF, good turf rubber, ROPS
MF	255			G	$4,400	8/06	SETN	Diesel
MF	261		1,564	G	$9,500	9/06	NWTN	Front loader
MF	2640	1983	6,515	F	$6,500	5/06	SEWY	MFWD, MF 256 loader w/ grapple
MF	2675			F	$5,000	3/06	NCMN	
MF	2705		8,000	G	$6,700	2/06	NWSD	Diesel, cab, air, radio, 3 pt., 3 hyd., electric outlet, 1,000 rpm, one owner
MF	2705		2,858	G	$8,100	1/06	NEIN	
MF	2705	1981	4,649	G	$9,000	6/06	NWMN	CAH, 3 pt., PTO, 3 hyd., front weights, 16.9-38
MF	2745	1979	4,864	F	$3,500	3/06	SEIA	2WD, cab, air, hub-mount duals
MF	275			G	$5,000	12/06	SCQB	Canadian sale, 2WD utility tractor, front loader, cab, 3 pt., PTO, converts to $4,365 U.S.
MF	275			G	$7,000	3/06	NCMN	
MF	275	1976	3,285	G	$10,500	2/06	NWIL	Utility, ROPS, canopy, 3 pt., Bush Hog 4000 loader, 66" bucket
MF	275	1977	3,272	G	$6,500	12/06	WCIL	Utility, 540 PTO, 2 hyd.
MF	282			G	$2,500	5/06	SCCA	Front weights, 3 pt., PTO, 2 hyd
MF	285			G	$2,700	8/06	WCNC	
MF	298			G	$5,000	11/06	SETN	
MF	3060		1,951	G	$12,500	9/06	SECA	Mower w/ Tiger attachment
MF	3545	1984	2,339	G	$14,000	2/06	NECO	Diesel, MFWD, loader, grapple, Westendorf TA 46
MF	3630			F	$7,500	1/06	SEPA	2WD, WF, CAH, good rubber
MF	3650	1988	3,241	G	$9,500	5/06	SEWY	MFWD, Autotronic, MF 856 loader & grapple
MF	3660			G	$19,500	3/06	NCMN	MFWD
MF	3680			G	$15,500	3/06	NWIL	MFWD, cab, air, weights, duals, diesel
MF	3690	1992	1,774	E	$31,000	3/06	ECIA	MFWD, diesel, super clean, fully-equipped cab, 18.4-42R, front weight bracket, 3 hyd., 170 hp.
MF	383			G	$6,000	8/06	SETN	ROPS
MF	390			G	$2,000	1/06	WCCA	Midmount cultivator, roll bar, 3 pt.
MF	390			G	$15,000	9/06	NEIN	Diesel, 4WD, 3 pt., MF 448 loader
MF	399	1990		G	$12,750	2/06	WCMN	MFWD, open station, MF 848 loader, 500 hours on OH and clutch
MF	4225		2,300	G	$8,400	3/06	SEPA	2WD, ROPS, fair turf rubber
MF	4255		1,018	G	$25,000	1/06	NCIL	MFWD, open station, reversible shuttle, 3 pt., 540/1,000 PTO, MF 1038 loader
MF	4270	1999	201	G	$31,500	12/06	SCNE	MFWD, open station, Westendorf loader, shuttle shift
MF	431		364	G	$12,200	10/06	WCGA	Loader
MF	4355	2002	1,900	G	$23,550	12/06	NWIL	
MF	4355	2002	2,200	G	$25,500	12/06	NWIL	MF 1070 loader
MF	4355	2003	1,700	G	$26,250	12/06	NWIL	MF 1070 loader
MF	4355	2003	1,700	G	$31,600	12/06	NWIL	MF 1070 loader
MF	4355	2003	1,200	G	$32,500	12/06	NWIL	MF 1070 loader
MF	4360	2002	1,100	G	$24,500	12/06	NWIL	No cab, MF 1080 loader, diesel
MF	451			G	$9,100	11/06	SETN	
MF	4840			F	$4,000	4/06	WCSD	4WD, 320 hp.
MF	4840			G	$6,100	10/06	SWOH	4WD, Cummins 250 hp., diesel, duals, EROPS, scraper hitch, 3 pt., PTO, 4 hyd.

Tractors

Make	Model	Year	Hrs.	Cond.	Price	Sale	Location	Comments
MF	4840			G	$9,200	2/06	NWSD	4WD, 903 Cummins, 265 hp., cab, air, motor OH at 4,600 hours, radio, rebuilt trans. at 5,100 hours, 3 hyd., extra lights, 20.8-38
MF	4840	1979	7,060	F	$4,000	3/06	NWKS	4WD, 18 speed, PS, 18.4-38
MF	4880	1981	5,063	G	$13,000	3/06	ECND	4WD, CAH, 12 speed, PS, 903 turbo, 4 hyd., return flow, Goodyear 20.8-38 duals (50%)
MF	5455	2004	850	G	$28,000	12/06	NWIL	MF 1070 loader, no bucket, diesel
MF	6150			G	$16,000	8/06	SETN	4WD, CAH
MF	6180	1997	1,751	G	$30,750	8/06	NEKS	2WD, Dynashift, 540/1,000 PTO, 18.4R-38, 11:00-16 front tires, cab, air, one owner, shedded
MF	6270	2002	2,900	G	$33,000	12/06	NWIL	MF 1080 loader, diesel
MF	6280	2001	2,600	G	$32,000	12/06	NWIL	MF 1080 loader, diesel
MF	6290	2002	4,300	G	$31,000	12/06	NWIL	Weights, diesel
MF	6480	2004	2,200	G	$39,000	12/06	NWIL	MF 1080 loader, diesel
MF	690			G	$9,000	8/06	SETN	CAH, front weights
MF	698			F	$8,000	3/06	NCUT	GB 660 loader
MF	750	1979		G	$1,000	8/06	NENE	Gray cab, hydrostatic, 354 turbo engine, raddle chain, chopper
MF	8245	2003	3,900	G	$40,000	12/06	NWIL	Diesel
MF	8245	2004	1,400	G	$59,000	12/06	NWIL	MF 1090 loader, diesel
MF	8280	2002	1,900	G	$57,700	12/06	NWIL	Duals, diesel
MF	8280	2003	2,000	G	$68,000	12/06	NWIL	Duals, diesel
Mitsubishi	D1500			G	$3,250	11/06	SECA	2WD, front weights, 2 pt., PTO
Same	75			G	$7,000	11/06	SECA	MFWD, Dowdy's push blade, 3 pt., PTO, 3 hyd.
Same	85			G	$1,500	5/06	SCCA	Row-crop mudder, canopy, 3 pt., 2 hyd.
Satoh	Beaver			G	$1,050	9/06	NECO	4WD, 3 pt., 5' blade, 1220 loader, diesel
Steiger	Bearcat			F	$7,800	3/06	NEMI	4WD, replaced Cat 3208 V-8, 225 engine, 3 hyd., duals
Steiger	CR1225			G	$8,000	11/06	SECA	Cab, air, 5 speed, PS, 3 pt.
Steiger	KM 225	1984	4,731	G	$14,500	11/06	WCMN	4WD, Cummins I10
Steiger	Panther	1985	6,192	G	$15,000	4/06	WCSD	CM 325, 4WD, cab, air, radio, 4 hyd., bareback, stand-alone aux., hydraulic system for air seeders, nice 20.8R-38
Steiger	Panther II	1975		G	$9,500	8/06	WCIA	4WD, 310 hp. Cummins, 3 pt., quick hitch, 3 hyd., 24.5-32 duals
Steiger	ST 220	1976	12,205	G	$7,500	4/06	NWMN	Bearcat, 4WD, Series III, 855 Cummins, 10-speed manual, 4 hyd., 20.8-34 duals (85%), extensive reconditioning
Steiger	ST 220	1977	3,160	G	$15,500	7/06	NWIL	4WD, Bearcat III, bareback, 3 hyd., full set of duals, 200 hours on complete new Cummins diesel engine
Steiger	ST 325	1979		F	$9,400	3/06	SEND	4WD, Panther, CAH, Cat engine, 4 hyd., 70% rubber, 24.5-32 duals, recent trans. & clutch repair
Steiger	ST 325	1984	6,735	G	$15,000	2/06	WCKS	4WD, duals, no 3 pt.
Steiger	ST 325	1984	6,002	G	$15,500	2/06	WCKS	4WD, duals, 3 pt.
Steiger	ST310	1974	10,000	G	$9,500	3/06	SEND	Panther II, 4WD, 855 Cummins, 10 speed, 3 hyd., 23.1-34 duals (85%)
Steiger	Tiger II	1974	5,740	G	$4,750	5/06	SEWY	Turbo Tiger II, 4WD, 3 pt., 12' dozer
Versatile	1150	1982		G	$41,500	3/06	ECMI	4WD, 30.5-32 duals, 5 hyd., bareback, 600 hp., in frame, Cummins, OH in 2005
Versatile	276	1985	5,610	F	$12,100	8/06	NECO	Bidirectional, 3 pt., PTO, loader
Versatile	276	1990	7,600	G	$11,500	7/06	WCMN	Bidirectional, Series II, good tires
Versatile	500	1979	4,000	G	$12,250	3/06	SEND	4WD, 12-speed gear, 3 hyd., 3 pt., PTO, deluxe air ride seat, 18.4-38 duals, Cummins 8.3 turbo installed

Tractors

Make	Model	Year	Hrs.	Cond.	Price	Sale	Location	Comments
Versatile	555			F	$4,700	8/06	NECO	4WD
Versatile	555	1983	5,613	G	$9,500	2/06	NWKS	4WD, Series 3, row crop, 3 pt., 1,000 PTO, 4 hyd.
Versatile	700	1973		F	$3,250	7/06	SEND	4WD, 3 hyd., 18.4-38 tires, 4 brand-new tires
Versatile	750	1976	9,412	G	$6,500	3/06	NWMN	4WD, 3 hyd., 20.8-38 duals (70%)
Versatile	800			F	$4,400	6/06	WCMN	4WD, Cummins, CAH, duals, 3 hyd.
Versatile	800	1974		G	$4,200	7/06	ECND	4WD, CAH, duals
Versatile	800	1975	6,543	G	$6,000	9/06	NWMN	4WD, CAH, 2 hyd., recent engine major, 30.5-32, 50% rubber
Versatile	800	1976	9,134	G	$5,000	7/06	NWMN	Series II, 4WD, 12-speed gear, 3 hyd., return flow, 18.4-38 duals, 30% rubber
Versatile	835			F	$7,500	4/06	NEND	4WD, 4 hyd., 18.4-38 duals, major OH at 6,941 hours
Versatile	835			G	$9,800	4/06	WCSD	4WD, 2,000 hours on new engine, Cummins 350 engine, new pressure plates and clutch
Versatile	835	1982	6,749	G	$10,000	7/06	SEND	4WD, 12-speed gear, 4 hyd., second hyd. pump and flow control, 480-80R-38 duals, 90% rubber
Versatile	835	1982	5,393	G	$10,500	11/06	NEKS	4WD, 12 forward and 4 reverse gears, 4 hyd.
Versatile	836	1985	7,599	G	$16,000	3/06	ECND	Designation 6, 4WD, L10A Cummins, 4 hyd., 18.4-38 duals, major work on reversed planetary drives, main bearings, rod bearings, injectors & turbo @ 7,100 hours
Versatile	846			G	$21,500	8/06	SCNE	4WD, front mount dozer blade, 4 hyd.
Versatile	850			F	$4,100	11/06	SCND	4WD, 250 hp., duals
Versatile	850	1974	4,300	G	$7,900	11/06	WCMN	4WD, 30% rubber .
Versatile	850	1976	9,106	F	$3,900	7/06	ECND	4WD, Series II, CAH, 2 hyd., duals, 3,000 hours on OH
Versatile	850	1976		G	$7,700	6/06	SEND	4WD, Series II, 3 hyd., 20.8-38 duals, R134A conversion, 4,000 hours on engine OH at 310 hp.
Versatile	850	1976	8,669	G	$11,500	7/06	NWMN	Series II, 4WD, 12-speed gear, 3 hyd., 24.5-32 duals, 80% rubber, 400 hours on engine OH
Versatile	855	1979		G	$8,900	9/06	NWMN	4WD, CAH, 4 hyd., 30.5R-32 inside tires, 70% rubber, 20.8R-38 duals, shows 5,748 hours
Versatile	875	1979	7,000	G	$10,500	7/06	NWMN	4WD, duals
Versatile	875	1979		G	$17,500	3/06	NWMN	Series II, 4WD, 3 hyd. w/ return, 1,500 hours on engine major OH, 20.8-38R duals
Versatile	875	1980		G	$12,000	2/06	NWKS	4WD, 20.8-38, clamp-on duals, 4 hyd., AM/FM, air, new clutch, new rods & mains
Versatile	875	1980		G	$14,000	2/06	NWKS	4WD, 20.8-38, clamp-on duals, 4 hyd., AM/FM radio, new clutch 200-300 hours ago, recent rods & mains
Versatile	875	1982	7,100	G	$10,400	7/06	NEND	4WD, 12-speed gear, 4 hyd., 20.8-38 duals
Versatile	875	1982		G	$10,500	11/06	ECND	4WD, 12-speed gear, 4 hyd., 20.8-38 duals
Versatile	875	1984	3,544	G	$18,750	2/06	SEKS	4WD
Versatile	876	1988	2,000	G	$30,500	1/06	NEIN	4WD, Designation 6
Versatile	876	1989	3,608	G	$40,000	4/06	WCMB	Canadian sale, L10 Cummins, 280 hp.
Versatile	895			G	$17,000	3/06	NWIL	4WD, bareback, duals
Versatile	895		3,812	G	$30,000	4/06	NEND	4WD, Series III, Cummins 855, CAH, 4 hyd. 20.8-38 duals
Versatile	895	1980	8,810	G	$11,000	7/06	SEND	4WD, 4 hyd., 24.5-32 duals
Versatile	895	1981	5,950	F	$9,500	12/06	WCMN	4WD, 3 pt., 3 hyd., 20.8-38 new insides, $7,300 motor & clutch work
Versatile	895	1982	8,624	F	$12,000	9/06	NEND	4WD, CAH, 20.8R38 duals, 5 hyd., 3 pt., PTO
Versatile	895	1982	9,200	G	$12,250	6/06	NWMN	4WD, 4 hyd., 20.8-38 duals, 3,900 hours on major OH
Versatile	900	1976	13,225	G	$5,300	7/06	NWMN	Series II, 4WD, 12 speed, 3 hyd., 20.8-38 duals, 30% rubber
Versatile	935	1980		F	$8,000	11/06	ECND	4WD, CAH, 12-speed gear, 4 hyd., 24.5-32 duals (50% rubber)

WHAT'S IT WORTH?

Tractors

Make	Model	Year	Hrs.	Cond.	Price	Sale	Location	Comments
Versatile	936	1988	5,554	G	$21,500	7/06	NWMN	Designation 6, 4WD, CAH, 12-speed gear, 4 hyd., return flow, 20.8-42 duals, 30% rubber
Versatile	936	1988	6,000	G	$22,000	7/06	NWMN	Designation 6, 4WD, CAH, 12-speed gear, 4 hyd., return flow, 20.8-42 duals, 30% rubber
Versatile	936	1988	2,540	G	$31,000	2/06	NWKS	4WD, Designation 6, 20.8R42 tires w/ duals, 4 hyd., AM/FM radio, air, new turbo rods & mains, new clutch, had oil sample analysis at every oil change
Versatile	945	1984		G	$18,250	11/06	NEND	4WD, Series III, 12-speed gear, 5 hyd. return flow, 24.5-32 Goodyear Dynatorques, 30% rubber
Versatile	945	1984	5,200	G	$18,500	7/06	NEND	4WD, Series III, 12 speed, 4 hyd., 24.5-32 duals
Versatile	955	1983	4,941	F	$13,500	7/06	SEND	4WD, PS, 4 hyd., 20.8-38 duals, new updated trans
Versatile	956	1985	7,923	G	$27,000	11/06	ECND	4WD, CAH, 12 speed, 4 hyd., 24.5-32 duals (65% rubber)
White	120		2,300	G	$29,000	1/06	NEIN	MFWD, cab, air, one owner
White	140	1989	1,938	G	$26,500	2/06	WCOH	MFWD, cab, 200 hours on new engine and duals
White	160	1988	3,065	G	$17,500	12/06	SCNE	2WD, 18 speed, 18.4-42, duals
White	185	1988		G	$22,500	8/06	NENE	MFWD, Cummins 505 diesel engine, 18.4-42 rear duals, 16.9-28 front, full set of front weights
White	185	1989	2,991	G	$34,600	3/06	NCIN	MFWD, CAH, 18.4R-42 factory duals, full front weights, quick hitch, 6 speed/3 range trans.
White	6085		2,513	G	$27,500	1/06	NEIN	MFWD, 676 loader
White	6144	1995	1,368	G	$33,000	12/06	SCNE	2WD, 32 speed, 18.4-38, duals
White	6195			G	$38,000	8/06	SCNE	MFWD, Farmhand XL1340 loader w/ joystick, 18 speed, PS, CAH, 3 pt., PTO, 3 hyd., 18.4-42 factory duals, 16.9-28 fronts
White	6195	1993		G	$21,500	11/06	SECA	MFWD, front weights, cab, air, PS, 3 pt, PTO
White	8710			G	$35,000	5/06	SCCA	MFWD, front weights, cab, air, PS, 3 pt, PTO
White	8710	1998	852	G	$61,500	1/06	SWOH	MFWD, fieldmaster, duals
Yanmar	1300			G	$1,700	11/06	SWCA	Diesel, rear tiller
Yanmar	1500			G	$3,750	11/06	SECA	2WD, 2 cyl.
Yanmar	1500			G	$4,250	12/06	NEMN	Loader box blade
Yanmar	155		220	G	$1,750	1/06	NWIL	2WD, compact utility
Yanmar	1700			G	$3,750	11/06	SECA	2WD, 2 cyl.
Yanmar	1700			G	$4,000	11/06	SECA	2WD, 2 cyl. 20 hp.
Yanmar	2200			G	$1,000	5/06	SWCA	Diesel, PTO, 3 pt.
Yanmar	240			G	$4,000	3/06	NWIL	Diesel, loader, rotary mower
Yanmar	F16D			G	$1,000	11/06	SWCA	17 hp., diesel, PTO, 3 pt.
Yanmar	F16D		1,236	G	$3,400	11/06	SWCA	20 hp., diesel, front bucket, rear scraper
Yanmar	YM1401		908	G	$800	11/06	SWCA	17 hp., diesel, PTO, 3 pt.
Yanmar	YM1401		908	G	$800	11/06	SWCA	17 hp., diesel, PTO, 3 pt., loader bucket, tiller
Yanmar	YM1600		339	G	$3,000	11/06	SWCA	Diesel, loader, rear scraper
Yanmar	YM1600		339	G	$3,000	11/06	SWCA	Diesel, loader, rear scraper
Yanmar	YM2000			G	$3,000	5/06	SWCA	PTO, 3 pt., rear scraper box, canopy
Yanmar	YM2000		62	G	$3,250	11/06	SWCA	Diesel, loader, rear scraper
Yanmar	YM2000			G	$3,750	11/06	SECA	23 hp., 2WD, front loader
Yanmar	YM2000		62	G	$5,000	11/06	SWCA	Diesel, loader, rear scraper
Zetor	205			G	$17,000	8/06	WCIL	Diesel, ROPS, new loader, warranty
Zetor	5211			F	$3,550	1/06	SEPA	WF, fair turf rubber
Zetor	5245	1992		G	$4,000	12/06	ECMO	MFWD, open, loader
Zetor	6320			G	$4,000	8/06	NWIL	Loader, diesel

Trailers

Trailers has always been one of our largest categories. I've lumped together all types of trailers here: implement trailers, stock trailers, combine header trailers, van trailers, car trailers, utility trailers . . . (Grain trailers are listed separately.) Check out the description in the far right-hand column for more about each trailer listed. Combine head trailers have been especially hot sellers at auction the last four to six months.

Trailers

Make	Model	Year	Cond.	Price	Sale	Location	Comments
Alloy	NA	1994	G	$7,000	3/06	WCWA	Ref. van trailer
Arne's	NA	1996	G	$21,000	3/06	WCWA	Flatbed, 32'×108"
Arne's	NA	1996	G	$21,000	3/06	WCWA	Flatbed, 32'×108"
Aztec	40'	1978	G	$6,600	3/06	NENE	Liquid transport trailer, (3) 1,600-gal. poly tanks, 30-gal. inductor, Briggs & Stratton 5.5-hp. 2" transfer pump, 10:00-22 tires, 70% brakes
Beall	1301	1973	G	$5,500	12/06	WCMN	Model 1301, 36' belly dump, 2 compartments, roll tarp, tandem axle
Beall	NA	1973	G	$6,900	1/06	SWNE	Fuel trailer, 9,500 gal., aluminum
Big Tex	NA		G	$2,750	9/06	ECMN	Gooseneck
Big Tex	NA	2004	E	$1,400	4/06	WCSD	6.5'×16' bumper utility trailer, like new
Bilt-Rite	NA	1985	G	$2,800	11/06	WCSD	28' horse trailer, 4-horse slant, minimal living quarters up front, tack room at back, side-load ramp
Birmingham	42'	1984	G	$7,500	3/06	NWMN	Double-drop on 8 aluminums, air ride
Birmingham	NA		G	$7,750	3/06	WCWA	20-ton, tandem-axle tilt-deck equipment trailer, air brakes
Bison	NA	1991	G	$12,500	12/06	WCKS	Double combine trailer, 53', triple-spread axle, 22.5 low-pro tires, steel rims, fold down ramps, pull-out outriggers
Bison	NA	1992	G	$19,500	3/06	ECND	53' combine trailer
Bison	NA	1993	G	$8,500	9/06	WCND	53', fold-up double combine trailer, tandems, spring ride, air dump, third axle
Bison	NA	1995	G	$7,800	9/06	WCND	53' tri-axle combine trailer, spring ride, tandem w/ rear axle dump, flip-up ramps
Bison	NA	2002	G	$10,000	3/06	ECND	28.5' combine trailer
Bison	NA	2002	G	$12,850	3/06	ECND	28.5', fifth wheel, tandem-axle combine trailer
Blair	Stock	1991	F	$2,600	9/06	NWIL	7'×20' livestock trailer, new tires
Boge	NA	1991	G	$5,750	11/06	NEIA	20×8 tandem-axle flatbed trailer, beaver tail
Borco	NA	1989	G	$51,500	5/06	ECMI	Converter dolly
Borco	NA	1989	G	$51,500	5/06	ECMI	Gooseneck lowboy, 75-ton, 4 axle
Boss	Stock	1999	G	$3,900	3/06	NCCO	16', bumper pull, divider, mats
Bri-Mar	NA	2000	G	$3,950	8/06	SETN	Tandem-axle dump trailer
Brown	40'		F	$400	9/06	ECMN	Tandem, flatbed, 8'×40'
Buckeye	NA		G	$1,700	3/06	NCOH	8'×20' grain trailer
Butler	NA		G	$2,000	10/06	SENJ	Tanker
Butler	NA	1984	G	$3,000	8/06	SETN	20', tandem, 2 axle, air brakes
Cancade	NA	2001	G	$21,750	4/06	NWMN	Tandem-axle steel end dump, roll tarp, comb. end gate, spring ride, 32'×60"x102"
Carry-On Corp.	NA	2006	G	$1,100	11/06	SEIA	7'×12' single-axle trailer, front and rear ramps
Chapparal	Stock		E	$2,300	8/06	WCOH	16', bumper trailer
Cherokee	NA		G	$8,500	5/06	SWCA	Pup trailer, 40,000 lb. GVW, 12' steel box, tandem axle, 8-wheel
Circle D	Stock	1996	G	$4,500	3/06	NCCO	16' bumper pull stock trailer
Circle M	NA		G	$1,700	6/06	NWKS	7'×18' car trailer, dovetail
City	30'	1977	G	$16,000	3/06	NEMI	Aluminum dump trailer, tandem, lift axle, 9-spread
City	42'	1982	G	$3,600	9/06	WCND	Aluminum spread axle flatbed, side kit, bows and tarp, air ride
City	NA	1986	G	$17,400	2/06	NWMN	Tri-axle aluminum end dump, 32' tub, 34' frame
Clement	NA		G	$5,250	5/06	SWCA	Pup trailer, 9-yard, tandem axle, 8-wheel, pintle hitch, refurbished
Clement	NA		G	$8,750	3/06	WCWA	End dump

Trailers

Make	Model	Year	Cond.	Price	Sale	Location	Comments
Cobra	32'	1984	G	$17,300	2/06	NWMN	Tri-axle aluminum end dump
Cole	NA		F	$850	3/06	NWIL	Head trailer
Cole	NA		F	$1,350	6/06	NWIL	Combine head trailer
Corn Pro	25'	1994	G	$4,700	7/06	WCOH	Grain trailer, wench, oak flooring, 18,000-lb. capacity
Corn Pro	Stock		G	$2,600	11/06	SWOH	16' bumper hitch livestock trailer
CWC	Stock		G	$5,200	12/06	NENE	7×26, gooseneck, 2 7,000-lb. axles
Dakota	44'	1980	G	$9,000	3/06	SEND	Drop deck implement trailer, hyd. beavertail, hyd. winch, flip-down sides, complete reconditioning, brakes, drums, decking
David Bradley	NA		G	$525	2/06	SEIN	Flatbed wagon, hoist
DCT	NA	2000	G	$4,100	11/06	ECND	20' trailer, dovetail, ramp, tandem axle, wood deck, hd, ball hitch
Delta	26'	1999	G	$4,000	3/06	SEND	Flatbed grain trailer, round bale sides, (2) 7,000-lb. axles, ramps
Delta	32'	2005	E	$7,000	12/06	WCMN	Fifth-wheel trailer, 23,400 GVW, beavertail w/ ramps, tandem dually
Delta	Stock		F	$750	4/06	WCSD	6'×16' bumper-pull horse trailer
Delta	Stock		F	$850	3/06	NCWI	16', tandem axle
Delta	Stock		F	$1,600	3/06	NCIA	7×20 tandem stock trailer, no floor
Diamond	20'		G	$1,800	1/06	WCPA	Office trailer
Diamond	Stock		F	$900	11/06	NWKS	16' stock trailer, 1978 model
Diamond	Stock		G	$1,100	4/06	WCKS	7×16', gooseneck
Diamond	Stock		G	$1,700	9/06	ECNE	6×16 bumper pull stock trailer
Diamond	Stock	1996	E	$5,700	1/06	SWNE	7×20 grain stock trailer, torsion axles, very nice
DN	NA		G	$3,400	5/06	SEND	Grain flatbed trailer, 32', steel deck, 4' beavertail, ramps, tandem-axle duals, spring suspension
Donahue	20'		F	$1,350	1/06	NCCO	Implement trailer
Donahue	24'		F	$475	3/06	NENE	10'×24' drop-down trailer
Donahue	28'		F	$400	1/06	NECO	
Donahue	28'		F	$450	4/06	NWMN	Tandem-axle trailer
Donahue	28'		F	$650	11/06	NWMN	Tandem axle, bed needs work
Donahue	28'		F	$700	4/06	SEND	
Donahue	28'		F	$700	1/06	SCMI	28'×10' transport trailer
Donahue	28'		G	$1,000	12/06	SCMN	
Donahue	30'			$3,500	3/06	SEMN	30' grain flatbed trailer, Model HF-30-BT, tandem axle
Donahue	36'		G	$900	3/06	WCKS	Implement trailer
Donahue	42'		F	$400	9/06	WCND	
Donahue	50'		G	$500	9/06	NWMN	Implement trailer
Donahue	NA		G	$750	12/06	NENE	2 axles, 4 wheels per axle
Donahue	NA		E	$4,350	1/06	NECO	Gooseneck, adjustable
Donahue	NA	1996	E	$10,000	12/06	SWIA	Tandem-axle grain trailer, 16', duals, 16' box, hoist, roll tarp, electric over hyd. for jack and box
Donahue	NA	2003	G	$5,700	3/06	NCCO	Grain tandem-axle swather trailer
Doonan	48'	1996	G	$14,500	12/06	WCKS	Drop deck trailer, 48', 10' deck, 4' dovetail, ramps, spread axle, 255/70R 22.5 low-profile tires, steel rims, aluminum side box
Dorsey	32'	1982	G	$9,800	3/06	ECIL	Tri-axle dump trailer, long frame, spring suspension
Dorsey	NA	1980	G	$9,500	11/06	ECND	Tandem-axle step trailer, 45', (2) 3,135-gal. Horvick tanks, chemical mix cone, 3" Honda pump

Trailers

Make	Model	Year	Cond.	Price	Sale	Location	Comments
Dorsey	NA	1995	G	$3,000	9/06	ECMN	Reefer Thermo King 5B2
Eager Beaver	20HA	1990	g	$6,500	11/06	SCCA	Equipment trailer
Eager Beaver	NA		G	$8,500	3/06	SCIN	Tandem-axle tag trailer, air brakes, 48,000 GVW
Eager Beaver	NA	1990	G	$5,500	3/06	ECMI	20-ton, tandem axle, air brakes
East	NA		G	$3,200	8/06	ECMN	Steel floor, steel frame
East	NA	1979	G	$7,750	12/06	SEND	Aluminum tri-axle dump trailer
Econoline	NA	1996	F	$2,300	1/06	NCCO	12-ton pintle hitch backhoe trailer, 22', 5' beavertail, ramps
Elmers	NA		G	$1,000	3/06	NWMN	Single-head transport trailer
Elmers	NA		G	$1,600	4/06	SEND	Header trailer
Exiss	Stock	2003	G	$8,100	3/06	SEND	Stock combo aluminum grain trailer, tack room, 16' livestock compartment, 7' wide
E-Z Trail	672		G	$1,325	1/06	WCIL	20' head transport
E-Z Trail	672		G	$1,700	2/06	NWIL	Head trailer
E-Z Trail	672		G	$1,750	2/06	NCIL	Head trailer
E-Z Trail	672		G	$1,800	2/06	NCIL	Head-hauling
E-Z Trail	672		G	$1,900	4/06	WCWI	Header trailer
E-Z Trail	NA		G	$1,600	12/06	ECKS	30' platform header trailer
E-Z Trail	NA		G	$2,100	8/06	NWIL	Combine header trailer
Featherlite	24'	1998	G	$4,500	8/06	SETN	Gooseneck, 20' flat, 4' dovetail
Featherlite	Stock		E	$13,000	4/06	NENE	2003 model, 7'×24' grain livestock trailer, always shedded, sharp
Featherlite	Stock	1996	E	$3,300	7/06	NWIL	16', bumper hitch
Featherlite	Stock	1998	G	$5,000	4/06	NEND	Grain steel livestock trailer, 6'8"W × 6'1"H × 20'L, center divider, torsion axles
Featherlite	Stock	1998	G	$7,000	11/06	SCND	20' aluminum stock trailer, 7'H ×7'W, center gate, rubber floor mats, super clean
Featherlite	Stock	2001	G	$10,000	3/06	NEMI	Aluminum 7'×24' tandem livestock trailer
Felling	FT20	2001	G	$3,900	11/06	WCMN	Tandem-axle grain trailer
Flow Boy	NA		G	$1,500	3/06	WCWA	Asphalt trailer
Fontaine	22'	1995	G	$32,000	4/06	SEND	Drop-deck detachable triple-axle semitrailer
Fontaine	48'	1989	G	$12,250	2/06	SEKS	DFT 3 8048A 48' drop-deck trailer, air ride, 255/70R22.5, hay racks & ramps
Fontaine	NA	1978	G	$4,500	3/06	SEMN	42'×96" flatbed trailer, new tires, spring ride
Fontaine	NA	1994	G	$8,500	5/06	ECMI	Tandem axle, step-deck equipment trailer
Fontaine	NA	1998	G	$31,000	7/06	WCTN	Lowboy, tri-axle, self-contained, gas engine, 100,000 lb.
Four Star	Stock	1990	G	$6,600	11/06	SEIA	7'×20' aluminum grain livestock trailer
Four Star	Stock	1995	G	$7,200	11/06	SEIA	8'×16' aluminum grain livestock trailer
Fruehauf	16'	1972	G	$2,000	3/06	ECMI	
Fruehauf	16'	1984	F	$3,100	4/06	WCSD	Aluminum, 3-axle end-dump pup trailer
Fruehauf	24'		G	$6,000	4/06	NWMN	Single axle, dry van, 3,000-gal. tank, Honda 2" pump, hose reel, air system
Fruehauf	28'		G	$4,500	5/06	SWCA	Equipment trailer, 4' beavertail, fold-down ramps
Fruehauf	28'	1971	G	$11,250	7/06	NWMN	Tri-axle end dump, poly-bedliner, spring suspension, quick dump, grain kit
Fruehauf	28'	1982	G	$2,300	3/06	SCIN	Dump trailer
Fruehauf	30'	1977	G	$12,000	7/06	NWMN	Tri-axle end dump, air up/down front axle, grain kit
Fruehauf	30'	1979	G	$11,500	7/06	NWMN	Tri-axle end dump, grain kit, spring suspension, quick dump
Fruehauf	30'	1979	G	$11,500	7/06	NWMN	Tri-axle end dump, grain kit, 10:00×20 tires, spring suspension, quick dump

Trailers

Make	Model	Year	Cond.	Price	Sale	Location	Comments
Fruehauf	30'	1983	G	$8,750	7/06	NWMN	Tandem end dump
Fruehauf	30'	1998	G	$16,500	12/06	SWMI	Aluminum box steel frame dump trailer, Shur-Lok roll tarp
Fruehauf	38'		F	$350	2/06	NWOH	Flatbed trailer, tandem
Fruehauf	42'		G	$4,000	3/06	WCWA	Tandem-axle flatbed
Fruehauf	45'		G	$1,500	12/06	ECMN	Sliding rear tandem, roll-up, 20" tube rubber, Dayton rims
Fruehauf	45'	1981	F	$4,800	1/06	SWNE	Flatbed trailer, bale racks
Fruehauf	45'	1984	G	$1,300	11/06	NCIN	Van trailer
Fruehauf	48'		G	$4,000	11/06	NWMN	Dry van, top vents
Fruehauf	48'	1989	G	$1,550	8/06	WCNC	
Fruehauf	48'	1989	G	$1,650	8/06	WCNC	
Fruehauf	48'	1989	G	$1,650	8/06	WCNC	
Fruehauf	53'	1988	G	$4,750	9/06	WCND	53'×102" dry van, e-track, air-ride, slider, 11×22.5 on polished aluminum
Fruehauf	8,000 gallon		P	$3,000	3/06	SEIA	Tanker trailer, 4 compartments, very rough
General	NA		G	$5,250	1/06	WCNH	20-ton tag-along, tandem axle
General	NA		G	$30,000	3/06	WCWA	Lowboy, hyd. detach. pony motor, center rail, 21' well
Golden Bell	NA		G	$1,200	12/06	WCKS	Header trailer, single axle
Golden Bell	NA		G	$1,200	12/06	WCKS	Header trailer, single axle
Golden Bell	40'		G	$1,400	1/06	WCPA	Van trailer, 8'×40', spring suspension
Great Dane	40'	1979	G	$7,750	3/06	ECMI	Single drop, tandem axle, beavertail
Great Dane	45'		G	$9,000	5/06	SWCA	50', refrigerated van trailer, 50'×102" box, Carrier refrigerator unit
Great Dane	45'	1989	G	$3,200	10/06	SENJ	Flatbed
Great Dane	48'	1978	G	$8,500	12/06	WCMN	Water van, 4 1,550-gal. poly tanks, 250-gal. ss mix tank, Honda engine and pump, 3" discharge, 40', 3' load-out hose
Great Dane	48'	1994	G	$7,000	3/06	WCWA	Refrigerated van trailer, Carrier refrigerator unit, sliding carriage
Great Dane	NA		G	$1,250	5/06	SWCA	25', refrigerated trailer, 25' box, Thermo King unit
Great Dane	NA		G	$9,000	5/06	SWCA	Refrigerated trailer, 50'×102" box, Carrier refrigerator unit, tandem axle
Great Dane	NA		G	$9,000	5/06	SWCA	Refrigerated van trailer, 50'×102" box, Carrier unit, tandem axle
Great Dane	NA		G	$9,000	5/06	SWCA	Refrigerated trailer, 50'×102", Thermo King carrier unit, tandem axle
H&H	16'	2004	G	$2,600	9/06	ECMN	Fold-down ramps, 12,000-lb. capacity
H&H	18'		G	$1,900	3/06	ECNE	Tilt-deck tandem-axle tag trailer
H&H	30'	2005	G	$7,750	9/06	SCNE	Grain flatbed, dual tandem-axle trailer, 5' beavertail, folding ramps, 16" tires, GVW 20,000 lb.
H&H	NA		G	$4,000	2/06	WCSD	34'×5' double-tandem trailer, dovetail
H&H	NA	2004	G	$950	12/06	SWIA	6×14 ramp trailer
H&H	NA	2005	G	$800	12/06	SWIA	Utility trailer, single axle, flip-up ramp, 5'×10', tongue jack
H&H	Stock	1998	F	$725	3/06	NCNE	16' tandem utility trailer
H&S	10'		G	$1,700	2/06	ECMN	Single-axle livestock trailer
Hale	Stock		P	$300	3/06	NWKS	Tandem axle, open-top livestock trailer
Hale	Stock		F	$800	3/06	WCKS	
Hale	Stock		F	$800	12/06	SCNE	6'×16' bumper pull stock trailer, new floor
Hale	Stock		P	$900	2/06	NCKS	6'×20', grain, really rough
Hale	Stock	1978	F	$875	10/06	SWNE	6'×16' bumper hitch, livestock trailer

Trailers

Make	Model	Year	Cond.	Price	Sale	Location	Comments
Hallmark	NA	1997	G	$2,100	8/06	ECNE	8'×16'×102" enclosed, tandem axle, bumper hitch, swinging doors
Hart	NA		G	$1,100	4/06	ECND	Single pole header trailer
Harvest H.	NA		G	$1,400	3/06	NCNE	Header trailer
Harvest H.	NA		G	$2,000	3/06	NEKS	30' adjustable header trailer
Haulmark	NA	2001	G	$3,900	3/06	WCMN	8.5'×24' tandem axle, bumper hitch enclosed trailer, side door, rear ramp door
Haulmark	NA	2005	E	$5,000	2/06	SWIN	24' enclosed car transport trailer, rear ramp door, side door, stone guard, chrome corners, roof vent, Torflex tandem axles, panel lined
Haynes	Stock		P	$100	11/06	SCSD	8'×20', grain, rough
Hercules	NA	1965	G	$4,000	5/06	ECMI	Tri-axle steel dump trailer
Hillsboro	20'		G	$4,000	3/06	ECNE	L300 20'×8' grain trailer, (2) 6,048-lb. axles
Hillsboro	Stock	1988	P	$1,100	6/06	NCIA	7×20 steel grain stock trailer, rusty
Hillsboro	Stock	1994	F	$550	10/06	SEMN	
Hillsboro	Stock	1998	G	$9,100	8/06	NCMI	7'×24' grain aluminum stock trailer, tandem 6,000-lb. axles, new brakes
Hobbs	38'	1973	P	$2,900	10/06	NCKS	Cattle pot, aluminum, 4 compartments, rough
Hobbs	40'	1967	F	$2,200	2/06	NCCO	Flatbed trailer
Hobbs	NA	1974	F	$3,200	2/06	NCCO	50' aluminum cattle pot trailer
Hull	16'		G	$750	8/06	ECMN	
Hurst	21'	1998	G	$3,000	12/06	NEMO	Grain flatbed trailer, wooden floor, tandem axles
Hurst	NA	1998	G	$1,500	12/06	SWMI	3 axle, 7'×18', 6 lug
Hyster	35T	1977	G	$9,500	3/06	SCIN	Detach lowboy, outriggers
Hyster	Lowboy		G	$7,500	7/06	WCCA	65-ton, hyd. neck
IHC	20'		E	$4,000	3/06	SWIN	Grain equipment trailer, 12,000-lb. tandem axles, beavertail, ramps, toolbox, nice solid trailer
Interstate	NA	2000	G	$3,700	3/06	SCIN	Tandem-axle tag trailer
Interstate	NA	2004	G	$7,200	3/06	SCIN	Tandem-axle tag trailer, dually
ITC	NA		G	$2,600	11/06	SEIA	8'×20' grain flatbed tandem-axle trailer, 4' beavertail, ramps
J&M	NA		G	$650	1/06	NECO	Platform head trailer
J&M	NA		G	$1,100	3/06	NESD	Header cart
J&M	NA		G	$1,800	12/06	ECNE	Header trailer, light, 6-bolt gear
Jackson	NA		F	$225	5/06	SEND	Swather transport trailer
Jantz	NA		G	$800	4/06	WCSD	Hd 3-axle steel flatbed 8×17 trailer, ramps & brakes
Jantz	NA		G	$1,300	11/06	NEND	Double-pole header tandem trailer
Jantz	NA	1990	G	$5,100	12/06	ECKS	20'×12' tandem-axle combine trailer, 24,000 lb. GVW, nonadjustable
Jantz	NA	1993	G	$4,500	12/06	ECKS	28'×12' tandem-axle combine trailer, adjustable, 8.5 ft. to 12 ft., ramps, air brakes, 9.50R16.5 tires, bought new
Jantz	NA	1993	G	$5,750	12/06	ECKS	28'×12' tandem-axle combine trailer, adjustable, 8.5 ft. to 12 ft., ramps, air brakes, 9.50R16.5 tires, bought new
Jantz	NA	1998	G	$8,200	3/06	NWKS	Combine trailer, pintle hitch, air, lights at rear
John Deere	101		G	$700	6/06	NCIL	Planter trailer, 28'
John Deere	201		G	$1,100	2/06	SCMI	Tandem-axle implement trailer
John Deere	21'		G	$675	2/06	ECIL	
John Deere	28'		G	$550	3/06	NCNE	Implement trailer
John Deere	30'		G	$800	12/06	NWIL	Implement trailer, square tube
John Deere	30'		G	$1,000	6/06	NWIL	Implement trailer

Trailers

Make	Model	Year	Cond.	Price	Sale	Location	Comments
John Deere	965		G	$1,500	12/06	NCIA	Head trailer
John Deere	NA		G	$1,600	2/06	NWIL	Combine head trailer
Johnson	NA		G	$750	6/06	ECND	Johnson Welding 16' tandem-axle flatbed trailer
Johnson	NA		G	$900	3/06	ECND	Single-pole header trailer
Johnson	NA		G	$1,700	6/06	ECND	Single-pole header trailer
Johnson	NA	2002	G	$1,500	9/06	WCND	30' single-pole header trailer
Kaufman	NA	2004	G	$9,600	10/06	SENJ	25-ton
Kiefer	29'	2000	G	$7,000	12/06	SWIA	Industrial grain trailer, tandem dual wheel
Kiefer	Stock		F	$0	3/06	WCSD	No sale at $700, 6'×16', steel, grain
Kiefer	Stock		P	$1,250	3/06	SEIA	6'×18' grain livestock trailer, rough
Kiefer	Stock		G	$1,900	8/06	NCIA	16' tandem stock trailer, bumper hitch
Kiefer	Stock	1978	G	$1,750	12/06	NEMO	20' grain livestock trailer, newer wooden floor
Kiefer	Stock	1987	G	$2,300	5/06	SEND	GN tandem-axle stock trailer, 22', torsion suspension
Kiefer	Stock	1988	F	$900	12/06	SWIA	Tandem-axle grain stock trailer, 7×20, single gate
Kiefer	Stock	2004	E	$17,000	8/06	WCIL	Horse trailer, 4 horse, aluminum, with front & rear tack, like new
Kilbros	1618N		G	$2,300	2/06	WCIL	30' transport head cart
Kilbros	300		G	$2,200	2/06	NWOH	30' header cart, dolly hitch
Kilbros	NA		G	$1,200	11/06	WCIL	Head trailer
Kilbros	NA		G	$1,500	2/06	WCIL	Head cart
Kilbros	NA		G	$1,550	12/06	ECNE	Adjustable header trailer, lights
Kilbros	NA		G	$1,700	2/06	WCIL	Head cart
King	20'		G	$5,000	7/06	WCPA	Equipment trailer, 20' deck, cable removable gooseneck, 24" rubber
Kuhn	NA		G	$1,200	3/06	SEND	32' transport, rear steer
LaCrosse	NA	1990	G	$3,500	6/06	NEIN	12-ton tag trailer
Landoll	32'		G	$16,500	12/06	ECMN	Hyd. sliding rear axles, drop deck
Landoll	48'	1999	G	$30,000	5/06	ECMI	Hyd. traveling axle equipment trailer, 48'×102", 20,000-lb. winch, air ride, forklift package
Ledwell	NA	2000	G	$600	10/06	WCFL	Water trailer, rear sprayers, trailer mounted
Load Trail	NA	2004	g	$900	8/06	SCIL	77×12, load ramp, 1 axle
Load Trail	NA	2006	E	$2,500	1/06	WCCA	2 axle
Load King	NA		G	$5,000	12/06	ECMN	Folding deck, 96" wide, main deck 20'6", rear deck 12'8", top deck 7'3"
Load King	NA	1988	G	$9,000	4/06	WCMB	Canadian sale, 32', Shur-Lok rollover tarp
Lorak	NA		F	$600	4/06	NEND	
Lowboy	NA		G	$300	5/06	SCCA	9'8"×25', tandem axle, flatbed
Lufkin	53'	1995	G	$5,000	8/06	ECMN	Insulated dry van
Mac-Lander	NA	1990	G	$4,250	12/06	ECMN	27' deck, beavertail, air or vac brakes
Mac-Lander	NA	2003	G	$3,000	12/06	WCIA	14', ramps
Magnum	20'	1987	G	$7,000	3/06	NEND	Pintle pup, roll tarp, new tires and brakes
Maurer	30'		G	$2,400	6/06	SCMN	Header trailer
Maurer	30'		G	$2,500	12/06	WCKS	Header trailer, single axle
Maurer	30'		G	$3,800	12/06	WCKS	Header trailer
Maurer	NA		G	$2,500	3/06	NESD	Single-header trailer
Maurer	NA		G	$2,600	3/06	NESD	Single-header trailer
Maurer	NA		G	$4,600	3/06	ECND	Combine head trailer
MD Products	NA		G	$3,700	12/06	WCKS	#636 header trailer, fifth-wheel running gear, tandem axle, 1 axle with brakes, holds 36' platform

WHAT'S IT WORTH?

Trailers

Make	Model	Year	Cond.	Price	Sale	Location	Comments
MD Products	NA	2004	G	$3,500	8/06	NCIA	Head trailer for 30' platform
MD Products	NA	2004	G	$3,750	12/06	WCKS	MD38 header trailer, fifth-wheel running gear, tandem axle, 1 axle with brakes
MD Products	NA	2005	G	$3,000	12/06	NEKS	30' header trailer, single axle, 2 front dolly wheels, adjustable hitch, lights
MD Products	NA	2005	G	$4,250	12/06	WCKS	#636 header trailer, fifth-wheel running gear, tandem axle, 1 axle with brakes, holds 36' platform
Merritt	Stock	1990	G	$16,000	3/06	SWNE	48' aluminum cattle pot, 1100R-24.5 tires
Miller	16'		G	$950	9/06	SWIA	Tilt-bed trailer, hd
Miller	NA		G	$4,400	12/06	WCIL	Tilt-top semitrailer, hyd. winch
Move Master	NA		F	$1,400	12/06	WCMI	25' header cart
Move Master	NA		G	$1,450	12/06	NWMO	25' trailer
Move-All	40'		G	$1,000	10/06	SWOH	25-ton equipment trailer, 8' wide, moving tandem deck powered by wetline, fifth-wheel pin
Mustang	NA	1995	G	$3,400	3/06	SCIN	Tandem-axle tag trailer, 12-ton
Mustang	NA	1999	G	$3,750	4/06	WCIA	Gooseneck, 20' flatbed, 5' fold up beavertail ramps, winch
Muv-All	NA	1980	G	$6,250	3/06	WCMN	Dovetail hyd. implement trailer, 40', steel deck, flip-ups
Natec	30'	1987	G	$19,750	4/06	NWMN	Tri-axle steel frame end dump, single pusher, tarp
Nelson	NA		G	$800	3/06	NEMI	8-ton wood porta box mounted on hd tandem trailer, hyd. hoist, poly unloading auger
Nelson	NA		G	$2,250	3/06	NEMI	Parkhurst/Nelson dual wheel tri-axle 24'+5' flatbed trailer, metal livestock sides, fifth wheel, electric brakes
Nelson	NA		G	$4,250	6/06	NEIN	50-ton detach lowboy, wet kit hook up
Nelson	NA	1998	G	$62,500	5/06	ECMI	Grain lowboy trailer, 80-ton capacity
Neville	24'	1995	G	$7,200	8/06	NCNE	Steel pup trailer, roll tarp, dolly hitch
Neville	53'	2006	E	$25,000	12/06	WCMN	Single-drop spread axle, air ride, beavertail, ramps
Nuttall	36'	1983	G	$15,000	4/06	ECND	60-ton lowboy trailer, outriggers, beavertail, ramps, 10:00-15 tires
O-C Scales	NA	1994	G	$5,500	3/06	SWMN	24' pop-up grain, 20,000-lb. tandem dually, beavertail, 102" wide
Oklahoma	NA	1997	G	$6,100	3/06	ECIL	30' grain trailer
OTM	NA	1998	G	$4,750	2/06	NECO	20' grain flatbed trailer, 4' dovetails, ramps
P&J	NA	2005	G	$5,850	1/06	WCCA	2-axle dump trailer
P&J	NA	2006	G	$1,400	9/06	ECMN	Tandem axle, beavertail, 2" ball
Pace	NA	1998	G	$6,000	3/06	WCWA	28', tandem-axle cargo trailer, electric brakes
Palmer	NA		G	$4,900	3/06	SWNE	600-gal. fuel trailer, Honda 5.5-hp. gas high-capacity transfer pump
Phelan	NA		G	$4,000	6/06	NEIN	25-ton lowboy
Phelan	NA		G	$4,500	6/06	NEIN	Lowboy
Phelan	NA		G	$4,500	3/06	SCIN	25-ton lowboy, fixed neck, beavertail, ramps
Phelan	NA		G	$5,700	3/06	SCIN	35-ton, lowboy, rigid neck
Phoenix	NA		G	$500	3/06	WCWA	End dump
Phoenix	NA	1990	G	$3,500	7/06	WCCA	Spread axle trailer
Pines	28'		F	$150	1/06	WCPA	Pup trailer, single axle
PJ	20'	2005	E	$5,200	3/06	NCCO	Grain trailer, 5'-pop up dovetail, 3-axle flatbed, ramps
PJ	30'	2003	G	$6,000	11/06	WCMN	Flatbed trailer, 5' beavertail, fifth wheel, 35' total, 2 axles, 20,000 lb., ramps
PJ	618D	2003	E	$2,900	3/06	NEND	Tandem-axle bumper hitch car trailer, 14,000 lb., ramps, like new

Trailers

Make	Model	Year	Cond.	Price	Sale	Location	Comments
PJ	NA	2003	G	$4,000	2/06	WCSD	6'×10' dump trailer
PJ	NA	2004	G	$3,300	11/06	WCMN	Dump trailer, electric hoist, 12'
PJ	NA	2005	G	$3,500	11/06	WCMN	Dump trailer, electric hoist, 12'
PJ	NA	2005	G	$3,800	11/06	WCMN	Dump trailer, electric hoist, 12'
PJ	NA	2006	G	$2,350	10/06	SEMN	S180
PK	NA		G	$2,500	12/06	SCNE	Head trailer for up to 30' grain or corn head
Ponderosa	NA		G	$4,100	11/06	NCKY	Special addition 2-horse trailer, living quarters
Rainbow	NA	2000	G	$2,800	11/06	NEND	Tandem-axle bumper trailer, 18', hyd. tilt deck, 6,000-lb. axles
Ranco	NA	1991	G	$7,500	4/06	WCSD	2-axle belly dump pup with duals
Ranco	NA	1994	G	$13,000	4/06	WCSD	Triple-axle belly dump trailer
Raven	34'	1983	G	$22,000	4/06	NWMN	Tri-axle aluminum end dump, single pusher, roll tarp
Raven	40'	1976	G	$2,750	1/06	WCPA	Equipment trailer, tandem axle, air ride
Raven	NA	1981	G	$4,500	3/06	SWNE	Aluminum 45' hay trailer, steel hay rails, 11R-24.5 tires
Rawhide	Stock		F	$350	4/06	WCSD	7×16 bumper horse trailer, floor needs repair
Reitnouer	NA	1989	F	$6,200	1/06	SWNE	Aluminum flatbed trailer 45' spread axle, bale racks
Rice	Stock		G	$1,200	11/06	SWIA	7'×20' grain livestock trailer, new floor & wiring
Roadmaster	NA		G	$2,003	11/06	WCMN	12' enclosed trailer
Rogers	NA		G	$22,000	6/06	NEIN	Nonground bearing, 60-ton tri-axle lowboy
Rogers	NA	1990	G	$4,500	3/06	ECMI	20-ton, tandem axle, 8×6
Rustler	NA	1987	G	$800	3/06	SCIN	2 horse, bumper pull, dressing room, ramp load
Schaben	1,000 gallon		G	$1,800	3/06	NENE	Tandem-axle liquid transport trailer, inductor, Briggs & Stratton 5-hp. gas motor
Schein	26'		G	$8,000	2/06	WCIL	Aluminum dump trailer, rear suspension, roll tarp
Siebert	NA		G	$19,000	5/06	SWCA	Lowbed trailer, 60-ton capacity, 21' Expando deck, 16-wheel, extra long & standard detachable goosenecks w/ Hyster jeep, 45-ton capacity, 16 wheel
Siebert	NA	1988	G	$10,000	5/06	ECMI	Double-drop lowboy, 48'×102", outriggers, air ride
Siebert	NA	1988	G	$10,000	5/06	ECMI	Double-drop lowboy, 48'×102", outriggers, air ride
Sled Bed	NA		G	$700	11/06	NEND	Snowmobile trailer
Sooner	Stock	2005	E	$13,900	12/06	WCMN	Aluminum fifth-wheel, livestock trailer, 3 compartment, tandem axle, 24'
Starlite	18'	2000	G	$3,450	3/06	SEMN	Grain flatbed trailer w/ beavertail
Starlite	NA		G	$1,400	4/06	ECND	20' tri-axle flatbed trailer
Starlite	NA	1999	G	$1,600	11/06	SCND	Tandem-axle car trailer, (2) 35,000-lb. axles, very nice
Steigers	NA	1996	G	$3,300	3/06	SCIN	10-ton tag trailer, pintle hitch
Strick	28'		G	$4,500	4/06	NWMN	Single-axle dry van, 2,000-gal. Pleasure Products, 1,350-gal. poly tanks
Strick	48'		G	$2,250	5/06	SWCA	Tandem axle, 8-wheel
Supreme	NA	1984	G	$3,800	12/06	ECMN	Gooseneck, tandem axle
Swartz	NA		G	$6,250	12/06	ECMN	35-ton hyd., beavertail
Talbert	NA		G	$1,000	10/06	SWOH	35-ton equipment trailer, 50-ton beams detachable, 22' well, wetline, new rear brakes
Talbert	NA	1988	G	$21,000	2/06	WCSD	40-ton lowboy trailer, tri-axle, 9' wide, detachable grain
Talbert	NA	1996	G	$30,000	1/06	WCPA	Equipment trailer, 50-ton capacity, 102" wide, 22.5' deck, outrigger brackets
Talbert	NA	2005	E	$57,000	7/06	WCPA	55-ton equipment trailer, 26' drop side deck, removable fourth axle
Temco	20'	1995	G	$9,700	3/06	SWNE	20'×7' tandem axle alum. grain trailer

Trailers

Make	Model	Year	Cond.	Price	Sale	Location	Comments
Temco	NA	1996	G	$1,500	2/06	SWNE	18'×7' wood deck flatbed trailer, (2) 5,000-lb. axles, ramps
Temco	NA	2003	G	$6,000	8/06	NECO	36' grain flatbed, 2,400-lb. trailer, convertible tail, ramps
Timpte	42'		F	$500	10/06	NCWI	Reefer trailer, spring suspension
Timpte	48'		G	$1,700	4/06	NWMN	Dry van tandem-axle storage trailer
Timpte	NA	2003	G	$18,250	3/06	ECND	28.5'
Timpte	NA	2003	G	$18,500	3/06	ECND	28.5'
Timpte	NA	2003	G	$18,500	3/06	ECND	28.5'
Titan	24'	1998	G	$8,750	12/06	NEMO	Grain flatbed trailer, wooden floor, dually tandem, beavertail, ramps
Titan	24'	2000	G	$4,500	2/06	NCCO	Grain flatbed trailer, 7,000-lb. tandem axles
Titan	35'	2004	G	$7,100	11/06	SCNE	Flatbed grain trailer, tandem duals
Titan	Stock	1998	G	$5,250	12/06	NEMO	20'×6' grain trailer
Towmaster	22'	2000	G	$4,250	12/06	ECMN	18,000-lb. tri-axle, fold-down ramps
Towmaster	C10	2005	G	$3,850	11/06	WCMN	Tandem-axle steel trailer
Towmaster	NA	1996	G	$3,000	12/06	ECMN	Gooseneck, 25' deck, tandem axle
Trail Boss	NA	2001	G	$12,750	11/06	SWCA	Equipment trailer
Trail-Eze	32'	1974	G	$7,000	4/06	SEIA	Tilt bed, triple axle, fifth-wheel trailer
Trail Eze	33'		G	$2,000	4/06	SEND	Grain triple-axle hyd. tilt trailer, winch
Trail-Eze	NA		G	$12,500	3/06	NWKS	Drop deck trailer, 76760 GVW
Trail-Eze	NA	1988	G	$13,000	3/06	ECND	Single drop
Trail-Eze	NA	1993	G	$18,500	3/06	WCWA	Tandem-axle step deck equipment traler, beavertail, hyd. step ramp, 10' upper deck
Trail King	NA	2000	G	$21,000	3/06	WCWA	Lowboy, 8'6" upper deck, 28' main deck, folding tail
Trail King	NA	2000	G	$29,000	4/06	ECND	TK60SSD triple-axle side dump trailer, 78,900-lb. GVW, 11R22.5 tires
Trail Max	T12UT	2002	G	$5,600	11/06	SECA	Flatbed
Trailmann	Stock	1988	F	$900	8/06	NEKS	16'×7' grain stock trailer, 7:00-15 tires
Trailmaster	NA	1984	G	$2,750	7/06	WCCA	Equipment trailer, 24' deck, flip ramps
Trailmaster	Stock		F	$1,100	3/06	ECNE	6'×22' tandem-axle grain livestock trailer
Trailmobile	40'	1969	F	$900	11/06	ECND	Dry van, for storage
Trailmobile	45'		G	$4,600	2/06	NWMN	1,650-gal. & (2) 1,550-gal. poly tanks, 1,000-gal. tank, air tank, mix cone, 2" hose reel, Briggs pump, 22.5 tires
Trailmobile	45'	1979	G	$3,000	7/06	NWMN	Dual slider, (4) 1,500-gal. poly tanks, transfer pump
Trailmobile	NA		G	$1,900	5/06	SWCA	Step deck equipment trailer, 7' upper deck, 18' lower deck, tandem axle, 8-wheel
Trailmobile	NA	1972	F	$1,400	5/06	ECNE	Van trailer
Trailmobile	NA	1979	G	$3,200	8/06	SETN	Flatbed
Trailmobile	NA	1988	G	$12,100	3/06	ECNE	Spread-axle flatbed trailer, wood deck, 255/70R22.5 tires
Trailstar	NA	1997	G	$26,500	2/06	NWMN	Aluminum tri-axle, aluminum end dump, third-axle air up/down, 32' tub, 34' frame, roll tarp
Trail Tech	NA		G	$1,600	3/06	ECND	Double header trailer
Trail Tech	NA	1995	G	$13,300	3/06	NESD	53', 3 axle, narrow frame, double combine trailer, 215/75R17.5 rubber
Trail Tech	NA	1998	G	$16,100	3/06	ECND	28.5'
Trail Tech	NA	1999	G	$10,600	3/06	NESD	3-axle fold-up, double header trailer
Trail Tech	NA	2000	G	$5,000	3/06	NESD	CT220 combine trailer, 13' slideouts, 255/70R22.5 tires
Trail Tech	NA	2001	G	$6,500	3/06	NESD	CT220 combine trailer, 13' slideouts, 255/70R22.5 tires
Trail Tech	NA	2001	G	$9,250	3/06	NESD	3 axle fold-up, double-header trailer for JD 635 headers
Transcraft	42'	1982	F	$3,100	1/06	NCCO	TI'-42', split-axle trailer

Trailers

Make	Model	Year	Cond.	Price	Sale	Location	Comments
Transcraft	45'	1995	G	$3,050	10/06	SENJ	Air ride
Transcraft	45'	1999	G	$6,000	3/06	ECMI	Flatbed, spread axle
Transcraft	48'	1991	G	$12,250	11/06	SCSD	8'×48' drop-deck
Transcraft	NA	1990	G	$16,000	5/06	ECMI	Gooseneck, drop-deck, 35-ton
Travalong	Stock		G	$3,500	10/06	NCKS	7×26 grain stock trailer, good floor, good rubber
Travalong	Stock	1988	G	$2,900	3/06	SENE	7'×16', bumper hitch
Travalong	Stock	1993	G	$3,250	3/06	ECNE	6×16' grain tandem-axle livestock trailer
Tri-Brook	32'	1976	G	$11,750	3/06	NEMI	Aluminum hyd. dump trailer, tandem, air lift, dual purpose gate, 33' aluminum frame, Shur-Lok roll tarp
Triggs	Stock		F	$550	5/06	SEND	6×16 grain stock trailer
Triggs	Stock	1991	F	$1,425	3/06	SEIA	20', title
Trinity	42'	2003	G	$48,000	2/06	WCIL	Stainless steel belt trailer, air ride
Uft	NA		G	$400	9/06	NEIN	Header wagon
United	30'		F	$2,600	3/06	WCMN	Tandem bump hitch enclosed trailer, 8' wide, e-track on inside, 2 side doors
United	NA	2001	G	$16,000	9/06	WCND	50' tri-axle grain race trailer, 20' living quarters, gas furnace, roof overhead storage, 10 KW diesel generator, ramp door
Unverferth	30'	2006	E	$3,000	12/06	SWIA	4-wheel header trailer, large tire option, light package
Unverferth	36'	2006	E	$4,700	12/06	WCMN	Road runner head trailer
Unverferth	HT 2500		G	$2,500	1/06	WCIL	Head trailer
Unverferth	HT12		G	$1,775	2/06	SCMI	Header cart
Unverferth	HT20		G	$1,800	2/06	NCIN	Head cart
Unverferth	HT25		G	$1,450	1/06	NWIL	Head trailer
Unverferth	HT25		G	$1,550	2/06	NEIN	Header cart
Unverferth	HT25		G	$1,600	3/06	SEIA	Head cart
Unverferth	HT25		G	$1,750	1/06	ECNE	Header trailer, 7.50-10 tires
Unverferth	HT25		G	$1,750	1/06	NWIL	Head trailer
Unverferth	HT25		G	$1,775	1/06	SWOH	25' head cart
Unverferth	HT25		G	$1,800	3/06	ECMI	Low-profile header cart
Unverferth	HT25		G	$2,300	3/06	NWOH	Header cart wagon
Unverferth	HT25	1995	G	$2,500	12/06	WCIA	Combine head mover
Unverferth	HT25	1998	G	$1,900	1/06	WCIL	Head cart
Unverferth	HT25	1998	G	$2,050	4/06	SEMI	Header cart
Unverferth	HT25	2003	G	$1,900	12/06	NCIL	Combine head trailer, 25'
Unverferth	HT30		G	$1,600	11/06	NCIN	Head cart
Unverferth	HT30		G	$1,800	2/06	SCMI	Header cart
Unverferth	HT30		E	$1,900	12/06	WCMN	Header trailer
Unverferth	HT30		G	$1,900	2/06	SCMI	Header cart
Unverferth	HT30		E	$2,000	12/06	WCMN	Header trailer
Unverferth	HT30		E	$2,100	2/06	ECMN	30' header cart, 4 wheels, one owner
Unverferth	HT30		G	$2,100	2/06	SEKS	30' head trailer
Unverferth	HT30		G	$2,150	6/06	SCMN	Header trailer
Unverferth	HT30		G	$2,300	3/06	ECMI	Low-profile header cart
Unverferth	HT30		G	$3,150	3/06	SEMN	4-wheel header transport cart
Unverferth	HT30		G	$3,300	3/06	SEMN	4-wheel header transport cart
Unverferth	NA		E	$2,100	3/06	ECNE	4-wheel head carrier trailer, dolly front wheels, hd, like new
Unverferth	NA		E	$4,600	11/06	SCNE	Roadrunner head trailer for 35' head, like new
Vern's	NA		G	$1,200	11/06	SENE	Vern's Manufacturing header trailer
Volzke	NA		G	$1,550	12/06	SCNE	24'×8', hd, lowboy trailer

Trailers

Make	Model	Year	Cond.	Price	Sale	Location	Comments
Vulcan	NA		G	$1,000	3/06	NEND	30' single-pole header trailer
Wells Cargo	NA	2006	G	$4,100	1/06	WCCA	2-axle enclosed trailer
Western	38'		G	$14,750	5/06	SWCA	End dump, 38' box, tandem axle, air gate
Western	NA	1999	G	$31,000	3/06	WCWA	48', tri-axle chip van trailer, aluminum wheels
Western	NA	1999	G	$31,000	3/06	WCWA	48', tri-axle chip van trailer, aluminum wheels
Westgo	14'	1973	G	$5,500	3/06	NWMN	Tandem pup trailer, hoist, air ride, roll tarp
Wilson	38'		G	$4,200	4/06	NWMN	Flatbed, spring ride
Wilson	43'	1973	F	$1,200	11/06	SCSD	Pot, new brakes, tires and lights OK
Wilson	46'	1983	G	$6,750	12/06	NENE	46×102, brakes, cattle pot trailer
Wilson	48'	1994	G	$16,000	2/06	SENE	Aluminum drop-deck trailer, 11R24.5 near-new tires on aluminum rims, spread axle, wood deck
Wilson	Stock	1971	F	$300	3/06	NEKS	42' double-deck steel cattle pot, 24.5 tires
Wilson	Stock	1983	G	$5,200	12/06	SEND	46' cattle trailer, LH load
Wilson	Stock	1993	G	$13,000	3/06	NWKS	48' livestock pot
Winnebago	NA		G	$2,700	11/06	WCMN	Fifth-wheel tri-axle trailer, 18,000-lb. GVW, stake bed w/ sides & rear, electric hoist
Wisconsin	NA		G	$3,500	6/06	NEIN	Tilt top, 12-ton
Witzco	50T		E	$25,500	10/06	NCWI	Tri-axle
Witzco	50T	2000	G	$18,000	5/06	ECMI	Triple axle, beam trailer
Witzco	NA	2006	E	$20,000	10/06	NCWI	35-ton equipment trailer, self-contained hyd. unit, air ride suspension, 24' scraper gooseneck, tapered front beam, tandem axle
Witzco	RG50	2007	E	$29,000	10/06	WCFL	Equipment trailer, removable gooseneck, 50-ton capacity, 8'6"
Witzco	RG50	2007	E	$29,000	10/06	WCFL	Equipment trailer, removable gooseneck, 50-ton capacity, 8'6"
WW	Stock		F	$1,200	1/06	NECO	16' bumper pull, wood floor
WW	Stock		G	$1,400	3/06	NENE	5'×16', bumper hitch livestock trailer, new floor
WW	Stock		G	$2,000	5/06	WCKS	6'×20' stock trailer
WW	Stock		E	$2,300	3/06	NCOK	Bumper pull stock trailer, excellent tires, good floor
WW	Stock	1978	G	$1,300	3/06	SEND	6'×16" tandem-axle stock trailer
WW	Stock	1993	F	$1,000	11/06	NCKS	6×16 livestock trailer
Yacht Club	NA		G	$700	5/06	SEND	4-place steel snowmobile trailer

Trucks

Have fun with this category. You'll find pickups, grain trucks, and semis all listed here. I thought auction sale prices on both grain trucks and semitrailers were exceptionally strong in late 2006 on into early 2007. On March 15, 2007, I saw a 2005 Chevy 2500 4×4 pickup with 449 miles sell for $30,250 on a sale in west-central Iowa. Do you suppose your father or grandfather would have believed a used pickup would ever sell for $30,250 at auction?

Trucks

Make	Model	Year	Cond.	Price	Sale	Location	Comments
Autocar	NA		F	$1,250	1/06	WCPA	Water truck, Cummins PT270 diesel, 9-speed trans.
Autocar	NA	1985	P	$1,800	4/06	WCSD	Truck tandem duals, 400 Cat engine, 13-speed, not running, needs batteries
Autcar	NA	1985	G	$6,000	3/06	ECMI	Tandem axle, 285 hp., L10 Cummins diesel, Allison aluminum box, electric tarp, double frame
Autocar	NA	1987	G	$16,000	7/06	WCPA	Heavy hauler truck, Cat diesel, 20-speed
Chevy	1500		G	$1,500	11/06	SECA	
Chevy	1500	1989	P	$350	11/06	WCMN	Extension cab, short box, 4WD, not running
Chevy	1500	1991	G	$1,400	2/06	SEIN	Silverado pickup, 175K miles, V-6 engine
Chevy	1500	1992	G	$600	4/06	NCOK	2WD, V-6, 5 speed, air, power windows & locks, super cab, 249,644 miles
Chevy	1500	1992	G	$1,300	8/06	SWCA	
Chevy	1500	1995	G	$2,300	8/06	NCOH	4WD, automatic, V-6, 170,000 miles
Chevy	1500	1995	G	$3,000	1/06	WCPA	Gas
Chevy	1500	1995	G	$5,500	2/06	SWNE	Silverado 2WD, standard cab, 105,000 miles, V-8, auto
Chevy	1500	1996	G	$2,400	11/06	SCNE	4×4, automatic, 350, V-8, 145,000 miles
Chevy	1500	1997	G	$1,700	3/06	WCWA	Silverado, V-8
Chevy	1500	1997	G	$7,500	2/06	SEKS	Cab, 4×4
Chevy	1500	2002	E	$11,250	4/06	NCOK	7,100 original miles, all power, V-6, automatic, mint condition
Chevy	1500	2002	G	$17,250	3/06	SWIN	Silverado 1500 Z71, 4WD, extension cab, 5.4 Vortec engine, automatic, tow package, grain & Reese hitches, running boards, line & bedliner, all power options, OnStar
Chevy	1500	2003	E	$15,400	8/06	WCKS	Pickup, automatic, 23K miles, extension cab, 5.3-liter motor
Chevy	20	1983	F	$925	2/06	SEIL	Pickup, 74,900 miles
Chevy	20	1990	P	$750	4/06	SEND	4×4, extension cab pickup, V-8, automatic
Chevy	2500		G	$1,750	5/06	SWCA	Utility, V-8, auto
Chevy	2500	1988	G	$1,750	12/06	NCIA	4×4, automatic, full power, high miles
Chevy	2500	1988	G	$2,000	11/06	SCCA	Flatbed, Meyer snowplow, 4WD
Chevy	2500	1988	G	$2,000	12/06	ECMN	Extension cab, 4WD, long box, Silverado, 120,000 miles, AM/FM
Chevy	2500	1990	G	$1,900	3/06	NENE	Cheyenne 4×4, 4 speed, 159,000 miles w/ 40,000 miles on OH
Chevy	2500	1990	G	$2,400	3/06	NENE	¾-ton, 4×4, 200 miles on 30,000 miles on OH
Chevy	2500	1991	F	$650	10/06	SEMN	4×4
Chevy	2500	1991	F	$950	8/06	SWCA	68,300 miles
Chevy	2500	1992	F	$2,900	7/06	SEND	Silverado, 4×4, 6.5 turbo diesel, 256,000 miles, new motor at 196,500 miles, new tires
Chevy	2500	1993	G	$1,900	3/06	WCWA	Toolbox, V-8
Chevy	2500	1994	G	$4,500	7/06	ECNY	4WD, Silverado, gas, auto
Chevy	2500	1995	F	$975	9/06	ECMN	Auto, AM/FM, toolbox, 4WD
Chevy	2500	1995	G	$4,100	8/06	SWCA	Cheyenne
Chevy	2500	1995	G	$4,800	8/06	SWCA	
Chevy	2500	1995	G	$5,600	4/06	ECND	Extension cab, 6.5 turbo diesel, auto, 4WD
Chevy	2500	1997	G	$2,100	10/06	WCMA	Cargo van, 124,106 miles
Chevy	2500	1998	G	$8,500	3/06	ECNE	Cheyenne, 4×4, Bradford-built steel flatbed, 350 Vortec V-8 gas, automatic, chrome guard
Chevy	2500	1999	G	$2,700	10/06	WCMA	Cargo van, 6 cyl., auto
Chevy	2500	1999	G	$3,100	10/06	WCMA	Cargo van, 6 cyl., auto

Trucks

Make	Model	Year	Cond.	Price	Sale	Location	Comments
Chevy	2500	1999	G	$3,900	10/06	WCMA	Cargo van, 6 cyl., auto
Chevy	2500	1999	G	$4,400	10/06	WCMA	Cargo van, 6 cyl., auto
Chevy	2500	1999	G	$5,700	10/06	WCMA	Cargo van, 6 cyl., auto
Chevy	2500	2000	G	$3,200	10/06	ECMO	4WD, air, 180,406 miles
Chevy	2500	2000	G	$10,750	11/06	ECND	LS extension cab, ¾-ton, 5.7 litre, automatic, 4WD, leather, 47,716 miles, leather 60/40 seat, cover
Chevy	2500	2000	G	$14,000	3/06	NWIL	Silverado 4×4, extension cab, 97K miles
Chevy	2500	2001	G	$16,000	2/06	WCSD	4 door, hd, Duramax at 99K miles
Chevy	2500	2003	G	$15,000	11/06	SCNE	4×4, hd, automatic, air, tilt, 61K miles
Chevy	2500	2004	E	$0	2/06	ECIL	No sale at $19,000 – wanted $21,000, Silverado, 4×4 pickup
Chevy	2500	2005	G	$25,000	12/06	WCKS	Duramax diesel engine, automatic, 4×4, quad cab, long box, dual climate control, pw/pl, seats, tilt, cruise, cloth interior, headache rack, trailer brakes, tow pkg., AM/FM/CD
Chevy	2500	2005	E	$25,000	12/06	WCMN	Duramax, hd, 6.6 diesel, 4WD, auto, under 30,000 miles, fifth-wheel ball, pw/pl, air overloads
Chevy	30	1978	G	$1,400	1/06	NWIL	2WD, 8' flatbed, 454 V-8, 74,465 miles
Chevy	30	1979	G	$1,800	4/06	SEND	4×4, 1-ton dually
Chevy	30	1979	G	$1,800	4/06	SEND	4×4, 1-ton dually, fuel pump
Chevy	30	1980	P	$500	2/06	ECIL	Custom deluxe
Chevy	30	1984	G	$2,600	2/06	SWNE	Scottsdale service pickup, 4 speed, 2WD
Chevy	30	1988	G	$2,500	8/06	NWIL	1-ton, 81K miles, 4 speed, hoisted stock rack
Chevy	30	1995	G	$4,400	8/06	SWCA	
Chevy	30	1995	G	$4,400	8/06	SWCA	
Chevy	3500		G	$3,000	11/06	SECA	Automatic, air
Chevy	3500		G	$3,500	11/06	SWCA	12' bed, 16" stake sides, gas
Chevy	3500		G	$8,600	5/06	SWCA	Flatbed, headache rack, auto
Chevy	3500	1982	G	$1,300	11/06	SCCA	Flatbed dumptruck, 12', 4 speed, side toolboxes
Chevy	3500	1989	F	$800	8/06	SETN	Utility bed, auto, 106,331 miles
Chevy	3500	1989	F	$1,500	7/06	SEND	Cab, chassis, dually, ambulance body, white
Chevy	3500	1990	G	$5,700	1/06	SCKS	Cheyenne 1-ton dually service/lube truck, 131,926 miles, 350 5.7-L V-8 gas, 235/R16 tires, auto, AM/FM, air, 470-gal. diesel tank, steel toolbox, Emglo air compressor w/ 5.5-hp. Honda gas engine, receiver hitch, VIN: 1GBHC34K2LE231162
Chevy	3500	1990	G	$6,900	11/06	NCOH	454 gas engine, automatic, 4×4, 95K miles
Chevy	3500	1993	F	$2,000	11/06	SCCA	Flatbed, duals, crew cab, fuel tank
Chevy	3500	1993	G	$2,750	3/06	ECIN	Crew cab, gas, 20,000 miles, auto
Chevy	3500	1993	g	$4,500	11/06	SCCA	Bucket truck, Altec AT250G boom
Chevy	3500	1993	G	$5,750	3/06	ECMI	6.5 diesel, 4 speed, 8'6" box
Chevy	3500	1995	G	$2,700	8/06	WCNC	158,106 miles
Chevy	3500	1995	G	$5,000	4/06	WCSD	Dually, dual 40-gal. tanks, electric pumps, 4×4, flatbed
Chevy	3500	1995	G	$9,400	4/06	NENE	1-ton dually, 4×4 extension cab, turbo, auto, grille guard, new tires
Chevy	3500	1996	G	$5,250	11/06	ECND	Cheyenne, 1-ton, standard cab, 5.7 liter, automatic, 4WD, 114K miles
Chevy	3500	1997	G	$3,000	3/06	WCWA	Swing crane
Chevy	3500	1997	G	$7,500	3/06	ECIN	Dump truck

Trucks

Make	Model	Year	Cond.	Price	Sale	Location	Comments
Chevy	3500	1997	G	$13,250	4/06	NEND	Silverado, 1-ton dually extension cab, 454, automatic, 4WD, 8' service bed, 300-gal. twin comp. fuel tank, twin pumps, 73,216 miles
Chevy	3500	1999	G	$7,500	11/06	SCCA	Van, dually, auto
Chevy	3500	2000	G	$10,000	10/06	ECMO	Versalift
Chevy	3500	2000	G	$10,500	10/06	ECMO	29' reach
Chevy	3500	2000	G	$10,500	10/06	ECMO	29' reach
Chevy	3500	2000	G	$12,000	10/06	ECMO	Versalift, 29'
Chevy	3500	2000	G	$13,000	10/06	ECMO	Versalift
Chevy	3500	2001	G	$9,500	3/06	ECMI	Siverado, 350, 300 hp., auto
Chevy	3500	2005	G	$25,000	12/06	WCKS	Duramax diesel engine, automatic, 4×4, quad cab, long box, dual-climate control, pw/pl, seats, tilt, cruise, cloth interior, headache rack, trailer brakes, tow pkg., AM/FM/CD, 57,500 miles
Chevy	4400		F	$200	10/06	SWNE	Box, hoist
Chevy	60	1976	F	$2,000	4/06	SEND	350, 4×2 speed, 5-yard gravel box
Chevy	60	1979	P	$450	7/06	SEND	Service body
Chevy	60	1986	P	$2,500	7/06	SEND	Pitman hot stick 46' double bucket
Chevy	60	1987	P	$900	7/06	SEND	Pitman hot stick 46' double bucket
Chevy	70	1980	G	$8,500	11/06	SCNE	5×2 speed, 366, V-8, Midwest 18' steel box, new twin cyl. hoist, 58,042 miles
Chevy	70	1981	G	$8,500	2/06	SWIN	Knapheide grain & livestock bed, quilted steel floor, 5×2 speed trans., V-8, good tires
Chevy	70	1981	G	$13,300	1/06	NECO	Tag axle, 20' steel box
Chevy	70	1982	E	$7,200	3/06	NEKS	V-8, bed
Chevy	70	1987	G	$4,100	6/06	NEIN	Single-axle dump truck, 10' dump bed, snowplow
Chevy	C20	1976	F	$1,600	2/06	NWMN	350 engine, 4 speed, 8' flatbed
Chevy	C20	1991	F	$400	9/06	NEIN	Van, auto, gas
Chevy	C2500	1990	G	$5,100	2/06	ECIL	Silverado, 4×4, auto, 5.7, 112K miles
Chevy	C30		G	$1,100	4/06	WCSD	Red pickup, 1-ton, dually, toolboxes, Omaha standard flat box
Chevy	C30	1983	F	$900	3/06	WCMN	1-ton dually flatbed, 350, 4 speed
Chevy	C30	1985	G	$6,000	8/06	SETN	Gas 350, V-8 engine, 4 speed, 19,756 miles
Chevy	C30	1995	G	$4,600	10/06	ECMO	6.5 diesel
Chevy	C30	1995	G	$5,750	3/06	SEMN	1-ton dually 4×4 pickup, 454V8, 5-speed trans., 4-10 posi rear end, 133,500 actual miles, bought new
Chevy	C30	1996	G	$2,400	10/06	ECMO	
Chevy	C3500	1994	G	$1,500	10/06	WCMA	Service truck, 8 cyl., auto
Chevy	C3500	1996	G	$1,600	10/06	NCWI	Dump truck, dual fuel, auto
Chevy	C60		P	$200	8/06	ECNE	Viking single-axle grain truck
Chevy	C60		F	$500	1/06	WCCA	Nurse truck, V-8
Chevy	C60		G	$800	9/06	NEIN	Grain box, gas
Chevy	C60		G	$1,750	9/06	WCTX	Diesel, single axle
Chevy	C60		F	$2,200	3/06	NWPA	16' wooden dump bed
Chevy	C60		G	$6,500	4/06	WCSD	20' bed, double hoist, Shur-Lok roll tarp, hyd. brakes
Chevy	C60	1976	G	$2,600	12/06	NWIL	350 V-8, 4×2 speed, 13.5' farm box, twin hoist, 8.25-20 tires, one owner, 88,875 miles, gas
Chevy	C60	1976	G	$2,700	5/06	SEND	Single axle, 350, V-8, 4×2 speed, 15' Omaha standard box, hoist, roll tarp, 51,289 miles

Trucks

Make	Model	Year	Cond.	Price	Sale	Location	Comments
Chevy	C60	1978	G	$2,900	3/06	NEKS	Custom single-axle truck, 16' wood box, Harsh single cyl. hoist, 350, 4×2 speed, 95,092 miles
Chevy	C60	1979	G	$3,000	3/06	SWNE	Single axle, 350 V-8 gas, 4×2 speed, 8.25-R20 tires, 1,500-gal. ss liquid fertilizer tank, 5.5-hp. Honda motor, 2" transfer pump
Chevy	C60	1979	G	$3,500	8/06	NCIA	366, 4×2 speed, recently rebuilt engine & flatbed, sold with Hillsboro 32' triple-axle grain trailer
Chevy	C60	1979	F	$3,900	4/06	NESD	16' steel box, wood floor, hoist, double acting hoist, 350 engine, 4×2 trans., 38,000 miles
Chevy	C60	1980	P	$450	7/06	SEND	Twin screw, double-reel carrier
Chevy	C60	1980	G	$1,700	10/06	SWNE	14' steel box, hoist, 350 gas engine, 4×2 speed, 8.25-20 tires
Chevy	C60	1982	F	$900	7/06	SEND	Single axle, 350 gas, 4×2 speed, enclosed service body
Chevy	C65		G	$1,000	11/06	SECA	Flatbed
Chevy	C65		G	$14,000	11/06	SCMN	Tag
Chevy	C65	1976	G	$1,600	2/06	WCME	14' dump body, 366 gas, 13 speed
Chevy	C65	1976	G	$3,000	7/06	NEND	Single axle, 366, 5×2 speed, 16' rugby box, hoist, roll tarp, 65,800 miles
Chevy	C65	1976	G	$3,000	12/06	SEIA	16' grain box
Chevy	C65	1976	G	$4,000	10/06	NCND	Twin screw truck, Logan live-bottom box, 5×4, 427, 28,000 actual miles
Chevy	C65	1976	G	$6,300	11/06	SCNE	5×2 speed, 366, V-8, Midwest 18' steel box, 61,674 miles
Chevy	C65	1976	G	$6,500	1/06	NWIL	14' farm box, hoist, 366V8, 5×2 speed trans., like-new tires, 50,150 miles
Chevy	C65	1976	G	$7,000	2/06	WCKS	Tandem truck, V-8 motor, 5×2 speed, 22' box, hoist, rollover tarp
Chevy	C65	1976	G	$9,000	10/06	NCND	Single axle, 5×2 speed, 16' steel box, hoist, 3-piece end gate, plumbed for drill fill, 10:00×20 rubber
Chevy	C65	1977	F	$1,500	2/06	WCIL	Tag axle, 81,000 miles, 366 motor, 5×2 speed, 21' bed, hoist
Chevy	C65	1977	G	$2,200	8/06	SCMN	Tandem-axle twin screw, 427 gas, grain box, hoist
Chevy	C65	1977	F	$2,750	6/06	NWMN	Twin screw tandem, 427, V-8, 5×2 speed, air shift, low differential, 19' Frontier beet equipped box, hoist, roll tarp
Chevy	C65	1977	F	$3,500	4/06	NWKS	366, V-8, 5×2 speed, 9:00-20 tires, 15'×42" Hillsboro box, hoist, rollover tarp
Chevy	C65	1977	G	$4,200	10/06	NCND	Twin screw, 15' gravel box, 427, 5×4, 32,000 actual miles
Chevy	C65	1977	G	$7,250	1/06	NWIL	15' farm box, hoist, 366 V-8, 5×2 trans., like-new tires, 71,040 miles, 3,663 miles on rebuilt engine
Chevy	C65	1977	G	$15,000	3/06	NWMN	Twin screw, 427, 5×4 speed, 19' box, twin post hoist, roll tarp, 71,751 miles
Chevy	C65	1978	G	$1,200	9/06	NEIN	Rollback, gas, 5×2 speed trans.
Chevy	C65	1978	F	$2,800	8/06	WCIA	350 gas, 4×2 speed, cheater axle, loaded box, 450-bu. corn
Chevy	C65	1978	G	$5,000	8/06	SCMN	Gas, 360 engine
Chevy	C65	1978	G	$12,000	2/06	ECIL	Tandem grain truck, 20' bed, 5×2 speed, air tag, cargo doors, 56,950 miles
Chevy	C65	1979	G	$1,800	2/06	WCME	20' metal bulk body, 427 gas
Chevy	C6500	1998	G	$7,100	8/06	WCNC	Rollback, 184,271 miles
Chevy	C70	1979	F	$1,000	4/06	WCSD	Fuel truck, 5×2 speed, needs batteries
Chevy	C70	1979	G	$3,750	2/06	WCME	14' dump body, 427 gas

Trucks

Make	Model	Year	Cond.	Price	Sale	Location	Comments
Chevy	C70	1979	G	$4,600	9/06	NENE	Grain truck, single axle, 16' wooden box, 54" sides, combination stock rack, twin cylinder hoist, 366 gas engine, 5×2 speed, 61,280 miles, one owner, tilt hood
Chevy	C70	1979	G	$10,200	8/06	NWIA	Electric roll tarp, 18' box & hoist with electric lift tag axle, 427 gas engine, 98K miles
Chevy	C70	1979	G	$11,500	3/06	NCND	Tag tandem, hyd. lift, 366, 5×2 speed, Omaha standard 20' box, hoist, roll tarp, 54,704 miles, plumbed for drill fill, 9:00-20 tires all around
Chevy	C70	1979	G	$13,000	3/06	ECND	Twin screw, tilt hood, 427, V-8, Eaton hd 10 speed, 20' box, hoist, roll tarp, swing end gate, 32,178 miles
Chevy	C70	1979	G	$14,500	12/06	SEND	Twin sleeper, 427, 5×2 trans., 20' strong box, roll tarp, 73,844 miles
Chevy	C70	1979	E	$18,900	8/06	WCKS	Tandem truck, 366 motor, 5×2 speed, 33,672 miles
Chevy	C70	1979	G	$21,500	4/06	NWMN	Twin screw, 427, Eaton 5×2 speed, 20' Buffalo box, hoist, roll tarp, 3-piece end gate, 61,064 miles, plumbed for drill fill
Chevy	C70	1981	E	$19,000	12/06	WCIA	366 engine, Steffen 18' wood box, 21,330 miles
Chevy	C70	1982	G	$7,750	4/06	SEMN	3-ton truck, Cancade box, roll tarp
Chevy	C70	1982	G	$11,500	3/06	NWMN	Twin screw, 427, V-8, 5×3 speed, 19' box w/ hoist and roll tarp, 85K miles
Chevy	C70	1983	E	$23,250	3/06	NWMN	Twin screw, 427, 5×4 speed, 19.5' Buffalo box, 3-piece end, gate, twin post hoist, roll tarp, twin fuel tanks, 47,975 miles
Chevy	C70	1986	F	$2,600	12/06	SEND	Single-axle truck, 366 V-8, 5 speed, 16' flatbed w/ hoist, 152,548 miles
Chevy	C70	1987	G	$6,000	8/06	SETN	Dump truck, diesel, 10' dump bed, 49,170 miles
Chevy	C70	1987	G	$10,500	12/06	NWIL	366 V-8, 5×2 speed, 15' farm box, roll tarp, twin hoist, 10.00R20 tires, 85,200 miles
Chevy	C70	1991	G	$1,500	10/06	ECMO	Kodiak, 2 toolboxes, 2 speed, gas
Chevy	C70	1991	G	$4,300	10/06	ECMO	2 axle
Chevy	C70	1992	G	$1,500	10/06	ECMO	2 drive, 1 toolbox
Chevy	C70	1992	G	$1,600	10/06	ECMO	Kodiak, gas, 5×2 speed
Chevy	C70	1993	G	$1,000	10/06	ECMO	Cab & chassis, 5 speed, gas
Chevy	C70	1993	G	$1,400	10/06	ECMO	Flatbed
Chevy	C70	1994	G	$1,500	10/06	ECMO	2 toolboxes, 8 cyl.
Chevy	C70	1994	G	$2,300	10/06	ECMO	2 axle, flatbed, 2 toolboxes
Chevy	C70	1995	G	$1,900	10/06	ECMO	2 toolboxes, 8 cyl.
Chevy	C70	1996	G	$2,400	10/06	ECMO	Flatbed, 2 axle, 2 door, hyd. brakes
Chevy	C80	1979	G	$5,000	7/06	ECNY	Boom truck, gas, 2-speed trans., Pitman HL500
Chevy	Cheyenne		F	$200	5/06	SCCA	Diesel
Chevy	Cheyenne		G	$2,750	5/06	SCCA	Diesel
Chevy	Cheyenne		G	$5,750	5/06	SWCA	3500, hd flatbed, 16' bed, headache rack, stake sides
Chevy	Cheyenne	1993	G	$8,750	8/06	WCNC	136,228 miles
Chevy	Cheyenne	1995	G	$3,100	8/06	WCNC	130,017 miles
Chevy	Cheyenne	1995	G	$4,250	8/06	WCNC	140,002 miles
Chevy	Cheyenne	1997	G	$2,250	12/06	ECMN	Extended cab, red, 4WD, long box, AM/FM
Chevy	Cheyenne	1998	F	$900	10/06	NCWI	Gas, auto, bed-mounted toolbox, rear tow hitch
Chevy	Cheyenne	1999	F	$2,300	9/06	SECA	2500, 4WD, 139,090 miles
Chevy	Custom	1976	F	$350	5/06	SEND	Custom deluxe pickup, V-8, 4 speed

Trucks

Make	Model	Year	Cond.	Price	Sale	Location	Comments
Chevy	Custom 30		G	$1,100	5/06	SWCA	Crew cab, V-8, auto
Chevy	HD3500	1997	G	$2,250	7/06	ECNY	Cheyenne, 7.4L Vortec, V-8, 5 speed, AM/FM radio
Chevy	HD3500	1999	G	$7,500	3/06	SCIN	4WD, gas, extended cab
Chevy	K10	1986	G	$2,800	3/06	ECNE	Blazer, V-8, auto, 55,804 miles, 4×4, air
Chevy	K10	1999	G	$2,300	10/06	ECMO	Extended cab
Chevy	K1500	1999	G	$1,200	10/06	WCMA	4WD, 6 cyl., air, auto
Chevy	K1500	1999	G	$1,200	10/06	WCMA	4WD, 6 cyl., air, auto
Chevy	K1500	1999	G	$1,800	10/06	WCMA	4WD, 6 cyl., air, auto
Chevy	K1500	1999	G	$3,450	10/06	WCMA	4WD, 6 cyl., air, auto
Chevy	K1500	1999	G	$13,250	3/06	ECNE	Silverado, 5.7 liter
Chevy	K20	1998	G	$1,400	10/06	ECMO	4WD, brakes, 224,739 miles
Chevy	K20	1998	G	$1,600	10/06	ECMO	4WD, auto, gas
Chevy	K20	1999	G	$4,200	10/06	ECMO	4WD, Weather Guard box, hyd. brakes, air, 8 cyl.
Chevy	K20	2000	G	$3,300	10/06	ECMO	4WD
Chevy	K2500	1988	P	$325	9/06	ECMN	¾-ton, 258,635 miles, tilt, air, cruise, AM/FM
Chevy	K2500	1992	E	$7,100	1/06	WCIL	Diesel pickup, 136,500 miles, clean
Chevy	K2500	1998	G	$1,750	10/06	WCMA	4WD service truck, 161,787 miles
Chevy	K2500	2005	E	$29,000	3/06	ECNE	Pickup, hd, Silverado package, Duarmax turbo engine, auto., regular cab, 4,244 miles, 4×4
Chevy	Kodiak		G	$6,000	1/06	WCCA	Nurse truck, Cat 3208
Chevy	Kodiak	1983	G	$1,400	10/06	ECMO	2 door, 5 speed, gas
Chevy	Kodiak	1985	E	$26,100	2/06	NENE	Full screw, Cat diesel, Scott 18' metal box w/ 60" sides, Allison auto, 3,000 miles on new trans., 30-ton hoist, 83,171 miles, Shur-Lok roll tarp
Chevy	Kodiak	1990	G	$13,500	12/06	ECIL	427 gas, hd, 5×2 speed, 11R22.5 rubber, air, 15' Midwest grain bed w/ 52" sides
Chevy	Kodiak	1990	G	$19,000	8/06	WCIL	Diesel grain truck, 5×2 speed, 3116 Cat engine, Knapheide 16' box, 11.00/22.5 tires, new clutch, bright red paint
Chevy	Kodiak	1991	G	$24,500	3/06	SCIA	Tag axle, 427 motor, 5×2 speed, 16' box, roll tarp, 21,280 miles
Chevy	Kodiak	1991	G	$30,000	1/06	SWOH	18' Omaha bed, Cat diesel, Allison auto. trans., tandem, 72,600 miles
Chevy	Kodiak	1992	G	$18,500	12/06	ECIL	427 gas, hd, 5×2 speed, 11R22.5 rubber, air tag power up & down axle, air brakes, like-new 16' Scott grain bed w/ 62" sides
Chevy	Kodiak	1994	G	$6,500	7/06	WCCA	Cat 3116 170-hp. diesel
Chevy	Kodiak	1995	G	$7,500	8/06	SETN	Flatbed, Cat diesel
Chevy	Kodiak	1996	G	$3,300	10/06	ECMO	2 toolboxes
Chevy	S10	1989	F	$700	10/06	NCWI	Gas, manual trans., air
Chevy	S10	1992	G	$1,000	10/06	SEMN	Pickup
Chevy	S10	1992	G	$1,050	8/06	NCNE	Blazer, 124,000 miles
Chevy	S10	1992	G	$1,550	8/06	SWCA	
Chevy	S10	1995	G	$2,700	8/06	SWCA	45,547 miles
Chevy	S10	1995	G	$3,300	8/06	SWCA	38,442 miles
Chevy	S10	1996	F	$1,550	3/06	SEND	Salvage title, topper
Chevy	S10	1996	G	$3,000	3/06	WCWA	Extended cab, toolbox, V-6
Chevy	S10	1997	G	$2,000	1/06	WCCA	Extended cab
Chevy	S10	1998	G	$3,600	9/06	SECA	3 door, extended cab, 149,213 miles
Chevy	Silverado	1980	F	$600	1/06	NEMO	4WD pickup

WHAT'S IT WORTH?

Trucks

Make	Model	Year	Cond.	Price	Sale	Location	Comments
Chevy	Silverado	1982	P	$350	7/06	NWMN	350, 4 speed, 4WD, lockout hubs
Chevy	Silverado	1988	G	$3,200	10/06	NCND	6.2, automatic
Chevy	Silverado	1991	G	$2,800	6/06	NWKS	4×4 pickup
Chevy	Silverado	1991	G	$2,900	4/06	WCSD	Club cab, white, 4×4, ½-ton, automatic, side toolboxes, running boards, 132K miles
Chevy	Silverado	1991	E	$5,500	2/06	WCIL	4WD dually pickup, automatic trans., air aluminum wheels, DMI bumper, 158K miles, new trans.
Chevy	Silverado	1992	P	$400	7/06	WCMN	½-ton, extended cab, 180,587 miles
Chevy	Silverado	1993	G	$2,500	4/06	NWMN	½-ton, extended cab, 350, auto, 4WD, dark blue, 189,000 miles, motor and trans. updates
Chevy	Silverado	1995	F	$700	9/06	ECMN	1500, V-8, auto, 4WD, extended cab, pw/ pl, PS, air, tilt, cruise, cassette
Chevy	Silverado	1996	F	$2,850	10/06	NCKS	Pickup, rough appearance, 3,000 miles on new 350 motor, automatic, 4×4, ¾-ton, 150,000 miles, good rubber
Chevy	Silverado	2000	G	$2,500	10/06	ECMO	8' pickup bed
Chevy	Silverado	2000	G	$9,000	2/06	WCKS	Z71, 4×4, automatic, extended cab
Chevy	Silverado	2001	G	$9,000	7/06	WCCA	Crew cab, V-8
Chevy	Silverado	2002	G	$7,750	11/06	SWCA	Flatbed, 10' bed w/ 12" stake sides
Chevy	Z71	1995	G	$2,100	12/06	WCMN	4×4, black, flare sides
Dodge	150		G	$900	8/06	SWCA	Ram charger
Dodge	150	1979	F	$650	4/06	ECND	Custom, reg. cab, 318, auto., 2WD, fiberglass topper, 134K miles
Dodge	1500	1995	G	$1,900	8/06	SCMN	4×4, 203,422 miles
Dodge	1500	1999	G	$3,350	6/06	NCIL	SLT Ram Laramie, V-8, 109,834 miles, 4×4 w/ Western 7.5' snowplow
Dodge	1500	2000	G	$6,100	8/06	NCIA	Short box, 4×4, steps, 5.9-L, all power, 69,000 miles
Dodge	1500	2003	G	$8,750	12/06	WCKS	5.7L Hemi gas engine, auto., 2×4, quad cab, long box, pw/pl, travel convenience pkg., cloth interior, nerf bars, grill guard, AM/FM/CD, tow pkg., heat, air, tilt, cruise, 73,100 miles
Dodge	250	1990	G	$3,000	1/06	NECO	Cummins, automatic, 4WD, 171,000 miles
Dodge	2500	1994	G	$2,700	6/06	NCIL	Ram Laramie SLT, V-8, Magnum, 4×4, 161,000 miles, new trans.
Dodge	2500	1995	G	$6,400	3/06	ECNE	Ram K2500, Laramie SLT service pickup, Cummins turbo diesel engine, auto. (rebuilt), 4×4, 169,056 miles
Dodge	2500	1998	G	$7,500	2/06	SEKS	Ram, Laramie SLT, 4×4, Revelator flatbed w/ removable bale spear
Dodge	2500	1998	G	$14,000	2/06	WCIL	Ram, SLT, 4×4, quad, cab, long bed, Cummins diesel, 145,000 miles, auto, leather interior, white
Dodge	2500	2001	E	$7,700	3/06	NEKS	Pickup, V-8
Dodge	2500	2003	G	$16,050	3/06	NWIL	4×4 regular cab pickup, hd, 37,500 miles
Dodge	3500	1992	G	$5,250	4/06	WCIA	Cummins engine, pw/pl, 141,500 miles
Dodge	3500	1995	G	$8,400	10/06	WCMA	4WD, enclosed service truck, Cummins 5.9L diesel, 5 speed
Dodge	3500	1996	G	$6,250	3/06	ECMI	4WD, auto, gas, 9' box
Dodge	3500	1996	G	$6,800	10/06	WCMA	Welder truck, Cummins 5.9L diesel, Lincoln 250-amp welder, diesel
Dodge	3500	1997	G	$9,500	3/06	NWKS	Ram, utility box, 88,000 miles, 5 speed, service truck, service body, 6-cyl. Cummins diesel turbo engine
Dodge	3500	2001	G	$16,250	7/06	SEND	Dually, Cummins 5.9-liter turbo, 6-speed manual trans., 2WD, 12' flatbed, 23,400 miles

Trucks

Make	Model	Year	Cond.	Price	Sale	Location	Comments
Dodge	500		F	$1,500	11/06	NEND	Single axle, wood box and hoist
Dodge	D300	1988	G	$750	3/06	ECMI	Bucket truck, V-8 gas, auto w/ 28' Versalift, utility box
Dodge	D600	1976	G	$4,500	4/06	SEND	360 engine, 2 speed, 15' Wilrich box, hoist, roll tarp, 37,600 miles
Dodge	Dakota	1993	G	$1,700	10/06	SEMN	
Dodge	Dakota	2001	G	$7,500	11/06	WCMN	4WD, V-8, 4 door, new tires, white, 85K miles
Dodge	Ram 150	1985	F	$350	8/06	SWCA	Cargo van, 97,336 miles
Dodge	Ram 150	1993	G	$2,000	8/06	SETN	169,415 miles, gas, 318 engine
Dodge	Ram 1500	2001	F	$2,750	9/06	ECMN	5.2 V-8, auto, 4WD, 4-door crew, air, tilt, cruise, AM/FM
Dodge	Ram 1500	2001	F	$2,750	9/06	ECMN	5.2 V-8, auto, 160,181 miles, 4 door, crew cab
Dodge	Ram 1500	2004	G	$11,750	9/06	NEND	4×4 pickup, regular cab, 5.7-litre Hemi, automatic, loaded, 27,500 miles
Dodge	Ram 250		F	$450	5/06	SCCA	Cummins diesel, manual trans.
Dodge	Ram 2500		G	$3,750	5/06	SCCA	Flatbed, Cummins diesel
Dodge	Ram 2500	1996	G	$5,000	11/06	SWCA	Cummins diesel
Dodge	Ram 2500	1998	F	$1,500	1/06	WCCA	Extended cab, Magnum V-8
Dodge	Ram 2500	1998	F	$1,500	1/06	WCCA	
Dodge	Ram 2500	2001	G	$10,250	11/06	SCCA	4WD, 8' bed, auto
Dodge	Ram 2500	2002	G	$8,200	9/06	SECA	94,377 miles
Dodge	Ram 350	1987	F	$800	10/06	SEMN	Pickup
Dodge	Ram 3500	1996	G	$6,250	6/06	NEIN	Dually, 4WD, diesel, new front end & trans., cruise, air
Dodge	Ram 3500	2001	G	$18,750	1/06	SCTN	Flatbed, 4WD, 40,175 miles
Dodge	Ram 3500	2003	G	$16,500	10/06	ECMO	Crew cab
Ford	550	2003	G	$22,000	3/06	SCIN	4WD
Ford	6000		G	$5,000	3/06	WCWA	Van truck, 6 cyl., diesel, 5 speed
Ford	6000	1986	G	$1,600	8/06	SETN	Cargo, seal coat truck, diesel, 5 speed, 760-gal. seal coat tank, 462,032 miles
Ford	700		G	$1,600	5/06	SWCA	Cab & chassis, Cat 3208 diesel, 5-speed trans.
Ford	700	1978	F	$1,200	4/06	SEND	Tilt cab, V-8, 5×2 speed, 24' enclosed van body
Ford	700	1991	G	$5,500	6/06	NEIN	Single axle, 5-2 trans.
Ford	700	1991	G	$5,500	3/06	SCIN	Dump truck, single axle, diesel, 5 speed
Ford	8000		G	$700	11/06	SECA	Water truck, Cat 3208, 5 speed
Ford	8000	1979	G	$2,000	9/06	NEIN	Dump truck, Cat V636 diesel, 210 hp., tandem axle, 13 speed
Ford	8000	1980	G	$17,000	3/06	SWNE	DT555, 225 hp. Cummins, 10 speed, 102,000 miles, tandem duals w/ Knapheide 600-bu. 20'×52" steel box
Ford	8000	1983	P	$2,800	7/06	SEND	Diesel, Pitman Polecat 1300 digger
Ford	8000	1984	G	$23,000	1/06	ECNE	Tandem-axle grain truck, 20' box, 50" sides, twin full screw, 13 speed, Cat 3208 diesel, 253,895 miles, dual fuel tanks
Ford	8000	1985	G	$3,000	7/06	WCCA	Feed truck, Cat 3208, 18230 mixer, scales
Ford	8000	1986	G	$13,000	1/06	WCIL	Tandem twin screw grain truck, Scott 18' bed w/ cargo doors, Cat engine, Fuller trans., roll tarp, 340,189 miles
Ford	8000	1995	G	$31,000	1/06	WCIL	Tandem twin screw grain truck, Scott 18' bed w/ cargo doors, Cat engine, Fuller trans., roll tarp, 145,847 miles
Ford	880	1976	F	$5,000	4/06	ECND	Twin screw, 475, 13 speed, air brakes, 20' Cancade box, hoist, roll tarp, 3-piece end gate
Ford	900		P	$550	10/06	SWOH	Dump truck, tandem axle, no engine or trans., camel-back rear suspension
Ford	900	1977	G	$4,000	11/06	SCCA	Cat 3208 diesel, aluminum box

Trucks

Make	Model	Year	Cond.	Price	Sale	Location	Comments
Ford	9000	1976	G	$4,800	4/06	SEND	Twin screw, Detroit, 13 speed, 10-yard gravel box
Ford	9000	1978	G	$5,700	2/06	NCIL	Custom cab, 290 Cummins, 10 speed, wet kit, 313,740 miles
Ford	9000	1979	G	$2,750	11/06	SCCA	Dump truck, Cummins 350 big cam, 13 speed
Ford	9000	1982	G	$4,000	3/06	SCIN	Tandem-axle dump truck, Cummins engine, 14' bed
Ford	9000	1982	G	$17,500	3/06	NEND	Louisville twin screw, 300 big cam, 8 speed, air ride seat, 20' Magnum box, scissor hoist, 3-piece end gate, rear pintle and air
Ford	9000	1993	G	$4,100	3/06	ECIN	Cummins diesel, heated mirrors, sleeper
Ford	9500	1998	G	$40,000	3/06	WCWA	Tri-axle roll-off truck
Ford	Aeromax		G	$6,000	5/06	SWCA	Diesel, 9 speed, air ride suspension
Ford	Aeromax		G	$9,000	5/06	SWCA	L9000 dump truck, 4-5 yard box, diesel, 9-speed trans.
Ford	Aeromax	1993	G	$2,600	12/06	ECMN	315 hp., air ride, L10 Cummins
Ford	Aeromax	1995	G	$3,800	12/06	ECMN	11,755 miles, air ride, air dump, locking rear
Ford	Aeromax	1997	G	$12,000	9/06	NEND	Semi tractor, Detroit 60 Series engine, 10 speed, day cab, air ride, excellent rubber, new rod bearings
Ford	C600	1981	G	$3,500	1/06	SCKS	Implement truck, 20' Schwarts flatbed, hyd. hoist, hyd. cylinder wench, 370 gas, 900R20 tires, 4×2 speed trans., 153,491 miles, 153" wheel base, 17,000-lb. GVW, VIN: 1FDMC60H3BVJ22111
Ford	C750	1996	F	$600	1/06	SCMI	16' flatbed, no hoist, 10 speed, gas, single axle
Ford	CF8000	1993	G	$3,750	11/06	SCCA	Van body, turbo diesel, 1 axle
Ford	F150		F	$200	10/06	SWOH	Gas, 5 speed
Ford	F150		G	$1,500	5/06	SCCA	Welding truck, V-8, 5 speed, Lincoln SA-200F-163 welder
Ford	F150	1978	F	$500	8/06	NCIA	Custom 4×4 pickup, topper, rebuilt 400 engine
Ford	F150	1978	F	$700	3/06	ECND	Ranger, V-8, automatic, 4WD, air, 20,000 miles on OH and front end
Ford	F150	1983	P	$250	6/06	NWMN	4×4, 6 cyl., 4 speed
Ford	F150	1983	F	$450	3/06	NEKS	Pickup
Ford	F150	1984	G	$1,000	3/06	WCMN	6 cyl., 4 speed
Ford	F150	1984	G	$1,400	3/06	WCMN	4WD, 6 cyl., 4 speed
Ford	F150	1986	F	$800	2/06	SWNE	2WD, 126,000 miles, V-8, auto
Ford	F150	1987	G	$3,650	8/06	SEMN	4×4
Ford	F150	1988	F	$650	4/06	NWMN	302, V-8, automatic, 4WD
Ford	F150	1989	F	$525	12/06	SEND	2WD, 6 cylinder, 5 speed, air, 213K miles, red
Ford	F150	1990	G	$500	12/06	NENE	Supercab
Ford	F150	1990	F	$500	12/06	WCKS	Gas, automatic
Ford	F150	1991	F	$900	3/06	WCWA	5 speed, electric lift gate
Ford	F150	1991	F	$1,100	10/06	SEMN	4×4, V-8, automatic
Ford	F150	1991	G	$2,600	4/06	ECND	Regular cab, 302, automatic, 4WD
Ford	F150	1992	F	$650	12/06	SEND	2WD, 5.0 V-8, automatic, air 155,800 miles, blue
Ford	F150	1992	G	$1,000	8/06	SWCA	86,915 miles
Ford	F150	1992	G	$1,200	9/06	ECMN	4WD, new front fenders, brush guard, fog lights, 182,000 miles, AM/FM, cassette, toolboxes, bedliner
Ford	F150	1992	G	$1,200	12/06	ECMN	4 speed, reg cab, tilt, air
Ford	F150	1992	G	$1,500	8/06	SWCA	106,053 miles
Ford	F150	1992	G	$1,500	8/06	SWCA	
Ford	F150	1993	F	$900	12/06	SEND	4WD, 5.0 V-8, automatic, air, 200,537 miles, brown
Ford	F150	1993	G	$2,900	10/06	NCND	4WD pickup

Trucks

Make	Model	Year	Cond.	Price	Sale	Location	Comments
Ford	F150	1994	P	$1,100	7/06	SEND	4×4, gas
Ford	F150	1995	G	$1,350	3/06	SCIN	½-ton, 6 cyl., 4WD, 5 speed, 173,000 miles
Ford	F150	1995	G	$2,400	11/06	SCIL	2WD pickup, 6 cyl., auto., 72K miles
Ford	F150	1995	G	$5,000	3/06	NCOK	121,285 miles, 4.9L straight 6 cyl., 5 speed, dual tanks, air
Ford	F150	1996	G	$4,500	8/06	SETN	4WD, V-8 engine, auto, air, 92,502 miles
Ford	F150	1997	G	$3,300	8/06	SWCA	
Ford	F150	1997	G	$3,500	11/06	SECA	½-ton
Ford	F150	1997	G	$3,500	11/06	SECA	2WD, ½-ton
Ford	F150	1997	G	$4,700	8/06	SWCA	89,200 miles
Ford	F150	1997	G	$6,000	1/06	WCCT	Extended cab, 2WD, 94,789 miles, third door, tilt, air
Ford	F150	1998	G	$2,650	12/06	SEIA	Lariat, 4.6L, auto, extended cab, 186,075 miles
Ford	F150	1999	G	$1,400	10/06	ECMO	Hyd. brakes
Ford	F150	1999	G	$2,800	10/06	ECMO	Extended cab
Ford	F150	1999	G	$4,500	1/06	WCCA	Extended cab, Triton V-8
Ford	F150	1999	G	$5,250	3/06	WCWA	Extended cab, 4WD, V-8
Ford	F150	1999	G	$10,000	9/06	ECNE	4×2, extended cab, air, pw/pl, 38,414 miles
Ford	F150	2000	G	$1,400	10/06	ECMO	2 door, hyd. brakes
Ford	F150	2000	G	$2,700	10/06	ECMO	8 cyl.
Ford	F150	2000	G	$3,000	10/06	ECMO	2 door, hyd. brakes
Ford	F150	2000	G	$4,250	1/06	WCCA	4WD
Ford	F150	2000	G	$4,250	1/06	WCCA	4WD
Ford	F150	2000	G	$5,500	1/06	WCNH	4WD, gas, PS
Ford	F150	2000	G	$5,700	10/06	NCWI	Gas, auto, PS
Ford	F150	2000	G	$6,000	1/06	WCNH	4WD, gas, PS
Ford	F150	2001	G	$5,000	1/06	WCCA	Extended cab, 4WD
Ford	F150	2002	G	$9,250	10/06	WCFL	4WD, gas
Ford	F150	2004	G	$14,500	9/06	NEMO	4WD, FX4 package, 23,765 miles
Ford	F150	2004	E	$22,000	12/06	SWIA	Lariat crew cab, 5.4 Triton, 4WD, leather, loaded, box cover, trailer pkg., 30,800 miles
Ford	F150 XL	1997	G	$4,900	9/06	SECA	98,313 miles
Ford	F150 XL	2001	G	$3,700	8/06	WCTX	Gas, V-8 engine, auto
Ford	F150 XL	2002	G	$7,000	8/06	SWCA	32,256 miles
Ford	F150 XLT	1986	G	$1,500	2/06	NWSD	4WD, gas, standard
Ford	F150 XLT	1986	G	$2,500	2/06	WCMN	4WD, 302 V-8, automatic, 2 door, air cruise, 80,392 miles, Brute ag hitch
Ford	F150 XLT	1990	F	$200	10/06	SWOH	Gas, bedliner
Ford	F150 XLT	1990	F	$950	10/06	SENJ	Extended cab, 4WD
Ford	F150 XLT	1991	F	$500	12/06	SEND	2WD, 5.0 V-8, automatic, 141,202 miles, brown/tan
Ford	F150 XLT	1992	G	$1,150	3/06	WCSD	4WD pickup, 160K miles, standard cab, gas, 6 cyl., bedliner
Ford	F150 XLT	1994	G	$1,600	8/06	NCNE	4WD, extended cab, auto, 140,889 miles
Ford	F150 XLT	1994	G	$3,800	12/06	NEMO	4WD pickup truck, 6' bed, red
Ford	F150 XLT	1995	G	$1,300	8/06	SWCA	202,687 miles
Ford	F150 XLT	2001	G	$8,250	11/06	ECND	Super cab 4 door, Triton 5.4, automatic, 4WD, 82,000 miles
Ford	F150 XLT	2003	G	$14,000	2/06	WCIL	4×4 pickup, 57,000 miles, 5.4, V-8, auto
Ford	F150 XLT	2004	G	$14,200	8/06	SWCA	Quad cab, 4WD, 71,508 miles
Ford	F250		P	$200	1/06	WCCA	V-8
Ford	F250		F	$325	3/06	ECNE	Pickup, 460 motor, automatic, 2WD, 83,443 miles
Ford	F250		G	$1,000	11/06	SWCA	Diesel, auto dual tanks
Ford	F250		G	$2,500	5/06	SWCA	5-speed trans., dual tanks, fuel tanks, Emigo air compressor

Trucks

Make	Model	Year	Cond.	Price	Sale	Location	Comments
Ford	F250	1976	G	$1,500	7/06	NWIL	4×4, big engine, gas
Ford	F250	1978	F	$850	4/06	NWMN	4WD, 110-gal. tank, pump
Ford	F250	1981	F	$750	2/06	SCKS	4×4, 4 speed, 8' flatbed, 5.8L
Ford	F250	1982	F	$850	7/06	ECND	4×4, regular cab, V-8, auto
Ford	F250	1982	G	$1,000	4/06	WCKS	162,030 miles, 400 engine
Ford	F250	1985	P	$525	7/06	NWMN	351, V-8, automatic, 4WD
Ford	F250	1987	F	$800	1/06	WCCA	Extended cab
Ford	F250	1988	F	$150	10/06	SWOH	4WD, gas
Ford	F250	1988	P	$250	9/06	ECMN	351, V-8, gas
Ford	F250	1988	G	$2,500	3/06	NWMN	351 V-8, 4WD, 103,395 miles
Ford	F250	1988	G	$3,400	4/06	NEND	4×4, V-8, 5 speed, auto, 94,460 miles
Ford	F250	1989	G	$950	10/06	ECMO	4WD, 114,646 miles
Ford	F250	1989	G	$1,500	3/06	WCWA	4WD, V-8
Ford	F250	1990	P	$700	11/06	WCMN	¾-ton pickup, 6 cyl., manual trans., 2WD, ladder rack, toolbox sides, 147K miles
Ford	F250	1990	G	$1,200	11/06	SCSD	Service truck, 2WD, 152K miles, 5 speed, 5,000 miles on rebuilt 351 engine
Ford	F250	1991	P	$700	11/06	SCSD	7.3 diesel turbo, extended cab, 8' box, auto, 175K miles
Ford	F250	1991	G	$725	10/06	SENJ	4WD, utility bed, auto, plow setup
Ford	F250	1991	G	$900	3/06	SCIN	4WD, 7.3 diesel
Ford	F250	1991	G	$1,500	3/06	ECMI	V-8 gas, auto, 4WD
Ford	F250	1992	G	$1,900	11/06	ECND	¾-ton, 5.8L, 2WD, 300-gal. tank w/ pump
Ford	F250	1993	G	$3,200	9/06	NCMI	4×4, gas
Ford	F250	1994	F	$1,500	7/06	SEND	2WD, 175,000 miles
Ford	F250	1995	G	$1,200	10/06	WCGA	Service body, 196,689 miles
Ford	F250	1995	G	$3,250	3/06	WCWA	4WD, 7.3L diesel
Ford	F250	1996	F	$800	7/06	WCCA	Super cab, V-8
Ford	F250	1996	G	$5,400	3/06	SENE	4×4, club cab, 75K miles
Ford	F250	1996	G	$6,000	3/06	WCWA	Extended cab, 4WD, V-8
Ford	F250	1997	G	$1,800	11/06	SWCA	Gas, auto
Ford	F250	1997	G	$2,000	3/06	ECIN	Van, gas
Ford	F250	1997	G	$2,100	1/06	WCCA	Utility
Ford	F250	1997	F	$2,500	1/06	WCCA	4WD
Ford	F250	1998	G	$3,500	1/06	WCCA	Extended cab, 4WD
Ford	F250	1999	G	$4,900	9/06	SECA	134,405 miles
Ford	F250	1999	G	$5,500	9/06	SECA	
Ford	F250	1999	F	$8,000	6/06	NCIA	4×4, salvage title, 7.3 Power Stroke, V-8, auto, air, 4 door, extended cab, 7' steel flatbed, 118K miles
Ford	F250	1999	G	$13,500	1/06	NECO	Extended cab, Power Stroke, 6 speed, 4WD, 129K miles
Ford	F250	2000	G	$10,000	8/06	SWIA	84K miles
Ford	F250	2001	G	$14,500	2/06	SEKS	4×4, 4 door, 77,000 miles
Ford	F250	2001	G	$17,000	12/06	ECKS	Super Duty, Lariat, crew cab, 4×4, 7.3L, PS, 154K miles
Ford	F250	2002	G	$10,500	11/06	WCMN	Extended cab, 4×4, pw, pl, 55,000 miles
Ford	F250	2003	G	$14,800	3/06	NESD	Extended cab, short box, 4×4, 50K miles
Ford	F250 XL	1986	G	$800	3/06	SWMN	4×4, 4 speed, 129,468 miles, diesel
Ford	F250 XL	1991	F	$850	5/06	SEND	Regular cab, 6 cyl., 5 speed, 100,000 miles
Ford	F250 XL	1993	P	$500	5/06	SEND	Regular cab, 6 cyl., 5 speed, 2WD, 159,000 miles
Ford	F250 XL	1994	G	$2,000	2/06	SEIA	4×4 pickup, dual tanks, air, color white, 170K miles

Trucks

Make	Model	Year	Cond.	Price	Sale	Location	Comments
Ford	F250 XL	1996	F	$2,600	5/06	SEND	Reg. cab, V-8, auto 4WD, figerglass body w/ pack rate, 185,000 miles
Ford	F250 XL	2001	G	$7,000	8/06	SWCA	Dog catcher truck, 79,273 miles
Ford	F250 XL	2002	G	$12,500	2/06	WCIL	Super Duty 2WD pickup, 17,500 miles
Ford	F250 XLT	1982	G	$2,600	3/06	SWMN	4×4, 4 speed, 73,829 miles, diesel
Ford	F250 XLT	1983	G	$1,900	3/06	SWMN	4×4, automatic, 139,349 miles, diesel
Ford	F250 XLT	1985	F	$2,400	3/06	SWMN	4×4, 4-speed manual trans., 70,055 miles
Ford	F250 XLT	1989	G	$1,800	3/06	NEND	Lariat, 460 gas, 5 speed, 4WD, low miles on OH motor and trans.
Ford	F250 XLT	1990	G	$2,300	3/06	WCMN	Lariat, 4×4, 351, V-8, auto, 170,550 miles, rebuilt engine, toolbox, fifth-wheel hitch
Ford	F250 XLT	1990	G	$3,400	6/06	NWMN	Lariat, extended cab, Northland Edition, 4×4, long box, 460 V-8, automatic, auto, pw/pl, 32K miles on Ford factory engine, 8K miles on Ford factory trans., shows 74,217 miles
Ford	F250 XLT	1992	F	$4,500	11/06	NEND	Super cab, 6.9 L, auto, 4WD, 194,000 miles, 180-gal. service tank and pump
Ford	F250 XLT	1992	G	$4,900	2/06	NWSD	Extended cab, 5 speed, fifth-wheel plate, extra grill guard, tires nearly new, running boards, clean inside, 213K miles
Ford	F250 XLT	1995	G	$2,000	9/06	SECA	Lift gate, 97,753 miles
Ford	F250 XLT	1995	G	$5,600	8/06	SCMN	Power Stroke diesel, ¾-ton, auto. trans., air club cab, 144,360 miles
Ford	F250 XLT	1995	G	$7,200	2/06	NWOH	4×4, Power Stroke diesel, extended cab, 150K miles
Ford	F250 XLT	1996	G	$2,250	3/06	WCWA	7.3L diesel, auto, electric lift gate
Ford	F250 XLT	1997	E	$21,500	3/06	SEMN	4×4, Power Stroke XLT, automatic, loader, 8' box, regular cab, fifth-wheel plate, ag bumper, 15,100 miles
Ford	F250 XLT	1999	G	$4,100	9/06	SECA	168,838 miles
Ford	F250 XLT	1999	G	$5,000	9/06	SECA	130,000 miles
Ford	F250 XLT	2000	G	$9,000	11/06	NCIN	4×4, Super Duty, 80K miles, 5.4, automatic
Ford	F250 XLT	2001	G	$6,700	9/06	SECA	154,347 miles
Ford	F250 XLT	2001	G	$7,000	9/06	SECA	147,037 miles, quad cab
Ford	F250 XLT	2001	G	$12,000	11/06	WCMN	Super Duty crew cab, 4×4, 61,000 miles
Ford	F250 XLT	2002	G	$17,000	5/06	NENE	Lariat pickup, 54,806 miles, 5.4, V-8, crew cab, leather seats
Ford	F250 XLT	2005	G	$23,500	12/06	NEMO	Super Duty 4WD pickup, 5.4L, V-8 engine, auto, full power, 25,658 miles
Ford	F250XL	2000	G	$8,000	8/06	SWCA	71,708 miles
Ford	F350		F	$500	1/06	WCCA	4 door, V-8
Ford	F350		G	$1,100	11/06	SWCA	Gas
Ford	F350		G	$1,250	11/06	SWCA	Diesel, auto
Ford	F350		G	$1,300	1/06	WCPA	Service truck, gas, 4 speed
Ford	F350		G	$1,300	5/06	SWCA	Diesel, auto
Ford	F350		G	$1,400	11/06	SWCA	Flatbed, 12' bed, headache rack
Ford	F350		G	$1,700	11/06	SWCA	Flatbed, 12' bed, headache rack
Ford	F350		G	$2,000	7/06	WCCA	Open top van, V-8, 4 speed
Ford	F350		G	$2,500	7/06	WCCA	Utility, V-8
Ford	F350		G	$4,300	11/06	SWCA	Diesel, auto
Ford	F350	1978	G	$2,600	12/06	SEND	1-ton flatbed pickup, 400 V-8, 4 speed, 12' flatbed, 107,700 miles, yellow

Trucks

Make	Model	Year	Cond.	Price	Sale	Location	Comments
Ford	F350	1978	G	$3,100	3/06	NWMN	Tonner dually, 351 V-8, 4 speed, 2WD, service bed to include (2) 110-gal. field service units, 7' side toolboxes, 66,423 miles
Ford	F350	1979	F	$500	11/06	SCSD	Service truck, 2WD, 460 engine, auto, 106K miles
Ford	F350	1982	G	$300	3/06	ECIN	Utility
Ford	F350	1984	G	$900	7/06	WCCA	4 speed, V-8, 8' bed
Ford	F350	1986	F	$1,000	3/06	WCWA	V-8 diesel, service body, air tank, hose reel
Ford	F350	1986	G	$1,900	4/06	WCSD	1-ton dually, 4×4, winch, rack on top, gas, 4WD
Ford	F350	1986	G	$3,000	8/06	SWCA	Service unit
Ford	F350	1986	G	$5,000	8/06	ECNE	4×4 dually, 460, automatic, aluminum 16" wheels, 10' Badger bed, 110,497 miles
Ford	F350	1987	F	$600	3/06	ECIN	Gas
Ford	F350	1987	F	$700	3/06	ECIN	Gas
Ford	F350	1987	F	$700	3/06	ECIN	Gas
Ford	F350	1987	G	$1,500	3/06	ECMI	Bucket truck, 460 V-8 gas, 32' Versalift, Onan generator
Ford	F350	1987	G	$1,750	3/06	ECMI	Bucket truck, 460 V-8 gas, auto, 32' Versalift, Onan generator
Ford	F350	1987	F	$2,500	7/06	SEND	Dually, 6.9 liter, 5-speed manual trans., 2WD, 12' flatbed, 92,200 miles, 31,600 miles on new engine
Ford	F350	1988	G	$4,250	12/06	NEMN	Boom truck, 33,520 miles
Ford	F350	1990	G	$1,250	3/06	ECIN	Gas, auto
Ford	F350	1990	G	$2,300	11/06	SCCA	Stake body truck, Power Stroke diesel, auto
Ford	F350	1991	G	$3,100	8/06	SWCA	End dump truck, 75,702 miles
Ford	F350	1991	G	$3,200	3/06	ECMI	5 speed, 3 yard dump, electric PTO
Ford	F350	1992	G	$1,500	3/06	ECIN	Flatbed
Ford	F350	1992	G	$2,750	3/06	WCWA	Service truck, 12' stake bed, lift gate, air compressor
Ford	F350	1993	F	$1,100	4/06	SEND	Crew cab pickup, V-8, automatic
Ford	F350	1994	F	$1,350	4/06	SEND	Crew cab pickup, V-8, automatic, service body
Ford	F350	1995	G	$1,400	3/06	NCCO	4 door, 1-ton dually, 7.3 diesel engine, automatic
Ford	F350	1995	G	$5,000	1/06	WCCA	V-8, auto, Harbo utility box
Ford	F350	1996	F	$200	9/06	WCTX	Service truck, Ford Power Stroke diesel
Ford	F350	1996	G	$4,750	11/06	SWCA	9' bed
Ford	F350	1996	G	$5,500	7/06	ECNY	Service truck, gas, 4WD, auto
Ford	F350	1996	G	$5,500	11/06	SWCA	9' bed
Ford	F350	1996	G	$8,300	8/06	SWCA	Crew cab, 3-yard dump
Ford	F350	1997	G	$1,500	10/06	ECMO	5 speed
Ford	F350	1997	G	$1,500	10/06	ECMO	2 axle
Ford	F350	1997	G	$2,100	10/06	ECMO	2 axle, 2 door, 2 toolboxes
Ford	F350	1997	G	$2,250	10/06	ECMO	Toolboxes, 131,000 miles
Ford	F350	1997	G	$2,250	10/06	ECMO	Toolboxes, 131,000 miles
Ford	F350	1997	G	$4,500	10/06	WCMA	Stake truck, 9' body, lift gate, arrow board
Ford	F350	1997	G	$7,250	11/06	SWCA	Extended cab, flatbed, dump truck
Ford	F350	1997	G	$7,400	4/06	SEIA	Dually, flatbed, 351, 5 speed, 103,000 miles
Ford	F350	1998	G	$4,500	9/06	SECA	14' box van, 86,053 miles
Ford	F350	1999	G	$8,250	12/06	NEMN	Extended cab
Ford	F350	1999	G	$9,500	12/06	NEMN	Extended cab
Ford	F350	1999	G	$16,000	2/06	SEKS	4×4, V-10, 66,000 miles, DewEze 382 bale spear body
Ford	F350	2000	G	$9,000	7/06	WCCA	Super Duty, Power Stroke
Ford	F350	2000	G	$11,000	3/06	WCWA	4WD, crew cab, 7.3L diesel

Trucks

Make	Model	Year	Cond.	Price	Sale	Location	Comments
Ford	F350	2001	G	$3,250	11/06	SWCA	Auto
Ford	F350	2001	G	$9,000	9/06	WCND	Lariat Super Duty 1-ton dually, 4 door, powerstroke diesel, auto, 4WD, lift kit, leather, loaded, 612,000 miles
Ford	F350	2005	E	$27,000	3/06	ECND	4 door, crew cab, 4×4, Lariat pkg., 40,800 miles, auto, short box
Ford	F350	2005	E	$27,000	3/06	ECND	4 door crew cab, 4×4, Lariat pkg., 35,500 miles
Ford	F350 XL	1991	E	$15,000	3/06	ECND	1-ton dually, 7.3 diesel, automatic, 4WD, 8' service bed, 141,324 miles, 280-gal. fuel tank, 12-V pump, fuel hose reel
Ford	F350 XL	1995	F	$1,900	9/06	SECA	111,301 miles
Ford	F350 XL	2000	G	$9,300	10/06	WCGA	Crew cab, Super Duty, service body
Ford	F350 XL	2001	G	$17,000	9/06	SCNE	Pickup, 4×4, Super Duty diesel, 1-ton, 106,920 miles, automatic, air, AM/FM, flatbed, round bale handler, live hyd. on back, toolboxes
Ford	F350 XLT	1994	G	$3,500	9/06	WCND	Centurion conversion, 1-ton dually, 4 door, 460 gas, auto., 4WD, fifth-wheel plate, aluminum wheels, 220,000 miles
Ford	F350 XLT	1995	G	$1,750	11/06	SCCA	Flatbed, dually, crew cab, 9' flatbed
Ford	F350 XLT	2000	G	$9,300	3/06	NESD	4-door super cab, 4×4, diesel, automatic, 171K miles, off-road pkg.
Ford	F350 XLT	2000	G	$10,500	3/06	NESD	4-door super cab, 4×4, diesel, automatic, 148,301 miles, off-road pkg.
Ford	F350 XLT	2000	E	$19,000	2/06	SWIN	Dually, 65K miles, red w/ gray interior, Power Stroke diesel V-8, low/high 4WD, automatic, tow pkg., cruise, CD player, pw/pl, aluminum rims, sharp
Ford	F350 XLT	2000	E	$22,750	11/06	SEIA	4 door, leather, Power Stroke diesel, loaded, Centurion conversion, fifth-wheel ball, 49,000 miles
Ford	F350 XLT	2006	E	$29,500	11/06	SEIA	Powerstroke turbo, fifth-wheel ball, 6,854 hours
Ford	F450		G	$1,100	11/06	SWCA	Diesel, 5 speed
Ford	F450		G	$1,250	5/06	SWCA	Diesel, 5 speed
Ford	F450		G	$2,400	5/06	SWCA	Super Duty flatbed, 12' bed, pipe rack, diesel
Ford	F450		G	$2,750	11/06	SWCA	Flatbed, 12' bed
Ford	F450		G	$4,000	11/06	SWCA	Power Stroke diesel, 5 speed
Ford	F450		G	$4,250	11/06	SWCA	Power Stroke diesel, 5 speed
Ford	F450		G	$5,000	11/06	SWCA	Power Stroke diesel, 5 speed
Ford	F450		G	$5,000	11/06	SWCA	Power Stroke diesel, 5 speed
Ford	F450	1993	G	$1,750	10/06	ECMO	Super Duty, air, 8 cyl.
Ford	F450	1993	G	$2,250	3/06	ECMI	Diesel, 5 speed, 12' dump box
Ford	F450	1995	G	$4,000	10/06	ECMO	Power Stroke, 8 cyl.
Ford	F450	1995	G	$7,000	11/06	SWCA	Dump truck, 3-yard bucket, diesel, auto
Ford	F450	1997	G	$4,000	11/06	SWCA	Power Stroke diesel, 5 speed
Ford	F450	1997	G	$7,000	7/06	SEND	Dually, 89,000 miles, 7.3 Power Stroke, new hd clutch and flywheel, 9' service body, good tires
Ford	F450	1998	G	$11,000	7/06	ECNY	Service truck, diesel, service body
Ford	F450	1999	G	$11,500	9/06	SECA	Super Duty flatbed diesel, 128,894 miles
Ford	F450	2000	G	$7,750	3/06	ECIN	7.3L diesel
Ford	F450	2000	G	$9,750	3/06	ECIN	7.3L diesel
Ford	F450	2000	G	$10,500	7/06	ECNY	Boom truck, V-8 diesel, single axle
Ford	F450XL	2000	G	$8,500	9/06	SECA	221,491 miles
Ford	F450XL	2000	G	$10,500	3/06	ECIN	Power Stroke diesel
Ford	F450XL	2001	G	$7,500	9/06	SECA	202,397 miles, diesel

WHAT'S IT WORTH?

Trucks

Make	Model	Year	Cond.	Price	Sale	Location	Comments
Ford	F450XL	2001	G	$10,000	9/06	SECA	127,953 miles
Ford	F450XL	2001	G	$10,500	9/06	SECA	200,680 miles, diesel
Ford	F450XL	2001	G	$12,000	9/06	SECA	4×4 stake bed, lift gate, 136,110 miles
Ford	F500		F	$350	10/06	SWOH	Single axle, gas, 4 speed, 8' steel dump box
Ford	F550		G	$8,400	10/06	SWOH	Utility, 4WD, single axle, Triton V-10 gas, auto
Ford	F550	1999	G	$7,750	3/06	ECIN	Flatbed
Ford	F550	1999	G	$9,000	3/06	ECIN	Super Duty
Ford	F550	2001	G	$17,000	9/06	SCNE	Super Duty pickup, 4×4, Power Stroke diesel, 130,400 miles, 5 speed, dually, DewEze flatbed, live hyd. on back, AM/FM, cattle guard
Ford	F550	2001	G	$18,000	7/06	ECNY	Boom truck, Power Stroke V-8 diesel
Ford	F550	2002	G	$11,250	11/06	SWCA	Flatbed, 12' bed, diesel, auto. trans.
Ford	F600	1976	G	$8,000	8/06	SCMN	21,075 miles, 16' Scott box, hoist
Ford	F600	1978	G	$1,800	4/06	WCSD	14' flatbed, 2-ton, 4×2 speed, 370 engine
Ford	F600	1979	G	$6,500	3/06	SWOH	Grain truck, one owner, only 29,650 miles, 14' steel bed, wood sides, 2 dump gates, 3-year-old hoist, 370-2-V engine
Ford	F600	1982	G	$15,100	1/06	SCKS	Grain truck, 24,146 actual miles, 370-4 V-8 gas engine, 5×2 speed trans., 189" wheel base, 21,200-lb. GVW, Knapheide 16' steel box with steel floor, Shur-Lok roll tarp, spare hyd. valve, Knaphoist single cyl. hoist, 900R20 tires, bought new, always shedded
Ford	F600	1983	G	$2,300	8/06	SWCA	10-yard box dump, diesel
Ford	F600	1984	G	$1,100	9/06	NEIN	Flatbed water truck, gas, 4 speed
Ford	F600	1986	G	$1,400	3/06	SCIN	20' bed, lift tailgate
Ford	F600	1988	G	$4,500	3/06	ECMI	Tandem axle, Cat engine
Ford	F600	1994	f	$800	9/06	NEIN	Cab & chassis, gas, 5-speed trans.
Ford	F600	1998	G	$5,000	3/06	ECMI	Single axle
Ford	F650		G	$1,700	4/06	WCSD	16' box and hoist
Ford	F650	2000	G	$33,000	3/06	ECIN	Dump truck, Cummins diesel, 8,800 miles
Ford	F650	2002	G	$27,500	11/06	SECA	Dump truck
Ford	F700		G	$12,500	11/06	SCMN	Tag, 20' Crysteel bed, hoist, 85,000 miles
Ford	F700	1976	G	$3,250	9/06	NEIN	Septic waste truck, 1,750-gal. waste tank, 250-gal. fresh water tank, new clutch, single axle, 5×2 trans.
Ford	F700	1976	G	$8,700	8/06	SCMN	20,493 miles, 16' Scott box, hoist
Ford	F700	1977	G	$5,500	2/06	ECIL	361 engine, 4×2 speed, 14.5' Midwest grain bed, hoist, roll tarp, 50,310 miles
Ford	F700	1978	G	$800	3/06	ECIN	Gas, single axle
Ford	F700	1978	F	$5,100	2/06	NCCO	Harsh 354 box, scales, 5×2 speed
Ford	F700	1979	F	$4,500	1/06	NCCO	Harsh 350 14' feed box, digital scale
Ford	F700	1980	P	$1,100	3/06	NEKS	Rough, 20' bed and hoist, 18" sides
Ford	F700	1982	G	$17,000	1/06	SCKS	Grain truck, 26,186 actual miles, 370 V-8 gas, 5-2 spd. trans., 189" wheel base, 24,500-lb. GVW, Knapheide 16' steel box w/ Shur-Lok roll tarp, 3-piece cargo doors, spare hyd. valve, 900R20 tires, bought new, always shedded
Ford	F700	1983	G	$4,000	4/06	SEND	3208, 5 speed, 16' steel flatbed
Ford	F700	1984	G	$10,500	11/06	SCCA	Detroit diesel, air brakes, auto
Ford	F700	1985	G	$1,300	8/06	SWCA	24' box, diesel, 224,613 miles
Ford	F700	1985	G	$8,100	11/06	WCSD	Allison automatic w/ Obeco steel box, 18'×5' tall, good steel silage box w/ end gate dump, steel grain end gate

Trucks

Make	Model	Year	Cond.	Price	Sale	Location	Comments
Ford	F700	1987	G	$13,500	3/06	ECMI	Bucket truck, auto, 60' Hi-Ranger lift, side boxes
Ford	F700	1988	G	$1,300	3/06	ECMI	Single axle, 14', 370 V-8, gas, auto
Ford	F700	1990	F	$500	9/06	ECMN	Cab & chassis, straight stick
Ford	F700	1990	F	$1,900	8/06	WCIL	10-ton dry tender box, rear auger, all hyd., gas engine, 5×2 speed, single axle
Ford	F700	1990	G	$5,000	8/06	NCIA	Turbo, Allison auto. 14' Jet box, hoist, tilt front end
Ford	F700	1991	G	$1,800	8/06	WCNC	
Ford	F700	1991	G	$3,500	3/06	ECMI	Diesel
Ford	F700	1992	G	$800	9/06	NEIN	Cab & chassis, gas, 5 speed
Ford	F700	1992	F	$950	9/06	NEIN	Cab & chassis, gas, 5 speed
Ford	F700	1992	G	$8,000	12/06	NEMN	
Ford	F700	1992	G	$11,500	3/06	ECMI	Bucket truck, turbo diesel, 5 speed, 55 Altec lift & 11' dump body
Ford	F700	1993	F	$2,200	9/06	SEIA	Cargo truck, auto, 24' cargo box
Ford	F700	1994	G	$1,550	3/06	NEKS	Diesel, flat steel bed
Ford	F700	1995	G	$2,700	10/06	ECMO	2 axle, hyd. brakes
Ford	F700	1995	G	$7,000	9/06	ECMN	2,000-gal. Engle tank w/ Masport pump, 3" inlet, 6" dump, side-mount secondary, 5-speed split trans.
Ford	F700	1995	G	$7,000	9/06	NEIN	Flatbed dump truck, 428 gas, wood sides, single axle
Ford	F7000	1985	G	$2,400	9/06	NEIN	Mechanic's truck, diesel, Knapheide enclosed body, 5×2 trans.
Ford	F7000	1986	G	$8,950	2/06	SEIL	
Ford	F750	1977	F	$900	11/06	SCIL	361 V-8, 15' bed, 44,800 miles
Ford	F750	1979	P	$600	2/06	NWIN	Grain truck, hoist
Ford	F750	2000	G	$23,000	9/06	SECA	Water truck, 11,125 miles
Ford	F750	2007	E	$60,000	10/06	WCFL	Water truck, Cummins 200-hp. diesel, 5.9L, Fuller FS-52-5A, 5 speed
Ford	F800		G	$13,000	11/06	SWCA	Dump truck, 5-7 steel box, diesel, 7 speed
Ford	F800	1978	G	$4,100	12/06	SEIA	Bulk feed truck, 10-ton Kraus feed body
Ford	F800	1978	G	$10,000	3/06	NEKS	Custom cab, single-axle grain truck, 59,022 miles, 18' steel box, 389 gas engine, 5×2 speed, dual fuel tanks, 10:00-20 tires
Ford	F800	1979	G	$1,200	3/06	ECMI	Lube truck
Ford	F800	1979	G	$18,000	12/06	ECMN	Crane, 125' 2-second telescoping boom, gas, tandems, downriggers, white, 42,000 miles
Ford	F800	1980	P	$2,200	7/06	SEND	Diesel, Pitman Polecat 1300 digger
Ford	F800	1982	P	$1,400	7/06	SEND	Reel truck, gas
Ford	F800	1983	G	$1,200	12/06	NEMN	Dump truck
Ford	F800	1983	G	$1,750	12/06	NEMN	
Ford	F800	1984	G	$7,250	3/06	ECMI	Bucket truck, V-8 gas, 5×2 speed, 55' Teco lift
Ford	F800	1985	G	$1,300	9/06	NEIN	Cab & chassis, diesel, 5×2 speed
Ford	F800	1985	G	$2,500	9/06	NEIN	Line truck, diesel, Pitman PC1300 Polecat outriggers, air brakes
Ford	F800	1985	G	$5,500	4/06	SEMI	80,746 miles, gas, 5 speed, 14' Scott steel box, hoist, 370-cubic-inch engine, single axle
Ford	F800	1986	G	$17,000	7/06	NWMN	Twin screw, 429, 5×2 speed, 20' Buffalo box, hoist, roll tarp, plumbed for drill fill, 10:00×20 tires, twin fuel tanks, beet equipped, 56K miles, one owner
Ford	F800	1987	G	$4,000	3/06	ECMI	Single-axle dump

Trucks

Make	Model	Year	Cond.	Price	Sale	Location	Comments
Ford	F800	1987	F	$5,000	8/06	WCIL	10-ton, 2-compartment dry tender box, rear auger, all hydraulic, 429 gas engine, 5×2 speed, single axle
Ford	F800	1987	G	$6,000	3/06	ECMI	Single-axle dump truck, Ford turbo
Ford	F800	1987	G	$8,000	12/06	NEMN	
Ford	F800	1987	G	$16,500	3/06	ECMI	Bucket truck
Ford	F800	1988	G	$5,750	12/06	NEMO	429 engine, 5×2 trans., 16' Knapheide bed, cargo doors, Shur-Lok roll tarp, 78,000 miles
Ford	F800	1989	G	$3,800	10/06	ECMO	Dump truck
Ford	F800	1989	G	$10,000	9/06	ECMN	7.8-liter 240 hp., 5×2, airbrakes, auger truck, upper & lower controls
Ford	F800	1990	G	$2,750	11/06	SCCA	Flatbed diesel, sleeper, 1 axle, 9 speed
Ford	F800	1991	G	$1,500	9/06	NEIN	Cab & chassis, air brakes, heated mirrors, air ride seats
Ford	F800	1991	G	$3,750	9/06	NEIN	Digger derrick, diesel, Pitman Polecat, dual outrigger
Ford	F800	1991	G	$7,000	10/06	WCMA	Stake truck, diesel, auto, 12' body
Ford	F800	1992	F	$3,100	8/06	WCIL	7.8L diesel engine, 8-ton, ss dry tender box, rear auger, cup auger for soybeans, all hyd., flip tarp, 5×2 speed
Ford	F800	1995	G	$2,600	10/06	ECMO	2 axle, 2 door
Ford	F800	1995	G	$2,700	10/06	ECMO	2 door, 2 axle
Ford	F800	1995	G	$3,100	10/06	ECMO	2 axle, 2 door
Ford	F800	1995	G	$4,000	10/06	WCMA	Enclosed utility truck, Cummins 5.9L diesel, auto, under deck air compressor
Ford	F800	1996	G	$4,250	10/06	NCWI	Utility truck, diesel, 6-speed trans., toolboxes
Ford	F800	1996	G	$7,600	10/06	WCMA	Dump truck, 5.9L diesel, auto
Ford	F800	1996	G	$11,000	1/06	WCNH	Dump truck, Cummins turbo diesel, 5×2 speed
Ford	F800	1996	G	$13,500	1/06	WCOH	Dump truck, Cummins turbo diesel, 5×2 speed
Ford	F800	1996	G	$30,000	3/06	WCWA	Boom truck, Cummins 6 cyl., diesel, 5×2 speed, 18' flatbed
Ford	F800	1997	G	$9,250	10/06	WCMA	Dump truck, Cummins 5.9L diesel, 4×6 yard body, 97,568 miles
Ford	F800	1998	G	$16,000	10/06	WCFL	Dump truck, Cummins 5.9L diesel, 6-speed trans.
Ford	F8000	1981	G	$15,000	2/06	SCKS	Tandem-axle truck, 22' steel box, tarp, 5×2 speed, 3208 Cat diesel, dual fuel tanks
Ford	F8000	1985	G	$25,500	1/06	WCPA	Service, diesel, 5 speed
Ford	F8000	1986	G	$8,000	1/06	SCKS	Single-axle truck tractor, 284 hours on Cat 3208 diesel engine OH, 5×2 speed trans., 130,046 miles, 295/75R22.5 tires, Rawson Koenig side toolboxes, chrome fenders, chrome bumpers, white w/ red stripe, VIN: 1FDXK87UXGVA39820
Ford	F8000	1986	G	$9,000	1/06	SCKS	Single-axle truck tractor, Cat 3208 diesel, 77,675 miles on OH, 5×2 speed, air brakes, 295/75R22.5 tires, Rawson Koenig side toolboxes, chrome fenders, chrome bumpers, white w/ red stripe, 201,748 miles, VIN: 1FDXK87U1GVA39818
Ford	F900	1979	F	$1,400	6/06	NCIA	5×4 speed, gas engine, twin screw, 15' gravel box & hoist
Ford	F900	1985	G	$2,750	3/06	ECIN	Dump truck, single axle
Ford	F9000	1990	G	$16,000	3/06	ECMI	Quad-axle dump truck, 3406 Cat diesel, 18' dump box
Ford	L8000		G	$7,000	11/06	SWCA	Dump truck, 5-6 yard box, diesel, 5 speed
Ford	L8000	1980	G	$2,000	12/06	NEMN	Dump truck, sander, plow
Ford	L8000	1986	G	$3,250	3/06	ECMI	Tandem-axle dump truck, 210 hp., diesel, 13 speed, Hendrickson suspension, 13' box

Trucks

Make	Model	Year	Cond.	Price	Sale	Location	Comments
Ford	L8000	1986	G	$4,500	8/06	NEIA	288K miles, Cat 3208, turbo, Allison trans.
Ford	L8000	1986	G	$7,750	10/06	NCWI	Dump truck, Cat engine, 225 hp., Allison trans., auto., single-axle spring suspension, 23K Eatons
Ford	L8000	1987	G	$2,250	12/06	NEMN	
Ford	L8000	1987	G	$6,700	11/06	SCNE	7.8 Ford engine, single axle, air brakes, 5×2 speed, 12' flatbed, grain ball hitch and fifth wheel
Ford	L8000	1987	G	$8,000	12/06	ECMN	Cat 3208, 7 speed, air brakes, 16-yard, 3208 Cat diesel pump, extra hose that comes with unit
Ford	L8000	1987	G	$20,500	12/06	WCMI	Grain truck, 18' Wheeler box, 3208 Cat engine, 161,034 miles, 10-speed road range trans.
Ford	L8000	1988	G	$8,500	3/06	SCIN	Tri-axle dump truck, 210 Ford diesel, 10 speed
Ford	L8000	1991	G	$15,000	9/06	SECA	2-axle water truck, diesel, 273,263 miles
Ford	L8000	1991	G	$16,000	9/06	SECA	2-axle water truck, diesel, 278,881 miles
Ford	L8000	1992	G	$5,750	7/06	ECNY	Boom truck, single axle, dual-tired boom truck, Ford diesel, auto
Ford	L8000	1992	G	$7,000	12/06	NEMN	Tanker truck
Ford	L8000	1994	G	$3,700	8/06	SWCA	Diesel
Ford	L900	1995	G	$30,000	1/06	NWIA	Aeromax Cummins diesel single-axle tractor, 10-speed Eaton Fuller trans., air seat, 427,302 miles, 2005 Jet 26' grain trailer
Ford	L9000		F	$1,750	10/06	SWOH	Tandem axle, V-8 engine, 2 stick, 10-speed trans, 14' steel dump box
Ford	L9000		G	$3,500	1/06	WCPA	Fuel/lube, tandem-axle fuel truck, 4,000-gal. fuel tank
Ford	L9000		G	$27,500	5/06	SWCA	4,000-gal. water truck, Cat 3406 diesel, 10-speed trans., never used tank
Ford	L9000	1977	F	$3,000	11/06	WCMN	Twin screw, 318 Detroit, 13 speed, 16' steel J Craft box
Ford	L9000	1979	G	$5,500	3/06	ECMI	Tri-axle dump truck, 285 hp., Cummins, 15 speed
Ford	L9000	1982	G	$5,000	3/06	ECMI	Tri-axle dump truck, tandem, lift axle, Cummins diesel, 10 speed
Ford	L9000	1982	G	$7,500	3/06	ECMI	Tri-axle dump truck, 350 Cummins, double frame, 15 spd., 16' box
Ford	L9000	1987	G	$3,000	10/06	SWOH	Dump truck, tandem axle, Cummins diesel
Ford	L9000	1987	G	$9,250	4/06	WCMB	Canadian sale
Ford	L9000	1988	G	$4,750	12/06	NEMN	Dump truck
Ford	L9000	1988	G	$5,500	3/06	ECIN	Dump truck
Ford	L9000	1988	G	$7,500	11/06	SCCA	Cat 3406 10 speed, wet kit
Ford	L9000	1988	G	$31,000	4/06	WCMN	Canadian sale, 15 speed, Cancade 20'×8.5' box, hoist, roll over tarp, blue
Ford	L9000	1988	G	$31,000	4/06	SWMB	Canadian sale, full tandem truck, 360 Cummins engine, 15-speed trans., Cancade 20'×8' box, hoist & rollover tarp, 11R22.5 tires, blue, very nice
Ford	L9000	1989	G	$9,000	12/06	NEMN	
Ford	L9000	1990	G	$22,500	3/06	ECMI	Tri-axle dump, 350 Cummins
Ford	L9000	1991	G	$4,500	3/06	SCIN	Single axle, 8 speed, L10 Cummins engine
Ford	L9000	1992	G	$10,000	9/06	NEND	Aeromax, twin screw, Detroit 60 Series, 9 speed, air ride, Jake, 24' flatbed, excellent rubber, new rod bearings
Ford	L9000	1993	G	$16,500	3/06	NEND	Twin screw, day cab, N14 Cummins, 430 hp., 9 speed, air ride, dual tanks, 383,993 miles, 11×22.5 tires
Ford	L9000	1994	G	$4,200	9/06	NEIN	Diesel Cat 3406 engine, Eaton 9 speed

Trucks

Make	Model	Year	Cond.	Price	Sale	Location	Comments
Ford	L9000	1994	G	$15,500	12/06	NEMN	185,018 miles, dump truck
Ford	L9000	1995	G	$4,400	1/06	WCCA	2 axle
Ford	L9000	1995	G	$6,250	9/06	ECMN	235,000 miles, 3406 Cat, 9 speed, headache rack
Ford	L9000	1995	G	$10,000	2/06	WCIL	Aeromax full locking twin screw truck, 370 hp., M11 Cummins, 13 speed, 18' litter spreader lime bed
Ford	L9000	1995	G	$12,500	11/06	SCCA	Flatbed dump truck, Cat diesel, 10 speed
Ford	LN7000	1982	F	$900	9/06	NEIN	Tire truck, V-8 gas, air compressor, lift gate
Ford	LN7000	1985	G	$3,500	9/06	NEIN	Vac truck, JD diesel,
Ford	LN7000	1988	G	$3,800	9/06	NEIN	Vac truck, JD diesel
Ford	LN800	1978	G	$3,500	11/06	SCSD	Grain truck, 534 gas, 5×2 speed, tandem, 20' box, roll tarp
Ford	LN8000	1977	F	$5,300	5/06	SEND	Twin screw dump truck, 3208 Cat, 13 speed, 15' gravel box, hoist
Ford	LN8000	1979	F	$3,000	3/06	WCKS	Fresh OH on 390 motor, 5-speed trans.
Ford	LN8000	1981	G	$19,000	2/06	SCMI	Straight truck, 180 thumb box/hoist, Cat motor, new tires front and rear, Shur-Lok tarp, 58,245 miles
Ford	LN880	1976	G	$10,000	4/06	NWMN	Twin screw, 477, V-8, Allison automatic, Buffalo 20' box, hoist, roll tarp, 3-piece end gate, 92,486 miles, 20K miles on trans. OH, 9:00-20 rears, 11×22.5 steering
Ford	LN9000	1977	G	$2,100	3/06	NECO	Cab & chassis, Cummins SC 299 engine, new 9-speed trans.
Ford	LN9000	1978	F	$14,200	2/06	NCCO	20' Peterson steel box, Detroit diesel, 13 speed, rebuilt engine
Ford	LN9000	1992	G	$7,750	9/06	NEIN	Single axle, dump truck, L10 Cummins, 10' bed
Ford	LT9000		G	$2,500	10/06	SWOH	Tandem axle, day cab, Cummins diesel, roadgrader trans., aluminum fenders
Ford	LT9000	1982	G	$6,750	3/06	NECO	18', Cummins 300 BC II engine, 10 speed, twin screw
Ford	LTL 9000	1982	G	$8,500	3/06	ECIN	Quad axle
Ford	LTL 9000	1987	F	$3,800	12/06	NWMO	Dump truck, 12-yard bed, Cummins diesel engine, Fuller trans., twin screw
Ford	LTL 9000	1993	G	$5,000	9/06	NEND	Semi tractor, 60 Series Detroit, 9 speed, double bunk removable sleeper
Ford	LTL9000		G	$11,500	5/06	SWCA	Dump truck, 10-yard box, diesel, Fuller 10-speed trans.
Ford	LTL9000		G	$43,500	5/06	ECMI	Tri-axle tractor, 13-speed trans., 279,483 miles
Ford	LTL9000	1984	G	$3,300	3/06	NEKS	400 Cummins, 13 speed, fifth wheel
Ford	LTL9000	1984	G	$14,000	3/06	NWMN	Twin screw, Detroit 8V92, 430 hp., 13 speed, 19' box, hoist, roll tarp
Ford	LTS9000	1989	G	$4,300	9/06	NEIN	Material handling truck, Cummins diesel, IMT 13031 crane, extended boom, rotating forks, 7-speed trans.
Ford	Ranger	1986	G	$600	8/06	SWCA	
Ford	Ranger	1988	G	$1,000	3/06	NCNE	Custom pickup, 4×4, 116,200 miles, red, automatic, 2.9L gas engine, AM/FM, lift kit
Ford	Ranger	1989	F	$900	4/06	NWMN	6 cyl., 5 speed, 4WD, front pole hitch
Ford	Ranger	1991	G	$1,900	1/06	NEMO	4WD
Ford	Ranger	1993	F	$650	10/06	SEMN	Pickup
Ford	Ranger	1993	G	$3,600	1/06	SCKS	XLT 4×4 pickup, 5-speed trans., 99,767 miles, 3.0L V-6 gas, sliding rear window, Century pickup box topper, rear/front tow bar hitch
Ford	Ranger	1994	P	$675	4/06	WCWI	Pickup, extended cab
Ford	Ranger	1994	G	$2,150	8/06	SWCA	45,334 miles

Trucks

Make	Model	Year	Cond.	Price	Sale	Location	Comments
Ford	Ranger	1994	G	$2,700	9/06	SECA	XL, 75,857 miles
Ford	Ranger	1998	G	$1,000	10/06	SENJ	
Ford	Ranger	2001	G	$2,500	10/06	ECMO	2 axle, 2 door, hyd. brakes
Ford	Ranger	2002	G	$6,400	8/06	SWCA	45,345 miles
Ford	Ranger	2002	G	$6,500	8/06	SWCA	42,024 miles
Ford	Ranger	2002	G	$8,500	8/06	SWCA	4WD, 20,446 miles
Ford	Ranger XLT	1988	G	$2,000	3/06	NCNE	Extended cab, 4×4, 5 speed, 2.9L gas engine, AM/FM, 163K miles, black
Ford	Ranger XLT	1996	G	$3,600	8/06	SWCA	Extended cab, 78,024 miles
Ford	Super Duty	1988	G	$3,100	8/06	SETN	Stake bed, lift gate, gas
Ford	Super Duty	1989	G	$800	3/06	ECIN	4 speed
Ford	Super Duty	1990	G	$2,500	11/06	SCCA	Enclosed box, Onan generator
Ford	Super Duty	1995	G	$3,500	3/06	ECIN	Flatbed
Ford	Super Duty	1997	G	$24,000	3/06	WCWA	Service body, 7.3L diesel, Bobcat 225 welder
Ford	Super Duty	1998	G	$6,800	9/06	SECA	14' box, lift gate
Freightliner	FL112	1999	G	$14,000	9/06	WCTX	Diesel
Freightliner	FL112	1999	G	$14,500	9/06	WCTX	Diesel
Freightliner	FL120	1996	G	$21,250	2/06	ECNE	Semi, day cab, 675,510 miles, 3406E Cat, air ride, 163" wheelbase, Jake brake, cruise control, computer info center
Freightliner	FL60	1994	G	$3,250	12/06	NEMN	Flatbed
Freightliner	FL60	1999	G	$10,500	9/06	SECA	24' bucket, lift gate, 59,453 miles
Freightliner	FL60	2000	G	$10,000	10/06	WCFL	Diesel, flatbed
Freightliner	FL60	2000	G	$11,500	11/06	SCCA	Flatbed, dumptruck, 1 axle, duals, Cummins
Freightliner	FL60	2000	G	$21,000	12/06	WCMN	3126 Cat, automatic Allison, 4-speed trans., 14' Frontier contractor's box, 104K miles
Freightliner	FL60	2002	G	$13,500	8/06	WCNC	112,876 miles
Freightliner	FL70		G	$4,250	5/06	SWCA	Cab & chassis, diesel, 7-speed trans.
Freightliner	FL70		G	$4,250	5/06	SWCA	Cab & chassis, Cummins diesel, 7-speed trans.
Freightliner	FL70		G	$9,100	10/06	ECMO	6 speed, cab chassis
Freightliner	FL70		G	$12,000	12/06	SEND	Single-axle truck, pusher, 6 speed, diesel, 18' stake box, hoist, 299,533 miles
Freightliner	FL70	1994	G	$3,700	12/06	ECMN	415,201 miles, 5.9L Cummins, 6-speed Allison trans., split-bench front seat, toolbox
Freightliner	FL70	1994	G	$8,500	3/06	WCWA	Tar truck, Cummins 6 cyl., asphalt patch system
Freightliner	FL70	1996	G	$8,500	12/06	NEMN	Dump truck
Freightliner	FL70	1998	G	$6,500	8/06	SETN	24' van body, Cummins diesel, 468,694 miles
Freightliner	FL70	1998	G	$27,900	1/06	WCCA	2,600-gal. water system
Freightliner	FL70	1999	G	$12,500	10/06	SWOH	Cat 3126 diesel, 246 hp., 7-speed trans.
Freightliner	FL70	2000	G	$13,000	7/06	WCCA	Cat 3126 5 speed, 10' flatbed
Freightliner	FL70	2000	G	$13,500	3/06	WCWA	Van truck, Cummins 8.6, 6 speed, 24' box
Freightliner	FL70	2000	G	$24,000	11/06	SECA	5-yard dump truck, Cat 3126 engine
Freightliner	FLC 112	1990	G	$18,500	12/06	ECKS	Day cab, Cummins N14, 350 hp., Fuller Roadranger, 13 speed, hyd. wet kit
Freightliner	FLC 112	1990	G	$30,000	12/06	ECKS	Knapheide 20' steel box, Harsh twin-cylinder hoist, Cummins N14, 315 hp., Fuller 9 speed, 492K miles
Freightliner	FLC 112	1990	G	$33,000	12/06	ECKS	Knapheide 20' steel box, Harsh twin cylinder hoist, Cummins N14, 315 hp. Fuller 9 speed
Freightliner	FLC 112	1995	G	$13,500	4/06	NWMN	Twin screw, day cab, N14 Cummins, 10 speed
Freightliner	FLC 112	1995	G	$15,000	4/06	NWMN	N14 Cummins, 10 speed, half fenders, 22.5 rubber

Trucks

Make	Model	Year	Cond.	Price	Sale	Location	Comments
Freightliner	FLC 112	1999	G	$19,000	2/06	SCMI	Semi tractor, gray, Cummins power, air, power windows, power heated mirrors, aluminum rims, 509,810 miles
Freightliner	FLC 11264ST	1995	G	$26,250	4/06	NWMN	Twin screw, third-axle single pusher steerable, N14 Cummins-350E, Eaton 9 speed, Cancade 21' box, 263,923 miles, roll tarp
Freightliner	FLC 120	1998	G	$10,500	12/06	ECMN	11.1 Detroit, 10 speed, white w/ blue stripe, 48" sleeper, new caps on rear
Freightliner	FLC 120	1998	G	$18,000	5/06	SWCA	Water truck, Detroit 55 diesel, 9-speed trans.
Freightliner	FLC 120	1999	G	$19,000	9/06	WCTX	Diesel
Freightliner	FLD 112	1987	G	$9,750	4/06	NWMN	Factory day cab, 300 Cummins, 9-speed spring ride
Freightliner	FLD 112	1995	G	$11,750	4/06	NWMN	Factory day cab, 350 Cummins, 9-speed, spring ride, low pro on steel, twin aluminum tanks
Freightliner	FLD 112	1998	G	$13,000	12/06	SEND	Day cab truck, M11 Cummins engine, Rockwell 10 speed, approximately 500K miles
Freightliner	FLD 112	1998	G	$13,000	12/06	SEND	Day cab semi tractor, M11 Cummins, Rockwell 10-speed trans.
Freightliner	FLD 120	1987	G	$8,000	3/06	ECNE	Conventional, day cab, Cummins 855 turbo, Eaton Fuller 9-speed Roadranger trans., 50,000 lb.
Freightliner	FLD 120	1988	G	$27,500	2/06	NWKS	Tri-axle grain truck, 13-speed trans., Cat diesel, 20' aluminum box, cargo doors
Freightliner	FLD 120	1989	G	$8,000	4/06	ECND	Conventional, 3406 Cat, 350 hp., 9 speed, air ride, air slide, 60" double bunk, twin aluminum tank
Freightliner	FLD 120	1991	G	$4,900	6/06	NEIN	Sleeper
Freightliner	FLD 120	1992	G	$8,000	3/06	NWKS	Tandem axle, 430 Cummins, 13 speed, air ride, air ride, 24.5 low-profile tires, aluminum wheels, 42" flat-top sleeper, recent engine/trans. & rear end work
Freightliner	FLD 120	1993	G	$9,000	6/06	NCPA	142,648 miles, Detroit 400 hp., Series 60, 8 speed, Hendrickson suspension, 22.5 Dayton tires, aluminum hub wheels, 25' frame, no box
Freightliner	FLD 120	1995	G	$7,400	12/06	SEND	3406 Cat, 9 speed, sleeper
Freightliner	FLD 120	1995	G	$14,000	3/06	NCNE	Truck tractor, 783,630 miles, Detroit 12.7L 470-hp. diesel engine, 13 speed, 358 rear ends, air ride, Jake brake, 70" sleeper, heated mirrors
Freightliner	FLD 120	1995	G	$14,000	3/06	NWMN	11.1L Detroit engine, 9 speed, air ride
Freightliner	FLD 120	1996	G	$7,500	12/06	NEMN	
Freightliner	FLD 120	1996	G	$18,500	2/06	WCMN	Cummins M11, RTX13609 trans., aluminum disks all around
Freightliner	FLD 120	1996	G	$27,500	3/06	WCWA	Roll-off chassis, Cat 3176, 10 speed
Freightliner	FLD 120	1997	G	$16,200	3/06	SEND	Day cab, 60 Series, 12.7 Detroit 10 speed, air ride cab, air ride suspension, air slide fifth, twin aluminum fuel tanks, 821,128 miles
Freightliner	FLD 120	1997	G	$26,000	12/06	ECMN	Dump truck, 330 hp., 10 speed, 16' box, airgate & air ride, 654,860 miles
Freightliner	FLD 120	1998	F	$7,000	12/06	WCKS	60 Series Detroit diesel engine, Super-10 speed, tandem axle, twin screw, power divider, air ride suspension, engine brake, cruise, single exhaust, 11R22.5 tires, steel rims, air ride seat, 210" wheelbase, air, heat
Freightliner	FLD 120	1998	G	$15,000	11/06	SCCA	Cummins 435 hp., 13 speed
Freightliner	FLD 120	1999	G	$15,000	7/06	WCPA	Cummins N14 370-hp. diesel

Trucks

Make	Model	Year	Cond.	Price	Sale	Location	Comments
Freightliner	FLD 120	1999	G	$15,000	10/06	NCWI	Cat C12 diesel, 10-speed trans, PS, low-profile 24.5 on aluminum, tandem axle
Freightliner	FLD 132	1999	G	$11,000	10/06	NCWI	Cummins N14 diesel, 500 hp., tandem axle, air ride suspension
GMC	1500		P	$100	8/06	NCNE	
GMC	1500	1982	F	$500	10/06	SWNE	Sierra Classic 1500 pickup, 6.2L diesel engine, 110,130 miles
GMC	1500	1983	F	$550	8/06	NENE	2WD pickup, 6.2L diesel, automatic, overdrive, matching topper, 185K miles
GMC	1500	1989	P	$750	11/06	WCMN	Regular cab, long box, 4WD
GMC	1500	1990	F	$750	7/06	ECNY	Gas, auto. trans.
GMC	1500	1996	G	$3,800	4/06	NWMN	SLE, extended cab, short box, 350, V-8, 2WD, 120,830 miles
GMC	1500	1999	G	$9,300	5/06	NCKY	SLT, Sierra, 3 door, extended cab, 4×4, 98,288 miles
GMC	2500		G	$1,100	5/06	SWCA	Utility, V-8, auto
GMC	2500	1991	P	$450	9/06	ECMN	Sierra, 4.3, 2 door, power locks, cruise
GMC	2500	1994	G	$5,000	12/06	NENE	Dually, 1-ton, 5-speed manual, 4×4, flatbed, gooseneck hitch
GMC	2500	1997	G	$4,900	5/06	SWCA	Utility, V-8, auto
GMC	2500	1998	G	$1,000	7/06	WCCA	¾-ton, long bed, 255-hp. Vortec, 4 speed, auto., 4 wheel, antilock brakes
GMC	2500	1999	G	$10,000	4/06	NWMN	Sierra, regular cab, 6.0, V-8, auto., 4WD, SLE option pkg.
GMC	2500	2001	G	$14,000	4/06	NWMN	Standard cab, 6.0L, auto, 4WD, 52,000 miles
GMC	2500	2003	G	$14,000	11/06	ECND	SLE, 4 door, extended cab, 6.0L auto, 4WD, cloth interior, running boards, 70,000 miles
GMC	3500		G	$1,300	5/06	SWCA	Diesel, auto. trans., lift gate
GMC	3500	1989	G	$750	8/06	SWCA	3×3 crew cab, utility, diesel
GMC	3500	1989	G	$1,300	3/06	ECIN	Auto
GMC	3500	1989	G	$10,000	11/06	SCCA	Service truck, 4WD, 454 engine, auto, 3,500-watt generator, hyd. oil dispenser, 34K miles, Tommy lift
GMC	3500	1990	G	$2,100	10/06	WCMA	Step van, 6.2L diesel
GMC	3500	1990	G	$2,400	3/06	NEKS	Flatbed
GMC	3500	1991	G	$3,500	8/06	SETN	177,490 miles, V-8, auto, gas
GMC	3500	1991	G	$4,500	3/06	ECND	1-ton service truck, duals, 150K miles, 40K miles on rebuilt 350 engine, 10K miles on brakes, wheel bearings & trans., no rust, service bed, toolbox & fifth wheel
GMC	3500	1994	G	$1,500	10/06	WCMA	Step van, 8 cyl., Honda EV6010 generator, gas
GMC	3500	1995	G	$1,800	8/06	SWCA	4×4, 106,220 miles
GMC	3500	1995	G	$2,700	8/06	SWCA	
GMC	3500	1995	G	$3,500	9/06	SECA	Vandura, 14' box van
GMC	3500	1995	G	$3,950	10/06	WCMA	4WD, enclosed service truck, lift gate, Start-All unit
GMC	3500	1995	G	$4,700	10/06	WCMA	4WD, enclosed service truck, lift gate, Start-All unit
GMC	3500	1995	G	$5,400	8/06	SWCA	Rack
GMC	3500	1995	G	$7,000	10/06	WCMA	4WD, enclosed service truck, lift gate, Start-All unit
GMC	3500	1995	G	$7,700	2/06	NEIN	4×4, 6.5 diesel, dual wheel pickup, automatic, extended cab, pw/pl, 111K miles
GMC	3500	1997	G	$3,000	10/06	ECMO	1-ton, flatbed
GMC	3500	1997	G	$3,250	5/06	SWCA	Diesel, auto, dual tanks
GMC	3500	1997	G	$13,000	4/06	WCMB	Canadian sale, diesel, 1-ton, flat deck, fifth wheel
GMC	3500	1999	G	$4,000	10/06	WCGA	Flatbed, Tommy lift

WHAT'S IT WORTH?

Trucks

Make	Model	Year	Cond.	Price	Sale	Location	Comments
GMC	3500	2000	G	$4,250	3/06	ECIN	Flatbed
GMC	3500HD	2000	G	$6,750	11/06	SWCA	Diesel, auto
GMC	3500SL	1990	G	$1,600	10/06	NCWI	Dump truck, diesel, auto, dump bed
GMC	5500		F	$200	1/06	WCCA	Flatbed
GMC	5500	1976	F	$500	9/06	WCND	Twin screw, V-8, auto, 20' French combination box, electric
GMC	6000	1976	G	$3,400	4/06	ECND	Sierra Grande, 350, V-8, 4×2 speed, 16' Scott box, hoist
GMC	6000	1977	F	$2,700	2/06	SWNE	Cab and chassis, V-8, 5×2 speed, single axle
GMC	6000	1979	G	$1,500	12/06	NWIL	350 V-8, 4×2 speed, 13.5' farm box, Knapheide scissor hoist, 20,000 miles on engine, gas
GMC	6000	1982	F	$1,100	2/06	SEIA	Sierra, V-8, 350 engine, 15' grain bed, twin hoist
GMC	6000	1985	F	$1,400	3/06	WCMI	Single-axle truck, 14' supreme aluminum van box, lift gate, V-8, Allison auto, low miles
GMC	6000	1988	F	$1,450	11/06	SCCA	Van body, 20' box
GMC	6500		F	$1,200	4/06	NWSD	Dump truck
GMC	6500	1976	F	$300	2/06	WCME	24' custom, built cover top steel bulk body, 366 gas, 5×2 trans.
GMC	6500	1976	G	$1,400	2/06	WCME	20' bulk body
GMC	6500	1977	F	$2,550	1/06	WCCA	Fire truck
GMC	6500	1977	G	$14,500	4/06	ECND	Lift tag tandem 427, auto, 20' Buffalo box, twin post hoist, 3-piece end gate, roll tarp, twin fuel tanks
GMC	6500	1977	G	$16,000	12/06	SCNE	Sierra Grande, 366 engine, 5 and 2 speed, 20' steel side box, hyd. tag axle, 67,156 one-owner miles
GMC	6500	1977	G	$17,500	3/06	ECNE	Grain truck, 427, 13 speed, 20' steel box, roll tarp, 39,600 miles
GMC	6500	1978	G	$7,000	11/06	SCNE	5×2 speed, 366, V-8, Midwest 18' steel box and hoist, 58,164 miles
GMC	6500	1978	G	$9,000	12/06	SCNE	427 engine, 5 and 2 speed, 20' steel side box, air brakes, air tag axle, cargo doors, roll tarp, 10:00 × 20" tires, 140,000 miles
GMC	7000		G	$2,500	5/06	SWCA	Flatbed dump truck, 18' bed, headache rack, V-8, 5-speed trans., 2-speed rear axle
GMC	7000	1979	G	$5,400	6/06	ECND	Sierra Grande single axle, 366, 5×2 speed, 16' Scott box, hoist, roll tarp, 60" sides, 3-piece end gate, 106,125 miles
GMC	7000	1979	G	$7,500	9/06	WCND	Dry floater, 2WD, 427, V-8, rebuilt Allison auto, twin fuel tanks, roll tarp, no title
GMC	7000	1980	G	$5,850	12/06	ECIL	5×2 speed, 10/20, 16' grain bed
GMC	7000	1980	G	$14,000	3/06	WCKS	Tandem truck, 39,500 miles, 427 motor, 13-speed trans., air brakes, twin screw, 20' bed, hoist, roll tarp
GMC	7000	1981	G	$7,900	3/06	ECNE	Single-axle grain truck, 19' wood box w/ steel floor, twin-cyl. hoist, Shur-Lok roll tarp, 427 gas engine, 5×2 speed, dual fuel tanks, air brakes, air pusher axle
GMC	7000	1981	E	$11,100	2/06	SENE	21' metal box, pusher axle, hoist, 73,460 miles, gas
GMC	7000	1982	G	$10,000	4/06	WCMB	Canadian sale, 5×2 trans., Midland 15'×8' box, roll over tarp, telescoping hoist, 68,000 miles
GMC	7000	1984	G	$18,600	4/06	NESD	Tri-axle truck w/ lift tag, air third axle, 20' Omaha steel box, hoist, 366 engine, 5×2 trans., power steering, roll tarp, swing-out end gate, pintle hitch, 84,395 miles, kept inside
GMC	7000	1985	G	$15,000	11/06	NCIN	Grain truck, 20' Omaha bed & hoist, 63K miles, 5×2 speed, single axle, air tag

Trucks

Make	Model	Year	Cond.	Price	Sale	Location	Comments
GMC	7000	1986	G	$2,500	3/06	SCIN	Single axle, 5×2 speed
GMC	7000	1989	G	$2,200	9/06	NCMI	Brigadier, cab & chassis, Cat 3208 diesel engine, 10-speed Roadranger, 23 rears, 127K miles, good rubber, long double-frame chassis
GMC	7000	1989	G	$12,750	9/06	NWOH	427 engine, Allison auto. trans., Knapheide 16' grain bed, hoist, air brakes, 109,893 miles, nice truck
GMC	7000	2001	G	$17,000	10/06	ECMO	Posi plus, 35' reach
GMC	7000	2001	G	$18,000	10/06	ECMO	Posi plus, 2 toolboxes
GMC	Astro	1985	F	$1,150	4/06	SEND	Single-axle tractor, 300 Cummins, 9 speed
GMC	Astro 95	1994	G	$3,100	3/06	NEKS	20' bed, hoist, steel
GMC	Brigadier	1979	F	$1,100	4/06	SWOH	Cummins, air brakes, 10 speed, shows 17,715 miles, single axle
GMC	Brigadier	1980	G	$14,000	4/06	NWMN	Twin screw, 6V92 Detroit, 7 speed, 20' box, hoist, roll tarp, 164,632 miles
GMC	Brigadier	1981	G	$4,600	10/06	SEMN	Tri-axle cab and chassis
GMC	Brigadier	1984	G	$3,250	12/06	NEMN	Dump truck, 280,202 miles
GMC	Brigadier	1984	G	$6,400	12/06	ECMN	855 Cummins, Eaton 9 speed, tri-axle, 311,000 miles, aluminum box, steel liner, air gate, spring up air down
GMC	Brigadier	1985	G	$1,150	1/06	WCNH	Gas, 8-yard sander, 10' snowplow
GMC	Brigadier	1985	G	$3,000	11/06	SCNE	Cummins, 7 speed, twin screw, air brakes
GMC	Brigadier	1985	F	$6,600	2/06	ECNE	20' box, air tag, 265K miles
GMC	C6500	1977	G	$3,800	12/06	WCIL	16' box, new tarp, gas
GMC	C6500	1998	G	$5,200	8/06	SWCA	24' box truck, 149,212 miles
GMC	C6500	1998	G	$9,500	3/06	ECIN	366 gas, single axle
GMC	C6500	2000	G	$19,000	10/06	ECMO	Chassis, posi plus 35' reach
GMC	C6500	2001	G	$17,500	10/06	ECMO	Chassis, posi plus lift, auto, diesel
GMC	C6500	2001	G	$19,000	10/06	ECMO	Chassis, posi plus bucket, 35' reach, 1 toolbox
GMC	C6500	2001	G	$25,000	10/06	ECMO	Chassis, posi plus bucket, 35' reach, 1 toolbox
GMC	C7500	1998	G	$8,250	3/06	ECMI	11' tow truck, V-8 gas, Century 601
GMC	General		G	$6,000	5/06	SWCA	Dump truck, 12-15 yard box, Detroit diesel, 9-speed trans.
GMC	General	1979	G	$6,400	3/06	NESD	V692, 13 speed, twin screw, Buffalo 20' box & hoist, 24.5 tires
GMC	General	1979	G	$9,300	3/06	NESD	892 Detroit, 13 speed, twin screw, Buffalo 20' box & hoist
GMC	General	1980	G	$8,100	3/06	NESD	892 Detroit, 13 speed, twin screw, Buffalo 20' box & hoist, 24.5 tires
GMC	K2500		G	$3,950	10/06	WCMA	4WD, extended cab, 8 cyl.
GMC	K2500		G	$5,300	10/06	WCMA	4WD, extended cab, 8 cyl.
GMC	Sierra		G	$4,000	11/06	SWCA	Dump truck, 3-5 yard box, Detroit diesel, auto
GMC	Sierra	1977	G	$1,000	3/06	NCWI	V-8, 4 speed, duals, flatbed, hoist
GMC	Sierra	1992	G	$5,750	11/06	SCCA	Rollback, 17' aluminum bed
GMC	Sierra	1994	G	$2,000	8/06	SWCA	
GMC	Sierra	1997	G	$1,600	10/06	NCWI	Gas, auto, air
GMC	Sierra 15	1976	P	$160	3/06	SWOH	Rough
GMC	Sierra G	1979	F	$550	3/06	NWKS	¾-ton pickup, 4×4, 350 V-8 gas engine, automatic, AM/FM, air, pw/pl, 138K miles
GMC	Sonoma	1994	G	$2,000	8/06	SWCA	4WD, extended cab
GMC	Sonoma	1995	G	$3,000	3/06	WCWA	Extended cab, V-6
GMC	Topkick		G	$2,750	11/06	SWCA	5-yard box, 5 speed
GMC	Topkick		G	$3,000	11/06	SWCA	7000 dump truck, 5 speed

Trucks

Make	Model	Year	Cond.	Price	Sale	Location	Comments
GMC	Topkick		F	$6,000	12/06	WCMN	Gas, contractor's box, automatic
GMC	Topkick	1980	G	$5,500	11/06	SCCA	Water truck, Cat 3208, 10 speed
GMC	Topkick	1981	G	$24,000	2/06	WCIL	Twin screw truck, 3208 Cat engine, Fuller 13-speed trans., 20' Knapheide grain box, 66" sides, roll tarp, 170,014 miles
GMC	Topkick	1981	G	$28,000	2/06	WCIL	Twin screw truck, 3208 Cat engine, Fuller 13-speed trans., 18' Knapheide grain box, 66" sides, roll tarp, 74,580 miles
GMC	Topkick	1982	F	$2,000	5/06	NENE	2-ton service truck, 3208 Cat motor, toolboxes, 5 speed, dual
GMC	Topkick	1986	G	$1,300	1/06	WCCA	10-bay beverage truck
GMC	Topkick	1986	G	$1,300	1/06	WCCA	10-bay beverage truck
GMC	Topkick	1986	G	$1,300	1/06	WCCA	10-bay beverage truck
GMC	Topkick	1990	G	$3,450	1/06	WCCA	10-bay beverage truck
GMC	Topkick	1990	F	$3,600	12/06	WCMN	Single axle, gas, 327 engine, Allison trans., roll up & side door, Tommy lift, 20' van body
GMC	Topkick	1991	F	$1,150	9/06	NEIN	Cab & chassis, 5-speed trans.
GMC	Topkick	1991	G	$5,100	8/06	NEKS	Single-axle grain truck, 16', 366, 8 cyl., 5×2 speed, hyd. tag, scissor hoist
GMC	Topkick	1991	G	$6,000	8/06	NEKS	Single-axle grain truck, 16' 450-bu. steel box, 266 8-cyl. engine, 5×2 speed, hyd. tag, scissor hoist, new motors
GMC	Topkick	1993	G	$4,050	8/06	SETN	Flatbed, gas, 16' dump bed
GMC	Topkick	1994	G	$6,000	11/06	SCCA	1 axle, Cat 3116, 6 speed
GMC	Topkick	1996	G	$5,500	11/06	SCCA	Cab & chassis, 1 axle, gas, 6 speed
GMC	Topkick	1996	G	$7,000	9/06	NEIN	Single-axle dump, gas, air tailgate, 5 speed
GMC	Topkick	1996	G	$7,500	11/06	SCCA	Rollback, 19' aluminum bed, stinger
GMC	Topkick	1998	G	$7,000	11/06	SCCA	Flatbed, Cat 3116 diesel, Allison auto
GMC	Yukon	2001	G	$8,000	1/06	WCCA	SLE
IHC	1600		F	$800	10/06	WCWI	Loadstar truck, hoist, gear box
IHC	1600		G	$1,000	12/06	WCIL	Loadstar, V-8 engine, 4×2 trans, 81,700 miles
IHC	1600	1976	G	$2,100	3/06	SENE	16' box, hoist, 78,100 miles, gas
IHC	1700	1976	G	$2,900	3/06	NECO	Loadstar, 20' bed, swing end gate, rollover tarp, 404 gas engine, 5×2 speed, hyd. tag
IHC	1700	1981	F	$900	10/06	SEMN	12' bed
IHC	1700	1984	G	$4,000	3/06	ECIN	Dump truck, diesel, tandem axle
IHC	1724	1979	G	$7,700	2/06	WCKS	V-8 motor, 5×2 speed, 20' bed, hoist, roll tarp
IHC	1750		G	$4,500	11/06	SWCA	Dump truck, 5-6 yard box, IHC 466DT diesel
IHC	1754		G	$7,500	10/06	NCWI	Utility truck, diesel, single axle, post driver on flatbed
IHC	1754	1986	G	$11,500	2/06	WCSD	Service truck, 5-ton crane, PTO drive, air
IHC	1800	1986	G	$1,250	3/06	ECMI	Sweeper vac
IHC	1800	1986	G	$11,000	3/06	WCWA	4WD, cab & chassis, 5×2 speed
IHC	1850	1976	F	$4,000	9/06	WCND	Twin screw tender truck, 466 diesel, 13 speed, direct PTO, new leader 16-ton twin compartment
IHC	1850	1981	G	$14,000	11/06	SENE	Cargostar, single axle, cabover grain truck, 22' aluminum box, rear cargo doors, tie-down tarp, Detroit DT466 diesel engine, 5×2 speed, recent engine OH
IHC	1854	1980	G	$30,500	3/06	SWNE	Feed truck, Harsh 502-cc-foot feed wagon DT466 diesel, auto, double auger discharge, power booster brakes
IHC	1900	1986	G	$7,000	11/06	SCCA	Crane truck, Altec D845TB boom, 1 axle

Trucks

Make	Model	Year	Cond.	Price	Sale	Location	Comments
IHC	1924	1979	G	$9,200	12/06	SEND	Twin screw truck, V-8 gas engine, Allison auto, 20' Frontier box, hoist, roll tarp
IHC	1924	1980	F	$1,600	6/06	NEIN	Single-axle dump truck, snowplow
IHC	1955	1989	G	$15,250	1/06	WCIL	Middle single-axle semi, 143,339 miles, sold with 1993 Jet 22' single-hopper bottom trailer
IHC	2275	1979	F	$1,800	3/06	WCMN	Twin screw, 290 Cummins, 9 speed, PTO
IHC	2275	1979	F	$3,800	2/06	SCMI	Tandem semi tractor, 267,510 miles
IHC	2275	1981	F	$3,500	2/06	WCIL	S Series, road tractor, 855 Cummins, 13 speed, 312,500 miles
IHC	2375	1984	G	$23,500	4/06	WCMN	Twin screw, new 20' box and hoist, tarp in 1999, air seat, air, 581,918 miles, L10 Cummins, 9 speed
IHC	2574		G	$18,500	11/06	SCCA	Dump truck, M11 Cummins, Allison auto, 12' snowplow
IHC	2574		G	$21,000	11/06	SCCA	Dump truck, M11 Cummins, Allison auto, 12' snowplow
IHC	2574		G	$21,000	11/06	SCCA	Dump truck, M11 Cummins, Allison auto, 12' snowplow
IHC	2574		G	$21,000	11/06	SCCA	Dump truck, M11 Cummins, Allison auto, 12' snowplow
IHC	2575	1977	G	$6,750	11/06	SCCA	Dump truck, Cummins, 9 speed
IHC	2654	1991	G	$14,000	3/06	WCWA	Dump truck, Cummins 6 cyl., 10/12 yard
IHC	2674	1991	G	$10,500	11/06	SCCA	Dump truck, 8 speed
IHC	2674	1999	G	$28,000	9/06	NEIN	Tri-axle, Cummins diesel, 8 speed
IHC	2674	1999	G	$44,000	10/06	ECMO	Crane truck, 13 speed, diesel, air, 6 cyl.
IHC	4070		P	$700	6/06	WCMN	Cabover, 6V71 Detroit, 13 speed
IHC	4070		F	$2,100	3/06	NWIL	Transtar, diesel, 50K miles on OH, good tires
IHC	4070B	1983	G	$1,100	12/06	ECMN	Cab over, live PTO, hyd. for trailer
IHC	4300	1977	G	$3,100	3/06	ECIN	Tandem axle
IHC	4300	1979	G	$3,000	5/06	ECMI	Stake bed, 15' deck, diesel
IHC	4300	1979	G	$17,000	3/06	ECND	Twin screw, third axle pusher, air up/spring down, 855 Cummins, 9 speed, spring suspension, Frontier LCG 20' box, hoist, roll tarp, 3-piece end gate, twin fuel tanks
IHC	4300	1980	G	$19,500	12/06	ECNE	Transtar tandem-axle grain truck, twin screw, 20' steel box, 52" sides, Schwartz twin-cyl. hoist, Cummins 350 diesel engine, 9 speed
IHC	4300	1983	G	$11,500	11/06	ECND	Transtar tri-axle, front lift duals, 855 Cummins, 13 speed, PS, 24' box, hoist, roll tarp
IHC	4300	1984	G	$3,250	3/06	ECIN	9 speed
IHC	4370	1982	G	$4,200	4/06	SEND	Transtar, twin screw, 855 Cummins, 13 speed
IHC	4600		G	$11,250	3/06	ECIN	
IHC	4700		G	$19,000	1/06	WCOH	Dump truck
IHC	4700	1990	G	$2,000	10/06	ECMO	Cab & chassis, hyd. brakes
IHC	4700	1990	G	$20,000	7/06	WCCA	Diesel
IHC	4700	1991	G	$8,500	11/06	SCCA	
IHC	4700	1992	F	$3,500	11/06	NCKY	18' refrigerated boxes
IHC	4700	1993	G	$1,000	10/06	ECMO	2-ton
IHC	4700	1993	F	$3,600	11/06	NCKY	18' Johnson refrigerated box
IHC	4700	1993	G	$11,500	3/06	ECIN	Dump truck, DT466 diesel, new bed, single axle, 5 speed
IHC	4700	1995	G	$7,000	3/06	ECMI	Single-axle dump truck, 5×2 speed, set up for snow, no blade
IHC	4700	1996	G	$9,500	5/06	SWCA	Van truck, 24' box, diesel, 6-speed trans.
IHC	4700	1996	G	$58,500	1/06	NCCO	Harsh 425H feed box, 25K miles, diesel, one owner
IHC	4700	1998	G	$12,000	9/06	SECA	Bucket truck, diesel, 129,508 miles

Trucks

Make	Model	Year	Cond.	Price	Sale	Location	Comments
IHC	4700	1998	G	$13,000	9/06	NEIN	Dump truck, DT466 diesel, new bed, single axle
IHC	4700	1998	G	$16,000	3/06	WCWA	Dump truck
IHC	4700	1998	G	$34,000	10/06	WCGA	15-ton
IHC	4700	1998	G	$37,500	11/06	SECA	Bale retreiver truck, DT466 Allison 4-speed auto.
IHC	4700	1999	G	$6,200	10/06	WCMA	Van body, diesel, auto air, 22' body & lift gate
IHC	4700	2000	G	$13,500	7/06	WCPA	Dump truck, diesel, 7 speed, hyd. split brake system
IHC	4700	2000	G	$14,500	10/06	NCWI	Dump truck, IHC DT466E 190-hp. diesel, 6-speed trans., 10' steel body, single axle
IHC	4700	2000	G	$16,500	7/06	WCPA	Dump truck, diesel, 7 speed, hyd. split brake system
IHC	4700	2000	G	$18,000	9/06	NEIN	Single-axle dump truck, 10' Rogers bed, 6 speed
IHC	4700	2000	G	$19,000	1/06	WCOH	Diesel, 5-6 yard dump body
IHC	4700	2000	G	$19,000	1/06	WCOH	Diesel, 5-6 yard dump body
IHC	4700	2000	G	$34,000	1/06	WCNH	Boom truck, diesel, 15-ton boom
IHC	4800	1990	G	$6,500	9/06	NEIN	Digger derrick, DT466 Detroit diesel, 4WD, front winch
IHC	4800	2000	G	$25,000	10/06	WCMA	4WD winch truck, 5 speed, Braden bed winch w/ rem., 47,239 miles
IHC	4900		G	$4,750	5/06	SWCA	Van truck, 24' box, diesel, 5 speed, Maxon rail lift
IHC	4900		G	$9,000	3/06	ECND	Navistar truck
IHC	4900	1989	G	$32,600	1/06	NWKY	Diesel, tandem dump 20' box, new OH
IHC	4900	1990	G	$33,000	11/06	NCOH	Tandem-axle DT466 diesel, 10-speed trans.
IHC	4900	1991	G	$10,000	10/06	SWOH	Fuel/lube truck, single axle, diesel, 5-speed trans.
IHC	4900	1991	G	$15,500	2/06	SWOH	Diesel grain truck, 466 engine, single axle, 6 speed, air brakes, air ride seat, Midland 16' bed, hoist, cargo doors, roll tarp, 490,183 miles
IHC	4900	1991	G	$16,500	8/06	SWCA	
IHC	4900	1993	G	$5,750	8/06	SETN	24' flatbed
IHC	4900	1993	G	$15,500	3/06	WCWA	Single-axle dump truck, 6 speed, PS, 5-6 yard box
IHC	4900	1994	G	$6,500	3/06	ECMI	Single-axle dump truck, 5×2 speed, 10' dump box, turbo diesel, PS
IHC	4900	1995	G	$30,000	12/06	WCKS	Service truck, DT466 diesel engine, 7 speed, single axle, air brakes, quad cab, PTO, 18' service body, 450-gal. fuel tank, air compressor, air hookups, Lincoln wire welder, headache rack, AM/FM, 146,100 miles
IHC	4900	1996	G	$7,000	3/06	ECIN	
IHC	4900	1996	G	$10,800	8/06	SETN	Refrigerated, 466E diesel
IHC	4900	1996	G	$18,500	11/06	SCCA	41,860 miles, dump truck, 9 speed
IHC	4900	1999	G	$37,000	5/06	SWCA	Bucket truck, Hi-Ranger, 500-lb. capacity, 5-speed trans., toolboxes
IHC	4900	2000	G	$16,250	5/06	SWCA	24' box, diesel, Fuller 6-speed trans.
IHC	5000	1986	G	$9,750	9/06	ECMN	Quad axle, Cat 306 DT, Fuller 10 speed, 16' box
IHC	7100	1990	G	$19,500	2/06	ECKS	Single axle, diesel truck, 1997 Neville 24' grain trailer
IHC	7100	1992	G	$14,250	1/06	SCKS	4×2 single-axle truck tractor, 466 D turbo diesel, 220 hp., 7-speed trans., 130,000 actual miles, 285/75R245 tires, 136" wheelbase, chrome mud flaps, red color, shedded
IHC	8100	1990	G	$8,500	3/06	SESD	Day cab, twin screw, L10 Cummins, 9 speed
IHC	8100	1991	G	$26,500	3/06	ECND	Tri-axle, third axle trailing, L10 Cummins, 9 speed, 22' Midland unibody, headlift hoist

Trucks

Make	Model	Year	Cond.	Price	Sale	Location	Comments
IHC	8100	1994	E	$38,500	6/06	NWMN	Tri-axle, Cummins L10, low hole, 9 speed, lifting fore third axle, 20' Loadline beet-equipped box, hoist, roll tarp, rear controls
IHC	8100	1995	G	$16,000	3/06	WCWA	20' flatbed, Cummins 6 cyl., 10 speed
IHC	8100	1997	G	$26,500	5/06	SWCA	Dump truck, new 5-7 yard box, 10 speed trans.
IHC	8200	1992	G	$19,000	3/06	WCWA	Tandem-axle dump truck, Cummins 330 hp., 9 speed, 10-12 yd. box
IHC	9100	1999	G	$34,500	5/06	SWCA	Conventional day cab, 3 axle, 410 hp., Cat C12 diesel
IHC	9100	2003	G	$57,000	10/06	WCGA	111,901 miles, 10 speed
IHC	9200		F	$9,800	3/06	ECND	Navistar semi
IHC	9200		G	$10,200	3/06	ECND	Navistar semi
IHC	9200		G	$11,500	3/06	ECND	Navistar semi
IHC	9200		G	$13,000	3/06	ECND	Navistar semi
IHC	9200	1994	G	$6,500	3/06	ECIN	Cummins diesel
IHC	9200	1994	G	$15,000	3/06	ECIN	Day cab, Cummins L1 diesel, 330 hp., 175" wheelbase
IHC	9200	1994	G	$15,500	3/06	ECIN	Day cab, Cummins L1 diesel, 330 hp., 175" wheelbase
IHC	9200	1995	G	$10,250	12/06	WCKS	Cummins M11 diesel engine, 10 speed, 10K miles on new tranny & clutch, 32K miles on in-frame OH, AC, twin screw, air ride, air slide fifth-wheel plate, 230" wheelbase
IHC	9200	1995	F	$11,000	10/06	SWOH	Dump truck, Cummins M11 diesel, 10-speed trans.
IHC	9200	1995	G	$11,500	11/06	WCMN	Eagle, day cab, 60 Series Detroit, 430 hp., 10 speed, air ride, 760K miles, new head gasket & injector cups fall of 2006
IHC	9200	1995	G	$16,500	3/06	ECIN	Day cab, Cummins diesel, 330 hp.
IHC	9200	1996	G	$15,000	3/06	ECIN	Day cab, Cummins 330-hp. diesel, 193" wheelbase
IHC	9200	1997	E	$53,500	6/06	NWMN	Tri-axle, Cummins M11, low hole, 9 speed, lifting trailing third axle
IHC	9200	1998	G	$18,000	11/06	NEND	60 Series, 12.7L Detroit, 430/470 hp., Eaton Fuller 10 speed, 703,558 miles, 205" wheelbase, 24.5 rubber, aluminum fronts
IHC	9200	1999	G	$49,000	3/06	ECIN	Eagle quad axle
IHC	9200	1999	G	$49,000	3/06	ECIN	Eagle quad axle
IHC	9200	2000		$59,500	3/06	ECIN	
IHC	9300		G	$7,750	8/06	WCNC	876,599 miles
IHC	9300	1985	G	$3,100	9/06	ECMN	7 speed, tandem
IHC	9300	1988	G	$4,250	8/06	WCNC	
IHC	9300	1989	G	$7,750	11/06	WCMN	Eagle, day cab, Cummins, 355 hp., 9 speed, air ride, 75% rubber
IHC	9300	1991	G	$4,600	8/06	ECMN	Day cab, 400 Cummins, 9 speed, wet kit
IHC	9300	1991	G	$10,500	3/06	ECIN	Day cab
IHC	9300	1993	G	$8,000	12/06	WCKS	Eagle, 60 Series Detroit diesel engine, 10 speed, tandem axle, twin screw, air ride suspension, air slide fifth wheel plate, 238" wheelbase, 11R24.5 tires, aluminum front rims, steel rears, power divider, cruise, engine brake
IHC	9370	1987	G	$15,000	2/06	WCIL	Eagle semi, 400 Cat engine, Fuller 13-speed Roadranger trans., 60" sleeper, (2) 120-gal. tanks, air ride, 862K miles
IHC	9400		G	$13,000	3/06	ECND	Navistar semi
IHC	9400	1992	G	$5,000	11/06	SCCA	Cummins N14, 9 speed
IHC	9400	1993	G	$15,750	4/06	NWMN	Day cab, 400 Cummins, new motor, 9 speed, wet kit, 566,000 miles

WHAT'S IT WORTH?

Trucks

Make	Model	Year	Cond.	Price	Sale	Location	Comments
IHC	9400	1993	G	$22,500	3/06	ECMI	Tri-axle dump truck, 17' box, double frame, 330-hp. Cummins
IHC	9400	1994	G	$7,600	10/06	NCWI	60 Series Detroit 12.7 diesel, Jake, 435 hp., air ride suspension
IHC	9400	1995	E	$10,000	2/06	NWOH	Sleeper, 860K miles, tandem, Cummins N14, 13 speed, wet kit
IHC	9400	1995	G	$15,500	3/06	ECIN	400-hp. Cummins diesel, wet kit, 9 speed
IHC	9400	1995	G	$28,000	3/06	SWNE	Conventional grain truck w/ N14, 370 hp., Cummins, 10 speed, twin screw, tandem duals, 450 Aulick 1857 18'×56" steel box
IHC	9400	1998	G	$10,500	9/06	NEIN	Sleeper
IHC	9400	2006	E	$92,500	3/06	SEMN	Conventional, 450 hp., 13 speed, 238" wheelbase, air ride, cab/suspension, air slide fifth wheel, 72" skyrise sleeper, 4,025 actual miles, trans. warranty
IHC	9600	1990	G	$8,000	3/06	SWMN	Cabover, semi w/ 400 Cummins, 644,771 miles, 13-speed Eaton Fuller trans., Jake brake, sleeper, bud rims, air ride
IHC	9600	1993	F	$4,300	3/06	NWIL	Diesel, 614K miles, good tires
IHC	9670	1982	G	$12,500	11/06	NEND	Cabover twin screw, third-axle single pusher, air up/down, Cummins power, 9 speed, PS, 21' Magnum box, roll tarp, 3-piece end gate, pintle hitch
IHC	9670	1984	G	$3,400	4/06	SWIN	Cabover, road tractor, 350 Cummins, live tandem, 9 speed, 588K miles
IHC	9670	1984	F	$6,700	2/06	NCCO	Cabover, 9 speed, Peterson 20' steel box, twin screw, Cummins 350, rebuilt engine
IHC	9670	1984	G	$8,500	2/06	WCIL	Eagle, semi w/ 400 Cummins engine, Fuller 13-speed Road-ranger trans., sleeper, (2) 150-gal. tanks, air ride, 692K miles
IHC	Eagle	1979	G	$9,100	3/06	SEMN	Cabover, 8V92 Detroit diesel, 13-speed aluminum bud wheels, 157,016 miles
IHC	Eagle	1981	G	$4,750	3/06	SWMN	Cabover semi, 400 Cummins, 947,402 miles, 13-speed Eaton Fuller trans., bud rims
IHC	Eagle	1984	F	$4,000	9/06	WCIA	Cabover diesel truck, 400 Cummins, 13 speed, 720K miles, runs good
IHC	Eagle	1984	G	$4,250	6/06	NWKS	855 Cummins, 300 hp., 9 speed, Fuller 185" wheelbase, sleeper, air ride, 376,000 miles
IHC	Eagle	1984	G	$4,750	7/06	NWMN	Conventional, 250 Cummins, 13 speed, 48" sleeper, wet kit, air ride, 11×24.5 rears, twin fuel tanks
IHC	Eagle	1993	G	$9,000	12/06	ECIL	Day cab, 9 speed, L10-330 Cummins, 22.5 tires, 330,975 miles
IHC	Eagle	1996	F	$6,800	6/06	NCIA	Sleeper, N14 engine, 548K miles, 10 speed, air ride, air seat, 2 of them, each sold for $6,800
IHC	Eagle	1996	F	$6,800	6/06	NCIA	Sleeper, N14 engine, 548K miles, 10 speed, air ride, air seat, 2 of them, each sold for $6,800
IHC	Eagle	1997	G	$10,500	6/06	NCIA	Pro sleeper, N14 engine rebuilt 30,000 miles ago, 10 speed, air ride, air seat, 729,000 miles
IHC	F2275	1988	G	$3,800	9/06	SECA	3-axle diesel, 501,767 miles
IHC	F2554	1980	G	$5,500	10/06	SWOH	Dump truck, tandem axle, IHC diesel, auto, 13' steel dump box

Trucks

Make	Model	Year	Cond.	Price	Sale	Location	Comments
IHC	F2575	1980	G	$18,750	8/06	NCNE	Tandem-axle grain truck, air up/down, third axle,
							20' steel box, roll tarp, rear cargo doors
IHC	Loadstar		F	$600	1/06	SCMI	Gas, dump truck, 5-yard box, single axle
IHC	Loadstar		G	$2,250	11/06	SWCA	Dump truck, 3-5 yard box
IHC	Loadstar		G	$3,250	11/06	SWCA	Dump truck, 3-5 yard box
IHC	S1600		G	$3,000	11/06	SECA	Flatbed, 8-cyl. diesel
IHC	S1600	1985	G	$3,300	11/06	SCSD	6.9L, automatic, 27K miles, set up to pull gooseneck
IHC	S1600	1986	G	$7,000	2/06	SCMI	Nurse truck, 600-gallon tank, (2) 35-gal. inductor tanks,
							5 hp., hitch, box racks, storage box, pallet platform,
							59,418 miles
IHC	S1700	1985	F	$850	10/06	NCWI	Van truck, 9L diesel, PS, auto
IHC	S1800	1981	G	$5,500	3/06	NWKS	Bulk feed box
IHC	S1900		F	$750	1/06	WCCA	Flatbed DT466, 6 speed
IHC	S1900		G	$2,000	5/06	SWCA	Cab & chassis, diesel, 5-spd. trans
IHC	S1900	1982	G	$2,400	9/06	NEIN	Digger derrick, DT466 diesel, PTO, air brakes
IHC	S1900	1984	G	$3,000	7/06	WCCA	Flatbed, DT456
IHC	S1900	1984	G	$15,000	4/06	NWMN	Twin screw, 466 diesel, auto, combination beet, grain, and
							potato box w/ hoist and roll tarp, recent engine major OH,
							11×22.5 rubber
IHC	S1900	1985	G	$3,600	9/06	NEIN	Bucket truck, Detroit diesel, air brakes, 45' lift
IHC	S1900	1985	F	$3,900	4/06	NCKS	DT466, 10 speed
IHC	S1900	1985	G	$25,000	2/06	NECO	Aulick 2057 combination box, single and bottom racks,
							hyd. end gate 466 diesel engine, 13 speed, 59,421 miles
IHC	S1900	1985	G	$27,000	1/06	WCIL	Twin screw tandem, 20' Kahn aluminum bed, Allison auto,
							165,426 miles
IHC	S1900	1986	G	$15,000	5/06	SEND	Single-axle feed truck, DT466, Allison auto, 2 speed,
							115,000 miles
IHC	S1900	1987	G	$7,000	3/06	ECMI	Bucket truck, DT466 turbo, 55' Altec lift, 2-man bucket
IHC	S1954	1985	G	$2,500	7/06	WCCA	DT466 210 hp., aftercool diesel engine, Allison auto,
							141" wheelbase
IHC	S1954	1986	G	$7,750	3/06	ECIN	Dump truck, Cat 3208 diesel, 14' bed
IHC	S2200	1977	G	$12,750	11/06	NEND	Twin screw, Cummins power, 13 speed, 21' box,
							roll tarp
IHC	S2200	1984	G	$18,100	5/06	SEND	Twin screw, L10 Cummins, 9 speed, 20' Frontier box,
							hoist, roll tarp, 3-piece end gate
IHC	S2300	1987	G	$35,000	2/06	WCMN	Tri-axle, 300 Cummins, 22' steel box, roll tarp, head lift
							hoist, 9-speed trans.
IHC	S2500		G	$16,500	5/06	SWCA	4,000-gal. water truck, 315-hp. diesel, 9-speed trans.
IHC	S2500	1978	G	$7,500	2/06	NWKS	Semi truck, 180" wheelbase, 13-speed trans.,
							Cummins 350
IHC	S2500	1981	G	$5,500	9/06	SECA	10-yard dump truck, 361,295 miles
IHC	S2500	1982	F	$7,200	3/06	NCCO	Twin screw, 20' steel box
IHC	S2500	1984	F	$2,000	2/06	NWOH	Day cab, 278K miles, Cummins, single axle, 10 speed
IHC	S2500	1985	G	$2,350	3/06	ECMI	300 Cummins diesel, 13 speed, 18' bed, 10×20 tires, hitch,
							toolbox, fuel tank
IHC	S2500	1987	G	$3,300	12/06	ECMN	Dump, DT466, stick, 2 speed, 53,000 miles, reversible
							11' plow, wing
IHC	Transtar 2	1976	F	$5,000	2/06	NCCO	Semi, Cummins 350, 13 speed

WHAT'S IT WORTH?

Trucks

Make	Model	Year	Cond.	Price	Sale	Location	Comments
IHC	Transtar 2	1978	G	$6,500	3/06	NWKS	Grain truck, service body, 350 Cummins, 20' Scott steel box, cargo doors, 10 speed, harsh hoist, twin screw w/ tag axle, roll over tarp
Isuzu	NA	1991	G	$1,850	2/06	NWSD	2WD pickup
Isuzu	NA	1994	F	$700	1/06	WCCA	Pickup
Isuzu	NA	2000	G	$13,000	3/06	WCWA	Flatbed truck, 4-cyl. diesel, turbo, 6 speed, 12' dump
Isuzu	NA	2000	G	$16,000	5/06	SWCA	NPR van truck, 15' box, diesel, auto
Kenworth	K100		P	$600	11/06	NEND	Cabover, Cummins, 9 speed, spring ride
Kenworth	T2000	1999	G	$17,750	11/06	NCIN	Semi, 475K miles, 10-speed Eaton, Cummins N14, Aero sleeper
Kenworth	T300	2000	G	$29,000	3/06	WCWA	Tandem axle, Cummins 6 cyl., 13 speed, wet kit
Kenworth	T400		G	$5,500	5/06	SWCA	Cat diesel, Fuller 9 speed, wet kit
Kenworth	T400	1990	G	$11,500	3/06	ECNE	Conventional, day cab, Cummins L10 turbo diesel engine, 270 hp., Eaton Fuller 9-speed Roadranger trans., 307,080 miles
Kenworth	T450	1990	G	$23,500	3/06	ECMI	Quad-axle dump truck, 3306 Cat, 13 speed, 18' box, Hendrickson suspension, air double frame
Kenworth	T600	1986	G	$11,000	4/06	SEND	42" flat-top sleeper, 3406 Cat, 425 hp., 13 speed, air ride, sliding fifth wheel, 200" wheelbase, 895,000 miles
Kenworth	T600	1986	G	$25,000	12/06	WCKS	Straight truck, 855 Cummins diesel engine, 9-speed, tandem axle, twin screw, power divider, engine brake, PTO, air brakes, 20' steel box, hoist, cargo doors, 11R24.5 tires, aluminum front rims, steel rears
Kenworth	T600	1988	G	$2,200	8/06	ECMN	
Kenworth	T600	1988	G	$2,200	8/06	ECMN	9 speed, day cab, Jake brake
Kenworth	T600	1988	G	$8,500	3/06	WCMN	Day cab, 365 Cummins, 13 speed, spring ride, low-profile 24.5 rubber, aluminum fronts, wet kit, 162' cab/trunion
Kenworth	T600	1988	G	$9,500	3/06	WCMN	Day cab, 350 Cummins, 10-speed, air ride, 22.5 rubber on aluminum, wet kit, 148" cab/trunion
Kenworth	T600	1988	G	$11,000	3/06	WCMN	Day cab, 365 Cummins, 9-speed, air ride, low-profile 24.5 rubber, aluminum fronts, wet kit
Kenworth	T600	1988	G	$23,500	2/06	NWMN	Third axle air, up/down pusher, L10 Cummins, 9-speed, 21' box, hoist, roll tarp, combination gate
Kenworth	T600	1988	G	$24,500	4/06	NWMN	Twin screw, 855 Cummins, 13-speed, dual exhaust, air ride, 544,653 miles, Loadline 20' box, hoist, roll tarp, 3-piece end gate, plumbed for drill fill, 11×24.5 on steel, 11×24.5 on polished aluminum, steering axle
Kenworth	T600	1989	F	$0	3/06	NEKS	No sale at $13,000, 13 speed, Cat 425, recent OH
Kenworth	T600	1989	G	$8,250	3/06	WCMN	Day cab, 365 Cummins, 13 speed, air ride, low-profile 24.5 rubber, aluminum fronts, 160" cab/trunion, cruise
Kenworth	T600	1989	G	$11,000	11/06	SCCA	Cummins, 18' bed
Kenworth	T600	1992	G	$7,500	9/06	NEIN	Diesel, Cat 3406 engine, 13 speed
Kenworth	T600	1993	G	$9,250	10/06	NCWI	12.7 diesel, 400 hp., 13 speed, Kenworth 8-bag air ride suspension
Kenworth	T600	1994	g	$8,000	9/06	NEIN	8 speed
Kenworth	T600	1995	G	$9,000	12/06	ECMN	Day cab, tandem, Cat 3406 motor, 9-speed Eaton Fuller trans.
Kenworth	T600	1996	G	$11,500	12/06	ECMN	Red top, Cummins 460 hp., Super 10 Aerodyne cab & sleeper

Trucks

Make	Model	Year	Cond.	Price	Sale	Location	Comments
Kenworth	T600	1996	G	$20,750	1/06	NECO	400 Cummins, 10 speed, 765K miles
Kenworth	T600	1998	G	$13,250	12/06	ECMN	3406 Cat, 13 speed, sleeper
Kenworth	T600	1999	E	$28,500	12/06	WCMN	Aerocab, 475 hp., Detroit 60 Series, Super-10 speed, auto shift, 6 aluminum wheels, 495,000 miles, new injectors
Kenworth	T600	1999	E	$30,500	12/06	WCMN	Aerocab, 475 hp., Detroit 60 Series, Super-10 speed, auto shift, low-pro, 6 aluminum wheels, 495,000 miles
Kenworth	T600	1999	E	$30,500	12/06	WCMN	Aerocab, 475 hp., Detroit 60 Series, Super-10 speed, auto shift, 530,000 miles
Kenworth	T600A	1986	G	$11,750	5/06	NENE	Day cab, 623,932 miles, 350 Cummins, OH, 9 speed, air ride, 150-gal. fuel tanks
Kenworth	T600A	1989	G	$13,500	3/06	ECNE	Cat 3406B, 400-hp. diesel, rebuilt Roadranger RTO, 13 speed, 186" wheelbase, 42" flat-top sleeper, 956,400 miles, blue
Kenworth	T800	1991	G	$42,000	12/06	NEKS	Service truck, 12.7 Detroit diesel, 9 speed, 22' Seyller service body, 800-gal. fuel tank, hyd. air compressor, bulk oil, used oil recovery, twin screw, power divider, air ride, 673,324 miles
Kenworth	T800	1993	G	$15,000	2/06	NWMN	60 Series Detroit, 9 speed, air ride, wet kit, 22.5 rubber, 930K miles
Kenworth	T800	1993	G	$18,000	3/06	NEMI	Day cab, 425 Cat, 3406B, 13 speed, air ride, long frame, air plate, wet kit, 285/24.5 rubber
Kenworth	T800	1993	G	$40,000	4/06	WCMB	Canadian sale, tandem, inner axle
Kenworth	T800	1995	G	$15,500	4/06	NWMN	Twin screw, day cab, M11 Cummins, 9 speed, air ride, wet kit
Kenworth	T800	1995	G	$25,000	2/06	SWNE	Cat 3406, 426 hp., 15 speed, Eaton direct, 607,000 miles
Kenworth	T800	1995	G	$36,000	3/06	WCWA	Detroit 60 Series, 10 speed
Kenworth	T800	1995	G	$38,000	3/06	WCWA	Water truck, Detroit 60 Series 435 hp., 18 speed, hose reel, R&S spray
Kenworth	T800	1997	G	$10,500	8/06	SETN	Stand-up sleeper, 525 Cummins 13 speed, Jake brake
Kenworth	T800	1997	G	$35,000	9/06	NEIN	N14 Cummins, Aerocab, Jake brake, aluminum bud wheels
Kenworth	T800	1998	G	$25,000	11/06	SCND	950K miles, 200K miles on complete OH, Cat 430-hp. engine, 10 speed, super sharp, super serviced local truck
Kenworth	T800	2000	G	$45,000	3/06	WCWA	Tandem axle, 435 hp., 15 speed, air ride
Kenworth	T800	2005	G	$80,000	11/06	SCCA	Cat C15, 15 speed
Kenworth	T800B	2002	G	$135,000	3/06	WCWA	Tri-axle, Cat C16 600 hp., 18 speed, full lockers
Kenworth	W900		G	$10,500	5/06	SWCA	Conventional cab, 60" sleeper, Cummins diesel, Road-ranger 9 speed, air ride suspension, air sliding fifth wheel, Jacobs engine brake
Kenworth	W900	1981	F	$1,500	6/06	WCMN	8V92, Detroit 10 speed, single axle, day cab
Kenworth	W900	1983	G	$11,000	9/06	WCND	Conventional, 400 Cummins, 13 speed, 60" flat-top sleeper, air ride, 15' service body, 700-gal. fuel tank, PTO pump, hose reel, pintle hitch, rear air
Kenworth	W900	1995	G	$22,000	2/06	WCSD	3406E Cat, 375 hp., 10 speed, wet kit, 700K miles
Kenworth	W900	1997	G	$27,000	11/06	SCCA	Cummins N14, 18 speed
Kenworth	W900	1997	G	$27,500	10/06	NCWI	Cummins N14 diesel, 15 speed, aluminum fenders, aluminum toolbox, 200" wheelbase
Kenworth	W900B	1988	G	$8,000	11/06	NWMN	Conventional, 3406B, 15 speed, Jake brake, 60" flat-top bunk, air ride, air slide

Trucks

Make	Model	Year	Cond.	Price	Sale	Location	Comments
Kenworth	W900B	1994	G	$13,000	11/06	NWMN	Conventional, 3406 Cat, 13 speed 60" bunk, air ride, air slide, Jake brake
Kenworth	W900B	2001	G	$70,000	3/06	WCWA	Log truck, Cat C15 475 hp., 18 speed, 8'6" bunks, electric scales
Kenworth	W900L	1990	G	$16,000	9/06	WCND	Conventional special edition, 425 Cat, 18 speed, 60" Aerobunk, air ride, air slide, Jake, wet kit, headache rack, twin aluminum fuel tanks, 612K miles
Mack	CH613	1990	G	$8,500	12/06	ECMN	Mack 350, 13 speed, 566,605 miles, air ride, condo sleeper
Mack	CH613	1990	G	$21,000	9/06	NEIN	Tri-axle dump truck, Mack diesel, 9 speed, air tailgate, auto tarp
Mack	CH613	1994	G	$9,000	6/06	NEIN	Flat-top 47' sleeper, Jake brake, 201" wheelbase
Mack	CH613	1996	G	$9,500	3/06	ECIN	E7 427 diesel, walk-in sleeper, air ride
Mack	CH613	1996	G	$11,000	9/06	ECMN	E7 350, 9 speed, Mack rear end, bull guard
Mack	CH613	1996	G	$33,000	9/06	NEIN	Tri-axle dump truck, Mack 310 hp., 10 speed
Mack	CH613	1997	G	$2,250	10/06	SWOH	E7 diesel, Jake brake, 9-speed trans., PS, air, tandem axle
Mack	CH613	1998	G	$19,000	1/06	NWIL	Tractor, 10 speed, twin screw, day cab, air ride, 350K miles
Mack	CH613	1998	G	$22,000	9/06	NEIN	Diesel, wet kit, tandem axle
Mack	CH613	2000	G	$20,000	9/06	NEIN	Tandem axle, 6-speed trans.
Mack	CH613	2000	G	$27,000	10/06	SWOH	Dump truck, Jake brake, 9 speed
Mack	CL700	1996	G	$40,000	10/06	NCWI	Dump truck, Mack 350 diesel, 10 speed
Mack	CS300	1986	E	$7,000	8/06	ECNE	224K miles, 538-cubic-inch 6-cyl. turbo diesel, 6-speed overdrive synchronized trans., 27K miles on complete OH @ Mack dealer ($5800)
Mack	DM685	1978	G	$9,000	7/06	WCPA	Mack diesel, 6-speed low-hole trans.
Mack	DM685	1986	G	$11,000	9/06	NEIN	Tri-axle dump truck, 5 speed
Mack	DM685SX		G	$7,750	7/06	WCPA	237 Mack diesel, 6-speed low-hole trans., twin piston hoist, 55K rears, tandem axle
Mack	DM685SX		G	$8,500	7/06	WCPA	237 Mack diesel, 6-speed low-hole trans., twin piston hoist, 55K rears, tandem axle
Mack	R	1978	G	$3,600	3/06	SWMN	Day cab, 237 Mack, 5 speed, PTO
Mack	R	1979	G	$5,300	10/06	SENJ	
Mack	R	1984	G	$8,000	9/06	NEIN	Tandem axle, 330-hp. Mack diesel, new short block OH
Mack	R600	1977	G	$9,000	7/06	NWMN	Twin screw, 300 Mack, 5 speed, 21' Buffalo box, hoist, beet equipped
Mack	R600	1980	G	$2,500	8/06	ECMN	Day cab, 300 engine, good tires
Mack	R600	1980	G	$4,250	7/06	NWMN	Twin screw day cab, 237 Mack, 15 speed, wet kit, PS, 11×24.5 rears, 11×22.5 fronts, twin tanks
Mack	R685ST	1978	G	$5,500	12/06	NEMN	
Mack	R686	1980	G	$9,750	9/06	ECMN	Dump truck, 16' box, air up & down, 285 Mack, 2-stick tranny, rear-air supply
Mack	R686S	1985	G	$13,000	9/06	NEIN	Tri-axle dump body, Mack diesel, Maxitorque range trans., double frame
Mack	R686ST	1977	G	$1,500	12/06	NEMN	466,207 miles
Mack	R686ST	1987	F	$5,100	9/06	NEIN	Mack diesel, tandem axle
Mack	R688	1986	G	$11,000	3/06	ECIN	Dump truck, diesel, tandem axle, 18 speed
Mack	R688S	1991	G	$15,000	11/06	SCCA	Mack 350 hp., wet kit
Mack	RD685S	1988	G	$12,000	10/06	WCMA	Dump truck, Mack diesel, Maxitorque extension range, 5-7 yard body

Trucks

Make	Model	Year	Cond.	Price	Sale	Location	Comments
Mack	RS600L		G	$1,900	5/06	SWCA	Transit mixer, truck, 10-yard Challenger mixing drum, Mack 25 diesel engine, Fuller trans.
Mack	Superliner		G	$9,000	5/06	SWCA	Dump truck, 10-12 yd, 350 hp. Cummins diesel, 13-speed trans.
Mack	Superliner	1979	G	$1,800	12/06	ECMN	5×2 speed trans., tandem axle, rear end & clutch rebuilt
Mack	Superliner	1988	G	$12,000	9/06	NEIN	Tri-axle dump truck, 300-hp. Mack diesel, Aerospring tarp
Mack	Superliner	1991	G	$9,100	10/06	SENJ	
Peterbilt	349	1987	G	$10,900	12/06	NEKS	3306 Cat diesel, 9 speed, tandem axle, twin screw, 22' steel box w/ 63" sides, cargo doors, Harsh RL112 hoist
Peterbilt	357	1990	G	$35,000	3/06	NEND	Tri-axle, air up/down pusher, Magnum 22' box, roll tarp, 350 Cummins big cam, 832 hours on engine & trans. OH, hd Allison automatic, 2 air ride seats, spring suspension
Peterbilt	359		G	$4,500	5/06	SWCA	Conventional cab, 3 axle
Peterbilt	359	1981	G	$4,500	11/06	NWMN	Conventional, Cat 3406, 15 speed, air ride, wet kit, PTO w/ 18' twin compartment drill fill, nonplug augers, side chutes
Peterbilt	362		G	$10,000	5/06	ECMI	Tri-axle, aluminum wheel, Cat diesel engine, 10-speed trans.
Peterbilt	362	1985	G	$4,000	5/06	ECMI	Cat engine, air dry, Dual axle
Peterbilt	375	1991	G	$7,700	3/06	SEND	Day cab, 3176 Cat, 9 speed, spring suspension, fixed plate, aluminum fuel tank
Peterbilt	377	1988	F	$6,750	3/06	NWKS	350 Cummins, 9 speed, air ride, 48" sleeper
Peterbilt	377	1989	G	$12,250	12/06	NEKS	855 big cam Cummins diesel, 9 speed, tandem axle, twin screw, 22' steel box w/ 63" sides, cargo doors, Harsh RL112 hoist, spring ride, AC, 829,678 miles
Peterbilt	377	1992	F	$8,250	3/06	NWKS	425 Cat, 10 speed, air ride, 60" sleeper, engine OH 3 years ago
Peterbilt	377	1994	G	$8,750	12/06	NEKS	12.7 Detroit diesel, 9 speed, tandem axle, twin screw, power divider, air slide fifth-wheel plate, air ride, 11R22.5 tires, steel rims, 675,524 miles
Peterbilt	377	1994	G	$16,000	2/06	SEKS	60 Series Detroit, 13 speed
Peterbilt	377	1994	G	$16,500	12/06	WCKS	3406E Cat diesel engine, 13 speed, tandem axle, twin screw, power divider, engine brake, cruise, power mirrors, 11R24.5 tires, all aluminum rims, air ride suspension, dual exhaust, air, heat
Peterbilt	377	1995	G	$10,000	12/06	WCKS	60 Series Detroit diesel engine, super 10-speed trans., tandem axle, twin screw, power divider, 11R22.5 tires, aluminum front rims, steel rears, air slide fifth-wheel plate, air ride suspension, Unibilt sleeper, AM/FM radio, cruise
Peterbilt	377	1995	G	$14,500	12/06	WCKS	60 Series Detroit diesel engine, 10 speed, tandem axle, twin screw, air ride suspension, 11R24.5 tires, aluminum front rims, steel rears, dual aluminum fuel tanks, engine brake, cruise, 640,660 miles
Peterbilt	377	1996	G	$34,500	4/06	SEND	Tri-axle, 3176 Cat, 365 hp., 13 speed, air ride, air cruise, 22' Frontier box, roll tarp
Peterbilt	377	1998	G	$37,500	3/06	WCWA	Water truck, Cat C10 365 hp.
Peterbilt	377	1999	G	$19,500	11/06	SWCA	Cat C12 diesel, 420 hp., air ride suspension
Peterbilt	378		G	$17,500	5/06	SWCA	Cummins diesel, Eaton Fuller 13 speed, engine brakes
Peterbilt	378	1990	G	$13,500	3/06	WCWA	Cat 3406E, 13 speed, air ride, air slide fifth

Trucks

Make	Model	Year	Cond.	Price	Sale	Location	Comments
Peterbilt	378	1998	G	$21,250	3/06	SEIA	500 Detroit engine, 10-speed trans., aluminum wheels, 63" stand-up sleeper, 782,500 miles
Peterbilt	378	2000	G	$35,000	5/06	SWCA	Conventional day cab, diesel, Fuller 10 speed
Peterbilt	378	2001	G	$47,000	3/06	WCWA	Tri-axle, Cummins 475 hp., 15 speed
Peterbilt	378	2001	G	$47,500	3/06	WCWA	Tri-axle, Cummins 475 hp., 15 speed, cab guard
Peterbilt	378	2001	G	$47,500	3/06	WCWA	Tri-axle, Cummins, 475 hp., 15 speed
Peterbilt	378	2001	G	$49,500	3/06	WCWA	Tri-axle, Cummins 475 hp., 15 speed
Peterbilt	379		G	$11,000	8/06	ECMN	
Peterbilt	379		G	$13,500	5/06	SWCA	3 axle, Cummins 365 diesel, Eaton Fuller 9-speed trans., wet kit, air ride
Peterbilt	379		G	$17,000	5/06	SWCA	3 axle, conventional cab, Cat diesel, Eaton Fuller 18 speed
Peterbilt	379	1982	G	$9,500	11/06	ECND	Flat-top sleeper, Cummins engine, 9 speed, PS, 584,421
Peterbilt	379	1982	G	$9,500	11/06	ECND	Flat-top sleeper, Cummins engine, 9 speed, PS, 609,300 miles
Peterbilt	379	1987	F	$9,000	3/06	NWKS	425 Cat, 310 hp., 9 speed, air ride, 42" sleeper
Peterbilt	379	1989	G	$11,750	2/06	SEKS	Cat, 475 hp., 13 speed
Peterbilt	379	1992	G	$16,000	12/06	NEKS	Extended hood, 3406 Cat diesel, 15 speed, twin screw, air ride, air slide fifth-wheel plate, AC, power divider, dual exhaust, 11R24.5 tires, aluminum rims
Peterbilt	379	1993	G	$11,000	8/06	ECMN	Extended engine work
Peterbilt	379	1994	G	$12,750	9/06	ECMN	N14, Eaton Fuller, 250" wheelbase
Peterbilt	379	1994	G	$15,750	3/06	NWKS	Long hood, 475 Cat, 10 speed, air ride, 60" sleeper, 24.5 tires, aluminum wheels
Peterbilt	379	1995	G	$29,000	10/06	NCWI	Detroit 12.7 diesel, 470 hp., 15 speed, PS, hyd. wet kit, aluminum headache rack, fenders aluminum
Peterbilt	379	1996	G	$25,000	12/06	NEKS	Extended hood, 3406 Cat diesel, 430 hp., 18 speed, tandem axle, twin screw, power divider, air slide fifth-wheel plate, air ride, 11R24.5 tires, all aluminum rims, dual exhaust, AC, 1,208,747 miles
Peterbilt	379	1996	E	$36,000	2/06	NWSD	Semi truck, 3406 Cat motor, 455 hp., 15-speed Eaton-Fuller, 60" stand-up Unibilt sleeper, very clean, 735K miles
Peterbilt	379	1997	G	$23,000	3/06	NWKS	Short hood, 475 Cat, 15 speed, 60" sleeper, 24.5 tires, aluminum wheels
Peterbilt	379	1998	G	$15,500	10/06	SWOH	475 hp., diesel, Jake, Fuller 10 speed
Peterbilt	379	1999	G	$19,000	12/06	WCKS	60 Series Detroit diesel engine, 10 speed, tandem axle, twin screw, power divider, air ride suspension, engine brake, dual exhaust, cruise, tilt, 11R24.5 tires, outside aluminum rims, air ride seat, air, heat
Peterbilt	379	1999	G	$20,000	12/06	WCKS	60 Series Detroit diesel engine, 10 speed, tandem axle, twin screw, power divider, air ride suspension, engine brake, dual exhaust, cruise, tilt, 11R24.5 tires, outside aluminum rims, air ride seat, air, heat
Peterbilt	379	1999	G	$21,000	12/06	WCKS	60 Series Detroit diesel engine, 10 speed, tandem axle, twin screw, power divider, air ride suspension, engine brake, dual exhaust, cruise, tilt, 11R24.5 tires, outside aluminum rims, air ride seat, AM/FM, air, heat

Trucks

Make	Model	Year	Cond.	Price	Sale	Location	Comments
Peterbilt	379	1999	G	$27,000	12/06	NEKS	Detroit 500-hp. Series 60 diesel engine, Super-10 speed, twin screw, AM/FM, AC, 60" sleeper, air slide fifth wheel, aluminum wheels, dual chrome stacks, clutch work, Texas bumper, 815K miles
Peterbilt	379	1999	G	$28,500	12/06	NEKS	550-hp. Cat diesel engine (in frame OH at 700K miles), Super-10 speed, twin screw, AM/FM, air, 60" sleeper, aluminum wheels, dual chrome stacks, Texas bumper, 1,013,128 miles
Peterbilt	379	1999	G	$28,500	12/06	NEKS	Cat 3406 diesel engine (240K miles on in frame OH), Super-10 speed, AM/FM, AC, 60" sleeper, air slide fifth wheel, aluminum wheels, 900K miles
Peterbilt	379	1999	G	$29,500	12/06	WCKS	60 Series Detroit diesel engine, 13 speed, tandem axle, twin screw, power divider, air ride suspension, engine brake, dual exhaust, cruise, tilt, 11R24.5 tires, outside aluminum rims, air ride seat, air, heat
Peterbilt	379	1999	G	$29,500	12/06	WCKS	C12 Cat diesel engine, 13 speed, tandem axle, twin screw, power divider, air ride suspension, engine brake, dual exhaust, cruise, tilt, 11R24.5 tires, outside aluminum rims, air ride seat, air, heat
Peterbilt	379	1999	G	$29,750	12/06	WCKS	60 Series Detroit diesel engine, 10 speed, tandem axle, twin screw, power divider, air ride suspension, engine brake, dual exhaust, cruise, tilt, 11R24.5 tires, outside aluminum rims, air ride seat, air, heat
Sterling	LT9500	1999	G	$36,000	10/06	WCFL	Dump truck, CC10 Cat diesel
Sterling	NA	1997	G	$26,500	12/06	SEND	Grain truck, 8.3 Cummins 300 hp., 9-speed trans., Chalmers suspension, 4:10 gears, new 20' Loadline box, headlift hoist, roll tarp, rear lift controls, 300K miles
Sterling	NA	1999	G	$92,500	5/06	ECMI	Terex Model TC 4792, 23-ton boom truck crane, diesel, 13,622 miles
Sterling	NA	2000	G	$27,750	5/06	SWCA	Conventional cab, 48" sleeper, 3 axle, Cat diesel, Fuller 10 speed
Terex	3066C		G	$50,000	10/06	WCFL	Articulated haul truck, 6×6, diesel, cab
Terex	TA25		G	$55,000	10/06	WCFL	Articulated haul truck, 6×6, cab
Terex	TA30	2000	G	$82,500	10/06	WCFL	Articulated haul truck, 6×6, Cummins M11 diesel
Terex	TA30	2001	G	$82,500	10/06	WCFL	Articulated haul truck, 6×6, Cummins M11 diesel
Terex	TA30	2002	G	$70,000	9/06	NEIN	Haul truck, diesel, 3,525 hours
Volvo	A25		G	$26,250	9/06	NEIN	Allison trans.
Volvo	A25	1989	G	$26,250	9/06	NEIN	Haul truck, 213 hp., Allison trans.
Volvo	A35C		G	$44,000	9/06	NEIN	Haul truck, rear gates
Volvo	F7	1987	G	$2,200	12/06	ECMN	Cab over, new tires
Western Star	4964F	1998	E	$50,000	6/06	NCPA	4964, Cat 425 hp., 8 speed, engine brake, Hendrickson suspension, 4.56 ratio, 24.5 tires, good rubber, all aluminum wheels, tri-axle, 20,000-lb. front axle, 46,000-lb. rear, in frame @ 60K miles
Western Star	NA		F	$2,500	7/06	WCPA	Heavy hauler truck, Cummins diesel, 24 speed
Western Star	NA	1987	G	$4,250	1/06	WCCA	3 axle
Western Star	NA	1991	G	$10,000	9/06	NEND	Semi tractor, walk-in sleeper, 3406 Cat, 13 speed, excellent rubber, aluminum wheels, new rod bearings
Western Star	NA	1992	G	$15,500	9/06	ECMN	82,500 miles, 55' working height, crane, 4 outriggers

WHAT'S IT WORTH?

Miscellaneous
Equipment

Cattle Equipment

Make	Model	Year	Cond.	Price	Sale	Location	Comments
Apache	NA		G	$700	11/06	SEIA	Creep feeder
Apache	NA		G	$1,375	8/06	NCMI	Portable creep feeder, 150-bu. capacity
Big Valley	NA		F	$45	3/06	ECNE	10' entrance panel w/ 4' gate
Big Valley	NA		F	$60	3/06	ECNE	(3) 12' corral panels
Big Valley	NA		F	$70	3/06	ECNE	(16) corral panels
Bowman	NA		G	$100	3/06	SWNE	Dipping vat
Daniels	NA		G	$850	3/06	SWNE	Daniels & Besler portable loading chute
Easy Way	NA		G	$4,100	4/06	WCMB	Canadian sale, 14' cattle self-feeder
Farm Master	NA		G	$80	3/06	NCOK	Feed bunk, plastic bottom
Farm Master	NA	2000	G	$1,800	11/06	NEIA	80-bu. creep feeder
Farnan	NA		F	$100	5/06	SCMI	Squeeze chute, hoof trimmer
Foremost	NA		G	$420	3/06	SEND	Self-catching headgate
Lynn	NA		G	$4,000	8/06	NCMI	Linn Mfg. custom-size hd bison squeeze chute, Digistar electric scale option and inspection panels
Miami	NA		G	$1,050	8/06	NCMI	Portable creep feeder, 250-bu. capacity, w/ panels, 3 sold @ $1,050 each
Miami	NA		G	$1,050	8/06	NCMI	Portable creep feeder, 250-bu. capacity, w/ panels, 3 sold @ $1,050 each
Miami	NA		G	$1,050	8/06	NCMI	Portable creep feeder, 250-bu. capacity, w/ panels, 3 sold @ $1,050 each
Mister Squeeze	NA		G	$1,000	4/06	ECND	Livestock chute
My-D Han-D	NA		G	$115	3/06	WCKS	Headgate for cattle chute
Palco	NA		G	$450	11/06	SEIA	Alleyway
Palco	NA		G	$800	8/06	NCIA	Self-closing head chute
Palco	NA		G	$825	8/06	NCIA	Self-closing head chute
Palco	NA		G	$2,100	11/06	SEIA	Working tub
Palco	NA		G	$2,800	11/06	SEIA	Headgate w/ scale
Pearson	NA		G	$1,850	11/06	SCNE	Squeeze chute
Powder River	NA		G	$425	1/06	WCNE	Cattle chute, head, catch, manual
Powder River	NA		G	$475	1/06	WCNE	Cattle chute, calf table
Powder River	NA		G	$1,500	2/06	NECO	Cattle chute
Powder River	N/A		G	$1,600	1/06	WCNE	Portable loading chute
Powder River	NA		G	$1,725	3/06	SEND	Squeeze chute
Pride of Farm	NA		G	$75	4/06	WCSD	Creep feeder
Rancher's Pride	NA		G	$800	8/06	NEKS	Creep feeder on cart
Rancher's Pride	NA		G	$800	8/06	NEKS	Creep feeder on cart
Sioux	NA		E	$160	3/06	NCOK	Round bale hay feeder
Sioux	NA		E	$160	3/06	NCOK	Round bale hay feeder
Sioux	NA		E	$165	3/06	NCOK	Round bale hay feeder
Sioux	NA		E	$165	3/06	NCOK	Round bale hay feeder
Sioux	NA		G	$665	3/06	SEND	(7) corral panels; $95 each
Sioux	NA		G	$963	3/06	SEND	(11) corral panels; $87.50 each
Sioux	NA		G	$1,900	11/06	SEIA	10'×19' calving pen
Two-W	NA		G	$4,000	8/06	NCMI	Portable livestock corral, 27 gates and panels, makes 60'×60' corral
Vern's	NA		G	$250	3/06	SEND	16.5' steel feed bunks
Vern's	NA		G	$250	3/06	SEND	16.5' steel feed bunks
Vern's	NA		G	$1,175	3/06	SEND	Creep feeder

WHAT'S IT WORTH?

Cattle Equipment

Make	Model	Year	Cond.	Price	Sale	Location	Comments
Vern's	NA		G	$1,175	3/06	SEND	Creep feeder
WW	NA		F	$250	11/06	SCNE	Squeeze chute

Drags

Make	Model	Year	Cond.	Price	Sale	Location	Comments
Brandt	5000	2003	E	$11,000	3/06	NEND	Contour Commander heavy harrow, 50', hyd. tine adjustable, large cart wheels, 5 rank
Brillion	24'		G	$800	3/06	NEMI	Transport folding field drag
Degelman	70'		E	$15,500	3/06	NCND	Strawmaster 70' hd harrow, adjustable pitch, flotation tires, new 9⁄16" hd teeth
DMI	24'		G	$3,600	3/06	NCIN	Crumbler, single rolling basket harrow, pt
DMI	28'		G	$4,200	3/06	NENE	Hydraulic fold crumbler
DMI	30'		G	$2,900	3/06	NWMN	Crumbler, adjustable pole
DMI	45'		G	$4,250	3/06	NEND	Crumbler, adjustable pole
DMI	45'	2003	E	$8,300	4/06	ECND	Case IH 45' crumbler, hyd. fold, adjustable pole
DMI	50'		G	$9,750	3/06	SWMN	Crumbler, triple fold
DMI	50'	1997	E	$9,000	2/06	WCMN	Crumbler
DMI	50'	2006	E	$12,500	12/06	WCMN	Crumbler, new
DMI	N/A		G	$3,500	3/06	NEIA	22.5' crumbler
Dunham	16'		F	$875	1/06	NCCO	Harrow, hd
Dunham	20'		G	$1,400	3/06	NCCO	Dunham Lehr hd harrow
Dunham	22'		F	$1,300	2/06	NCCO	Harrow, hd
Dunham	24'		F	$600	9/06	NECO	Roller harrow, pt, solid front, crow rear
Flexi-Coil	65'		G	$1,550	4/06	SEND	Hyd. harrow
Flexi-Coil	85		G	$3,100	4/06	NCSD	Harrow, 50'
Flexi-Coil	85	1995	G	$11,000	4/06	WCMN	Canadian sale, heavy harrows, 50', 20" tine teeth
Fuerst	35'		G	$700	12/06	NEMO	Harrow
Fuerst	NA		G	$350	6/06	NECO	8'-tine drag
Fuerst	NA		G	$2,300	9/06	SCNE	10'×8' harrow
Herman	42'		G	$1,900	4/06	WCSD	Harrow, all new teeth
Herman	55'		G	$450	3/06	ECND	Harrow, 500-gal. tank, 5-bar harrow
Herman	60'		F	$450	4/06	NEND	Hyd. fold harrow
Herman	60'		G	$700	4/06	NEND	Hyd. fold
Herman	60'		G	$1,150	4/06	NWMN	Harrow
Herman	98'		G	$1,600	3/06	NEND	Hyd. fold harrow, adjustable sections, tanks, hyd. pump
IHC	310		G	$650	1/06	ECNE	5 section, hyd. cart
John Deere	200	2005	E	$9,000	12/06	WCMN	Crumbler, 38.5'
Lindsay	20'		G	$400	3/06	NCIL	Hyd. drag cart
Lindsay	24'		G	$685	1/06	NWIL	Harrow and cart
Lindsay	40'		G	$1,450	2/06	ECMN	7-section steel lever drag on hyd. cart
Lindsay	60'		F	$400	9/06	NWMN	Harrow, spray attachment
Lindsay	NA		G	$1,300	6/06	SCMN	7-section steel lever drag on a hd cart
McFarland	22'		G	$450	9/06	NWIL	Harrow
McFarland	24'		G	$1,750	2/06	NWIL	Longfellow drag, 24', 8 bars, hyd. lift

Drags

Make	Model	Year	Cond.	Price	Sale	Location	Comments
McFarland	30'		G	$1,750	3/06	NWIL	30'
McFarland	60'		G	$10,750	12/06	SEND	60' harrow, low acres
McFarlane	26'		G	$4,000	3/06	NCIL	Drag cart, 8-bar spike tooth
McFarlane	28'		F	$350	3/06	NEMI	Folding fence harrows, cart
McFarlane	28'		G	$3,000	3/06	NCIL	8-bar spike drag
McFarlane	30'		G	$1,900	8/06	NWIL	Harrow
McFarlane	32'		G	$6,900	12/06	NWIL	5-bar harrow
Melroe	35'		F	$75	5/06	SEND	Hydraulic harrow
Melroe	35'		F	$160	5/06	SEND	Harrow
Melroe	403		G	$1,500	3/06	SWMN	60', 12-section spring tooth drag
Melroe	403		G	$1,850	3/06	NWMN	Hyd. fold harrow, 60'
Melroe	45'		F	$450	3/06	ECND	Harrow, hyd. fold
Melroe	45'		G	$1,050	4/06	NWMN	Hyd. harrow
Melroe	45'		G	$1,100	4/06	WCMN	Drag, hyd. cart
Melroe	45'	1980	G	$390	3/06	SEND	Hyd. harrow
Melroe	450		G	$400	8/06	WCMN	30', 3 bar, hd sections
Melroe	48'		F	$400	9/06	NWMN	Harrow
Melroe	55'		F	$350	7/06	NWMN	Hyd. fold harrow
Melroe	55'		F	$500	4/06	NWMN	Harrow cart, hd Summers adjustable sections
Melroe	60'		F	$400	7/06	NWMN	Hyd. fold harrow, Boss sections
Melroe	60'		G	$1,050	4/06	NWMN	Cart, Summers adjustable sections
Noble	24'		G	$175	2/06	WCNE	3-8', 2 bar, rear attachments
Noble	24'		G	$250	2/06	WCNE	Spring tooth, 3 bar, folding
Noble	60'		G	$400	2/06	NWKS	Jumbo cultimatic spring tooth
Pepin	NA		G	$2,600	3/06	WCMN	66' cart, Melroe spring tooth drag section
Phillips	NA		G	$4,000	10/06	NCND	Rotary harrow, 43', hyd. fold, one owner
Phillips	NA		G	$15,500	12/06	ECMO	30' rotary harrow
Remlinger	24'		G	$1,050	2/06	NWIL	Hyd. fold harrow
Summers	50'		G	$2,250	11/06	NWMN	Hyd. adjustable 3-rank Danish, 5-bar adjustable harrow, 1,000-gal. tank, pump
Summers	60'		E	$4,600	6/06	SCMN	
Summers	60'		G	$5,200	6/06	ECND	Super harrow, hyd fold, ½" tines
Summers	67'		F	$500	7/06	NEND	Hyd. fold harrow
Summers	70'		G	$1,900	9/06	NWMN	Harrow, 5-bar adjustable sections, late model, very nice
Summers	72'		G	$13,000	4/06	NEND	Super harrow, 9/16" tooth, hyd. pressure down
Summers	72'	1995	G	$15,750	3/06	ECND	Super harrow plus, hyd. angle adjustable hyd. frame up/down
Summers	72'	1996	G	$12,000	11/06	ECND	Super harrow, 9/16" shank, 1 season
Unverferth	20'		E	$5,600	2/06	SEMI	Hyd. fold rolling harrow, roll baskets
Unverferth	230		E	$14,500	2/06	SEKS	42' rolling harrow, like new
Unverferth	25'		G	$3,800	2/06	NCIN	Double rolling basket harrow
Unverferth	26'	1998	G	$4,100	2/06	NWIN	Rolling harrow
Unverferth	36'		G	$6,000	2/06	SEKS	Rolling harrow
Western	56'		G	$400	9/06	NEND	Hyd. harrow
Wilrich	35'		G	$6,500	12/06	SCMN	Crumble

WHAT'S IT WORTH?

Feed Wagons

Make	Model	Year	Hrs.	Cond.	Price	Sale	Location	Comments
BJM	C900T			G	$7,200	5/06	SEND	Mixer feeder, single axle, hyd. gate & chute, electric scale, 540 PTO, relined in 2000, right-hand hyd. fold discharge, creep feed auger, flotation & road tires
Blair	NA			G	$600	3/06	NEKS	
Brady	10'			F	$525	1/06	NECO	4×10, pt, PTO
Butler	1830			F	$300	8/06	NCMI	Ensilamixer feed cart
Gehl	7190			F	$2,200	1/06	NEIN	Mix wagon
Gehl	7190			F	$3,100	4/06	WCSD	540 PTO
Gehl	7210			G	$4,000	2/06	NWOH	Scales
Gehl	BF190			F	$300	2/06	WCNE	5'×10', pt, PTO
H&S	20'			P	$800	11/06	NEIA	
H&S	20'			F	$1,250	8/06	NEIA	Silage inserts
H&S	20'			G	$1,800	11/06	NEIA	
Haybuster	256			G	$4,750	11/06	SEIA	Feeder
Henke	160			F	$3,900	4/06	NENE	Mixer-feeder wagon, digital scale
Kelly Ryan	4×10			F	$50	3/06	ECNE	Shedded
Kelly Ryan	4×10			F	$200	11/06	SWIA	
Kelly Ryan	4×8			G	$1,100	8/06	NEKS	540 PTO
Kelly Ryan	5×10			F	$110	3/06	ECNE	
Kelly Ryan	5×12			F	$700	3/06	SEND	Single-axle bunk feeder, 540 PTO
Kelly Ryan	5×12			G	$1,800	3/06	ECNE	10:00-20 tires
Kelly Ryan	5×14			G	$2,900	11/06	SCNE	
Knight	3030	2002		E	$11,000	2/06	SCNY	TMR
Knight	3030	2003		G	$11,000	1/06	NENE	540 PTO, 3-auger discharge, scale, pt
Knight	3300			G	$7,500	11/06	SCND	Mixer feed wagon, Weigh-Tronix 715 digital scale
Oswalt	250			G	$7,500	8/06	SCNE	Pt
Oswalt	250	1998		G	$11,000	12/06	WCIA	No scale, 4 augers
Pequea	520			G	$1,500	8/06	SEPA	Round bale feeder wagon
Rissler	450		1,275	G	$1,200	3/06	NEMI	Self-propelled feed cart, scales, 8-hp. Honda motor
Schuler	125			E	$500	3/06	NEIA	
Schuler	125			F	$2,250	3/06	NWIL	
Schuler	175			G	$5,000	12/06	SEIA	175BF, single axle
Schuler	354			G	$15,000	9/06	SWIA	SRM 354 remix complete w/ 2-scale readouts, remote display, all new bearings & chains, A1 condition
Schwartz	NA			P	$200	2/06	WCNE	5'×10', PTO, pt, for parts
Schwartz	130			F	$300	3/06	NENE	4'×12'
SI	NA			G	$3,050	10/06	SEMN	24'

Generators

Make	Model	Year	Hrs.	Cond.	Price	Sale	Location	Comments
Ag Tronic	27P1			G	$650	2/06	WCNE	21 KW generator, PTO, 110V
Coleman	4000 watt			G	$380	11/06	NCKS	Used very little
Cummins	NA			G	$1,500	9/06	ECMN	75 KW, fuel cell
Detroit	NA			G	$800	8/06	SCFL	12 KW
Detroit	NA			G	$2,400	8/06	SCFL	12 KW
Generac	40 KW			G	$1,700	1/06	SCMI	PTO generator, cart
Generac	40 KW			G	$2,200	3/06	SEPA	40/80 KW generator on cart, PTO

Generators

Make	Model	Year	Hrs.	Cond.	Price	Sale	Location	Comments
Homelite	4400			F	$150	3/06	NWKS	LR4400
John Deere	276			G	$4,200	3/06	ECNE	276D diesel power unit on cart, 65 hp., radiator, clutch, new complete engine OH 2005
John Deere	4045T	2005	401	E	$7,600	3/06	ECNE	Diesel power unit on cart, radiator, clutch, like new
John Deere	6059			G	$3,900	3/06	ECNE	6059D diesel power unit
Katolight	25 KW			G	$1,000	8/06	NCIA	PTO on cart
Katolight	25 KW			G	$3,200	12/06	WCMI	PTO drive
Katolight	35 KW			G	$1,900	9/06	WCWI	Alternator, running gear
Katolight	55 KW			G	$1,300	9/06	NEND	PTO alternator on trailer
Katolight	55 KW			G	$2,850	8/06	NCIA	On cart
Lima	10 KW			G	$3,250	8/06	SCMI	10 KW, Deutz power unit
Onan	15 KW			G	$600	1/06	NECO	62.5A, PTO
Onan	6 KW			G	$400	9/06	WCND	4-wheel light plant, 6 KW, aux. lights, quick disconnect
Pincor	20 KW			F	$1,400	3/06	NWOH	PTO drive on cart
Pincor	50 KW			G	$1,450	4/06	NWKS	PTO on trailer
Winco	12 KW			F	$2,000	8/06	SCMI	Deutz power unit
Winco	15 KW			G	$1,300	6/06	SEND	PTO, 540/1,000 PTO shaft
Winco	17KW			G	$1,600	10/06	SENJ	Tow-behind
Winco	20 KW			F	$550	3/06	NCWI	PTO on transport
Winco	20 KW			G	$950	1/06	SCNE	Maxi-Watt PTO, continuous watts
Winco	30 KW			F	$650	8/06	NEKS	20/30 KW, 540 PTO-powered on cart, Lincoln gas arc welder runs (but not working)
Winco	45 KW			G	$3,200	11/06	ECND	3-phaser
Winco	45 KW	2000		E	$3,500	3/06	NCND	PTO
Winco	NA			G	$600	3/06	ECNE	3-phase 440V
Winco	NA			G	$700	3/06	SEND	540 PTO
Winco	NA			G	$2,000	3/06	WCMN	3,500-watt on cart, PTO
Winpower	12 KW			G	$700	11/06	ECND	12 KW single-phase
Winpower	12 KW			G	$500	4/06	ECND	PTO
Winpower	12 KW			G	$1,875	4/06	NWSD	On two wheels, 100' power cord
Winpower	12PT2			G	$500	6/06	NCIL	PTO
Winpower	20 KW			G	$1,500	3/06	ECND	PTO, 20KW start, 12KW continuous, trailer
Winpower	39436			G	$700	1/06	NECO	20 KW, 280 amp, PTO
Winpower	39436			G	$1,075	2/06	NECO	On trailer
Winpower	25 KW			G	$650	6/06	NWKS	PTO
Winpower	25 KW			G	$1,750	3/06	NWMN	
Winpower	25/15			G	$1,000	2/06	NEIN	25/15 KW PTO, no cart
Winpower	40 KW			G	$2,600	3/06	SEND	40/80 KW surge generator, 1,000 PTO
Winpower	80/50	1991		G	$2,100	5/06	SCMI	50 KW

Hog Equipment

Make	Model	Year	Hrs.	Cond.	Price	Sale	Location	Comments
Big Huskee	NA			G	$275	3/06	ECNE	Feeder, no-waste bottom
Big Huskee	NA			G	$275	3/06	ECNE	Feeder, no-waste bottom
Big Huskee	NA			G	$275	3/06	ECNE	Feeder, no-waste bottom
Big Huskee	NA			G	$275	3/06	ECNE	Feeder, no-waste bottom
Big Huskee	NA			G	$275	3/06	ECNE	Feeder, no waste bottom
Big Huskee	NA			G	$275	3/06	ECNE	Feeder, no-waste bottom
Big Huskee	NA			G	$300	3/06	ECNE	Feeder, no-waste bottom
Big Huskee	NA			G	$300	3/06	ECNE	Feeder, no-waste bottom
Huskee	NA			G	$60	3/06	ECNE	Small feeder
Lifetime	16'			G	$1,000	2/06	WCIL	8'×16' hyd. hog cart
Lifetime	20'			F	$350	8/06	NWIL	20' hyd. hog cart
Pride of the Farm	NA			F	$15	10/06	SWNE	Hog waterer

Irrigation Equipment

Make	Model	Year	Hrs.	Cond.	Price	Sale	Location	Comment
Ag Rain	NA	2002		G	$16,000	12/06	SWMI	1320' hard-nosed tandem-axle traveler, twin 202 plus gun Model T40A/1320 travel
Ag Rain	T45A			G	$1,900	3/06	WCMI	T45 ¼-mile irrigation traveler
Ames	NA			G	$3,036	11/06	ECNE	2640' of 9" aluminum pipe, gated 40", some plain, $1.15 per foot
Berkeley	NA			G	$375	11/06	ECNE	Two Berkley 3×4 booster pumps, PTO on trailers, both good
Berkeley	NA			G	$650	12/06	ECMO	Irrigation pump
Boss	NA			F	$150	10/06	SWNE	Traveling big gun, cart
Boss	NA			F	$4,250	2/06	SCMI	¼-mile irrigation traveler, vertical reel, one piece, 3 years use on hose
Boss	NA			F	$6,000	2/06	SCMI	¼-mile irrigation traveler, horizontal reel, one piece
Chevy	454	1995		E	$1,000	6/06	NWKS	Engine
Chevy	454	1997		E	$1,300	6/06	NWKS	Engine
Chevy	454	2000		E	$2,100	6/06	NWKS	Engine
Chevy	454	2002		E	$2,700	6/06	NWKS	Engine
Chevy	454	2002		E	$3,000	6/06	NWKS	Engine
Chevy	454	2003		E	$3,000	6/06	NWKS	Engine
Crisafulli	NA			G	$1,700	4/06	WCMT	PTO drive, Crisafulli irrigation pump trailer, mounted, 50' of 12" rubber discharge hose
Diamond	NA			G	$1,836	11/06	ECNE	1,530' of 8" PVC pipe, gated 20", $1.20 per foot
Ford	300			G	$1,750	11/06	SENE	6-cyl. power unit on cart
Ford	460			F	$400	11/06	ECNE	Power unit, older, LP
Gorman Rupp	NA			F	$2,300	8/06	SCMI	MB4A20, irrigation pump, Perkins power unit
Heinzman	NA			G	$1,650	11/06	ECNE	44 length 8" aluminum pipe, 1,320', gated 20"
Isuzu	NA			G	$1,700	10/06	NECO	Irrigation engine, no turbo, 10 KW, 3-phase generator, 4,677 hours
John Deere	329			G	$3,400	3/06	WCMI	6-cyl. diesel power unit, clutch
Lockwood	NA			G	$11,000	12/06	ECNE	9-tower full-length pivot, 11-22.5 tires, Model 7900, manual shutoffs on sprinklers
NA	NA			G	$195	11/06	SENE	Pipe trailer
NA	NA			G	$378	11/06	SENE	360' of 8" pipe @ $1.05 per foot, 40" gates
NA	NA			G	$400	11/06	ECNE	Micrometer 6" water meter

Irrigation Equipment

Make	Model	Year	Hrs.	Cond.	Price	Sale	Location	Comments
NA	NA			G	$600	11/06	ECNE	Pipe trailer
NA	NA			G	$648	11/06	SENE	720' of 8" pipe @ 90¢ per foot, 40" gates
NA	NA			G	$653	11/06	SENE	870' of 6" pipe @ 75¢ per foot
NA	NA			G	$690	11/06	SENE	690' of 8" pipe @ $1.00 per foot, 40" gates
NA	NA			G	$798	11/06	SENE	570' of 6" pipe @ $1.40 per foot, new 30" gates
NA	NA			G	$891	11/06	SENE	810' of 8" pipe @ $1.10 per foot, 40" gates
NA	NA			G	$1,500	3/06	ECMI	Water winch ¼-mile irrigation traveler
NA	NA			G	$2,400	3/06	WCMI	Water winch, ¼-mile irrigation traveler, newer hose
NA	NA			G	$2,625	3/06	ECMI	2500' of 6" aluminum hook and latch irrirgation pipe, 30' pieces
NA	NA			G	$6,864	3/06	WCMI	2 miles of aluminum irrigation pipe @ 65¢ per foot, including brands such as Sur-Rane, Rainway
Reinke	NA			F	$700	8/06	SCMI	200' irrigation line, 5-hp. gas motor
Reinke	NA			F	$6,000	8/06	SCMI	1,000' center pivot irrigation line
Reinke	NA			F	$7,000	8/06	SCMI	#414, 2-line center pivot irrigation line
Reinke	NA			F	$21,000	8/06	SCMI	2-line center pivot irrigation line
Valley	NA	1982		G	$12,700	11/06	SCNE	#4855 8-tower pivot system, low pressure drops, ⅝" pipe
Vermeer	NA			P	$700	3/06	ECMI	¼-mile irrigation traveler hose, rough
Zimmatic	NA	1998		G	$26,500	6/06	NWKS	7-tower sprinkler
Walton	NA			G	$1,100	3/06	NEKS	Tedder

Posthole Diggers

Make	Model	Year	Hrs.	Cond.	Price	Sale	Location	Comments
Bobcat	12			G	$1,700	3/06	SEND	12" bit
Bobcat	15C			G	$2,250	12/06	WCMN	Hyd. power auger, 18" bit
Bush Hog	2102			E	$950	2/06	SWIN	Like new
Bush Hog	NA			G	$525	12/06	ECMO	12" auger
Bush Hog	NA			G	$675	12/06	SEIA	10" & 12" augers, 3 pt., PTO
Bush Hog	NA			E	$700	4/06	SEIA	3 pt. posthole digger, new
Danuser	NA			G	$450	3/06	NWKS	3 pt. posthole digger
Danuser	NA			G	$700	3/06	WCKS	3 pt., large & small auger
Danuser	NA			G	$825	4/06	NWSD	2 bits
Danuser	NA			G	$850	3/06	WCSD	2 auger bits
Farm Star	NA			E	$300	1/06	WCIL	3 pt.
John Deere	NA			F	$350	9/06	NECO	3 pt., 8" auger
Lowe	NA	2003		G	$1,300	2/06	WCSD	For Caterpillar skid steer, 15" & 24" augers
McMillan	NA			G	$1,375	4/06	SWSD	Hyd. post digger, 9" & 12" bits
Melroe	1200			G	$1,400	4/06	ECND	Bobcat, hyd. unit, no bits
Rhino	NA			E	$1,050	3/06	ECNE	New 3 pt. posthole digger, 8" auger
Worksaver	12"			G	$375	4/06	SWIN	12"

Rock Pickers

Make	Model	Year	Hrs.	Cond.	Price	Sale	Location	Comments
Big Otto	NA			G	$3,400	4/06	NEND	Fork style
Crown	NA			F	$1,900	11/06	NEND	3-bat, hyd. drive
Degelman	6000			G	$7,000	8/06	NCMI	Hyd. driven
Degelman	6000			E	$9,300	2/06	SCMI	Signature 6000 stone picker, PTO driven, 3 years use, one owner
Degelman	R570			G	$1,450	3/06	NCWI	
Haybuster	L106			G	$5,500	4/06	NWMN	Low lift, 10' windrow bar
Highline	XL6084			G	$7,700	2/06	SCMI	5' throat
Leon	NA			G	$4,000	4/06	SCMN	Reel type, nice
Riteway	45			E	$18,500	4/06	NWMN	Rock roller
Riteway	RR900	2005		E	$9,750	3/06	SEMN	Hydro reel, hd, hyd. tongue, used three years, looks new
Rockomatic	NA			G	$1,050	4/06	WCMN	Canadian sale, reel type, high lift
Rockomatic	NA			G	$2,250	11/06	NWMN	3 bat, PTO drive, hd
Schulte	NA			F	$4,250	8/06	SCMI	5' throat
Schulte	RS320	2000		G	$10,000	5/06	SCMI	
Schulte	SRW 1400	2000		E	$10,500	5/06	SCMI	Stone windrower
Schulte	WR4			F	$4,100	8/06	SCMI	12' rock rake
Schulte	WR5			G	$3,500	2/06	NEIN	14' rock rake
Summers	700			G	$3,500	3/06	NEND	Hyd. drive, 3-bat
Summers	NA			G	$400	4/06	ECND	Fork style
Summers	NA			G	$1,000	4/06	NWMN	
Summers	NA	1990		G	$6,500	4/06	ECND	Hyd. 3-bat reel, back stop
Uft	570			G	$2,050	3/06	ECND	Fork chain style
Westgo	4210			G	$4,150	3/06	NCIA	Hyd.
Westgo	NA			G	$3,100	3/06	SEND	3-bat, hyd. drive

Snowblowers

Make	Model	Year	Hrs.	Cond.	Price	Sale	Location	Comments
Allied	NA			G	$1,100	8/06	NCMI	8.5' 3 pt., hyd. turn auger
Alloway	8'	2001		G	$1,400	4/06	NWMN	3 pt., PTO
Bervac	876			G	$900	2/06	WCNE	3 pt.
Bervac	SA98			G	$1,600	2/06	NCIN	8', 3 pt.
Buhler	9620	2002		G	$2,500	12/06	SWIA	2 stage, hyd. spout, 540 PTO, used twice
Erskine	6'			G	$425	9/06	NEND	3 pt., two stage
Farm King	7'			G	$425	9/06	SCMN	3 pt., single auger, red
Farm King	8'			G	$500	6/06	ECND	3 pt., 540 PTO, hyd. spout
Farm King	8'			G	$1,200	8/06	NCIA	Late model, double auger, hyd. spout
Farm King	8'			G	$1,900	3/06	WCMN	Double auger, hyd. spout, like new
Farm King	8600			F	$600	6/06	SEND	3 pt., 540 PTO, hyd. spout
Farm King	960			F	$900	4/06	NESD	8', hyd. spout
Farm King	960			E	$1,250	12/06	SWWI	Like new
Feterl	NA			G	$950	12/06	WCMN	Double auger
Feterl	NA			G	$1,250	8/06	WCMN	2 stage, hyd. spout
Feterl	NA			G	$10,000	12/06	SEMN	3 pt., double auger
IHC	80			F	$500	3/06	ECND	540 PTO
IHC	80			G	$950	7/06	NCIA	PTO
IHC	80			G	$2,600	11/06	SENE	7', 3 pt.

WHAT'S IT WORTH?

Snowblowers

Make	Model	Year	Hrs.	Cond.	Price	Sale	Location	Comments
John Deere	275			F	$500	2/06	ECIL	3 pt.
John Deere	47			G	$1,450	11/06	WCMN	425, 445, 455 mounts
John Deere	686			G	$1,500	3/06	NWMN	8', 540 PTO
Loftness	8'			G	$500	3/06	SEMN	3 pt., 96", 540 PTO, 2 augers
Loftness	8'			G	$550	10/06	SEMN	3 pt.
Loftness	8'			G	$625	9/06	SCMN	3 pt., single auger
Loftness	8'			G	$675	10/06	SEMN	3 pt.
Loftness	961	2000		E	$2,200	2/06	ECMN	961B-TS, 8', 3 pt., hd, 540 with 1,000 hookup, like new, very sharp
Loftness	NA			G	$2,850	3/06	SEMN	Commercial double auger, hd, 3 pt., 1,000 PTO, 195-hp. rating
Lorenz	8'			G	$3,600	3/06	ECND	
Lorenz	9'			E	$5,000	12/06	WCMN	Hyd. spout, 1,000 PTO
Lorenz	984			E	$2,100	2/06	ECMN	New owner
Lucknow	9'			G	$1,900	12/06	SWMI	9', hd, 3-pt. double auger, large 1,000-rpm shaft
Lucknow	NA			G	$1,000	2/06	NCIL	6'-8', 3 pt.
New Holland	716C			G	$2,300	3/06	ECND	3 pt., 1,000 PTO, hyd. spout, 2 stage
Red Devil	8'			G	$1,300	12/06	NCIA	
Red Devil	9654B			G	$1,800	2/06	NWIA	8', 3 pt., twin stage, hyd. spout, like new
Red Devil	9664			G	$600	12/06	SEMN	
Red Devil	9664C			G	$2,100	12/06	WCMI	8' double auger
Schulte	1100			E	$3,100	4/06	NESD	9', hyd. spout, 1,000 PTO, kept inside
Schulte	7400			G	$900	11/06	SCND	Front mount skid steer
Schulte	8'			F	$500	1/06	NECO	3 pt., 2 stage, hyd. spout
Schulte	9600			F	$1,000	11/06	NEND	3 pt.
Westgo	8'			G	$750	4/06	ECND	3 pt., 96", hyd. spout control, 540 PTO
Wildcat	NA			G	$2,750	3/06	NCIA	Twin fan, two spout

Sugar Beet Equipment

Make	Model	Year	Hrs.	Cond.	Price	Sale	Location	Comments
Alloway	NA			G	$1,400	8/06	WCMN	12R-22 defoliator, front steel, flails
Alloway	NA			G	$1,700	12/06	WCMN	8R-22 defoliator, front chopper knives
Alloway	NA			G	$3,000	3/06	ECND	6R defoliator, steel fronts, 150 acres on new steel flails, knife scalpers, rebuilt gear box
Alloway	NA			G	$3,900	6/06	NWMN	Defoilator, 6R, triple drum, steel front, 300 acres on new flails
Alloway	NA			G	$4,000	12/06	WCMN	12R-22 defoliator
Alloway	NA			G	$4,000	12/06	WCMN	12R-22 defoliator
Alloway	NA			G	$5,500	2/06	NWMN	Beet topper, 12R-22, steel front, front stabilizer wheels
Alloway	NA			G	$11,750	2/06	NWMN	Beet topper, 12R-22, steel front
Alloway	NA	1991		G	$2,500	4/06	NWMN	6R-22 defoliator
Alloway	NA	1997		G	$8,000	4/06	SEND	Beet defoliator, 12R-22, center hangers
Alloway	NA	2001		G	$13,250	4/06	NWMN	12R-22 steel front
Alloway	Topmaster			F	$500	7/06	NWMN	Topmaster II, triple, all rubber
Amity	NA	2004		G	$17,500	4/06	NWMN	12R defoliator
Amity	NA	2004		G	$41,000	4/06	NWMN	Lifter, 8R, used 2 seasons
Amity	R998	2003		G	$39,000	2/06	NWMN	Beet lifter, 8R-22, belted chain
Amity	R998	2003		G	$41,000	2/06	NWMN	Beet lifter, 8R-22, belted chain
Artsway	680A			F	$700	7/06	NWMN	Beet harvester, 6R-22, row finder
Artsway	680B			G	$0	8/06	WCMN	No sale at $5,900, 6R lifter w/ row finder
Artsway	690	1996		G	$14,000	6/06	NWMN	Lifter, 6R-22 H&S bed cleaner, w/ poly insert, H&S truck bed watering tank, Artsway row finder
Artsway	692			G	$0	8/06	WCMN	No sale at $17,500, 8R beet lifter, grab wheels, lifter wheels recently redone, 1 year new ferris wheel, cvc PTO shaft
Artsway	692B	2000		G	$29,000	3/06	ECMI	6R harvester
Artsway	784A			F	$700	3/06	ECMI	4R beet defoliator
Artsway	NA	1994		G	$5,500	4/06	NWMN	6R-22 beet lift loader
Elmers	NA			F	$850	1/06	NCCO	6R beet cultivator
Fruehauf	42'	1983		G	$8,250	12/06	WCMN	Beet trailer
Fruehauf	42'	1983		G	$9,250	12/06	WCMN	Beet trailer
Fruehauf	NA	1980		G	$5,000	3/06	SWMN	Beet trailer, no plate
H&S	NA	1999		G	$28,500	6/06	NWMN	24-ton beet cart w/ H&S truck bed watering tank
H&S	NA	2002		G	$23,500	3/06	ECMI	Beet cart, 37 ton, large super flotation tires
John Deere	223			P	$200	3/06	SWMN	Beet lifter cart, needs repair for parts
John Deere	4310			P	$900	9/06	NECO	Beet harvester, hyd. controls
Melroe	NA			G	$800	4/06	SEND	Beet thinner, 66'
Meyer Bilt	NA	1991		G	$4,500	4/06	SEND	12R-22 defoliator, center hangers, steel on front, field ready, not used in last 2 years
Orthman	NA			G	$1,000	8/06	NECO	Beet cutter
Pickett	NA	1999		G	$15,000	4/06	NWMN	24R beet thinner, hyd fold
Pickett	NA	2000		G	$3,250	4/06	NWMN	Beet manager, mechanical thinner, 12R-22, 3 pt.
Red River	NA			G	$3,600	3/06	NCCO	4R-30 defoliator
Red River	NA	1986		F	$1,600	4/06	SEND	Wide frame lifter, 6R-22, rock protectors
Red River	NA	1990		F	$3,250	4/06	SEND	Wide frame lifter, 6R-22
Red River	NA	1993		G	$6,500	4/06	SEND	Beet lifter, 6R-22
Richardton	960	1994		G	$7,250	4/06	SEND	Dump cart, 12 ton
Richardton	975	1997		G	$9,250	4/06	SEND	Dump cart, 15 ton

WHAT'S IT WORTH?

Sugar Beet Equipment

Make	Model	Year	Hrs.	Cond.	Price	Sale	Location	Comments
WIC	626C			G	$1,200	3/06	ECND	Harvester, 6R, hyd. load, dee row finder
WIC	822C			F	$1,000	7/06	NWMN	Triple drum rotobeaters, 12R, all rubber
WIC	822C			F	$2,000	7/06	NWMN	Triple drum rotobeaters, 12R, all rubber
WIC	822C			G	$3,000	7/06	NWMN	Triple drum rotobeater, 12R, all rubber
WIC	826C			F	$1,000	7/06	NWMN	Harvester, 6R-22, row finder
WIC	826C			F	$1,600	7/06	NWMN	Harvester, 6R-22, row finder
WIC	826C			F	$1,600	7/06	NWMN	Harvester, 6R-22, row finder
WIC	826C	1986		F	$1,000	4/06	NWMN	Lifter, 8R, field ready
WIC	H2837			G	$17,000	3/06	SWMN	6R sugar beet lifter
WIC	NA			F	$400	7/06	NWMN	24R-22 beet cultivator, cutaways, tunnel shields, lift assist, hyd. fold
WIC	NA			G	$2,000	8/06	WCMN	12R-22 beet topper
WIC	NA			G	$8,500	3/06	SWMN	12R beet defoliator
WIC	NA			G	$12,000	3/06	SWMN	24R-22 beet cultivator, Youngkranz shields
WIC	NA	1993		G	$2,200	12/06	WCMN	12R defoliator
WIC	NA	1994		G	$8,500	12/06	WCMN	6R lifter, rear scrub, large hopper
Wilrich	NA	1998		G	$7,500	4/06	SEND	Wilrich Red River rear scrub lifter, 6R-22, completely reconditioned 1/06, 1 year on scrub chain

Notes

V-Rippers

Make	Model	Year	Hrs.	Cond.	Price	Sale	Location	Comments
Bakker	NA			G	$5,250	8/06	WCMN	Incline ripper, adjustable, 12R-22 or 8R-30, with pull hitch & coulters
Big Ox	NA			G	$550	4/06	NCOK	3 pt., 7 shank
Big Ox	NA			F	$650	3/06	NWKS	7 shank
Big Ox	NA			G	$750	1/06	WCNE	3 pt., 7 shank
Big Ox	NA			F	$500	3/06	NCCO	Subsoiler, double gauge wheels, 9 shank
Big Ox	NA			G	$550	5/06	SCCA	3 pt., gauge wheels, 9 shank
Big Ox	NA			G	$650	4/06	NCOK	3 pt., 9 shank
Blu-Jet	NA			F	$600	3/06	SWNE	9-shank 30" ripper, rear sweeps
Blu-Jet	NA			F	$850	3/06	NWKS	7 shank
Blu-Jet	NA			F	$1,500	3/06	SWNE	9-shank 30" ripper, rear sweeps
Blu-Jet	NA			G	$1,800	12/06	SCNE	7-shank subtiller/ ripper
Blu-Jet	NA			G	$2,750	9/06	NWIL	SubTiller II, 5 shank
Blu-Jet	NA			G	$3,200	1/06	SCNE	SubTiller II, 7 shank, gauge wheels
Blu-Jet	NA			E	$3,650	4/06	NEIA	5-shank deep ripper
Blu-Jet	NA			G	$4,200	3/06	NENE	5-shank subsoiler, dual gauge wheels
Blu-Jet	NA			E	$4,250	1/06	SCNE	SubTiller II, 3 pt., 7 shank, new points
Blu-Jet	NA			E	$4,400	1/06	WCIL	SubTiller II 5 shank, pull type
Blu-Jet	NA			G	$5,000	11/06	SCNE	SubTiller II, 9 shank, coulters, 3 pt.
Blu-Jet	NA			E	$5,500	9/06	SCNE	Unused 3 pt. 7-shank SubTiller II
Blu-Jet	NA	1990		G	$3,600	6/06	NWKS	SubTiller II, 7-shank ripper, with prop blades
Brillion	NA			F	$1,750	2/06	NCCO	7 shank
Bush Hog	NA			F	$750	1/06	NCCO	5 shank
Case IH	10			F	$1,000	8/06	NWIL	5 shank
Case IH	14			G	$1,700	3/06	NECO	7 shank
DMI	NA	1987		F	$2,250	11/06	WCMN	Subsoiler, 3 heavy-duty shanks, 3 coulters, 3 pt.
IHC	11			G	$1,050	8/06	NCIA	7 shank V-ripper, auto reset, 3 pt.
IHC	5			F	$1,100	3/06	SEPA	6 shank, hd
IHC	NA			F	$1,450	2/06	NCCO	7 shank
John Deere	90			G	$850	9/06	NECO	7 shank, 3 pt.
John Deere	90			G	$900	3/06	NWKS	9/11 shank
John Deere	900			F	$200	1/06	WCCA	3 pt., 5 shank
John Deere	900			F	$650	3/06	NEKS	7 shank
John Deere	900			G	$900	5/06	SCCA	5 shank, gauge wheels, 3 pt.
John Deere	900			F	$950	3/06	SWNE	9 shank, 3 pt.
John Deere	900			G	$950	11/06	SWIA	7 shank, gauge wheels
John Deere	900			G	$1,750	1/06	WCCA	7 shank, gauge wheels
John Deere	910			G	$2,100	6/06	NWIL	7-shank, leveler bar harrow
John Deere	915			G	$1,650	8/06	NCIA	5 shank, 3 pt., toggle trip, gauge wheels
John Deere	915			G	$1,700	1/06	WCNE	7 shank, 3 pt.
John Deere	915			G	$1,850	1/06	WCIL	7 shank, 3 pt. ripper
John Deere	915			G	$2,150	12/06	ECMO	7 shank, 3 pt.
John Deere	915			G	$2,600	3/06	NESD	5 shank
John Deere	915			G	$2,650	1/06	WCIL	9 shank, 3 pt. ripper
John Deere	915			F	$2,700	4/06	SEPA	5-tooth ripper
John Deere	915			F	$3,300	1/06	NCCO	7 shank
John Deere	915			G	$4,700	1/06	NCCO	7 shank

V-Rippers

Make	Model	Year	Hrs.	Cond.	Price	Sale	Location	Comments
Landoll	1500			G	$4,400	2/06	SEIN	4-shank ripper, 3 pt.
Landoll	7 shank			F	$800	2/06	WCSD	Mounted, 12-14'
M&W	NA			G	$2,250	2/06	NWIL	6 shank, 12.5'
Orthman	635-073			G	$1,100	9/06	SCNE	635-070, 9-shank 30" ripper w/ liquid fert. pump & hoses, gauge wheels
Orthman	NA			F	$600	8/06	SCNE	9-shank ripper
Orthman	NA			G	$650	1/06	WCNE	3 pt., 7 shank
Orthman	NA			F	$800	3/06	NWKS	13 shank
Orthman	NA			G	$900	9/06	NECO	9-shank ripper, 3 pt.
Orthman	NA			F	$1,000	8/06	NECO	9-shank inner row ripper
Orthman	NA			G	$1,500	8/06	WCKS	9 shank
Orthman	NA			F	$1,500	10/06	NECO	8R-30 inner row ripper, guide disk
Orthman	NA			G	$1,700	1/06	NECO	7 shank
Orthman	NA			G	$2,500	1/06	NECO	9-shank 8-row inner row ripper, 30" centers
Unverferth	NA			G	$3,650	8/06	NWIL	5-shank subsoiler, 3 pt.